Mifflin
Harcourt

Teacher Edition

SCIENCE
FUSiON

fusion [FYOO • zhuhn] a combination of two
or more things that releases energy

Program Advisors

Paul D. Asimow
*Professor of Geology and
    Geochemistry*
California Institute of Technology
Pasadena, California

Bobby Jeanpierre
*Associate Professor of Science
    Education*
University of Central Florida
Orlando, Florida

Gerald H. Krockover
*Professor of Earth and Atmospheric
    Science Education*
Purdue University
West Lafayette, Indiana

Rose Pringle
Associate Professor
School of Teaching and Learning
College of Education
University of Florida
Gainesville, Florida

Carolyn Staudt
Curriculum Designer for Technology
KidSolve, Inc./The Concord
    Consortium
Concord, Massachusetts

Larry Stookey
Science Department
Antigo High School
Antigo, Wisconsin

Carol J. Valenta
*Associate Director of the Museum
    and Senior Vice President*
Saint Louis Science Center
St. Louis, Missouri

Barry A. Van Deman
President and CEO
Museum of Life and Science
Durham, North Carolina

Classroom Reviewers

Surbhi Madia Barber
Cottage Grove Elementary
Cottage Grove, Wisconsin

Michael J. Bodek
Green Ridge Elementary
Mechanicsburg, Pennsylvania

Abby Cunningham
Anderson Island Elementary
Anderson Island, Washington

Mark T. Esch
Cottage Grove Elementary
Cottage Grove, Wisconsin

Tina M. Gilbert
Cottage Grove Elementary
Cottage Grove, Wisconsin

Timothy J. Gollup
Cottage Grove Elementary
Cottage Grove, Wisconsin

A J Hepworth
Mineola Middle School
Mineola, New York

Wendy Hughes
Cottage Grove Elementary
Cottage Grove, Wisconsin

Nan Kaufman
Livonia Public Schools
Livonia, Michigan

Diane S. Kohl
M.J. Gegan Elementary School
Menasha, Wisconsin

Joseph C. Kubasta
Rockwood Valley MS
Wildwood, Missouri

Dustin C. LeBlanc
Sporting Hill Elementary
Mechanicsburg, Pennsylvania

Susanne Moar
Rockwood School District
Science Department
Eureka, Missouri

Pamela Pauling
Wheatland Elementary
Andover, Kansas

Allen G. Rauch
*Associate Professor of Science
    Education*
Molloy College
Rockville Centre, New York

Tim Rupp
Gordon Elementary
Marshall, Michigan

Michelle A. Salgado
National Board Certified Teacher
Chloe Clark Elementary
DuPont, Washington

Brent Schacht
Cottage Grove Elementary
Cottage Grove, Wisconsin

Power up with

SCIENCE FUSiON

Print

The **Write-in Student Edition** teaches science content through constant **interaction** with the text.

Labs and Activities

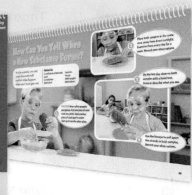

Digital

The parallel **Digital Curriculum** provides **e-learning digital lessons and virtual labs** for every print lesson of the program.

Program Advisors

Paul D. Asimow
Professor of Geology and Geochemistry
California Institute of Technology
Pasadena, California

Bobby Jeanpierre
Associate Professor of Science Education
University of Central Florida
Orlando, Florida

Gerald H. Krockover
Professor of Earth and Atmospheric Science Education
Purdue University
West Lafayette, Indiana

Rose Pringle
Associate Professor
School of Teaching and Learning
College of Education
University of Florida
Gainesville, Florida

Carolyn Staudt
Curriculum Designer for Technology
KidSolve, Inc./The Concord Consortium
Concord, Massachusetts

Larry Stookey
Science Department
Antigo High School
Antigo, Wisconsin

Carol J. Valenta
Associate Director of the Museum and Senior Vice President
Saint Louis Science Center
St. Louis, Missouri

Barry A. Van Deman
President and CEO
Museum of Life and Science
Durham, North Carolina

Classroom Reviewers

Surbhi Madia Barber
Cottage Grove Elementary
Cottage Grove, Wisconsin

Michael J. Bodek
Green Ridge Elementary
Mechanicsburg, Pennsylvania

Abby Cunningham
Anderson Island Elementary
Anderson Island, Washington

Mark T. Esch
Cottage Grove Elementary
Cottage Grove, Wisconsin

Tina M. Gilbert
Cottage Grove Elementary
Cottage Grove, Wisconsin

Timothy J. Gollup
Cottage Grove Elementary
Cottage Grove, Wisconsin

A J Hepworth
Mineola Middle School
Mineola, New York

Wendy Hughes
Cottage Grove Elementary
Cottage Grove, Wisconsin

Nan Kaufman
Livonia Public Schools
Livonia, Michigan

Diane S. Kohl
M.J. Gegan Elementary School
Menasha, Wisconsin

Joseph C. Kubasta
Rockwood Valley MS
Wildwood, Missouri

Dustin C. LeBlanc
Sporting Hill Elementary
Mechanicsburg, Pennsylvania

Susanne Moar
Rockwood School District
Science Department
Eureka, Missouri

Pamela Pauling
Wheatland Elementary
Andover, Kansas

Allen G. Rauch
Associate Professor of Science Education
Molloy College
Rockville Centre, New York

Tim Rupp
Gordon Elementary
Marshall, Michigan

Michelle A. Salgado
National Board Certified Teacher
Chloe Clark Elementary
DuPont, Washington

Brent Schacht
Cottage Grove Elementary
Cottage Grove, Wisconsin

Power up with

SCIENCE FUSION

Print

The **Write-in Student Edition** teaches science content through constant **interaction** with the text.

Labs and Activities

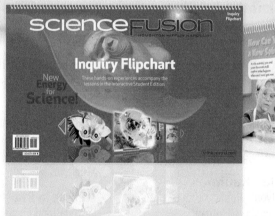

Digital

The parallel **Digital Curriculum** provides **e-learning digital lessons and virtual labs** for every print lesson of the program..

Energize your students through a multi-modal blend of Print, Inquiry, and Digital experiences.

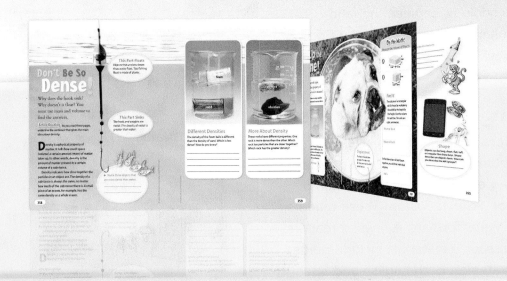

Assessment

Formative Assessment

Student Edition
Sum It Up!
Brain Check

Summative Assessment

Student Edition
Unit Review

Assessment Guide
Lesson Quizzes
Unit Test

The Inquiry Flipchart and Virtual Labs

provide meaningful and exciting hands-on experiences.

Performance Assessment

SHORT OPTION: Teacher Edition
LONG OPTION: Assessment Guide

RTI Response to Intervention

RTI Strategies

Online Assessment

Test-taking and automatic scoring
Banks of items from which to build tests

What's New?

ScienceFusion K–8 © 2017

Here are some of the exciting new features in the © 2017 update of *ScienceFusion*.

21st-Century Skills

An important component of many STEM careers is the meaningful understanding of the foundations of technology, engineering, and computer coding. A new spiraled curriculum on "Technology and Coding" has been added for Grades 1–8 to address this need. In addition, Kindergarten has a new "Technology and Engineering" section.

New Science & Engineering Leveled Readers

Science & Engineering Leveled Readers bring engaging science and engineering content to all students, whether they need extra support, are working at grade level, or are seeking enrichment. Thirty or more readers per grade are available as part of *ScienceFusion*. These readers are also available separately in print or digital formats. A leveled readers app for iPad® is also available. Teacher resource materials include guided reading and vocabulary development strategies. Both English and Spanish are supported.

Google Expeditions

HMH is among the first to develop K–8 content for Google® Expeditions. Using a simple Google cardboard device and a smartphone, students are swept away into immersive virtual worlds where learning and engagement are maximized. Teachers have a lot of flexibility in customizing the experience for each classroom.

Next Generation Science Standards (NGSS)

ScienceFusion was initially developed at a time when the National Research Council (NRC) *Framework for K–12 Science Education* was published. The NRC's work serves as the foundation to the NGSS in the form of Disciplinary Core Ideas, Crosscutting Concepts, and Science and Engineering Practices. *ScienceFusion* incorporates these three dimensions of learning and can serve as a solid preparation for a full NGSS curriculum. To facilitate this transition, correlations to the three dimensions are provided in the Teacher Editions and online materials.

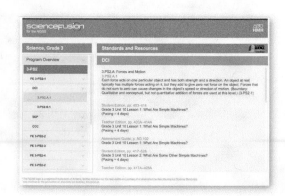

 **Print**

The **Write-in Student Edition** teaches science content through constant **interaction** with the text.

Write-in Student Edition

360° of Inquiry

The *ScienceFusion* write-in student edition promotes a student-centered approach for

- learning science concepts and vocabulary
- building inquiry, STEM, and 21st Century skills
- incorporating math and writing in each science lesson

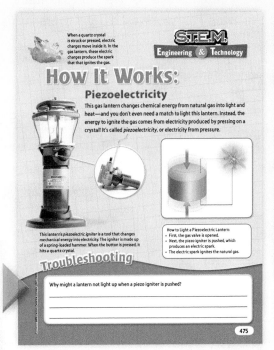

S.T.E.M.

Engineering & Technology

ScienceFusion features a STEM unit that focuses on

- engineering and technology
- learning science concepts and vocabulary
- building inquiry, STEM, and 21st Century skills

Big Ideas & Essential Questions

Each unit is designed to focus on a Big Idea and supporting Essential Questions.

Graphic Organizers

As they read, students summarize and organize their science ideas in charts, tables, diagrams, and other graphic organizers.

Active Reading

Annotation prompts and questions throughout the text teach students how to analyze and interact with content.

Do the Math!

Students practice and apply math skills as they are doing science.

Interactive Glossary

Students deepen their understanding of vocabulary by adding their own notes and context to glossary definitions.

Build On It!

ScienceFusion's multimodal approach connects a hands-on experience to the STEM lesson in the student edition.

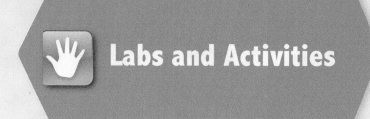
The **Inquiry Flipchart** and **Virtual Labs** provide meaningful and exciting hands-on experiences.

Labs and Activities

360° of Inquiry

Inquiry Flipcharts

The inquiry flipcharts deliver three levels—directed, guided, and independent—of hands-on inquiry for every lesson. The laminated, 11 x 17 flipcharts, also available digitally, can be placed on a table for centers or small group areas so students can work as lab partners or in collaborative groups.

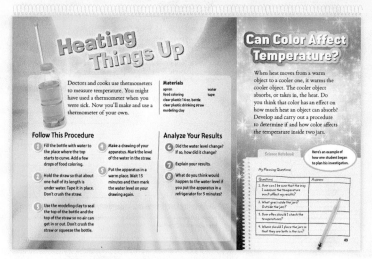

Directed or Independent Inquiry

Guided Inquiry

Inquiry Lesson and Virtual Lab

Each inquiry lesson in the student edition has a corresponding virtual lab to provide a multimodal approach for learning science concepts and skills.

Inquiry lesson

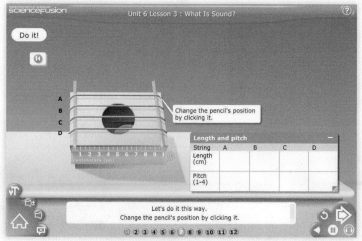

Virtual Lab

The parallel **Digital Curriculum** provides
e-learning digital lessons and virtual labs
for every print lesson of the program.

360° of Inquiry

Digital Lessons and Virtual Labs

An e-Learning environment of interactivity, videos, simulations, animations, and assessment designed for the way digital natives learn. An online Student Edition provides students anytime access to their student book.

Digital Lessons

Online Student Edition

Video-Based Projects

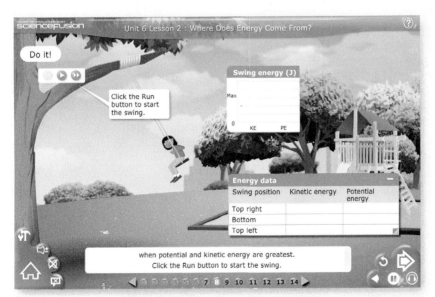

Virtual Labs

Also available online:

- NSTA *SciLinks*
- Digital Lesson Progress Sheets
- Video-Based Projects
- Virtual Lab Datasheets
- People in Science Gallery
- Media Gallery
- Extra Support for Vocabulary and Concepts
- Leveled Readers

All paths lead to a full suite of print and online Assessment Options right at your fingertips.

Classroom Management
Integrated Assessment Options

The *ScienceFusion* assessment options give you maximum flexibility in assessing what your students know and what they can do. Both the Print and Digital paths include formative and summative assessment. See the **Assessment Guide** for a comprehensive overview of your assessment options.

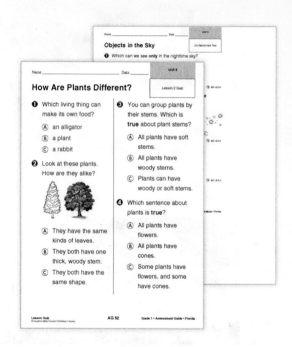

Teacher Online Management Center

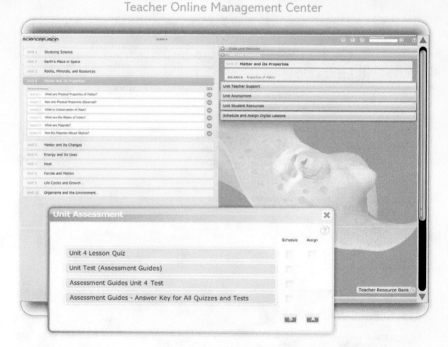

Print Assessment

The print **Assessment Guide** includes

- **Lesson Quizzes**
- **Unit Tests**
- **Unit Performance Assessments**

Online Assessment

The **Digital Assessment** includes

- **assignable leveled assessments for individuals**
- **customizable lesson quizzes and unit tests**
- **individual and whole class reporting**

Customizing Assessment for Your Classroom

Editable quizzes and tests are available in ExamView and online at ⊙ **thinkcentral.com.** You can customize a quiz or test by adding or deleting items, revising difficulty levels, changing formats, revising sequence, and editing items. Students can also take quizzes and tests directly online.

Choose Your Options

with two powerful teaching tools—a comprehensive **Teacher Edition** and the **Teacher Online Management Center.**

Classroom Management Teacher Edition

Each lesson has a wealth of teaching support, including activities, probing questions, misconception alerts, differentiated instruction, and vocabulary support.

- Lessons organized around a 5E lesson format

-  Science Notebooking strategies focusing on vocabulary and inquiry

- Strategies for helping young science students build and develop science concepts and inquiry skills for every lesson

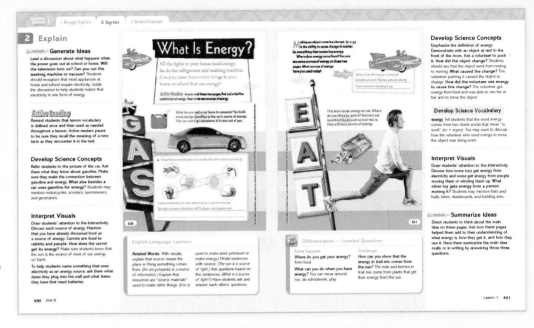

National Science Teachers Association

SCiLINKS
THE WORLD'S A CLICK AWAY

- Easy access to NSTA's e-professional development center, *The Learning Center*
- SciLinks provide students and teachers content-specific online support.

☑ **RTI** Response to Intervention

Response to Intervention is a process for identifying and supporting students who are not making expected progress toward essential learning goals.

 Professional Development

Unit and lesson level professional development focuses on supporting teachers and building educator capacity in key areas of academic achievement.

Online Management Center

- Program resources can be easily previewed in PDF format and downloaded for editing.

- Assign and schedule resources online, and they will appear in your students' inboxes.

- All quizzes and tests can be taken and automatically scored online.

- Easily monitor and track student progress.

Student Edition Contents

Levels of Inquiry Key ■ DIRECTED ■ GUIDED ■ INDEPENDENT

THE NATURE OF SCIENCE AND S.T.E.M.

LIFE SCIENCE

PHYSICAL SCIENCE

© Houghton Mifflin Harcourt Publishing Company (b) ©Corbis

ScienceFusion

Video-Based Projects

⊘ **Available in Online Resources**

This video series, hosted by program authors Michael Heithaus and Michael DiSpezio, develops science learning through real-world science and engineering challenges.

Ecology

Leave your lab coat at home! Not all science research takes place in a lab. Host Michael Heithaus takes you around the globe to see ecology field research, including tagging sharks and tracking sea turtles. Students research, graph, and analyze results to complete the project worksheets.

Grade	Video Title
3	Exploring the Galápagos Islands Tent-Making Bats
4	Alligators Up Close Rainforest Habitats
5	The Sea Turtles of Shark Bay

S.T.E.M. Science, Technology, Engineering, and Math

Host Michael DiSpezio poses a series of design problems that challenge students' ingenuity. Each video follows the engineering design process. Worksheets guide students through the process and help them document their results.

Grade	Video Title
3	Take It to Great Heights
4	It's a Bird! It's a Plane!
5	No Gas Needed Get Focused! A Cut Above **

** In Partnership with Children's Hospital Boston

Designed for Grades 3-5, the videos may also be viewed by primary-grade classes if appropriate.

ScienceFusion

Program Scope and Sequence

ScienceFusion is organized by five major strands of science. Each strand includes Big Ideas that flow throughout all grade levels and build in rigor as students move to higher grades.

ScienceFusion Grade Levels and Units

	GRADE K	GRADE 1	GRADE 2	GRADE 3
Nature of Science	**Unit 1** Doing Science	**Unit 1** How Scientists Work	**Unit 1** Work Like a Scientist	**Unit 1** Investigating Questions
STEM	**21st Century Skills:** Technology and Engineering	**Unit 2** Technology All Around Us **21st Century Skills:** Technology and Coding	**Unit 2** Technology and Our World **21st Century Skills:** Technology and Coding	**Unit 2** The Engineering Process **21st Century Skills:** Technology and Coding
Life Science	**Unit 2** Animals **Unit 3** Plants **Unit 4** Habitats	**Unit 3** Animals **Unit 4** Plants **Unit 5** Environments	**Unit 3** All About Animals **Unit 4** All About Plants **Unit 5** Environments for Living Things	**Unit 3** Plants and Animals **Unit 4** Ecosystems and Interactions

GRADE 4	GRADE 5	GRADES 6-8

Unit 1 Studying Science	**Unit 1** How Scientists Work	**Module K** Introduction to Science and Technology
		    Unit 1 The Nature of Science
		    Unit 2 Measurement and Data

Unit 2 The Engineering Process **21st Century Skills:** Technology and Coding	**Unit 2** The Engineering Process **21st Century Skills:** Technology and Coding	**Module K** Introduction to Science and Technology **Unit 3** Engineering, Technology, and Society **21st Century Skills:** Technology and Coding

Unit 3 Plants and Animals
Unit 4 Energy and Ecosystems
	Unit 3 Cells to Body Systems
	Unit 4 Living Things Grow and Reproduce
	Unit 5 Ecosystems
	Unit 6 Energy and Ecosystems
	Unit 7 Natural Resources
		Module A Cells and Heredity
		    Unit 1 Cells
		    Unit 2 Reproduction and Heredity
		Module B The Diversity of Living Things
		    Unit 1 Life over Time
		    Unit 2 Earth's Organisms
		Module C The Human Body
		    Unit 1 Human Body Systems
		    Unit 2 Human Health
		Module D Ecology and the Environment
		    Unit 1 Interactions of Living Things
		    Unit 2 Earth's Biomes and Ecosystems
		    Unit 3 Earth's Resources
		    Unit 4 Human Impact on the Environment

ScienceFusion Grade Levels and Units

	GRADE K	GRADE 1	GRADE 2	GRADE 3
Earth Science	**Unit 5** Day and Night **Unit 6** Earth's Resources **Unit 7** Weather and the Seasons	**Unit 6** Earth's Resources **Unit 7** Weather and Seasons **Unit 8** Objects in the Sky	**Unit 6** Earth and Its Resources **Unit 7** All About Weather **Unit 8** The Solar System	**Unit 5** Changes to Earth's Surface **Unit 6** People and Resources **Unit 7** Water and Weather **Unit 8** Earth and Its Moon
Physical Science	**Unit 8** Matter **Unit 9** Energy **Unit 10** Motion	**Unit 9** All About Matter **Unit 10** Forces and Energy	**Unit 9** Changes in Matter **Unit 10** Energy and Magnets	**Unit 9** Matter **Unit 10** Simple and Compound Machines

GRADE 4	GRADE 5	GRADES 6-8
Unit 5 Weather **Unit 6** Earth and Space	**Unit 8** Changes to Earth's Surface **Unit 9** The Rock Cycle **Unit 10** Fossils **Unit 11** Earth's Oceans **Unit 12** The Solar System and the Universe	**Module E** The Dynamic Earth **Unit 1** Earth's Surface **Unit 2** Earth's History **Unit 3** Minerals and Rocks **Unit 4** The Restless Earth **Module F** Earth's Water and Atmosphere **Unit 1** Earth's Water **Unit 2** Oceanography **Unit 3** Earth's Atmosphere **Unit 4** Weather and Climate **Module G** Space Science **Unit 1** The Universe **Unit 2** The Solar System **Unit 3** The Earth-Moon-Sun System **Unit 4** Exploring Space
Unit 7 Properties of Matter **Unit 8** Changes in Matter **Unit 9** Energy **Unit 10** Electricity **Unit 11** Motion	**Unit 13** Matter **Unit 14** Light and Sound **Unit 15** Forces and Motion	**Module H** Matter and Energy **Unit 1** Matter **Unit 2** Energy **Unit 3** Atoms and the Periodic Table **Unit 4** Interactions of Matter **Unit 5** Solutions, Acids, and Bases **Module I** Motion, Forces, and Energy **Unit 1** Motion and Forces **Unit 2** Work, Energy, and Machines **Unit 3** Electricity and Magnetism **Module J** Sound and Light **Unit 1** Introduction to Waves **Unit 2** Sound **Unit 3** Light

Program Pacing

The following pacing guide recommends days for the core print and digital instructional elements of each unit. Additional days can be added for optional inquiry, activities, and extensions.

DAYS	NATURE OF SCIENCE S.T.E.M.
Unit 1 Studying Science	
9	Print or Digital Lesson Content
4	Inquiry Lesson or Virtual Lab
1	Unit Review and Assessment
Unit 2 The Engineering Process	
5	Print or Digital Lesson Content
4	Inquiry Lesson or Virtual Lab
1	Unit Review and Assessment
24 DAYS	

DAYS	LIFE SCIENCE
Unit 3 Plants and Animals	
9	Print or Digital Lesson Content
4	Inquiry Lesson or Virtual Lab
2	S.T.E.M. /Engineering and Technology
1	Unit Review and Assessment
Unit 4 Energy and Ecosystems	
9	Print or Digital Lesson Content
4	Inquiry Lesson or Virtual Lab
2	S.T.E.M. /Engineering and Technology
1	Unit Review and Assessment
32 DAYS	

DAYS	EARTH SCIENCE
Unit 5 Weather	
7	Print or Digital Lesson Content
2	Inquiry Lesson or Virtual Lab
2	S.T.E.M. /Engineering and Technology
1	Unit Review and Assessment

DAYS	EARTH SCIENCE (continued)
Unit 6 Earth and Space	
7	Print or Digital Lesson Content
4	Inquiry Lesson or Virtual Lab
2	S.T.E.M. /Engineering and Technology
1	Unit Review and Assessment
26 DAYS	

DAYS	PHYSICAL SCIENCE
Unit 7 Properties of Matter	
5	Print or Digital Lesson Content
4	Inquiry Lesson or Virtual Lab
2	S.T.E.M. /Engineering and Technology
1	Unit Review and Assessment
Unit 8 Changes in Matter	
5	Print or Digital Lesson Content
4	Inquiry Lesson or Virtual Lab
2	S.T.E.M. /Engineering and Technology
1	Unit Review and Assessment
Unit 9 Energy	
7	Print or Digital Lesson Content
6	Inquiry Lesson or Virtual Lab
2	S.T.E.M. /Engineering and Technology
1	Unit Review and Assessment

DAYS	PHYSICAL SCIENCE (continued)
Unit 10 Electricity	
7	Print or Digital Lesson Content
4	Inquiry Lesson or Virtual Lab
2	S.T.E.M. /Engineering and Technology
1	Unit Review and Assessment
Unit 11 Motion	
3	Print or Digital Lesson Content
2	Inquiry Lesson or Virtual Lab
2	S.T.E.M. /Engineering and Technology
1	Unit Review and Assessment
62 DAYS	

DAYS	21ST CENTURY SKILLS:
2	TECHNOLOGY AND CODING

Correlation of *ScienceFusion* to the NRC Framework's 3 Dimensions of Learning

The National Research Council (NRC) published the *Framework for K-12 Science Education,* which has served as the foundation of the Next Generation Science Standards. This framework defines and describes best practices in the teaching of science and outlines the 3 Dimensions of Learning which should be taught together for best student understanding: Disciplinary Core Ideas (DCI), Science and Engineering Practices (SEP), and Crosscutting Concepts (CCC). The 3 Dimensions of Learning were the basis for the Next Generation Science Standards (NGSS), and have also been used as a structure for science standards of several non-NGSS states. *ScienceFusion* integrates the three dimensions of learning throughout the lessons in the book, making the program an effective transition and springboard for a full NGSS curriculum. The correlation identifies the dimensions and where they are taught within this grade level of *ScienceFusion*.

UNIT	DCI/SEP/CCC
Unit 1 Studying Science	**SEP** **Engaging in Argument from Evidence** Student Edition, pp. 41–42 **CCC** **Scale, Proportion, and Quantity** Student Edition, pp. 17–26, 45–54
Unit 2 The Engineering Process	**DCI** **3-5.ETS1.B.1 Research on a problem should be carried out before beginning to design a solution. Testing a solution involves investigating how well it performs under a range of likely conditions.** Student Edition, pp. 63–78 Teacher Edition, pp. 63A–78A Assessment Guide, pp. AG 14–AG 15 **3-5.ETS1.B.2 At whatever stage, communicating with peers about proposed solutions is an important part of the design process, and shared ideas can lead to improved designs.** Student Edition, pp. 63–76 Teacher Edition, pp. 63A–76A Assessment Guide, p. AG 14

UNIT	DCI/SEP/CCC
Unit 2 The Engineering Process (*continued*)	**3-5.ETS1.B.3 Tests are often designed to identify failure points or difficulties, which suggest the elements of the design that need to be improved.** Student Edition, pp. 63–76 Teacher Edition, pp. 63A–76A Assessment Guide, p. AG 14 **SEP** **Asking Questions and Defining Problems** Student Edition, pp. 63, 66–67, 77–78 Teacher Edition, pp. 77A–78A **Developing and Using Models** Student Edition, pp. 77–78 Inquiry Flipchart, p. 9 **Planning and Carrying Out Investigations** Student Edition, pp. 93–94 Teacher Edition, pp. 93A–94A
Unit 3 Plants and Animals	**DCI** **4.LS1.A.1 Plants and animals have both internal and external structures that serve various functions in growth, survival, behavior, and reproduction.** Student Edition, pp. 103–114, 117–132, 135–148, 151–166 Teacher Edition, pp. 103A–114A, 117A–132A, 135A–148A, 151A–166A Assessment Guide, pp. AG 25–AG 26, AG 28–AG 30 **SEP** **Planning and Carrying Out Investigations** Student Edition, pp. 165–166 Inquiry Flipchart, p. 18 **Analyzing and Interpreting Data** Student Edition, pp. 165–166 Inquiry Flipchart, p. 18

UNIT	DCI/SEP/CCC
Unit 3 Plants and Animals (*continued*)	**CCC** **Structure and Function** Student Edition, pp. 103–114 **Patterns** Student Edition, pp. 133–134 **Stability and Change** Student Edition, pp. 151–166, 173–188
Unit 4 Energy and Ecosystems	**DCI** **4.ESS2.E.1 Living things affect the physical characteristics of their regions.** Student Edition, pp. 207–234 Teacher Edition, pp. 207A–234A Assessment Guide, pp. AG 42–AG 43 **4.ESS3.A.1 Energy and fuels that humans use are derived from natural sources, and their use affects the environment in multiple ways. Some resources are renewable over time, and others are not.** Student Edition, pp. 207–220 Teacher Edition, pp. 207A–220A Assessment Guide, p. AG 41 **SEP** **Planning and Carrying Out Investigations** Student Edition, pp. 233–234 Teacher Edition, pp. 233A–234A
Unit 5 Weather	**SEP** **Using Mathematics and Computational Thinking** Student Edition, p. 249 **CCC** **Cause and Effect: Mechanism and Explanation** Student Edition, pp. 221–232 Teacher Edition, pp. 221A–232A

UNIT	DCI/SEP/CCC
Unit 5 Weather (*continued*)	**Systems and System Models** Student Edition, pp. 245–258 **Patterns** Student Edition, pp. 287–288
Unit 6 Earth and Space	**CCC** **Patterns** Student Edition, pp. 297–312 **Systems and System Models** Student Edition, pp. 327–340
Unit 7 Properties of Matter	**SEP** **Constructing Explanations and Designing Solutions** Student Edition, pp. 383–384 Inquiry Flipchart, p. 41 **CCC** **Scale, Proportion, and Quantity** Student edition, pp. 351–366 **Energy and Matter: Flows, Cycles, and Conservation** Student Edition, pp. 371–372
Unit 8 Changes in Matter	**SEP** **Obtaining, Evaluating, and Communicating Information** Student Edition, pp. 419–420 Inquiry Flipchart, p. 46
Unit 9 Energy	**CCC** **Energy and Matter: Flows, Cycles, and Conservation** Student Edition, pp. 429–444 **Cause and Effect: Mechanism and Explanation** Student Edition, pp. 459–460

UNIT	DCI/SEP/CCC
Unit 10 Electricity	**DCI** **4.PS3.B.3 Energy can also be transferred from place to place by electric currents, which can then be used locally to produce motion, sound, heat, or light. The currents may have been produced to begin with by transforming the energy of motion into electrical energy.** Student Edition, pp. 483–496 Teacher Edition, pp. 483A–496A Assessment Guide, p. AG 109 **CCC** **Energy and Matter: Flows, Cycles, and Conservation** Student Edition, pp. 497–498 **Structure and Function** Student Edition, pp. 497–498, 501–514 **Cause and Effect: Mechanism and Explanation** Student Edition, pp. 517–528
Unit 11 Motion	

Teacher Notes

UNIT **1** Studying Science

Big Idea and Essential Questions

This Unit was designed to focus on this Big Idea and Essential Questions.

Take It Home!
A School-Home Connection letter is provided in Online Resources.

Big Idea

Scientists answer questions about the world around us by carrying out careful investigations.

Essential Questions

L1 **What Do Scientists Do?**

L2 **What Skills Do Scientists Use?**

L3 **How Do Scientists Collect and Use Data?**

L4 **Why Do Scientists Compare Results?**

L5 **What Kinds of Models Do Scientists Use?**

L6 **How Can You Model a School?**

 ### Professional Development

Houghton Mifflin Harcourt and **NSTA,** the **National Science Teachers Association,** have partnered to provide customized professional development resources for teachers using *ScienceFusion*.

The Professional Development Resources include:

- Do-it-yourself resources, where you can study at your own pace
- Live and archived online seminars
- Journal articles, many of which include lesson plans
- Fee-based eBooks, eBook chapters, online short courses, symposia, and conferences

  Access to The NSTA Learning Center is provided in the *ScienceFusion* Online Resources.

National Science Teachers Association

The **NSTA** Learning Center

Unit Planning

Options for Instruction

Two parallel paths meet the unit objectives, with a strong Inquiry strand woven into each. Follow the Print Path, the Digital Path, or your customized combination of print, digital, and inquiry.

	LESSON 1	LESSON 2	LESSON 3
Essential Questions	What Do Scientists Do?	What Skills Do Scientists Use?	How Do Scientists Collect and Use Data?
Print Path	☐ Student Edition pp. 3–16 • The Role of Scientists • Making Observations and Asking Questions • Experiments • Other Kinds of Investigations • Scientists Share Their Results as Evidence	☐ Student Edition pp. 17–26 • Everyday Science Skills • Think Like a Scientist • Math and Science Skills	☐ Student Edition pp. 27–40 • Research Is the Key • Science Tools • Measurement Tools • Recording and Displaying Data • Using Data
Hands-On Inquiry	Inquiry Flipchart p. 2 **Spin-a-Copter** ☐ Directed Inquiry **Design Your Own** ☐ Independent Inquiry	Inquiry Flipchart p. 3 **Pendulum Swing** ☐ Directed Inquiry **Pantry Investigation** ☐ Independent Inquiry	Inquiry Flipchart p. 4 **Rain, Rain, Come Again** ☐ Directed Inquiry **Who's Wet? Who's Dry?** ☐ Independent Inquiry
Digital Path	☐ Digital Lesson Online Resources Interactive presentation of lesson content	☐ Digital Lesson Online Resources Interactive presentation of lesson content	☐ Digital Lesson Online Resources Interactive presentation of lesson content

🧑 People in Science, p. 43

💿 Online Resources

LESSON 4

☑ **Guided Inquiry**

Why Do Scientists Compare Results?

LESSON 5

What Kinds of Models Do Scientists Use?

LESSON 6

☑ **Guided Inquiry**

How Can You Model a School?

☐ **Student Edition**
pp. 41–42
• Scaffolding for Inquiry

☐ **Student Edition**
pp. 45–54
• Models and Science
• Other Models Scientists Use

☐ **Student Edition**
pp. 55–56
• Scaffolding for Inquiry

Unit Assessment

Formative Assessment
Sum It Up! and Brain Check
Student Edition, end of each lesson

Summative Assessment
Lesson Quizzes
Assessment Guide,
pp. AG 1–AG 6

Inquiry Flipchart
p. 5

Why Do Scientists Compare Results?
☐ Guided Inquiry

Inquiry Flipchart
p. 6

Bridge Building
☐ Directed Inquiry

Stress Test
☐ Independent Inquiry

Inquiry Flipchart
p. 7

How Can You Model a School?
☐ Guided Inquiry

Unit 1 Review
Student Edition, pp. 57–60

Unit 1 Test
Assessment Guide,
pp. AG 7–AG 11

Performance Assessment
SHORT OPTION: Teacher
Edition, p. 59
LONG OPTION: Assessment
Guide, pp. AG 12–AG 13

RTI Response to Intervention

RTI Strategies p. 1K

☐ **Virtual Lab**
Online Resources
Interactive scaffolded inquiry

☐ **Digital Lesson**
Online Resources
Interactive presentation of lesson content

☐ **Virtual Lab**
Online Resources
Interactive scaffolded inquiry

💿 Online Assessment
Test-taking and automatic scoring
Banks of items from which to build tests

Planning for Inquiry

Use the following preview of Inquiry Activities and Lessons to gather and manage the materials needed for each lesson.

Activity	Inquiry and Design Process Skills Focus	Materials	Prep Tips, Troubleshooting, and Expected Results
Lesson 1 DIRECTED INQUIRY Flipchart **p. 2** **A** **Spin-a-Copter** OBJECTIVE Follow directions for an investigation to make a paper-spinning helicopter. ⏱ 25 minutes 👥 individuals	• Observe • Infer • Compare • Experiment • Plan and Conduct a Simple Investigation	• index card or heavy paper • scissors • safety goggles • small paper clip	**Prep Tips** Direct students to the diagram on the Flipchart for a guide to cutting and folding an index card to make a helicopter. Be sure students write their names on their helicopters. **Caution!** Remind students to use scissors with care. Students should wear goggles when testing their own helicopters or when others are testing helicopters. **Troubleshooting** You may wish to do this activity outside or in a gymnasium or a room with a high ceiling and room for students to move around. **Expected Results** Students will observe that adding mass (the paper clip) to the helicopter causes it to spin and descend faster. If throwing the helicopter upward, students will notice that it will not travel very far before it begins to spin and descend toward the ground.
INDEPENDENT INQUIRY Flipchart **p. 2** **B** **Design Your Own** OBJECTIVE Plan and conduct an experiment to determine whether the mass of a helicopter's base affects its motion. ⏱ 25 minutes 👥 individuals	• Plan and Conduct a Simple Investigation • Hypothesize • Draw Conclusions • Experiment • Gather, Record, Display or Interpret Data	• paper helicopter • paper clips • meterstick • stopwatch or clock with second hand	**Prep Tips** Review the concept of mass before beginning this activity. Suggest that students use the helicopter they made in the Spin-a-Copter Directed Inquiry for this activity. **Caution!** Students should wear goggles when testing their own helicopters or when others are testing helicopters. **Troubleshooting** Guide students to consider adding one paper clip at a time to the helicopter base. Students should conduct at least three trials for each mass. **Expected Results** Students may come up with a variety of ideas on how to test their helicopters. Spin speed will be difficult to quantify, but students should be able to notice qualitative differences (faster, slower, etc.).

Additional teaching support for all inquiry activities is available in **Online Resources.**

Notebook Science Notebook Strategies
- Lists of Kit-Supplied Materials
- Meeting Individual Needs
- Investigate More—Extensions and Variations and More!

Activity	Inquiry and Design Process Skills Focus	Materials	Prep Tips, Troubleshooting, and Expected Results
Lesson 2 DIRECTED INQUIRY Flipchart **p. 3** **A Pendulum Swing** OBJECTIVE Follow directions for an investigation to determine what characteristics affect a pendulum's swing. ⏱ 45 minutes 👥 pairs	• Observe • Control Variables • Gather and Record Data	• small and large metal washers (1 each per group) • string (2 50-cm lengths per group) • ruler • scissors • stopwatch or clock with second hand	**Prep Tips** You may wish to cut the 50-cm lengths of string beforehand. The extra length will be used to tie and secure the string. Thin string will work best. Heavy gauge thread can be used instead of string. Each pair of students will need two metal washers, one with a larger size and mass than the other. Be sure the larger washer has a larger mass than the smaller washer. Locate an area in which students can test their pendulums. **Troubleshooting** If students cut the string, make sure they cut the same length of string for each pendulum. Some students may need help tying the string onto the washer. Make sure they secure the washer with a tight knot. If students have difficulty holding the string steady while the pendulum is swinging, suggest they tape the end of the string to a table top, making sure to leave the washer and string hanging at 40 cm and 10 cm as appropriate. Have students make sure there are no obstacles when they are ready to start the pendulum. **Expected Results** Students will observe that when the lengths of string are the same, both pendulums swing at the same rate. When the strings are shortened, both washers swing faster.
INDEPENDENT INQUIRY Flipchart **p. 3** **B Pantry Investigation** OBJECTIVE Plan and conduct an investigation of mixtures. ⏱ 25 minutes 👥 individuals	• Plan and Conduct a Simple Investigation • Observe • Draw Conclusions • Experiment	• vinegar • students may choose items such as sugar, baking powder, or baking soda • Science Notebook	**Prep Tips** In order to conserve resources, you may want to tell students to limit the amount of kitchen supply samples to just a spoonful of each. Cover surfaces with paper towels or newspapers. **Caution!** Wear goggles. Students should have adult supervision. Explain to students that they should have the approval and supervision of a parent or trusted adult when doing this activity outside the classroom. **Expected Results** Students will find that some mixtures, such as vinegar mixed with baking powder or baking soda, will bubble. There is no observable reaction with other mixtures, such as vinegar mixed with sugar.

Planning for Inquiry (continued)

Activity	Inquiry and Design Process Skills Focus	Materials	Prep Tips, Troubleshooting, and Expected Results
Lesson 3 DIRECTED INQUIRY Flipchart p. 4 **A Rain, Rain, Come Again** **OBJECTIVE** Follow directions for an investigation to make and use a rain gauge. 🕐 25 minutes to make and set up the gauge; 15 minutes daily for one week for observations 👥 small groups	• Observe • Compare • Plan and Conduct a Simple Investigation • Measure • Gather, Record, Display or Interpret Data	• tall, clear deli container (1 per group) • waterproof clay (1 stick per group) • waterproof marker • ruler	**Prep Tips** Find a location outside where rain gauges will be undisturbed and students will be able to make regular observations. After placing the rain gauges outside, allow 15 minutes each day for one week for students to measure and record the water collected, and pour off the water to bring the level back to the zero mark. **Troubleshooting** Step 4: Keep in mind that if the rain gauge is left outside for several days and there is no rain, some of the existing water may evaporate so measuring the waterline will provide false data. If doing this activity during your area's dry season, consider placing the rain gauges where a lawn sprinker system is active several times a week. Students can measure and record the water for a one-week period. **Expected Results** Results will depend on weather conditions or sprinkler systems. Have students focus on measuring accurately, reporting results clearly, and building a well-labeled bar graph.
INDEPENDENT INQUIRY Flipchart p. 4 **B Who's Wet? Who's Dry?** **OBJECTIVE** Plan and conduct an investigation to determine rainfall in other parts of the world. 🕐 45 minutes 👥 small groups	• Communicate • Plan and Conduct a Simple Investigation	• media center resources or National Weather Service records • Science Notebook	**Prep Tips** Explore with students the differences between primary data and secondary data. Explain that primary data are data collected by a scientist. Using a thermometer to measure air temperature is an example of primary data. Secondary data are data collected by others. Explain that scientists carefully follow and document their procedures for gathering data so that other scientists can evaluate the data's accuracy and reliability. Explain that in this investigation, students may use both primary and secondary data. **Expected Results** Results will depend on the locations measured. Students should focus on the brainstorming process, writing the procedure clearly, and carrying it out scientifically.

Additional teaching support for all inquiry activities is available in Online Resources.

Activity	Inquiry and Design Process Skills Focus	Materials	Prep Tips, Troubleshooting, and Expected Results
Lesson INQUIRY 4 GUIDED INQUIRY **Flipchart** p. 5 **Student Edition** pp.41-42 **A Why Do Scientists Compare Results?** OBJECTIVES • Measure an object using several different types of tools (standard and non-standard units of measurement) and compare the results with other groups. • Communicate the importance of accuracy in measurements and reasons why differences may take place. ⏱ 25 minutes 👥 small groups	• Observe • Measure	• classroom object (1 per group) • pan balance • spring scale • ruler	**Prep Tips** Demonstrate the use of the pan balance and accompanying set of masses before distributing them to groups. Be sure and include objects that can be attached to the hook of a spring scale when gathering materials. **Troubleshooting** Step 3: Students must be able to hook this object to the spring scale. Students may measure a different object from the one selected in Step 1. Step 3: When students make up their non-standard units, they must also identify the property the unit measures. Instruct students to record their results in all steps so the results can be compared. **Expected Results** Students may find differences in their measurements due to the choice of units and their accuracy in using the measurement tools and in counting. Students should follow the prompts and record their responses on Student Edition pages 41–42.

Go Digital! Virtual Lab

Why Do Scientists Compare Results?

Key Inquiry Skills: Compare, Measure, Design and Conduct Simple Investigations, Record Data

Students measure a backpack to determine whether it will fit into a new locker. They compare three different sets of measurements taken to discover that human error is often responsible for differences in measurements.

Additional teaching support for all inquiry activities is available in Online Resources.

Activity	Inquiry and Design Process Skills Focus	Materials	Prep Tips, Troubleshooting, and Expected Results
Lesson 5 DIRECTED INQUIRY Flipchart **p. 6** **A Bridge Building** **OBJECTIVE** Follow directions for an investigation to build a model of a bridge. ⏱ 45 minutes 👥 small groups	• Formulate or Use Models • Measure	• plastic straws (15–20 per group) • masking tape • paper clips • scissors • ruler • 2 desks or tables	**Prep Tips** One type of bridge that students can make is a truss bridge. Direct students to cut a straw into thirds and tape the ends together to form a triangle. Explain that this form is called a *truss*, a very strong construction unit. Tell students they can use trusses and straight straws to build their bridges, but they cannot make a bridge using bundled straws. If you plan to have students complete the Independent Inquiry that follows, direct them to leave a space in the center of the bridge large enough to fit a paper cup. **Troubleshooting** Students will need to test their bridges for strength as they build them. Suggest that students use markers or pencils for weights. **Expected Results** Students will observe that triangles are able to resist greater forces than straight straws, and they can construct a bridge that will span the 25 cm if they combine the triangular trusses.
INDEPENDENT INQUIRY Flipchart **p. 6** **B Stress Test** **OBJECTIVE** Plan and conduct an investigation to test the strength of a bridge. ⏱ 20 minutes 👥 pairs	• Plan and Conduct a Simple Investigation • Formulate or Use Models • Draw Conclusions	• paper cup (1 per group) • pennies or other uniform masses (10 per group) • straws • masking tape • paper clips • Science Notebook • bridge constructed in the Directed Inquiry activity	**Prep Tips** If students completed the Bridge Building activity, have them use that bridge as a starting point for Stress Test. If they did not complete that activity, explain how to build a truss by cutting a straw into thirds and taping the ends together to form a triangle. Small paper cups will work best for this activity. A variety of designs may be suggested by student groups. For example, some groups may wish to suspend their cup from the bridge instead of balancing the cup on the bridge. Provide a variety of materials to meet these needs. **Expected Results** Students will find that bridges vary in strength depending on their design. The bridge they built may or may not be able to support the weight of one or more pennies in a cup.

Activity	Inquiry and Design Process Skills Focus	Materials	Prep Tips, Troubleshooting, and Expected Results
Lesson 6 GUIDED INQUIRY **Flipchart** p. 7 Student Edition pp. 55–56 **A How Can You Model a School?** **OBJECTIVES** • Measure the classroom using metric tools such as tape measures and metersticks. • Construct a model of a classroom. • Compare the models made and note differences based on spatial awareness or measurements made. ⏱ 30–40 minutes to gather data on day 1; 40 minutes to make the model on day 2 👥 small groups	• Formulate or Use Models • Communicate • Measure • Draw Conclusions	• drawing paper • graph paper • tape measure • cardboard boxes • computer drawing or modeling program	**Prep Tips** Prepare students by giving them some examples of a model, including scale models, physical models, dioramas, and mental models. If you think the scale of the activity may be too great for students, scale it down. Have students model the classroom, some other room in the school or at home, or a sports field. To reduce the amount of supplies needed, you may want to assign each group to make just one model that they can compare with those made by others. Have students confer with you as they plan their model so you can ensure that many types of models will be available for comparison. **Troubleshooting** Allow students to practice using the tape measure to understand the scale, the units, and how to record measurements accurately. You may want to have students gather measurement data one day and make their models the following day. If a team chooses to make a mental model, tell them they need to write directions for others to use the same mental model. When choosing the types of models they will make, have students consider whether the colors they use are important and how each type of model can include color information. Taking students outside may be challenging, so restrict the amount and degree to which you allow students to do measurements outdoors or around the school. **Expected Results** Students will find they can communicate some kinds of information more easily with a particular kind of model. Students should follow the prompts and record their responses on pages 55–56.

Go Digital! Virtual Lab

How Can You Make a Model?
Key Inquiry Skills: Use Models, Predict, Use Numbers
Students use a model to determine how quickly a cyclist must go in order to get to a destination on time.

Differentiated Instruction

Customize and Extend

You can extend and customize science instruction for your students using the following resources.

Leveled Readers

The **Science & Engineering Leveled Readers** can be used to provide additional nonfiction reading practice in the subject area of Unit 1.

ON-LEVEL This Reader reinforces unit concepts. It includes student response activities for your students.

TEACHER GUIDE

The accompanying **Teacher Guide** provides teaching strategies and support for using all the Readers, as well as English and Spanish worksheets that focus on vocabulary development. A correlation to the Disciplinary Core Ideas of the Next Generation Science Standards is included.

EXTRA SUPPORT This Reader shares title, illustrations, vocabulary, and concepts with the On-Level Reader. However, the text is linguistically accommodated to provide simplified sentence structures and comprehension aids. It also includes response activities.

 DIGITAL VERSIONS

All of these Leveled Readers are available online. They are also available in an innovative and engaging format for touchscreen mobile devices. Contact your HMH Sales Representative for more information.

ENRICHMENT This high-interest nonfiction Reader enriches and extends unit concepts. It reinforces some of the unit vocabulary, includes *stretch vocabulary*, and includes response activities.

RTI Response to Intervention

Response to Intervention is a process for identifying and supporting students who are not making expected progress toward essential learning goals.

The following *ScienceFusion* components have the flexibility to be used to provide Core Classroom Instruction (Tier 1), strategic intervention (Tier 2), and intensive intervention (Tier 3).		
Component	**Location**	**Strategies and Benefits**
Student Edition, Active Reading prompts, Sum It Up!, Brain Check	Active Reading throughout each lesson, Sum it Up! and Brain Check at the end of each lesson	Student responses can be used as screening tools to assess whether intervention is needed.
Assessment Guide, Lesson Quizzes	pp. AG 1–AG 6	Student responses can be used as screening tools to assess whether intervention is needed.
Inquiry Flipcharts	Inquiry Flipchart pp. 2, 3, 4, 6	Directed Inquiry for students who learn best through directed or teacher-led hands-on activities.
Teacher Edition, Unit Review Answer Strategies	TE pp. 57–60	Suggestions for intervention, guidance, and remediation for each review question.
Leveled Readers	TE p. 1J	Content support for students not meeting the learning needs during core classroom instruction.
Leveled Readers, Teacher Guides and Vocabulary Worksheets	TE p. 1J	Direct instruction with small groups of students needing additional content at various readability levels.
Extra Support for Vocabulary and Concepts (online worksheets)	Online Resources	Support for individualized instruction with practice in essential content.
Online Student Edition with Audio	Online Resources	Provides learners with multiple-modality access to science concepts and information.
Interactive Digital Lessons and Virtual Labs	Online Resources	Provides individualized learning experiences. Lessons make content accessible through simulations, animations, videos, audio, and integrated assessment.

Differentiated Instruction

English Language Learners

Choose from these instructional strategies to meet the needs of English language learners. Suggestions are provided for adapting the activity for three proficiency levels. Point-of-use strategies also appear within unit lessons.

☑ Unit Vocabulary

Lesson 1	Lesson 2	Lesson 3	Lesson 5
scientist	inference	microscope	model
science		pan balance	two-dimensional model
observation		spring scale	three-dimensional model
investigation		data	computer model
hypothesis			

Vocabulary Cards are provided in Online Resources.

Vocabulary Activity

Play Tic-Tac-Toe

Play variations of tic-tac-toe with the vocabulary terms. Examples:

- Use pictures or drawings; players win the square if they say the term.
- Use terms; have players select the correct picture.
- Use terms; to win the square, players must write or say a correct sentence (as evaluated by other students or by you) using the term. The sentence must demonstrate that the player understands the term's meaning.

Beginning	Intermediate	Advanced
Use pictures or drawings on the game board. Provide labels for each vocabulary term. Students win the square if they match the labels with the pictures.	Make a large game board. Post a list of the vocabulary terms. On index cards, write sentence frames for each term. Students will draw a card, choose the correct term to complete the sentence, and write the term on a square of the game board.	Have students write each vocabulary term on an index card. Collect the cards, and form teams. A team member draws a card. Team members must define or discuss the term on the card without using the term itself. They get two points if the other team guesses the term; the other team gets one point. Use checkmarks in different colors to indicate team points. The winning team has the most points on the game board.

☑ Model Concepts

Many Kinds of Scientists

Remind students of the three kinds of scientists mentioned in the unit: earth scientists, physical scientists, and life scientists. Form three groups. Each group is to find and describe a current investigation being conducted in one branch of science. Provide leveled, illustrated books, magazines, newspapers, and other appropriate research materials. Allow time for presentations.

Beginning	Intermediate	Advanced
Supply students with picture-based sources, such as picture books, magazines, illustrated newspapers, and websites. Ask them to create a sequence of pictures that describes a specific scientific project. Help them to label each picture.	Ask groups to present their research on a large, illustrated poster. Posters should be entitled _____ Scientists Study _____. Require labels for each illustration or chart on the poster. Ask students to include at least two sentences describing the investigation they researched.	Ask students to present their research as a skit in which scientists describe their investigation. Require them to write scripts and to practice the skits. Have them include visual aids, including websites, which help to explain the project's goals and findings.

☑ Model Inquiry Skills

Measure

Give students various measurement tools: ruler, pan balance, spring scale, tape measure, or thermometer. Ask them to measure and describe various objects in or features of the classroom. Have students display data in graphs. Graphs should have titles and labels.

Beginning	Intermediate	Advanced
Give students partially completed graphs of various measurements. Ask them to complete the measurements and the graphs. Supply labels, or ask students to complete labels that have a word or two missing.	Ask students to write on each graph a clear sentence that explains what was measured and how the measurement was done. For example: I measured _____ using a _____.	Ask students to compare measurements using words such as longer, heaviest, smallest, and so on. Have them write on each graph at least two sentences explaining the comparative values they found.

Studying Science

I Wonder Why

Use the images and the question to stimulate interest in the unit topic. Ask students if they can identify the large object shown. Tell them it is a submersible, which is a vehicle that allows scientists to explore deep beneath an ocean's surface—much deeper than a person with scuba gear could dive. The technician in the inset photo manipulates the crane, which lifts the submersible out of the water to the deck of the ship. Discuss how information gathered by scientists in the field provides raw data for scientists to interpret in the lab.

Here's Why

Have students turn the page and read the response to the question. You may wish to share the following background with students.

More About...

Submersibles

Submersibles such as the one shown here carry researchers deep below the ocean's surface. A few of these vessels can dive to a depth of 6,000 meters. An average dive lasts eight hours. It takes about one hour to descend 1,600 meters, and about the same amount of time to return to the surface. The interior of these vessels is very cold. At the depths these vessels reach, the water outside the vessel is just a few degrees above freezing.

UNIT 1

Studying Science

Big Idea

Scientists answer questions about the world around us by carrying out careful investigations.

© Houghton Mifflin Harcourt Publishing Company · (bg) ©Ralf Hettler/Getty Images; (inset) ©Chris Howes/Wild Places Photography/Alamy Images Photostock

I Wonder Why

Why is the work of a scientist doing field research like the work of a scientist doing research in a laboratory? *Turn the page to find out.*

1

🍎 **Professional Development** **Science Background**

Use the keywords to access

- Professional Development from **The NSTA Learning Center**
- SciLinks for additional online content appropriate for students and teachers
- Teacher Science Background in the back of this Teacher Edition and in the Planning Guide

Keywords

inquiry skills
scientific methods
scientific tools

SCi LINKS.
THE WORLD'S A CLICK AWAY

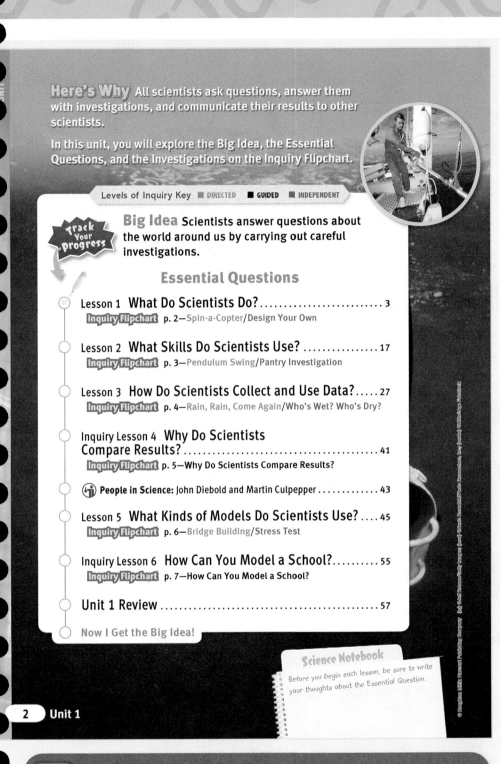

Here's Why All scientists ask questions, answer them with investigations, and communicate their results to other scientists.

In this unit, you will explore the Big Idea, the Essential Questions, and the Investigations on the Inquiry Flipchart.

Levels of Inquiry Key ▨ DIRECTED ■ GUIDED ▨ INDEPENDENT

Track Your Progress

Big Idea Scientists answer questions about the world around us by carrying out careful investigations.

Essential Questions

Now I Get the Big Idea!

Science Notebook
Before you begin each lesson, be sure to write your thoughts about the Essential Question.

Go Digital

For a complete digital curriculum and resources that provide full coverage of the objectives for this unit, see the Online Resources for this program.

What Do Scientists Do?

Vocabulary
science   scientist
observation   investigation
hypothesis

investigation, and hypothesis.
Click each word to find out more about it.

Big Idea and Essential Questions

Big Idea Scientists answer questions about the world around us by carrying out careful investigations.

Post the Unit Big Idea on the board. Have students read the Essential Questions, which are also the titles of the lessons in this unit.

- Discuss how the Essential Questions can help them focus on the Big Idea.

- Have students read the Big Idea statement. The statement describes the main science concept they will be learning.

- Have students predict other ideas that will be taught in the lessons based on the titles, or have them give examples of pictures they expect to see.

Once they have completed all the lessons, they should have a better understanding of the Big Idea.

Essential Questions You may use the following Science Notebook strategy for working with the Essential Questions before students begin the unit or lessons in the unit.

- Strategies for revisiting the Big Idea and Essential Questions are provided in Enduring Understandings on page 57A.

Notebook **Science Notebook**

- Have students copy the Essential Questions into their Science Notebooks. Suggest they leave writing lines between questions.

- Ask students to write responses to the Essential Questions. Urge students not to worry about whether their responses are correct. They should expect their ideas to change as they work in the unit. Comment that students will be able to review and revise their answers to the Essential Questions at the end of the unit.

- Tips and strategies for using Science Notebooks are provided throughout this unit, in the Planning Guide, and in Online Resources.

Options for Inquiry

FLIPCHART P. 2

Students can conduct these optional investigations at any time before, during, or in response to the lesson in the Student Edition.

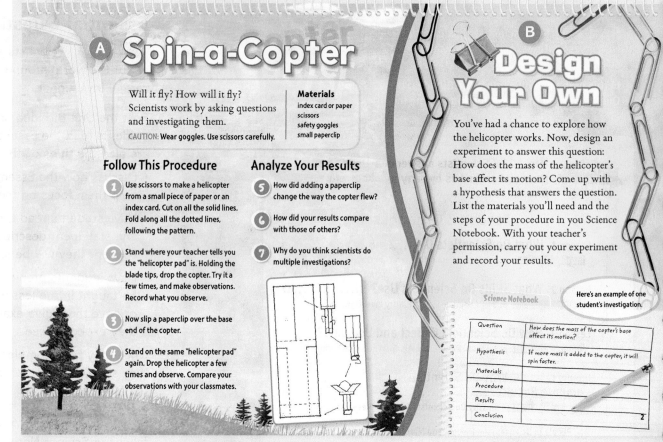

A Spin-a-Copter

Will it fly? How will it fly? Scientists work by asking questions and investigating them.

CAUTION: **Wear goggles. Use scissors carefully.**

Materials
index card or paper
scissors
safety goggles
small paperclip

Follow This Procedure

1. Use scissors to make a helicopter from a small piece of paper or an index card. Cut on all the solid lines. Fold along all the dotted lines, following the pattern.

2. Stand where your teacher tells you the "helicopter pad" is. Holding the blade tips, drop the copter. Try it a few times, and make observations. Record what you observe.

3. Now slip a paperclip over the base end of the copter.

4. Stand on the same "helicopter pad" again. Drop the helicopter a few times and observe. Compare your observations with your classmates.

Analyze Your Results

5. How did adding a paperclip change the way the copter flew?

6. How did your results compare with those of others?

7. Why do you think scientists do multiple investigations?

B Design Your Own

You've had a chance to explore how the helicopter works. Now, design an experiment to answer this question: How does the mass of the helicopter's base affect its motion? Come up with a hypothesis that answers the question. List the materials you'll need and the steps of your procedure in you Science Notebook. With your teacher's permission, carry out your experiment and record your results.

Here's an example of one student's investigation.

Science Notebook

Question	How does the mass of the copter's base affect its motion?
Hypothesis	If more mass is added to the copter, it will spin faster.
Materials	
Procedure	
Results	
Conclusion	

2

Directed Inquiry

A Spin-a-Copter

🕐 25 minutes
👥 individuals

Prep and Planning Tips

You may wish to have students fly their helicopters outdoors or in a gymnasium, where they can spread out.

Expected Results

Students will observe that when they try to throw the spin-a-copter like a ball it does not go very far before it starts to spin and descend. They may find that adding mass (the paper clip) to the copter causes it to fly a little farther away from them and to spin a little faster on its descent.

Independent Inquiry

B Design Your Own

🕐 25 minutes
👥 individuals

Prep and Planning Tips

See the Planning for Inquiry page for more information. Guide students to consider adding one paper clip at a time to the helicopter tail. They might use a meterstick to measure the distance they can throw the copter and record this data in a table.

Science Notebook

Students can use the Science Notebook as a model for designing their own investigation. Point out that their questions and hypotheses do not have to follow the model. Have them consider whether the materials should include measurement tools (metersticks, stopwatches). Assure them that if results are inconclusive, they can write in the Conclusion row that more investigations are needed.

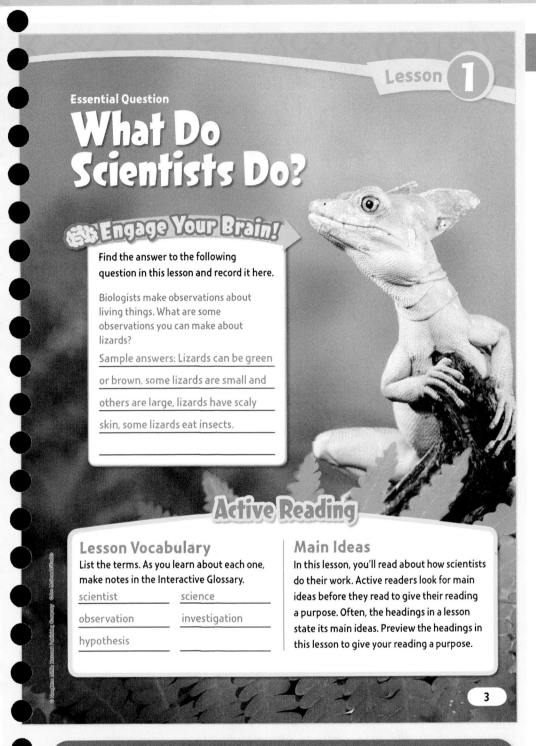

Essential Question

What Do Scientists Do?

Engage Your Brain!

Find the answer to the following question in this lesson and record it here.

Biologists make observations about living things. What are some observations you can make about lizards?

Sample answers: Lizards can be green or brown, some lizards are small and others are large, lizards have scaly skin, some lizards eat insects.

Active Reading

Lesson Vocabulary

List the terms. As you learn about each one, make notes in the Interactive Glossary.

scientist	science
observation	investigation
hypothesis	

Main Ideas

In this lesson, you'll read about how scientists do their work. Active readers look for main ideas before they read to give their reading a purpose. Often, the headings in a lesson state its main ideas. Preview the headings in this lesson to give your reading a purpose.

3

Go Digital

An interactive digital lesson is available in Online Resources. It is suitable for individuals, small groups, or may be projected or used on an interactive white board.

What Do Scientists Do?

Vocabulary
science   scientist
observation   investigation
hypothesis

investigation, and hypothesis.
Click each word to find out more about it.

Objectives

- Describe that science focuses on the natural world only.
- Explain that scientists make observations, ask questions, conduct investigations, and produce evidence that guides scientific thought and theory.
- Communicate that scientists conduct multiple types of investigations (traditional experiments involving fair testing, inventing, documenting, trial and error, etc.).
- Recognize that scientific knowledge requires evidence.

Engage Your Brain!

Explain to students that the precise answer to this question is not in their book. Challenge them to find the page in this lesson that discusses scientific methods and how scientists answer questions. Record students' ideas in a chart or on the board. Remind students to record their final answer to the question when they answer it using the sixth page of this lesson.

Active Reading   Annotations

Remind students that active readers "make texts their own" by annotating them with notes and marks that help with comprehension. Encourage students to use pencil, not pen, to make annotations as they read. The goal of annotation is to help students remember what they have read.

Vocabulary and Interactive Glossary

Remind students to find and list the yellow highlighted terms from the lesson. As they proceed through the lesson and learn about the terms, they can add notes, drawings or sentences in the extra spaces provided in the Interactive Glossary.

2 Explain

Notebook ▸ Generate Ideas

Have students think about the people in their community, state, and country and then brainstorm a list of careers. If students do not mention scientist, add it to the list. Next, ask students to tell what scientists do. Record their ideas in a chart or on the board. Correct any inaccuracies after they have read the lesson.

Active Reading

Preview Headings

Remind students that active readers preview headings to establish expectations and purposes for reading. Reading with a purpose helps active readers focus on understanding and recalling what they read in order to fulfill the purpose.

Develop Science Concepts

Explain to students that when scientists say they ask questions about the *natural world,* they are referring to all the parts of the physical world that can be observed and investigated, including the following: plants and animals, the atmosphere, ecosystems, bridges, cities, robots, galaxies, and energy.

Direct students to look at the photo and picture themselves in that classroom. Have them read the questions in the word balloons and then write a different question they might ask the scientist in the photo. Emphasize that students are expected to write their questions on the student page in the space provided in the interactivity box.

The Role of Scientists

It's career day for Mr. Green's fourth-grade class! Mr. Green invited a scientist named Dr. Sims to talk to the class. The students are ready, and they have many questions to ask.

Active Reading As you read these two pages, turn the heading into a question in your mind. Then underline the sentence that answers the question.

What do scientists do?

▸ Write a question you would ask a scientist.
Sample answers: How long did you go to school? What is the best part of your job? Is being a scientist hard work?

4

© Houghton Mifflin Harcourt Publishing Company

English Language Learners

Understand the Natural World
Discuss the word *nature,* prompting with examples of plants, animals, oceans, mountains. Then discuss the word *natural.* Ask: What is the *natural world?* (the physical universe)

Ask for other terms using *natural* as an adjective, or describing word: natural resource, natural history, natural gas. Have students use each term in a sentence.

"Thank you for inviting me to your school! My name is Dr. Sims, and I am a scientist. A **scientist** asks questions about the natural world. There are many kinds of scientists and many questions to ask!

Science is the study of the natural world. Earth scientists study things like rocks, weather, and the planets. Physical scientists study matter and energy. Life scientists, like me, study living things. I am a wildlife biologist, which means I study animals in the wild.

Scientists work alone and in teams. Sometimes, I travel alone on long hikes to watch animals. At other times, I ask other biologists to go with me. I share ideas with other scientists every day.

Science is hard work but fun, too. I like being outdoors. Discovering something new is exciting. The best part, for me, is helping animals. The best way to explain what a scientist does is to show you."

▶ For each area of science, write a question a scientist might ask.

Earth Science

Sample answer: How far is Earth from

Neptune?

Life Science

Sample answer: What kind of bird lays

the largest egg?

Physical Science

Sample answer: What kind of simple

machine would I use to put a heavy box

in the back of a moving truck?

Do you work all by yourself?

Is it fun to be a scientist?

© Houghton Mifflin Harcourt Publishing Company

5

Develop Science Vocabulary

science Explain that the English word *science* comes from a Latin word *scientia*, meaning *knowledge*.

scientist Explain that the suffix –*ist* mean "one who does." Therefore, a *scientist* is "someone who does science."

Direct students to find the two science vocabulary terms. Have them describe how the words *science* and *scientist* are similar and different. Students should recognize that a version of the word *science* is in both of them.

Develop Inquiry Skills

CLASSIFY Before having students write questions that scientists would ask in each category, you may wish to have the class generate a single list of questions. Work with your class to help them classify each question by marking it with an E for Earth science, L for Life science, or P for Physical science.

Notebook ▶ Summarize Ideas

Direct students to think about the main idea of these two pages. Ask if their ideas about what scientists do have changed since they read this section. Have them summarize the main idea orally or in writing, using the words *science* and *scientists*.

Differentiation — Leveled Questions

Extra Support

Think about a park, a pond, or a river. What animals might a wildlife biologist study there? Sample answers: ducks, geese, swans, hawks, alligators, snakes

Challenge

What are some reasons why scientists might need to work in teams? Sample answer: because sometimes the questions they are asking are too complicated or would take too long for one person to investigate

2 Explain (continued)

Notebook ▸ Generate Ideas

Ask students to write down one observation of something inside the classroom or outside a window. Then, challenge them to ask one question about what they observed.

Develop Science Concepts

What are the five senses you use to make observations? sight, smell, hearing, taste, and touch

Invite students to share the five things they observed in the photo of the classroom. If any statements are not directly observable, point out that these are called inferences. Have students correct their lists to eliminate inferences.

Making Observations and
Asking Questions

Dr. Sims looks around the classroom. She observes everything for a few moments. Then she asks questions about what she sees.

How does that plant produce offspring?

Does the lizard's skin ever change colors?

Does the goldfish spend more time near the top of the tank or the bottom of the tank?

Dr. Sims

▶ Ask your own question about the classroom in the photo.
Sample answer: Does the plant with flowers need more water than the plant that does not have flowers?

6

Scientists make observations about the world around them. An **observation** is information collected by using the five senses.

Scientists ask questions about their observations. Notice that Dr. Sims' questions are about the living things in the classroom. That's because she is a wildlife biologist. Your questions might be different if you observed different things than she did.

Dr. Sims asks, "How would you find an answer to my question about the goldfish?" She and the students talk about watching the fish. Someone suggests writing

▶ Name five things you observe in this classroom.
Sample answer: plants, a goldfish tank, posters, a bookcase, a lizard in a terrarium

observations in a notebook. Someone else says a stopwatch can help.

Dr. Sims says, "I could do all these things in an investigation." Scientists conduct an **investigation** to answer questions. The steps of an investigation may include asking questions, making observations, reading or talking to experts, drawing conclusions, and sharing what you learn.

7

Writing Connection

Letter To help students develop their abilities to ask questions based on observations, take them on a tour of the school or the school grounds. Have students take notes about the history or structure of the school or the layout of the school grounds.

Have them write down their questions. Later, have students use their notes to write a one-page letter to an expert asking for help in answering one or more of their questions. Remind students of the parts of a friendly letter: a greeting, a body, and a closing.

Develop Science Vocabulary

observation Point out that the word *observation* is a noun (a person, place, or thing) but is closely related to the verb (an action, or state of being) *observe,* which is a science inquiry skill.

investigation Write this word and *observation* on the board, and invite a student to underline the common suffix. Explain that adding *–tion* turns a verb into a noun.

Interpret Visuals

When students look at the classroom in the photo, make sure they understand that they can write down anything they can observe in the photo—living or nonliving things.

Notebook ▶ **Summarize Ideas**

Give each student three slips of paper. Direct them to write one of the following on each: *ask questions, make observations, do investigations.* Direct students to sequence the slips of paper on a sheet of paper and draw arrows to show how these activities are related. Have them summarize the main idea orally or in writing.

2 Explain (continued)

Notebook ▶ Generate Ideas

Ask students what Dr. Sims means when she mentions "doing an experiment." List students' examples of experiments or the activities that take place during experiments.

Active Reading

Remind students that lesson vocabulary is defined once and then used as needed throughout a lesson. Active readers pause to be sure they recall the meaning of a new term as they encounter it in the text.

Develop Science Concepts

Help students understand the meaning of an experiment as a fair test.

Suppose I went into my kitchen and mixed baking soda, salt, and vinegar together in a bowl to see what happens. Why is that not an experiment? because you didn't change one factor to show what caused something to happen

Now what if I used two bowls, one with baking soda, salt, and vinegar and the other with just baking soda and vinegar? Why is it an experiment this time? because you changed one factor, by putting salt in one bowl and leaving salt out of the other bowl

Explain to students that scientific methods are a collection of tools that scientists use to carry out investigations, similar to the collection of tools a carpenter wears on a belt when building a house. The carpenter uses only the tools needed for a particular job. The order in which the tools are used also depends on the job.

Experiments

Dr. Sims seems very excited to talk about investigations. She says, "Describing what you see is one kind of investigation. Other investigations include doing an experiment."

Active Reading As you read these two pages, circle the lesson vocabulary word each time it is used.

A Fair Test

An *experiment* is a fair test. It can show that one thing causes another thing to happen. In each test, you change only one factor, or *variable*. To be fair and accurate, you conduct the experiment multiple times.

To test something else, you must start a new experiment. Being creative and working in teams can help scientists conduct experiments.

Carlos is conducting an experiment. He gives the lizard fruit and crickets to see which will be eaten. The food is the only variable that is changed. Each day, the lizard gets two different types of food at the same time and in the same amounts.

8

English Language Learners

Understand a Fair Test
Students may not understand *fair test*. Ask them to discuss what they think of as *fair* and *unfair* and why they think so. Introduce and explain *accurate* as one synonym for *fair*. Clarify that in science, a test means an experiment. Ask them to find the sentence that tells how to do a fair test: "To be fair and accurate, you conduct the experiment at least three times." Invite discussion.

Scientific Methods

Scientific investigations use scientific methods. Scientific methods may include the following activities:

- make observations
- ask a question
- form a hypothesis
- plan and conduct an experiment
- record and analyze results
- draw conclusions
- communicate results

Sometimes, these steps are done in this order. At other times, they're not.

A hypothesis is an idea or explanation that can be tested with an investigation. Dr. Sims gives the students an example from their classroom. She says, "I hypothesize that this lizard eats more insects than fruit."

▶ Talk with other students in your class. Then write a hypothesis to explain what makes the lizard in the photo change color. Students may suggest that

changes in light, temperature, or

mood cause the color change.

_____

_____

_____

9

Develop Science Vocabulary

hypothesis Write the word *hypothesis* on the board. Point out to students that this is another word related to a science inquiry skill. *Hypothesis* is the noun, and *hypothesize* is the skill verb. Have students write the two words, underline the parts that are the same, and circle the parts that are different.

Develop Inquiry Skills

HYPOTHESIZE Guide students to write their own hypotheses by providing a fill-in-the-blank sentence for them to complete, such as: A change in the color of the lizard is caused by _____ (Sample answer: temperature, background color, stress).

You may wish to have the class brainstorm ideas and hold some discussion before students write their own hypotheses about the lizard's color change.

 Notebook ▶ **Summarize Ideas**

Direct students to think about the main ideas on these two pages. Have them state a main idea about experiments and a main idea about scientific methods orally or in writing.

Differentiation — Leveled Questions

Extra Support

State a hypothesis to explain why some kinds of balls bounce higher than others. Sample answer: Balls that are firmer and filled up with more air will bounce higher than balls that are softer or partially deflated.

Challenge

Describe an experiment to test the hypothesis that leaves of trees change color when the temperature drops. Sample answer: Keep a small potted tree that drops its leaves in a greenhouse that can be chilled.

2 Explain (continued)

Notebook ▶ Generate Ideas

Have students tell you what they know about investigations that do not involve experiments. **Ask: How does a scientist investigate whether other stars have planets orbiting them?** They look for planets through powerful telescopes.

Active Reading

Explain that signal words show connections between ideas. *One example is* and *here's another* are phrases that signal examples of an idea. *Also* and *in fact* signal added facts. Remind students that active readers remember what they read because they are alert to signal words.

Develop Science Concepts

Students may not be familiar with identification guides. Obtain a field guide to birds or trees from your library, and allow students to look through it. Alternately, you can find identification guides on the Internet.

What kinds of models are there? Sample answers: model cars and trucks, model airplanes and ships, model rockets, globes, models of atoms and cells, models of the human body

Where would you go and whom would you ask if you wanted to do research? Sample answers: to the library and ask the reference librarian, to a museum or planetarium and ask an expert, online to visit a reliable website

Other Kinds of Investigations

Dr. Sims smiles. She says, "I hope this doesn't confuse anyone, but doing an experiment isn't always possible."

Active Reading As you read these two pages, circle the clue words or phrases that signal a detail such as an example or an added fact.

Many science questions cannot be answered by doing an experiment. (Here's one question:) What kind of lizard have I found? This question can be answered by using an identification guide. (Here's another question:) What causes the sun to seem to rise and set? This question can be answered by making and using a model of Earth and the sun. (Here's another:) At what time of year does a state get the most rain? This question can be answered by looking for patterns through many years of rainfall records. (Here's another:) How did people who lived 100 years ago describe Mars? This question can be answered with research. Research includes reading what others have written and asking experts.

What is the surface of Mars like? This question is hard to answer with an experiment. NASA scientists sent robot spacecraft to Mars. Cameras on these spacecraft take pictures of the planet for scientists to observe.

10

Interpret Visuals

Make sure students know that the photos of the lizards on this page are not positioned over their correct names and descriptions.

Why is it impossible to identify the lizards by color? Two of the three lizards can be found in many colors. All three lizards can be brown.

Guide students to compare the descriptions of the lizard species and find features that they might use to distinguish them.

Develop Inquiry Skills

OBSERVE **Guide students to better understand how making observations can answer a question. Ask them to plan an investigation to answer the question, What kinds of birds visit a bird feeding station in September?** Students should explain they can answer the question by observing and recording the kinds of birds at the feeding station each day in the month of September.

Notebook ▶ Summarize Ideas

Direct students to think about the main idea and details on these two pages. Have them use the main heading phrase "other kinds of investigations" in a a verbal or written sentence. Then, ask them for two to four details that name some types of investigations.

Use an Identification Guide

Draw lines to match the lizard with its description.

Texas Horned Lizard

- Colors: brownish
- Body: wider and flatter than other lizards
- Tail: straight and shorter than the body
- Spines: several short horns on head, spiny scales on sides of body

Common Chameleon

- Colors: green, yellow, gray, or brown
- Eyes: big and bulge out from side of head
- Body: tall and flat, a ridge of scales along the backbone
- Tail: curls for grasping branches

Common Iguana

- Colors: green, gray, brown, blue, lavender, or black
- Spines: along center of back and tail
- Body: Large flap of skin under the chin

11

123 Math Connection

Make a Graph To extend the question "At what time of year does a state get the most rain?" list on the board the following average monthly rainfall data for Florida: Jan., 2 in.; Feb., 2 in.; March, 2 ½ in.; April, 2 ½ in.; May, 4 in.; June, 6 in.; July, 9 in.; Aug, 10 in.; Sept., 10 in.; Oct., 5 ½ in.; Nov., 2 ½ in.; Dec., 2 in.

Have students convert the fractions to decimals and then graph the data.

2 Explain (continued)

 Notebook **Generate Ideas**

With students, brainstorm possible answers to Dr. Sims' question in the introductory paragraph: **How do you know?** Record their ideas about what information they might need to predict the weather.

....

Active Reading

Remind students that the main idea may be stated in the first sentence or it may be stated elsewhere. To find a main idea, active readers ask: What is this paragraph mostly about?

....

Develop Science Concepts

Students may be familiar with the concept of evidence as related to criminal investigations and presentations in a legal trial or hearing.

What do detectives do when they gather evidence? They look for objects or information that can help them decide who committed a crime.

Explain that scientific evidence also consists of facts, or pieces of verifiable information. In science investigations, the evidence is used to show that a hypothesis is correct or not correct.

Scientists Share Their Results as Evidence

Dr. Sims says, "Tell me something you know." You tell her that it is going to be stormy tomorrow. She says, "*How* do you know?"

Active Reading As you read these two pages, draw two lines under the main idea.

When scientists explain how things work, they must give evidence. *Evidence* is data gathered during an investigation. Evidence might support your hypothesis, or it might not. For example, think about the class with their lizard. The students tell Dr. Sims a hypothesis: Lizards eat more insects than fruit. They carry out an experiment, putting tiny crickets and fruit in the lizard's tank. After two hours, they observe how much food is left, and then repeat the experiment each day for a week.

The students tell Dr. Sims that their lizard ate more crickets than fruit. She says, "What is your evidence?" The students share their recorded results. They report that the lizard ate 13 crickets and no fruit.

12

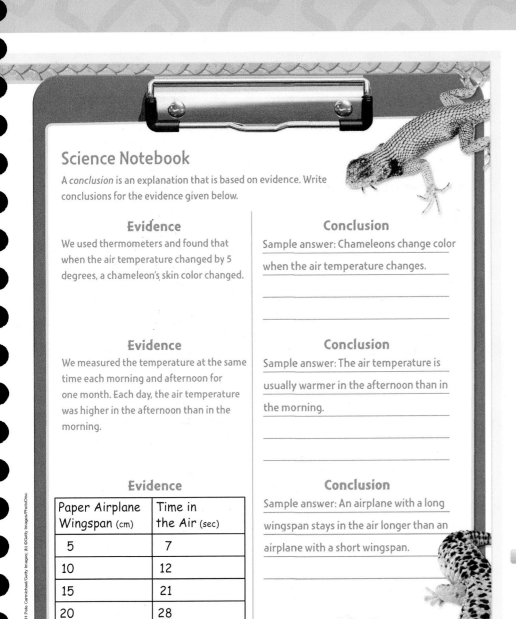

Science Notebook

A *conclusion* is an explanation that is based on evidence. Write conclusions for the evidence given below.

Evidence

We used thermometers and found that when the air temperature changed by 5 degrees, a chameleon's skin color changed.

Conclusion

Sample answer: Chameleons change color when the air temperature changes.

Evidence

We measured the temperature at the same time each morning and afternoon for one month. Each day, the air temperature was higher in the afternoon than in the morning.

Conclusion

Sample answer: The air temperature is usually warmer in the afternoon than in the morning.

Evidence

Paper Airplane Wingspan (cm)	Time in the Air (sec)
5	7
10	12
15	21
20	28

Conclusion

Sample answer: An airplane with a long wingspan stays in the air longer than an airplane with a short wingspan.

13

Develop Inquiry Skills

DRAW CONCLUSIONS In the last paragraph on the previous page, have students circle the evidence (the lizard ate 13 crickets and no fruit) and underline the conclusion (their lizard ate more crickets than fruit).

When writing what evidence would support the conclusion that chameleons change color when the air temperature changes, direct students to think about observations that could be made by placing a thermometer inside the lizard's tank.

Before writing a conclusion based on the evidence that air temperatures are usually warmer in the afternoon than in the morning, have students think about investigations they could carry out over several days or weeks.

Guide students to draw a conclusion from the wingspan and time-in-the-air data in the table at the bottom of this page. Have them complete an if-then statement: **If the wingspan is ____, then the time in the air will ____.** increased, increase

Notebook ▸ Summarize Ideas

Direct students to look again at the main idea they underlined for Active Reading. Then, have them look at the activity on this page and summarize orally or in writing the connection between evidence and conclusions.

3 Extend/Evaluate

Sum It Up!

- If students are unfamiliar with cloze passages, tell them to look for contextual clues and to use their knowledge of the lesson content to fill in the missing words and phrases and to write the missing sentence. You might also point out that all the science vocabulary terms highlighted in this lesson are needed to complete the summary.

- If students are not sure how to complete item 3, tell them to go on to item 4. Once they understand that the students in the story are doing research, they should realize that research is a kind of investigation.

- Make sure students understand that item 9 requires them to write a whole sentence and that the answer cannot be found in their lesson.

- Once students have completed the summary, have them pair up and read their summaries to one another. Then, they can discuss any differences and make corrections.

- Suggest to students that they cover up the answer key and try to fill in as many blanks as they can, first without references and second by looking back at the lesson pages for clues. Once they have completed as much as they can, they can use the Answer Key to check and revise their answers. Point out that the revision step is very important because when the page is correct, it can be used as a summary of the lesson from which to study for tests.

- If students find part of the cloze passage to be particularly difficult, make certain to review the relevant concepts before allowing students to proceed to the Brain Check.

When you're done, use the answer key to check and revise your work.

Fill in the missing words to tell what scientists do.

Summarize

Mr. Brown's fourth-grade class wants a pet in their classroom. Their teacher says they have to think like a (1) ___scientist___ to care for animals. The students know that means (2) ___asking questions___ about the natural world. The class wonders what kinds of animals make good classroom pets. They decide to do an (3) ___investigation___ to find out. They go to the library and use books and websites to (4) ___research___ pets.

The class concludes that guinea pigs are the best pets for their classroom. Mr. Brown asks them what (5) ___evidence___ they have to support their conclusion. The students explain that guinea pigs are quiet and gentle. They are also active in the daytime and sleep at night.

Once the guinea pigs are in the classroom, the students watch and listen. They keep a science journal and list all their (6) ___observations___. Then, students ask (7) ___questions___ based on what they observe. One is: What does it mean when the guinea pigs make squeaking sounds? Two students have a (8) ___hypothesis___ : guinea pigs make that noise when they want to be fed.

Mr. Brown suggests that the students record the time when they hear the sound and write down what they are doing at the same time. After a few days, the students see that their guinea pigs make that noise just as the zippered bag that holds the fresh vegetables is opened. So, what do you think the sound means? (9) ___It means they want to eat the vegetables right away.___

Answer Key: 1. scientist, 2. asking questions, 3. investigation, 4. research, 5. evidence, 6. observations, 7. questions, 8. hypothesis, 9. It means they want to eat the vegetables right away.

🧠 Brain Check

Name _____

Word Play

1 Use the words in the box to complete the puzzle.

Across

5. An explanation based on evidence
7. Scientists do one of these to answer questions

Down

1. An idea or explanation that can be tested with an investigation
2. To share the results of investigations
3. A person who asks questions about the natural world
4. You ask this
6. A kind of investigation that is a fair test

Crossword answers:

Down 1: HYPOTHESIS
Down 2: COMMUNICATE
Down 3: SCIENTIST
Down 4: QUESTION
Down 6: EXPERIMENT
Across 5: CONCLUSION
Across 7: INVESTIGATION

communicate   conclusion   experiment*   hypothesis*

investigation*   question   scientist*

* Key Lesson Vocabulary

© Houghton Mifflin Harcourt Publishing Company

15

Answer Strategies

Word Play

1. To make the puzzle more challenging, have students cover up the word box at the bottom of the page. If students need help, direct them to the page in the lesson on which each term is defined and discussed.

Assessment

Scoring Guide

You may wish to use this suggested scoring guide for the Brain Check.

Item	Points
1	35 (5 points each item)
2	20
3	20
4	25
Total	100

Lesson Quiz

See Assessment Guide, p. AG 1.

3 Extend/Evaluate (continued)

Answer Strategies

Apply Concepts

2. You may wish to pass out a set of objects for students to choose from. Make sure their observations are attributes that can be directly observed, not inferences. Have students think to themselves: What would a scientist ask about this object?

3. Explain to students that they are to develop a hypothesis. Have them write if-then statements to show a cause and effect. If they are not sure what a hypothesis is, have them review the seventh page of this lesson.

4. Point out to students that they can compare the popularity of each food by comparing the size of the sections of the circle, or by comparing the percent numbers.

Take It Home!

See *ScienceSaurus*® for more information about scientific investigations. *ScienceSaurus* is a "mini-encyclopedia" students can use to find out more about unit topics. It contains numerous resources including concise content summaries, an almanac, many tables, charts, and graphs, history of science, and a glossary.

Apply Concepts

2 Choose an object to observe. List some observations. Then ask some questions related to your observations.

Name of Object: _____   Questions: _____

Observations: _____   _____

Answers will vary. Verify that the observations are accurate for the object selected.

3 Your family uses steel wool soap pads for cleaning pots and pans. Often they get rusty after use. What could you do to stop the pads from rusting? Write a hypothesis you could test. Hypotheses will vary. Students may say that the pads need to be well dried or sealed in a plastic bag, wrapped in aluminum foil, or put in the freezer.

4 The graph shows the results of a national online poll in which students were asked to name their favorite lunch food. What conclusions can you draw? Sample answers: Students prefer pizza over the four other lunch items. Students like pita pockets the least. Students like lasagna and grilled cheese about the same. Hamburgers are the second-favorite lunch.

Pita pockets
Grilled cheese
Pizza
Lasagna
Hamburgers

Take It Home! See *ScienceSaurus*® for more information about scientific investigations.

16

Make Connections

Easy
Art Connection

Investigate Colors

- Provide watercolor paints, brushes, cups of water, and paper to students. Demonstrate how to mix two colors from the set and observe the resulting color. Then, have students list the color combination they plan to test and carry out their plans.

- Have students display their color mixing results and share conclusions.

Average
Math Connection

Use Fractions

- Have students investigate the question, Which lunch do students in our class prefer: hamburger, pizza, grilled cheese, lasagna, or pita pockets?

- Guide students to collect data and record it on tally charts. Have them find the number of students that prefer each lunch and compare each number to the total number of students in the class. Guide them to draw diagrams to find the fraction of the group that voted for each food.

Average
Health and Physical Education Connection

Investigate Physical Activity Levels

Have each student keep a physical activity log for a week, noting how many hours and minutes they spend in each activity for seven days. Activities that qualify include walking, running, playing outdoor sports, riding bikes, lifting and carrying packages, gardening, cleaning homes, and so on.

Challenging
Social Studies Connection

Find Scientists from My State

- Have students do Internet searches to find out about scientists (living and historical) from their own state.

- To prepare, discuss appropriate keywords to submit to search engines and identify directories recommended for Grade 4 students.

- Have students work in teams to complete their research, record their notes, and share their results.

Options for Inquiry

FLIPCHART P. 3

Students can conduct these optional investigations at any time before, during, or in response to the lesson in the Student Edition.

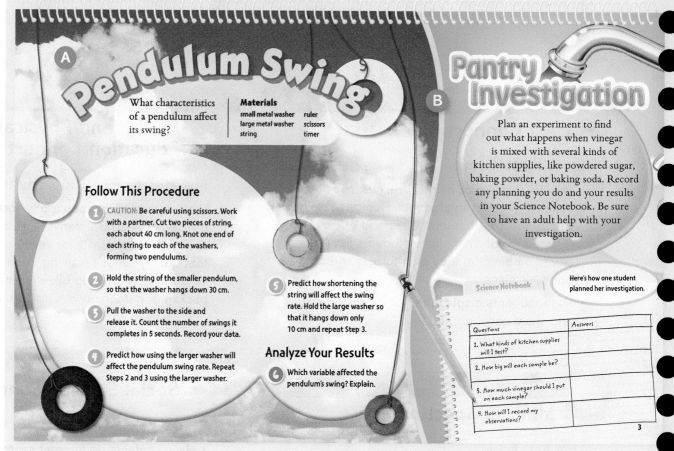

A Pendulum Swing

What characteristics of a pendulum affect its swing?

Materials
small metal washer   ruler
large metal washer   scissors
string   timer

Follow This Procedure

1. CAUTION: Be careful using scissors. Work with a partner. Cut two pieces of string, each about 40 cm long. Knot one end of each string to each of the washers, forming two pendulums.

2. Hold the string of the smaller pendulum, so that the washer hangs down 30 cm.

3. Pull the washer to the side and release it. Count the number of swings it completes in 5 seconds. Record your data.

4. Predict how using the larger washer will affect the pendulum swing rate. Repeat Steps 2 and 3 using the larger washer.

5. Predict how shortening the string will affect the swing rate. Hold the large washer so that it hangs down only 10 cm and repeat Step 3.

Analyze Your Results

6. Which variable affected the pendulum's swing? Explain.

B Pantry Investigation

Plan an experiment to find out what happens when vinegar is mixed with several kinds of kitchen supplies, like powdered sugar, baking powder, or baking soda. Record any planning you do and your results in your Science Notebook. Be sure to have an adult help with your investigation.

Here's how one student planned her investigation.

Science Notebook

Questions	Answers
1. What kinds of kitchen supplies will I test?	
2. How big will each sample be?	
3. How much vinegar should I put on each sample?	
4. How will I record my observations?	

3

Directed Inquiry

A Pendulum Swing

🕐 20 minutes
👥 pairs

Prep and Planning Tips

Each pair of students will need two metal washers, one with a larger size and mass than the other. Make sure each student pair cuts the same length of string for each pendulum.

Expected Results

The pendulum with the larger washer should have the same swing rate as the pendulum with the smaller washer. In other words, the time of a to-and-fro swing—the pendulum's *period*—is independent of the pendulum's mass. Shortening the string will result in a shorter period (the swing rate will increase).

Independent Inquiry

B Pantry Investigation

🕐 25 minutes
👥 individuals

Prep and Planning Tips

See the Planning for Inquiry page for more information. In order to conserve resources, you may want to tell students that the mass of the kitchen supply samples cannot be more than 5 oz.

Science Notebook

Students can use the Science Notebook as a model for designing their own investigation. They may wish to brainstorm the kinds of kitchen supplies that they think might react with vinegar. Students should also plan how they will make observations. Ask if they plan to wait a few minutes or observe right away.

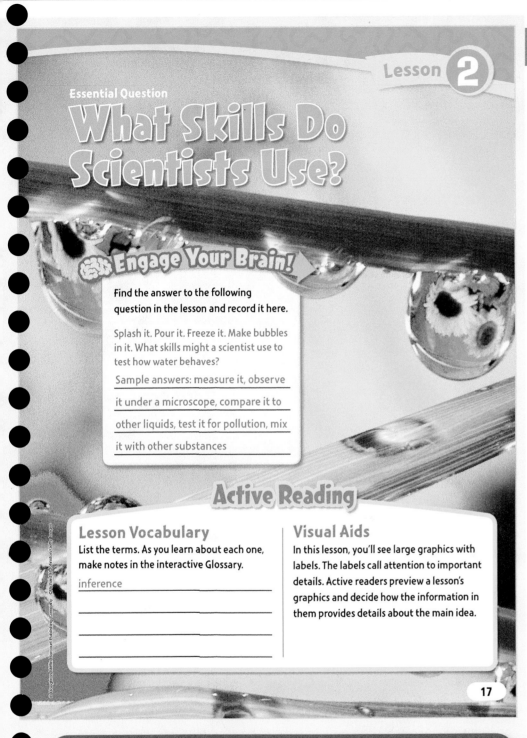

Lesson 2

Essential Question

What Skills Do Scientists Use?

Engage Your Brain!

Find the answer to the following question in the lesson and record it here.

Splash it. Pour it. Freeze it. Make bubbles in it. What skills might a scientist use to test how water behaves?

Sample answers: measure it, observe it under a microscope, compare it to other liquids, test it for pollution, mix it with other substances

Active Reading

Lesson Vocabulary

List the terms. As you learn about each one, make notes in the interactive Glossary.

inference

_____

_____

_____

Visual Aids

In this lesson, you'll see large graphics with labels. The labels call attention to important details. Active readers preview a lesson's graphics and decide how the information in them provides details about the main idea.

17

Go Digital

An interactive digital lesson is available in Online Resources. It is suitable for individuals, small groups, or may be projected or used on an interactive white board.

What Skills Do Scientists Use?

Vocabulary
inference

The vocabulary word for this lesson is inference.
Click the word to find out more about it.

Objectives

• Explain that inquiry skills are used in daily life.

• Identify examples of skills used to carry out common tasks.

Engage Your Brain!

Guide students to consider how life, earth, and physical scientists might test water in different ways. For example, a life scientist might look for microscopic life, an earth scientist might see how it erodes rocks, and a physical scientist might test how it freezes.

Remind students to record their final answers to the question when they read about how scientists investigate on the fourth and fifth pages of this lesson.

Active Reading Annotations

Remind students that active readers "make texts their own" by annotating them with notes and marks that help with comprehension. Encourage students to use pencil, not pen, to make annotations as they read. The goal of annotation is to help students remember what they have read.

Vocabulary and Interactive Glossary

Remind students to find and list the yellow highlighted terms from the lesson. As they proceed through the lesson and learn about the terms, they can add notes, drawings or sentences in the extra spaces provided in the Interactive Glossary.

2 Explain

 ▶ **Generate Ideas**

Have students preview the images and labels on these two pages. **What are the scientists doing in each picture?** observing, inferring, communicating, and comparing

Point out that not only are these science skills but they are also the skills 21st century citizens need to use every day in their own lives.

How do you use these skills in your own life? With students, list situations when they use these skills, such as observing how an expert does a job, communicating how to fix a computer problem, and comparing healthy food choices.

Active Reading

Remind students that a term may be highlighted or italicized. Active readers focus on highlighted and italicized terms because a definition is often provided at that point in the text.

Develop Science Concepts

How do you use your senses other than smell to observe? to see colors of flowers, to taste sweet and sour foods, to hear high and low sounds, to touch to feel whether objects are rough or smooth

Have students practice making inferences by stating an observation and asking students what they can infer from that observation. **You hear a distant and deep rumbling sound. What might you infer?** Sample answers: A truck is coming down the road, there is going to be a thunderstorm, or there is traffic on the highway.

You touch the soil around a plant and it feels dry. What can you infer? I can infer that the plant needs water.

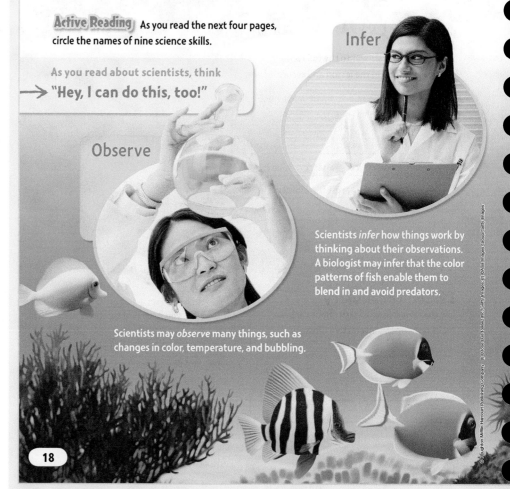

Everyday Science Skills

Do you ask questions about the world around you? If so, you use these science skills all day, every day—just like a scientist!

Active Reading As you read the next four pages, circle the names of nine science skills.

As you read about scientists, think → "Hey, I can do this, too!"

Infer

Observe

Scientists *infer* how things work by thinking about their observations. A biologist may infer that the color patterns of fish enable them to blend in and avoid predators.

Scientists may *observe* many things, such as changes in color, temperature, and bubbling.

18

English Language Learners

Practice Comparing Give students magazines, pictures, or classroom objects. Ask them to find two objects, places, animals, or people with valid points of comparison. For example: an urban place and a rural place, a police officer and a firefighter, a horse and a zebra, a stapler and a pencil sharpener. Offer various compare-and-contrast graphic organizers to help students make comparisons. Ask small groups to complete organizers and present them to the class.

Scientists use inquiry skills every day—and so do you. When you (observe) you use your five senses to get information. Let's say you smell cheese, bread, and spicy odors. You (infer) "I think we are having pizza for lunch today!" An **inference** is a statement that explains an observation.

When you think about how things are the same and different, you (compare) them. For example, your family wants to adopt a new kitten. You compare different kittens, looking for one that is playful and friendly. When you decide which kitten is the best, you (communicate) that decision to your family. You can communicate by speaking, writing, and by using pictures or models.

Compare

Scientists *compare* objects and things that happen.

▶ Practice the skill of *comparing*. List ways these two fish are similar and different.

Powder-Blue Tang   Porcupinefish

Similarities	Differences
Sample answers: Both fish have large eyes. Both fish have fins and scales. Both fish breathe through gills.	The blue tang is colorful and sleek in shape. The porcupinefish is white and tan in color and covered in spines.

Communicate

▶ Scientists *communicate*, or share, their results and inferences with other scientists. What did you communicate today?

Sample answer: I told my teacher that I finished my homework from last night.

19

Differentiation — Leveled Questions

Extra Support
You smell the odor of burnt toast. What can you infer?
Sample answers: Someone left the bread in the toaster too long.

Challenge
You are an astronomer. You see a streak of light cross the sky and infer it was a meteor. Could anyone else make the same inference? maybe not, if they didn't know as much about objects in the sky as an astronomer does

Develop Science Vocabulary

inference Point out to students that the word *inference* is a noun (person, place, or thing) related to the verb (action word) *infer*. The thinking skill is to *infer*, and the result of that thinking is the idea called an *inference*.

Develop Inquiry Skills

COMPARE To help students better understand how to compare and contrast, write the words *spring* and *fall* on the board. Have students draw a Venn diagram, made of two interlocking circles, with the intersection labeled *similarities* and the outer parts of the two circles labeled *differences*. Direct students to compare what they know about these two seasons and to fill in the Venn diagram. Sample answers: similarities—they last the same amount of days, the air temperatures are about the same, school is open; differences—spring usually starts cold and gets warmer while fall starts warm and gets colder, it might rain more in one season than the other, more plants flower in spring than in fall

As students answer the question in the Communicate box, remind them that people can communicate in different ways. They can speak, use non-verbal communication, or communicate ideas in writing or in pictures.

When students compare the powder-blue tang and porcupinefish in the photos, challenge them to show how their statements are based on observations rather than inferences.

Notebook ▶ Summarize Ideas

Have students look again at the photos, labels, and captions. Invite them to think about the information presented and then summarize the main idea orally or in writing.

2 Explain (continued)

 Generate Ideas

With students, brainstorm some answers to a question based on the main heading: **What do people do when they think like a scientist?** Record ideas on the board and have students return to them and correct any inaccuracies after they have read the lesson.

Develop Science Concepts

Students are likely to be familiar with the skill *predict*. Make sure they understand that science predictions are based on observations, not guesses or random choices.

Explore the experiment mentioned under Use Variables. Explain to students that all other conditions, or factors, are kept the same. Ask: **What factors should be kept the same in this experiment?** the kind of fruit juice, the kind of ice pop molds, the size of the molds and the amount of juice poured into them

Elaborate on the discussion of Plan and Conduct Investigations. **What materials would you need?** a glass of tap water, salt, a measuring spoon, and an egg

Guide students to develop a procedure. **What steps would you follow?** First, put one spoonful of salt into the water and stir to dissolve it. Then, put the egg in the glass and see if it floats. If it does not, add another spoonful of salt. Repeat until the egg floats.

Think Like a Scientist

Scientists use these skills every day in their investigations. Find out what they are and when you might use them.

Predict

Scientists use their observations and existing research to make predictions about what will happen in the future. For example, a meteorologist uses weather patterns to determine whether it will rain over the weekend.

Use Variables

When scientists plan experiments, they think, "What is the one thing I will change?" That one thing is a variable. Let's say you want to find out how cold a freezer has to be to make fruit pops. The variable that you will change is the temperature inside the freezer.

Some science skills are part of doing science investigations, including experiments. They may sound unfamiliar to you. But when you read about these skills, you might realize that you already use them.

20

© Houghton Mifflin Harcourt Publishing Company

 Writing Connection

Letter Help students understand what scientists might communicate to one another by having them do research about a famous scientist and then write a one-page letter that a scientist might write to another telling about his or her discoveries.

For example, students could write a letter as Thomas A. Edison, inviting a friend to visit his lab to see the electric lights he is working on. Remind students to include the parts of a friendly letter: a greeting, a body, and a closing.

Plan and Conduct Investigations

Scientists plan and conduct investigations that will answer science questions. Say you want to know how salty water must be to make an egg float. First, you think about the steps you'll take to find the answer. Next, you gather the materials you'll use. Then, you test the amount of salt.

▶ You are a marine biologist. You study living things in the ocean. What is one investigation you might plan?

to find out what a fish eats or how it
protects itself

Predict what a marine biologist might look for on a dive.

fish, crabs, lobsters, plankton, shrimp,
eels, sharks, coral

Hypothesize

Scientists hypothesize when they think of a testable statement that tries to explain an observation. Suppose you notice that water seems to evaporate at different rates from containers with different shapes. What would you hypothesize is a cause?

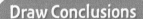

Draw Conclusions

Scientists draw conclusions when they use evidence to evaluate a hypothesis. If you investigate how the size of a sail affects how quickly a toy boat moves, you might conclude that boats with larger sails move faster because larger sails collect more wind.

© Houghton Mifflin Harcourt Publishing Company

21

Interpret Visuals

What details in the underwater scene give you ideas for investigations? the fish and other sea life; the camera for taking pictures

Make sure students understand that marine biologists investigate ocean life. Consider having students brainstorm ideas in teams, listing as much marine life as they can before choosing one investigation they might plan.

Notebook ▸ **Summarize Ideas**

Have students think about the five science skills discussed on these two pages. Ask them to choose one and to give examples of how scientists and students might use it in an investigation. Have them summarize the main idea orally or in writing.

Differentiation — Leveled Questions

Extra Support

In the investigation about the salt water and egg, how would you use measuring spoons? I would use them to measure the amount of salt I add to the water each time.

Challenge

Why should you report the amount of water used and the amount of salt? Help students understand that the water's salinity depends on how much salt is added per unit volume of water.

2 Explain (continued)

 Generate Ideas

Have students add to the list of math skills in the introductory paragraph. Record their ideas on the board. Point out that scientists use all these skills, too.

Active Reading

Remind students that active readers preview headings to establish expectations and purposes for reading. Reading with a purpose helps active readers focus on understanding and recalling what they read in order to fulfill the purpose.

Develop Science Concepts

Challenge students to brainstorm how scientists in fields other than marine biology use mathematics.

Suppose you are a space scientist who wants to send a robot to Mars to test soil samples. How might you use math? to measure the distance to Mars, to find the speed of the spacecraft, to measure the force of gravity on Mars, to use a clock to keep time

Suppose you are a weather scientist. How would you use numbers in your investigations? to measure air temperature in degrees, to measure rainfall in inches and centimeters, to describe wind speed and air pressure, to find average weather conditions for a season, to show scale on maps

Math and Science Skills

Using rulers and balances. Putting things in order. Measuring the speed of a car. Making tables and graphs. Sounds like math, but it's science, too!

Active Reading As you read this page, turn the heading into a question in your mind. Then underline the parts of the text that answer the question.

Every scientist uses math. Let's say you are a marine biologist who studies whales. You *classify* whales by how much they weigh or how long they are from head to tail. You put them in *order* when you arrange them by length from smallest to largest. You *use numbers* to tell how many are alive today. You *use time and space relationships* to investigate when and where they migrate each year. You *measure* how long they are and how much food they eat. You *record and display* the results of your investigations in writing and in tables, graphs, and maps.

Classify and Order

You classify things when you put them into groups. To put things in order, you may make a list in which position matters, such as ordering bird species by how fast they fly or move.

Measure

In science and math, you measure by using tools to find length, width, height, mass, weight, volume, and elapsed time.

Use Numbers

You use numbers when you observe by counting or measuring. You also use numbers to compare and order. And, you use numbers to describe speed and force.

22

English Language Learners

Examine Cohesion Links
Students may have trouble understanding pronoun referents and words that are understood but not written. Refer students to the paragraph about studying whales. Read the first three sentences aloud. Then, examine the fourth and fifth sentences. Help students understand that *them* in the fourth sentence refers to whales. In the fifth sentence, *how many* means "how many whales."

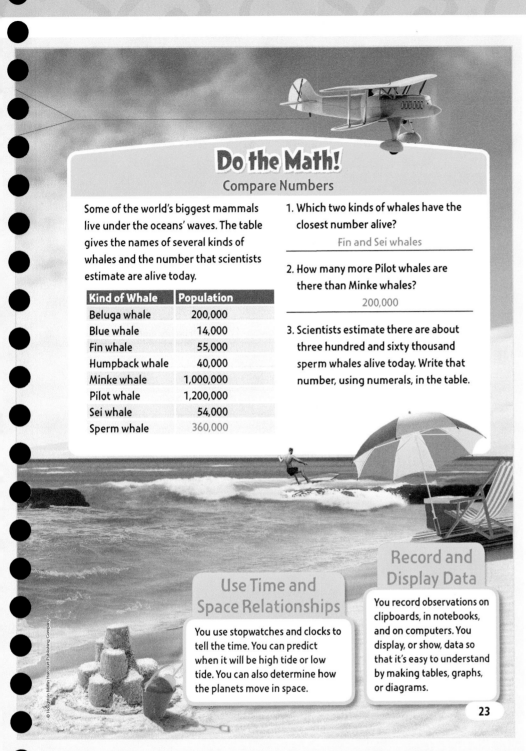

Do the Math!
Compare Numbers

Some of the world's biggest mammals live under the oceans' waves. The table gives the names of several kinds of whales and the number that scientists estimate are alive today.

Kind of Whale	Population
Beluga whale	200,000
Blue whale	14,000
Fin whale	55,000
Humpback whale	40,000
Minke whale	1,000,000
Pilot whale	1,200,000
Sei whale	54,000
Sperm whale	360,000

1. Which two kinds of whales have the closest number alive?

   Fin and Sei whales

2. How many more Pilot whales are there than Minke whales?

   200,000

3. Scientists estimate there are about three hundred and sixty thousand sperm whales alive today. Write that number, using numerals, in the table.

Use Time and Space Relationships

You use stopwatches and clocks to tell the time. You can predict when it will be high tide or low tide. You can also determine how the planets move in space.

Record and Display Data

You record observations on clipboards, in notebooks, and on computers. You display, or show, data so that it's easy to understand by making tables, graphs, or diagrams.

23

Math Connection

Represent Relative Sizes

Provide students with data for the average length of an adult male of each species listed on the student page, as follows: beluga whale, 4 m; blue whale, 25 m; fin whale, 20 m; humpback whale, 12.9 m; minke whale, 9 m; pilot whale, 5.6 m; sei whale, 16 m; sperm whale, 16 m.

Have students draw a number line and place the whales by length. Remind them to read the numbers carefully, including the decimals, and to use the units of measurement correctly.

Develop Inquiry Skills

USE NUMBERS Have students use the whale data in the table on this page to compare relative population sizes. **Which estimated whale population is the largest?** the pilot whale population

Which estimated whale population is the smallest? the blue whale population

Help students understand that all these numbers are estimates. **To what place value are all these numbers rounded?** to the thousands

Do the Math!

Compare Numbers

To find the two kinds of whales that are closest in numbers, have students rewrite the list in numerical order and then check adjacent pairs.

To find the difference in two whale populations, students can subtract the smaller number from the larger number, or they can count from the smaller number until they reach the larger number.

When students write three hundred and sixty thousand in digits, have them check their placement of the comma.

Notebook ▶ Summarize Ideas

Direct students to think about the main idea on these two pages. Ask them if their ideas about how math is used outside of school have changed. Have them summarize the main idea orally and in writing.

3 Extend/Evaluate

Sum It Up!

- Tell students to use their knowledge of the lesson content to fill in each column of the table with the correct skills. You might want to point out that all these skills appear as headings throughout the lesson.

- Once students have completed the table, have them pair up and read their tables orally to one another. Then, they can discuss any differences and make corrections.

- Suggest to students that they cover up the answer key and try to fill in as many of the correct skills as they can, first without references and second by looking back at the lesson pages for clues. Once they have completed as many as they can, they can use the Answer Key to check and revise their answers. Point out that the revision step is very important because when the page is correct, it can be used as a summary of the lesson from which to study for tests.

- If students find completing the table to be particularly difficult, make certain to review the relevant concepts before allowing them to proceed to the Brain Check.

When you're done, use the answer key to check and revise your work.

Fill in the missing skills in the column where they belong.

Summarize

Scientists Use Skills

Everyday Science Skills	Science Investigation Skills	Math and Science Skills
1. infer	5. predict	10. measure
2. communicate	6. use variables	11. classify and order
3. compare	7. plan and conduct investigations	12. record and display data
4. observe	8. draw conclusions	13. use time and space relationships
	9. hypothesize	14. use numbers

Answer Key: 1–4. infer, communicate, compare, observe; 5–9. predict, use variables, plan and conduct investigations, draw conclusions, hypothesize; 10–14. measure, classify and order, record and display data, use time and space relationships, use numbers

 **Brain Check** — Lesson **2**

Name _____

Word Play

1 It's easy to get tongue-tied describing what scientists do. Look at the statements below. Switch the red words around until each statement about inquiry skills makes sense.

In order to sort his beakers and other tools, Dr. Mallory hypothesizes each object by size and shape. __classifies__

Gabriella measures that her dog will want his favorite food for dinner, because she has observed him eat it quickly many times before. __predicts__

Kim predicts when planning an experiment with her older brother. She keeps everything the same during their procedure, except for the one factor being tested. __uses variables__

After completing an experiment and summarizing her findings, Dr. Garcia classifies what she has learned with other scientists. __communicates__

Dr. Jefferson studies the age of rocks and fossils. She uses variables to tell how old each specimen is. __uses time and space relationships__

Before conducting his experiment for the science fair, Derrick uses time and space relationships about which sample of fertilizer will make his tomato plant grow the fastest. __hypothesizes__

To find out how long it takes Deshawn to ride his bike 100 m, Jessica communicates the time with a stopwatch. __measures__

25

Answer Strategies

Word Play

1. If students need help, guide them to look for contextual clues.

- Suggest that students think of a synonym for the word *sort* to solve the first statement.

- Point out that Gabriella is thinking about what will happen in the future in the second statement.

- For help with the third statement, direct students to the fourth page of this lesson.

- For help with the fourth statement, direct students to the third page of this lesson.

- For help with the fifth statement, direct students to the seventh page of this lesson.

- Point out to students that the sixth statement is about making an educated guess about what causes something else to happen.

- Direct students to use the words *how long*, *time*, and *stopwatch* as clues to solve the last statement.

Assessment

Scoring Guide
You may wish to use this suggested scoring guide for the Brain Check.

Item	Points
1	35 (5 points each)
2	35
3	30
Total	100

Lesson Quiz
See Assessment Guide, p. AG 2.

3 Extend/Evaluate (continued)

Answer Strategies

Apply Concepts

2. Have students discuss what they know and don't know about octopuses and identify questions that can be answered with numbers: how many arms they have, how big they get, how fast they move. Ask students about the size of bubbles and how long they last before they pop. Have students discuss how the scooter moves and think about ways its movement can be measured.

3. Have students explain how they could record the shape changes of the moon on a calendar. Ask students to think about what they might observe before and after the scene showing the birds. Have students consider all the weather conditions that can be observed from day to day.

....

 Take It Home!

Suggest to students that they go with a family member to the biography section of the children's room in their public library. Have them make paper bookmarks to mark the places in the book where science skills are used. Suggest that they take notes on each bookmark.

 Apply Concepts

2 Write how you would use numbers to investigate each object.

Sample answer: count arms, measure mass, calculate speed

Sample answer: measure diameter of bubbles, time how long bubbles last before they break

Sample answer: measure distance it rolls, time how long it can stand up, calculate speed

3 For each one, what kinds of observations could you record on a calendar?

Sample answer: record the changing shapes of the moon each night

Sample answer: record when the birds build nest, young hatch, and young fly away

Sample answer: record which days have rain and which do not; record the amount of rain that falls in a week or month

Take It Home! There are many books in the library about scientists and how they think about the world around them. Pick a book with a family member. Find examples of the skills you learned about and make a list.

26

Make Connections

Social Studies Connection

Map Science Sites

- Have students research places in their state where they can be inspired to think like a scientist, including science museums, zoos, botanical gardens, and wildlife refuges.

- Provide students with state maps. Have them locate and label sites of scientific interest. Have them write a title for the map and make a key to the symbols and abbreviations they use.

Easy

Math Connection

Find Elapsed Time in Years

Read to students: Jacques Cousteau was a famous ocean explorer who used science skills every day. He was born in 1910 and died in 1997. In 1943, Cousteau and another man invented SCUBA gear. In 1950, Cousteau took over an old navy ship that he used to explore the world's oceans until 1996.

How many years did Jacques Cousteau live? 87

How old was he when he invented SCUBA? 33

How many years did he explore on his boat? 46

Average

Art Connection

Construct Mobiles

- Have students write each science skill on a file card and use markers to decorate the cards. Then, have them punch one hole in the top of each card.

- Provide yarn or string and wooden chopsticks, twigs, or plastic straws. Show them how to tie lengths of string on the cards and hang them from cross pieces. Give students time to balance their mobiles by sliding the strings along the cross pieces.

Challenging

Writing Connection

Create a How-to Manual

- Challenge students to write their own how-to-think-like-a-scientist manuals. Urge them to discuss the skills words found in this lesson (observe, infer, communicate, predict, use variables, plan and conduct investigations, hypothesize, draw conclusions, classify/order, use numbers, use time and space, measure, and record) and provide their own examples of when they might be used.

- Have students illustrate their manuals.

Options for Inquiry

FLIPCHART P. 4

Students can conduct these optional investigations at any time before, during, or in response to the lesson in the Student Edition.

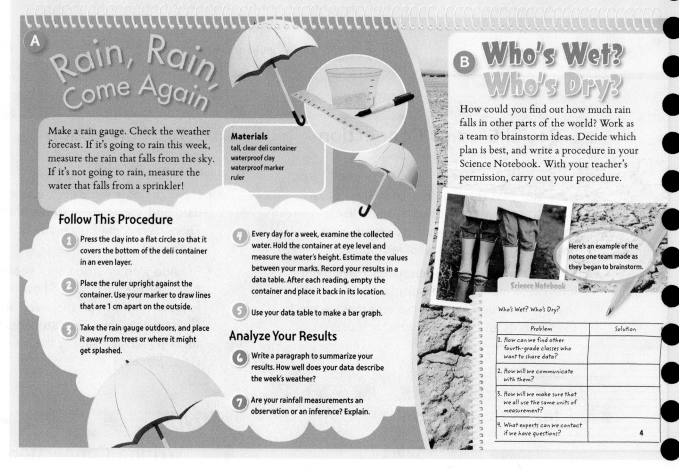

A Rain, Rain, Come Again

Make a rain gauge. Check the weather forecast. If it's going to rain this week, measure the rain that falls from the sky. If it's not going to rain, measure the water that falls from a sprinkler!

Materials
tall, clear deli container
waterproof clay
waterproof marker
ruler

Follow This Procedure

1. Press the clay into a flat circle so that it covers the bottom of the deli container in an even layer.
2. Place the ruler upright against the container. Use your marker to draw lines that are 1 cm apart on the outside.
3. Take the rain gauge outdoors, and place it away from trees or where it might get splashed.
4. Every day for a week, examine the collected water. Hold the container at eye level and measure the water's height. Estimate the values between your marks. Record your results in a data table. After each reading, empty the container and place it back in its location.
5. Use your data table to make a bar graph.

Analyze Your Results

6. Write a paragraph to summarize your results. How well does your data describe the week's weather?
7. Are your rainfall measurements an observation or an inference? Explain.

B Who's Wet? Who's Dry?

How could you find out how much rain falls in other parts of the world? Work as a team to brainstorm ideas. Decide which plan is best, and write a procedure in your Science Notebook. With your teacher's permission, carry out your procedure.

Here's an example of the notes one team made as they began to brainstorm.

Science Notebook

Who's Wet? Who's Dry?

Problem	Solution
1. How can we find other fourth-grade classes who want to share data?	
2. How will we communicate with them?	
3. How will we make sure that we all use the same units of measurement?	
4. What experts can we contact if we have questions?	4

Directed Inquiry

A Rain, Rain, Come Again

⏱ 25 minutes
👥 small groups

Prep and Planning Tips

After placing the rain gauges outdoors, allow 15 minutes each day for a week for students go outdoors, measure and record the water collected, and pour off the water to bring the level back to the zero mark. If you place the gauges where they will collect water from an automatic sprinkler system, students can also measure and record the water for several days.

Expected Results

Results will depend on weather conditions or sprinkler systems. Have students focus on measuring accurately, reporting results clearly, and building a well-labeled bar graph.

Independent Inquiry

B Who's Wet? Who's Dry?

⏱ 45 minutes
👥 small groups

Prep and Planning Tips

See the Planning for Inquiry page for more information. To find out how to use email to safely connect with classrooms around the world, visit Internet pen pal services.

Science Notebook

Students can use the Science Notebook as a model for designing their own investigation. Point out that their procedure does not have to follow the one suggested. Instead of collecting rainfall data themselves, students may decide to do research and find existing data online or in the library. Average yearly rainfall data is readily available for states, regions, and other countries in almanacs and encyclopedias.

Essential Question

How Do Scientists Collect and Use Data?

Lesson 3

Engage Your Brain!

Find the answer to the following question in this lesson and record it here.

Are the ladybugs on this tree identical to each other? How would you investigate this question?

Sample answer: I would make
observations, take measurements, use
tools such as hand lenses, and think
about my results.

Active Reading

Lesson Vocabulary

List the terms. As you learn about each one, make notes in the Interactive Glossary.

data

microscope

pan balance

spring scale

Main Idea and Details

Details give information about a topic. The information may be examples, features, or characteristics. Active readers stay focused on the topic when they ask, What facts or information do these details add to the topic?

27

Go Digital

An interactive digital lesson is available in Online Resources. It is suitable for individuals, small groups, or may be projected or used on an interactive white board.

Objectives

- Determine that scientists often conduct research as part of an investigation.
- Identify different tools that scientists use to study objects and properties.
- Communicate that data gathered are based on measurement and observation, not inferences.
- Record data in appropriate tables and charts based on the purpose of the data.
- Describe that measurements and recording methods need to be accurate because data are used as evidence for scientific explanation.

Engage Your Brain!

Guide students in brainstorming ways to attack this science problem. Record their ideas in a chart or on the board.

Remind students to record their final answers to the question when they read about how scientists do research on the second and third pages of this lesson or use tools on the fourth and fifth pages of this lesson.

Active Reading   Annotations

Remind students that active readers "make texts their own" by annotating them with notes and marks that help with comprehension. Encourage students to use pencil, not pen, to make annotations as they read. The goal of annotation is to help students remember what they have read.

Vocabulary and Interactive Glossary

Remind students to find and list the yellow highlighted terms from the lesson. As they proceed through the lesson and learn about the terms, they can add notes, drawings or sentences in the extra spaces provided in the Interactive Glossary.

2 Explain

Notebook ▸ Generate Ideas

Have students brainstorm some questions they would like answered about fireflies. You might want to mention that fireflies are also known as lightning bugs.

Then, direct students to preview the pictures on these two pages. **What hints do you see about what science research means?** It means going online to look things up, reading newspaper and magazine articles, and going to see what is in a museum.

Develop Science Concepts

How would you use an encyclopedia to research fireflies? Sample answer: Look under "F" for firefly, "L" for lightning bug, or "I" for insects.

What kinds of resources can a librarian show you related to fireflies? nonfiction science books, magazine articles, encyclopedia articles, websites

Suppose you could talk to an expert at a natural history museum. What questions would you ask about fireflies? Sample answers: How does the light help fireflies survive? How do they make light? Do they give off heat as well as light? How many kinds of fireflies are there?

Research Is the Key

Tiny insects fly and flash on a summer night. Are you curious about them? Do you wonder how to find out what they are and how they light up? Do some research!

28

English Language Learners

Examine the Understood *You*
Read the first paragraph aloud. Direct students' attention to the last sentence. Tell them that *you* is often left out of English sentences. Students must mentally add the word. For example: *You* do some research! Explain that imperatives, or command sentences, usually have an understood subject: *you*. Invite examples, such as: Go home; Send me an email; Hand in your homework.

Natural history museums have insect collections as well as scientists who can answer questions about them.

Often scientists ask themselves, "What do other scientists know about this?" To find out, they do *research*. When you research, you use reference materials and talk to experts to learn what is known. So, if you want to learn what scientists know about fireflies, you can do these things:

- Use an encyclopedia.
- Read a book.
- Read science articles.
- Visit a museum.
- E-mail a scientist.
- Visit science websites.

These kinds of resources may have plenty of information about fireflies. But you will still have questions they do not answer. That's when you conduct your own investigations.

Do the Research!

You just saw bees flying in and out of a hole in an old tree. You know it's not a good idea to get too close. So, how can you find out what bees do inside a tree? What research resource would you go to first? Explain why.

Sample answer: An "ask-a-scientist"

webpage, because I could ask the exact

questions I have.

_____

29

Students may have heard the word *research* used in different ways. Some people, including many scientists, refer to all aspects of science investigations as *research*. Make sure students understand that here the word refers only to the process of finding out what other scientists have already concluded and reported.

Develop Inquiry Skills

COMMUNICATE Explain to students that scientific communication is a two-way process. Not only do scientists tell others what they have learned by writing reports and giving talks, they also communicate by answering other scientists' questions and discussing how to conduct investigations.

When students consider how to find out what bees do inside a tree, ask **To whom might you communicate your questions?** Sample answers: ask a beekeeper, ask an insect scientist, call a local nature center, post a question on a science website

Notebook ▸ Summarize Ideas

Have students look again at the main heading on these two pages. Invite them to think about how research is key and summarize the main idea orally or in writing.

Writing Connection

E-mail a Scientist Explain to students that there are many scientific labs, museums, and universities where students may contact a scientist and get a reply. Have the class generate a list of questions they wish to research and choose one or more to ask a scientist. Guide students in composing a group email message. and send the email from your teacher account. Remind students they should always ask permission before communicating on the Internet.

2 Explain (continued)

Notebook ▸ Generate Ideas

With students, brainstorm possible answers to the question **What are some tools scientists use?** Record ideas on the board and have students return to their list and add to it after they have read the lesson.

Active Reading

Remind students that lesson vocabulary is defined once and then used as needed throughout a lesson. Active readers pause to be sure they recall the meaning of a new term as they encounter it in the text.

Develop Science Concepts

Distribute hand lenses, magnifying boxes, and small squares of newspaper to students so that they can compare the images they can see with each tool. Demonstrate how to hold the hand lens near the eye and bring the newsprint up to it until it the surface of the paper is in focus. Have students place a small square of newsprint in the bottom of the magnifying box and replace the lid. If the print is on the bottom of the box, it should be in focus when students look through the lens in the top of the box.

Which lens magnifies the newsprint more? Since the magnification of these lenses can vary, answers will depend on the particular tools students try.

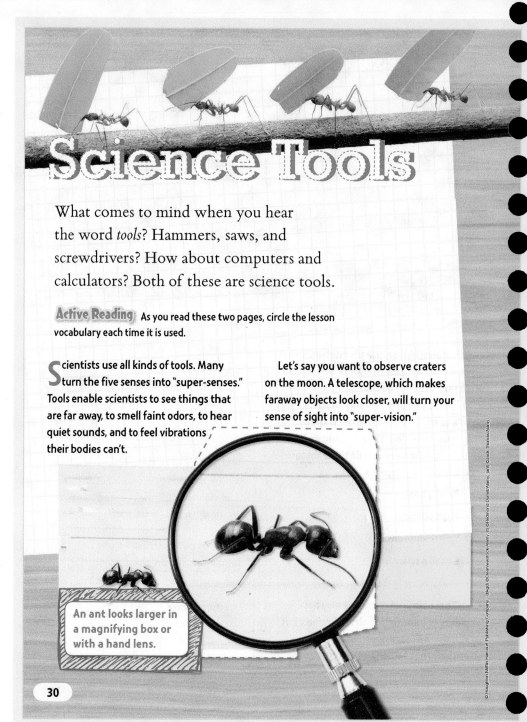

Science Tools

What comes to mind when you hear the word *tools*? Hammers, saws, and screwdrivers? How about computers and calculators? Both of these are science tools.

Active Reading As you read these two pages, circle the lesson vocabulary each time it is used.

Scientists use all kinds of tools. Many turn the five senses into "super-senses." Tools enable scientists to see things that are far away, to smell faint odors, to hear quiet sounds, and to feel vibrations their bodies can't.

Let's say you want to observe craters on the moon. A telescope, which makes faraway objects look closer, will turn your sense of sight into "super-vision."

An ant looks larger in a magnifying box or with a hand lens.

30

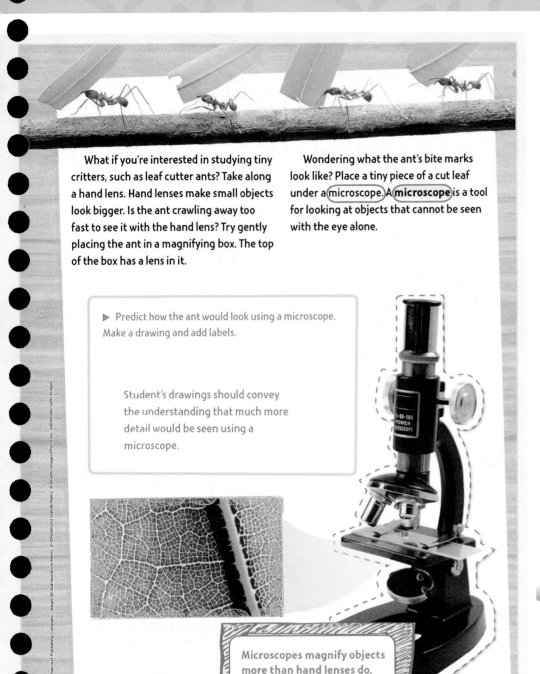

What if you're interested in studying tiny critters, such as leaf cutter ants? Take along a hand lens. Hand lenses make small objects look bigger. Is the ant crawling away too fast to see it with the hand lens? Try gently placing the ant in a magnifying box. The top of the box has a lens in it.

Wondering what the ant's bite marks look like? Place a tiny piece of a cut leaf under a microscope. A microscope is a tool for looking at objects that cannot be seen with the eye alone.

▶ Predict how the ant would look using a microscope. Make a drawing and add labels.

Student's drawings should convey the understanding that much more detail would be seen using a microscope.

Microscopes magnify objects more than hand lenses do.

31

Develop Science Vocabulary

microscope Write the word microscope on the board with a space between *micro* and *scope*. Explain that *micro* means "small" and *scope* means "to look at."

What other words have either micro or scope in them? microscopic, microchip, microwave, telescope, horoscope, kaleidoscope, periscope, stethoscope

Interpret Visuals

Direct students' attention to the call-out photo of the chewed leaf on this page. Explain that a call-out photo is often used to show an enlarged detail related to another image. In this case, the detail shows what might be seen through the microscope.

Point out to students that there are many kinds of microscopes, some magnifying more than others. If they were to use a microscope like the one in the photo to view an ant, they would only be able to view a part of the ant at one time. Have students draw a close-up drawing of one part of an ant.

 Notebook ▸ **Summarize Ideas**

Have students think about the kinds of science tools described on these two pages and summarize the main idea orally or in writing.

Differentiation — Leveled Questions

Extra Support

What is one difference between a hand lens and a microscope? Sample answer: Microscopes have much stronger magnification than hand lenses.

Challenge

What kinds of living and nonliving things, or their parts, are microscopic? All answers should be organisms or structures that cannot be seen with the eye alone. Sample answers: bacteria, germs, cells, dust particles.

2 Explain (continued)

 Generate Ideas

Tap students' prior knowledge by having them brainstorm answers to the question, **How do scientists find exact answers?** Record ideas on the board, and have students add to the list as they read and discuss the lesson.

Develop Science Concepts

Students may ask why they cannot use customary units such as inches, feet, gallons, and pounds to measure in science. Explain that these units are used in very few countries. Because scientists need to communicate with other scientists all over the world, they have agreed to all use the International System of Units.

⚡ Misconception Alert ⚡

Students may think that *mass, volume, weight, heaviness,* and *size* all describe the same attribute. The word *size* is particularly ambiguous because students may think of clothing sizes.

Common usages of descriptive words such as *big* and *small* may also contribute to misconceptions about measurement.

Explain to students that scientists have exact meanings and tools for each type of measurement. For example, *mass* (the amount of matter in an object) is measured with a balance, and *weight* (the force of gravity on an object) is measured with a spring scale.

Measurement Tools

What's the biggest bug in the world? How far can a grasshopper hop? How long can a butterfly fly? How do scientists find exact answers?

Scientists use measurement tools to make their observations more exact. Think about it this way. You and your friend watch two grasshoppers hop. Your friend says, "This one jumped farther." But you think the other one jumped farther. To find out for sure, you need to measure.

There are tools to measure length or distance, mass, force, volume, and temperature. Most scientists use metric units with these tools. For example, a **pan balance** is used to measure mass with units called grams (g). A **spring scale** is used to measure force in units called newtons (N).

Pan Balance

Place the object you want to measure on one pan. Add gram masses to the other pan until the two pans balance. Add the masses together to find the total in grams (g).

32

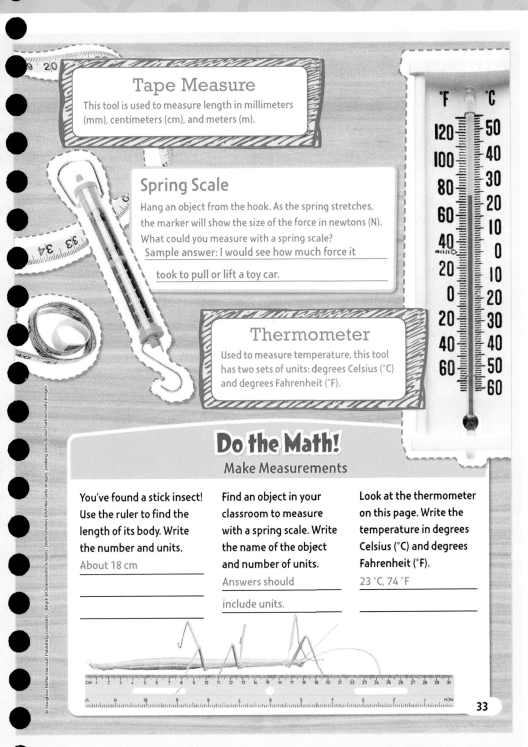

Tape Measure

This tool is used to measure length in millimeters (mm), centimeters (cm), and meters (m).

Spring Scale

Hang an object from the hook. As the spring stretches, the marker will show the size of the force in newtons (N). What could you measure with a spring scale? Sample answer: I would see how much force it took to pull or lift a toy car.

Thermometer

Used to measure temperature, this tool has two sets of units: degrees Celsius (°C) and degrees Fahrenheit (°F).

Do the Math!
Make Measurements

You've found a stick insect! Use the ruler to find the length of its body. Write the number and units.
About 18 cm

Find an object in your classroom to measure with a spring scale. Write the name of the object and number of units.
Answers should include units.

Look at the thermometer on this page. Write the temperature in degrees Celsius (°C) and degrees Fahrenheit (°F).
23 °C, 74 °F

33

 Math Connection

Compute Differences Guide students to use an encyclopedia or online sources to find out the average lengths of other common insects (ladybugs, house flies, etc.). Have students use subtraction to compare the lengths of these insects with the length of the stick bug.

Develop Science Vocabulary

pan balance Draw a board on top of a fulcrum (seesaw) on the board. Draw a box on either end of the board. Ask: **What does it mean when both ends of the board are at the same height from the ground?** It means the boxes are balanced. Point out that balanced means they have the same mass or amount of matter in them.

spring scale Point out that the spring scale in the picture does not work by balancing. This is because it does not compare mass. A spring scale has a spring that is stretched by a force, such as the force of gravity.

Do the Math!
Make Measurements

To measure the stick insect, have students use the scale on the ruler that shows centimeters or millimeters.

When students look for an object in the room to measure with a ruler, ask: **How can you measure the length of an object that is longer than the ruler?** borrow rulers from others and put them end to end; use the same ruler repeatedly, marking where it ended each time

Show students how to record the number of degrees, the symbol for degrees, and the abbreviation for Fahrenheit or Celsius.

Notebook ▶ Summarize Ideas

Direct students to think about the main idea on these two pages. Ask them if their ideas about how measurement is used in science have changed. Have them summarize the main idea orally or in writing.

2 Explain (continued)

Notebook ▸ Generate Ideas

What kinds of observations would you want to keep track of in the jungle? Sample answers: the number of butterflies, the kinds of butterflies, what the butterflies do

How would you save your observations, so you don't forget them? Sample answers: using paper and pencil or a notebook and pen to write notes, using a digital audio recorder or video recorder

Active Reading

Remind students that active readers preview headings to establish expectations and purposes for reading. Reading with a purpose helps active readers focus on understanding and recalling what they read in order to fulfill the purpose.

Develop Science Concepts

What are some other kinds of data in the form of numbers? Sample answer: measurements such as temperature

What are some ways you have learned to display data in mathematics? Sample answers: tables, pictographs, bar graphs, line plots

Recording and Displaying Data

You're crawling through a tropical jungle. A butterfly flutters by. Then another appears. How will you keep track of how many you see?

Active Reading As you read these two pages, turn each heading into a question that will point you to the main idea. Underline the answers to your questions in the text.

A poster is one way to display data.

head   antenna   pronotum   eye   elytra   leg   wing   abdomen

34

English Language Learners

Explore Meanings of Do
The word *do* in questions can be confusing. Help students see how turning headings into questions often requires the addition of *do*. Guide them in turning "Recording Data" into a question, noting the use of do: How do scientists record data? Continue with the other headings on these pages. Then, practice turning statements into questions using *do*. For example: I have five dollars. Do I (or, Do you) have five dollars?

Recording Data

The bits of information you observe are called **data**. Some data are in the form of numbers. For example, the number of butterflies you see in an hour is a piece of data. Other data are in the form of descriptions. Examples include written notes, diagrams, audio recordings, and photographs.

Only observations are data. So when you think, "There are more butterflies here than in Canada," that's a guess, not data.

Displaying Data

The data you record as you investigate may be correct, but not easy to understand. Later, you can decide how to display the data. For example, you might use your scribbled notes from the jungle to draw a map showing where you saw each butterfly. You might compare the number of each kind of butterfly you found in a circle graph. You might use a bar graph to show the number of butterflies you saw each hour.

Data Two Ways

The table on the left lists six butterflies and the number of wing flaps each one made as it passed by an observer. The bar graph on the right can display the same data. Use the data in the table to complete the graph.

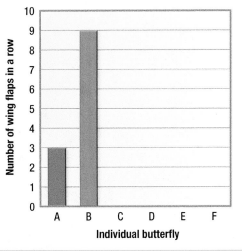

Individual Butterfly	Number of Wing Flaps in a Row
A	3
B	9
C	4
D	3
E	3
F	10

Check students' completed graphs for accuracy.

Develop Science Vocabulary

data Explain to students that the word *data* is plural. If students need to refer to a single observation, tell them to say "this piece of data."

When students refer to several related pieces of data, such as the data in the table on this page, they can call it a *data set*.

Review the steps needed to make a bar graph, and record them on the board so students can refer to the list while creating their own bar graphs: write a title, label the vertical axis, label the horizontal axis, decide on the scale, draw the bars.

Develop Inquiry Skills

RECORD AND DISPLAY DATA Have students use the same table with data about the butterflies to construct a line plot. Have them determine the scale by looking at the range of numbers in the right column (0–10 would work). Have them draw a horizontal line and divide it into 10 equal parts. Then, place an X over the correct number of wing flaps for each butterfly.

Notebook ▸ Summarize Ideas

Direct students to think about the main ideas on these two pages. Invite them to review the main heading and subheadings and summarize orally or in writing the main ideas.

2 Explain (continued)

Notebook → ### Generate Ideas

Direct students to preview the pictures and captions on these two pages. **What details can help you answer the question about how scientists use data to solve problems?** Sample answers: They exchange data using computers. They compare their data to information in museums. They work on teams to solve problems.

Develop Science Concepts

Explain that honeybees live in large groups called colonies. There are wild colonies, but most of the bees live in hives, which are boxlike structures, built by farmers. Farmers harvest and sell honey from the hives, but the most important function of honeybees is as pollinators for apples, nuts, berries, onions, cabbages, peppers, beans, melons, and many other fruits and vegetables. Without honeybees, people might not have these foods to eat.

How do you think scientists collect the data on the number of bees? Sample answer: by counting the number of bees in farmers' hives, by counting the number of hives, by talking to farmers who keep bees, by talking to farmers who grow the plants that need bees

Scientists observed that the number of bees in a hive can drop quickly. **What conclusion would you draw if you found out that honeybees in hives where this happens are infected with the same virus?** Sample answer: I would conclude that the virus is killing them.

Using Data

You see on the news that the number of honeybees in the United States is decreasing. What is happening to them? How do scientists use data to solve problems and share information?

Drawing Conclusions

You've recorded your data. You've displayed it in a way that is easy to understand. Your next step is to analyze, or look for patterns in, the data. You might identify a trend, or a direction in the data over time. For example, you might conclude that the number of honeybees in your hometown has decreased by 30% in the last five years. What's next?

Communicating

Scientists communicate in many ways. They may work together to collect data. They compare their data with other scientists doing similar investigations. They report their results and conclusions by giving talks and writing reports. Conclusions often lead to new questions to investigate. Scientists are still studying why the number of honeybees is decreasing.

Scientists can share data as they make observations by using electronic devices.

> Dr. Ruiz,
> Just checked the hives on Elm Street. There are many dead bees, and fewer honeycombs than last month.
> Dr. Preston

36

Differentiation — Leveled Questions

Extra Support

You measure the temperature outside at noon for a week. The results are: 59°F, 57°F, 54°F, 53°F, 51°F, 47°F, and 45°F. What is the trend? The temperature dropped 2–3°F each day.

Challenge

What can scientists ask about honeybees in order to draw conclusions about the cause of their disappearance? Sample answers: Do they have a disease? Is something eating the bees? Do the bees have enough food?

Scientists may work alone or in teams to analyze data and draw conclusions.

▶ A database is a collection of information or objects. Databases are organized so they are easy to search— like a search website. How would you search a database of insect facts to see what others have learned about the decrease in the number of honeybees? I could search by location, by the number of hives over time, by current events, or by honeybee diseases.

Museums often have large collections of specimens, so scientists can compare what they have found to what's in a museum.

37

Develop Science Concepts

Draw a simple table with rows and columns on the board. Explain that databases are collections of information stored in computers. Each item described in the database is called a *record*. A record is like a row in this table. Each fact about the record is in a *field*. The fields are cells created by the intersection of the rows and columns in the table.

In an insect database, each row might be a different kind of insect. The fields might tell where the insects are found, how many live in each place, what diseases they get, how they are affected by pollution, which scientists are investigating them, and so on.

What combinations of keywords would you use to search the database? Sample answers: honeybee + location, honeybee + disease, honeybee + news, honeybee + hives, honeybee + population

Develop Inquiry Skills

COMMUNICATE Use the following activity to begin a discussion of the importance of good communication skills. Write the following on a sheet of paper, and post it on the wall:

Dinner special: red beans and rice $7.95, chicken or beef $8.95, children $5.95.

Suppose you read this on the window of a restaurant. What is the problem with it? It seems to say that children are one of the dinner specials.

What did they mean it to say? Children pay only $5.95 to eat any special.

What should the sign say? Sample answer: Children's dinner costs only $5.95.

Notebook ▶ Summarize Ideas

Invite students to think about how scientists draw conclusions and communicate, and then have them summarize the main idea orally or in writing.

3 Extend/Evaluate

Sum It Up!

- Make sure students understand how outlines are structured to show relationships. For example, an indented statement is a detail of the statement above it.

- Direct students to cover the answer key and try to fill in as many blanks as they can. Then, they can use the Answer Key to check and revise their answers.

- To answer items 2–6 under I.B, suggest students look back at the second and third pages of this lesson.

- To answer items 2–4 under II.B, refer students to the fourth and fifth pages of this lesson.

- To answer items III and D, refer students to the sixth and seventh pages of this lesson.

- Items 2 and 3 under IV.B can be answered by reviewing the eighth and ninth pages of this lesson.

When you're done, use the answer key to check and revise your work.

The outline below is a summary of the lesson. Complete the outline.

Summarize

I. Research Is the Key

    A. Scientists do research to find out what others know.

    B. Reference sources you can use:

        1. encyclopedias

        2. books

        3. science articles

        4. museums

        5. contact a scientist

        6. science websites

II. Science Tools

    A. Scientists use tools to make the senses more powerful.

    B. Tools that aid the sense of sight:

        1. telescope

        2. hand lens

        3. magnifying box

        4. microscope

III. Measurement Tools

    A. pan balance

    B. spring scale

    C. tape measure/ruler

    D. thermometer

IV. Recording and Displaying Data

    A. Data are the bits of information you observe.

    B. Ways to display data:

        1. tables

        2. maps

        3. graphs

Answer Key: I.B.2–6 (in any order) books, science articles, museums, contact a scientist, science websites II.B.2–4 (in any order) hand lens, magnifying box, microscope III. Measurement Tools III.D. thermometer IV.B.2–3 (in any order) maps, graphs

Brain Check

Lesson 3

Name_____

Word Play

1 Put the mixed-up letters in order to spell a science term from the box.

tada   D A T A

eama supteer   T A P E   M E A S U R E

crasheer   R E S E A R C H

priclg harce   C I R C L E   G R A P H

croopsmice   M I C R O S C O P E

gripes clans   S P R I N G   S C A L E

montumceica   C O M M U N I C A T E

axingbynim fog   M A G N I F Y I N G   B O X

metermother   T H E R M O M E T E R

lap cannaeb   P A N   B A L A N C E

circle graph	communicate	data*	magnifying box	microscope*
pan balance*	research	spring scale*	tape measure	thermometer

*Key Lesson Vocabulary

39

Answer Strategies

Word Play

1. If any students are having challenges with unscrambling the science terms, suggest that they count the number of letters in each scrambled word and then look for words in the box that have the same number of letters. When students have unscrambled all the words, challenge them to use each one in a sentence.

Assessment

Scoring Guide

You may wish to use this suggested scoring guide for the Brain Check.

Item	Points
1	50 (5 points each)
2	25 (5 points each)
3	25 (5 points each)
Total	100

Lesson Quiz

See Assessment Guide, p. AG 3.

3 Extend/Evaluate (continued)

Answer Strategies

Apply Concepts

2. Provide hints to students who need them.

- Ask students how printed encyclopedias are organized (alphabetically). If students are more familiar with electronic encyclopedias, they may answer that they would use keywords to search them.

- For websites, ask students to think about the keywords they would use to search.

- Mention that for books the table of contents and index might help them find the information they need.

- Point out that in some cases, a scientist might need a sample of the rock to correctly identify it.

- Point out to students that museums also have experts who have knowledge about the museums' collections.

3. Direct students to review the uses of these science tools on the fourth through seventh pages of this lesson.

Take It Home!

Suggest that students work with a family member to identify measurement tools in their home, including those that are parts of appliances such as microwave ovens. In the kitchen, they can look for measuring spoons and cups, thermometers, and timers. In other rooms, they can look for bathroom scales, fever thermometers, clocks, rulers, and tape measures.

Apply Concepts

2 Someone gives you an object. You think it's a rock, but you aren't sure. Write how you could use each resource to do research.

 encyclopedia

Sample: I could look in the R volume for "rocks."

 websites

Sample: I could search online images using the keywords "rock crystals."

 books

Sample: I could find a book about rock collecting.

 contact a scientist

Sample: I could take a photo of it and e-mail the photo to a scientist and ask him or her to help me identify the rock.

 museum

Sample: I could take the object to a museum and compare it with the collections there.

3 Draw lines to match the tool to its use.

pan balance — to measure force
spring scale — to look closely at insects outdoors
thermometer — to measure mass
microscope — to find temperature
hand lens — to view objects too small to be seen with the eye alone

Take It Home!

Tell your family about the measurement tools scientists use. Discuss ways your family measures at home. Find and learn to use these tools. Hint: Does your kitchen have tools for measuring foods?

40

Make Connections

Language Arts Connection

Write a Recipe

- Students will build communication and technical writing skills by developing a recipe for a favorite food. Have them list the ingredients, including measurements, followed by a step-by-step procedure that includes a time allotment for each step.

- Allow students to exchange recipes and peer-edit them to improve the clarity of the recipes.

Math Connection

Measure Perimeter

- Have students measure the perimeter of the top of a table or desk, using a tape measure or metric ruler and centimeters units. Remind them to record their measurements and to use the correct unit abbreviation (cm).

- You may wish to have some students use a ruler to measure in millimeters (mm).

Social Studies Connection

Research Climate

- Direct students in Internet or library research to find out how your state's climate differs from those of other states. Have students use keywords *(home state name) + climate* to locate websites where they can find low and high temperatures, number of sunny days, and rainfall averages.

- Have them research the same data in other states and draw some conclusions.

Health and Physical Education Connection

Investigate Throwing Balls

- Have students plan and carry out an investigation in which they collect data about how far and how accurately they can throw balls of various sizes.

- Guide students to decide what materials they will need and the procedure they will follow. Have them record their data in a table and then use that data to make a graph.

Guided Inquiry

FLIPCHART P. 5

🕐 25 minutes

👥 small groups

Students follow the directions on the Flipchart. The accompanying Lesson Inquiry pages in the Student Edition provide scaffolding for guided inquiry.

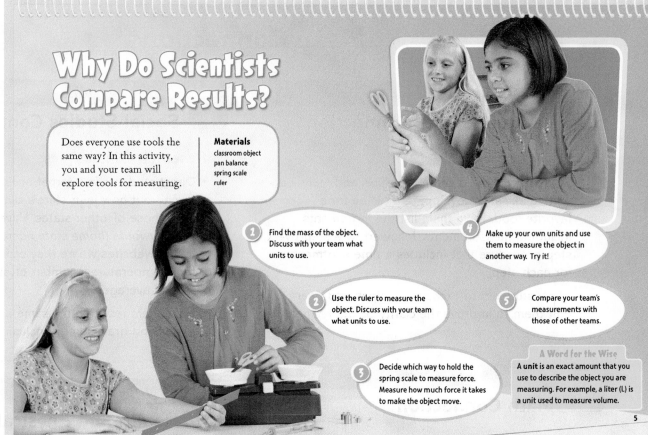

Why Do Scientists Compare Results?

Does everyone use tools the same way? In this activity, you and your team will explore tools for measuring.

Materials
classroom object
pan balance
spring scale
ruler

1. Find the mass of the object. Discuss with your team what units to use.

2. Use the ruler to measure the object. Discuss with your team what units to use.

3. Decide which way to hold the spring scale to measure force. Measure how much force it takes to make the object move.

4. Make up your own units and use them to measure the object in another way. Try it!

5. Compare your team's measurements with those of other teams.

A Word for the Wise
A **unit** is an exact amount that you use to describe the object you are measuring. For example, a liter (L) is a unit used to measure volume.

5

Inquiry Skills Focus Observe and Measure

Objectives

- Measure an object using several different types of tools (standard and non-standard units of measurement) and compare the results with other groups of students.

- Communicate the importance of accuracy in measurements and reasons why differences may occur.

Prep and Planning Tips

See the Planning for Inquiry page for more information.

- Demonstrate the use of the pan balances and accompanying sets of masses before distributing them to student groups.

- When students make up their own units, they must also identify the property they are measuring: mass, length, force, and so on.

Expected Results

Students may find differences in their measurements due to the choice of units and their accuracy in using the measurement tools and in counting.

---

1   Engage/Explore

Attention Grabber

Tell students that if they weigh 80 pounds on Earth, they would weigh 30 pounds on the planet Mercury and 189 pounds on Jupiter. This is because weight is a measurement of the force of gravity and the planets' forces of gravity differ. On the other hand, if they had measured their mass with a balance, they would have a measurement that does not change wherever they are in the solar system.

Preview Activity

Before beginning the investigation, have students review the directions on the Inquiry Flipchart and the accompanying Student Edition response pages. Then, have them complete the response pages as they follow directions on the Flipchart.

Inquiry Flipchart page 5

Lesson 4
INQUIRY

Name _____

Essential Question

Why Do Scientists Compare Results?

Set a Purpose
What will you learn from this investigation?
how to measure using tools

Think About the Procedure
Which tool will you use to measure mass?
a pan balance

Which units of length will your group use? Explain your choice.
Answers will vary. Students should justify
their choice of millimeters or centimeters
by discussing the object they need to
measure.

Record Your Data
In the space below, make a table in which you record your measurements.

Answers will vary depending upon the object and tool used. Check all measurements for accuracy.

© Houghton Mifflin Harcourt Publishing Company

41

1 Engage/Explore (continued)

Guide the Investigation

Develop Inquiry Skills

OBSERVE Have students practice the skill of observing by having them describe each measurement tool as you distribute them. **What do you observe about this tool?** Answers may include the material it is made from, its color, its shape, its size, its number of parts, any marking or text on the tool, and so on.

MEASURE Help students to understand that when they measure, they must think about the property (mass, length or distance, or force) they want to measure, the right tool for measuring that property, and the units they will count.

What property will you measure in step 2? length

How will you hold the spring scale in step 3? Students should decide if they will hang the object by holding the scale vertically in the air (measuring the force of gravity) or by placing the classroom object on a surface and holding the spring scale parallel to the surface to measure how much force it takes to pull it.

GATHER AND RECORD DATA The table in which students record their measurements should have two columns—a column for the tool they used or property they measured and a column for the actual measurement. Have students check twice that the units are correct.

Go Digital

A virtual lab experience is available with the Online Resources for this program.

Why Do Scientists Compare Results?

2 Explain

Develop Inquiry Skills

DRAW CONCLUSIONS When deciding which measurement tool was the hardest to use, students should consider how accurately the tools were used. For example, if there was wide disagreement among the measurement data of students, the reason may be that the tool is harder to use than the students realized.

ANALYZE AND EXTEND Discuss students' responses to the items.

1. Explain to students that scientists compare their results and discuss differences.

2. Tell students that, in addition to errors made in measuring, measurement tools may have slight differences or may be broken.

3. You could measure its volume using a graduated cylinder.

3 Extend/Evaluate

4. Would you measure solids or liquids with these tools and why? Sample answer: I could measure liquids or solids I can pour such as sugar or salt.

5. Invite students to share the questions they would like to ask about science tools.

Assessment

Lesson Quiz
See Assessment Guide, p. AG 4

Draw Conclusions

Of the three measurement tools you used, which did you find the easiest to use? Which was the hardest? Explain.

Answers will vary. Students may find the ruler the easiest to use because it is familiar. They may say the spring scale is the hardest because it is the least familiar.

Analyze and Extend

1. Why is it helpful to compare results with others?

to check if our measurements were correct

2. What should you do if you find out that your measurements are very different than those of other teams?

measure again and compare again

3. What other characteristics of the object can you measure?

Sample answer: I can measure the object's volume.

4. The picture shows two more measurement tools. Write about what you could measure with each one.

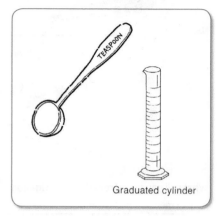
Graduated cylinder

Answers will vary. Students may say that they can measure small amounts of liquid with both.

5. What other questions would you like to ask about science tools?

Sample answer: How can I measure the mass of an object that is too large for a classroom balance?

42

Differentiated Inquiry

Easy

Estimate Distance

- Give groups a dried bean and a meterstick. Students take turns gently hitting the bean along the floor.

- When the bean comes to a halt, each student in a group records an estimate of how many centimeters it moved in a data table.

- Then, the person who hit the bean measures the distance with the meterstick. Students record the distance.

- When everyone has had a few turns, have students analyze the results to see if their estimation skills improved, got worse, or stayed the same.

Easy

Measure Elapsed Time

- Provide stopwatches. Have students practice finding the amount of time various events last (walking to another room, doing a math problem).

- Discuss how to find elapsed time by using a clock that is not a stopwatch. Show how to record the time when an event begins and ends. Then, they can count hours and minutes from start to end.

- Have students check work to build accuracy.

Average

Measure Temperature

- Give groups of students thermometers and a list of places to find the air temperature (in a closet, in a hallway, on a windowsill, and so on).

- Allow time for students to develop a procedure, make a data table, and make measurements.

- Have groups share their results and discuss reasons for discrepancies, such as differences in accuracy in reading the thermometers, temperature scale used, and location of measurements.

Challenging

Finding Nonstandard Units

- Challenge students to find an object or group of objects that are approximately the same measure as a standard unit. Possible answer: A small metal paper clip might be about the same mass as one gram.

- Have students look at the parts of their hands to find a way to estimate centimeters. Possible answer: The width of a finger might be about 1 cm.

- To estimate one newton of force, students can use trial and error by hanging various objects from the spring scale. Possible answers: 20 nickels, a medium-sized apple or orange, or 100 small metal paper clips.

People in Science

Objectives

- Describe the roles of scientists.
- Describe that scientists come from all backgrounds.
- Determine the role of technology in the work of scientists.

Notebook ▸ Generate Ideas

Have students brainstorm a list of places where scientists may work, such as labs, colleges and universities, hospitals, and industries. Lead them to consider that many scientists work outside in places such as forests, swamps, prairies, and other natural environments.

Background

- As a young man, John Diebold tried to make a living in the entertainment industry, but he had little success. He then took a job maintaining ships and equipment for ocean research. This job led to his interest in marine and earth sciences.

- Scientists use air guns to map the shape of the ocean floor and to identify deposits of oil and natural gas underneath it. Air guns release sound waves that travel at different speeds through different materials. Computers process the data and make detailed images of the ocean floor.

- Martin Culpepper owns patents for many of his inventions. A patent gives an inventor the legal right to an invention. Patents help inventors get paid for their work.

- The prefix *nano-* means "one billionth." The term *nanotechnology* describes the manipulation of matter on a molecular scale.

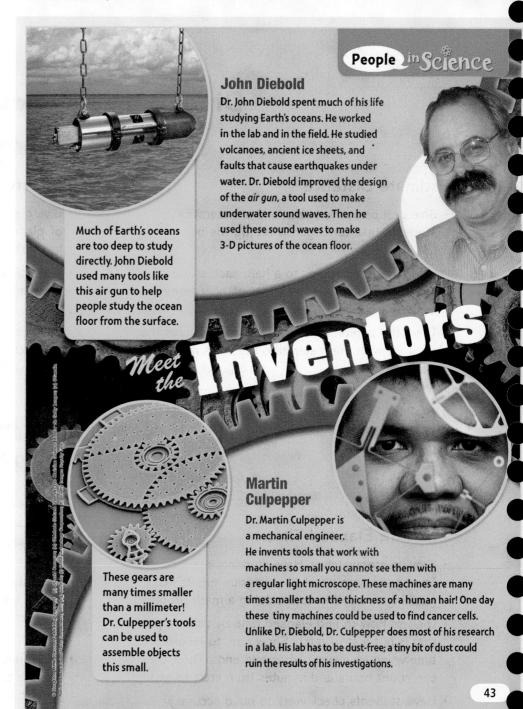

Meet the Inventors

Much of Earth's oceans are too deep to study directly. John Diebold used many tools like this air gun to help people study the ocean floor from the surface.

John Diebold

Dr. John Diebold spent much of his life studying Earth's oceans. He worked in the lab and in the field. He studied volcanoes, ancient ice sheets, and faults that cause earthquakes under water. Dr. Diebold improved the design of the *air gun*, a tool used to make underwater sound waves. Then he used these sound waves to make 3-D pictures of the ocean floor.

These gears are many times smaller than a millimeter! Dr. Culpepper's tools can be used to assemble objects this small.

Martin Culpepper

Dr. Martin Culpepper is a mechanical engineer. He invents tools that work with machines so small you cannot see them with a regular light microscope. These machines are many times smaller than the thickness of a human hair! One day these tiny machines could be used to find cancer cells. Unlike Dr. Diebold, Dr. Culpepper does most of his research in a lab. His lab has to be dust-free; a tiny bit of dust could ruin the results of his investigations.

43

Writing Connection

Write a Letter Have students write a letter to Martin Culpepper. Encourage students to ask the scientist questions about his work, such as how he became interested in science and whether he prefers working in a laboratory or in the field. Remind students that a letter has three parts: a greeting, the body of the letter, and a closing. Explain to them that a letter can be written in a formal or informal style, depending on the contents of the letter and the intended recipient.

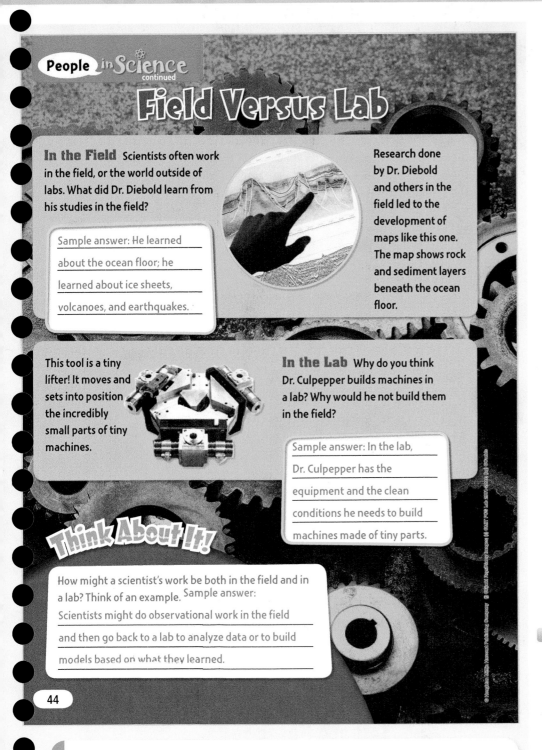

People in Science *continued*

Field Versus Lab

In the Field Scientists often work in the field, or the world outside of labs. What did Dr. Diebold learn from his studies in the field?

Sample answer: He learned about the ocean floor; he learned about ice sheets, volcanoes, and earthquakes.

Research done by Dr. Diebold and others in the field led to the development of maps like this one. The map shows rock and sediment layers beneath the ocean floor.

This tool is a tiny lifter! It moves and sets into position the incredibly small parts of tiny machines.

In the Lab Why do you think Dr. Culpepper builds machines in a lab? Why would he not build them in the field?

Sample answer: In the lab, Dr. Culpepper has the equipment and the clean conditions he needs to build machines made of tiny parts.

Think About It!

How might a scientist's work be both in the field and in a lab? Think of an example. Sample answer: Scientists might do observational work in the field and then go back to a lab to analyze data or to build models based on what they learned.

44

Develop Inquiry Skills

COMPARE As students prepare to answer the questions on this page, explain that scientists often must choose the best environment for carrying out experiments and research. **What are some advantages of working in the field? What are some advantages of working in a lab?** Sample answer: The field is where scientists can find and observe the plants, animals, rocks, weather, and other things and events that cannot be simulated in a lab. In a lab, scientists can control the environment and work safely with chemicals, machines, and other equipment.

Develop Science Concepts

Before students complete the Think About It! Interactivity, discuss how some scientists work in both the field and in labs. **Why might a scientist do some work in the field and then continue that work in a lab? Give an example.** Sample answer: A marine biologist might observe an unusual type of seaweed in the field and then take a sample of it to the laboratory for further study. An engineer might visit the site of a new bridge or skyscraper and then build and test a model in a lab.

Notebook ▸ Summarize Ideas

Have students compare and contrast both the work and the working environments of John Diebold and Martin Culpepper. Have them summarize their ideas orally or in writing.

Science, Technology, and Society

Costs and Benefits

New technology can have both positive and negative effects on Earth's living things. Air guns, for example, are now used to search for underwater deposits of oil and natural gas. However, air gun explosions can damage the hearing of whales and dolphins, which they use to communicate and navigate. Have students choose an example of recent technology, such as computers or mobile telephones, and list the positive and negative impacts this technology has on living things.

Options for Inquiry

FLIPCHART P. 6

Students can conduct these optional investigations at any time before, during, or in response to the lesson in the Student Edition.

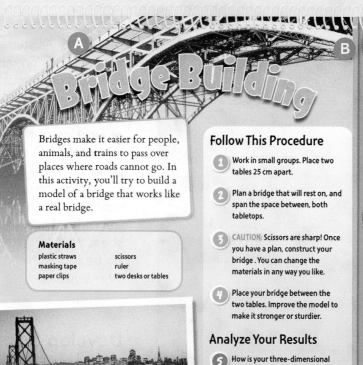

A

Bridge Building

Bridges make it easier for people, animals, and trains to pass over places where roads cannot go. In this activity, you'll try to build a model of a bridge that works like a real bridge.

Materials

plastic straws	scissors
masking tape	ruler
paper clips	two desks or tables

Follow This Procedure

1. Work in small groups. Place two tables 25 cm apart.

2. Plan a bridge that will rest on, and span the space between, both tabletops.

3. CAUTION: Scissors are sharp! Once you have a plan, construct your bridge. You can change the materials in any way you like.

4. Place your bridge between the two tables. Improve the model to make it stronger or sturdier.

Analyze Your Results

5. How is your three-dimensional model like a real bridge? How is it different?

6. Did each group build their bridge in the same way? Explain.

B

Stress Test

A bridge has to be strong enough to hold up a load of cars, trucks, and people. How strong is a model bridge made of straws? As a team, plan a procedure to answer this question using a paper cup and pennies. Write any planning you do in your science notebook. Then, try your plan and record your results.

Science Notebook

Here's an example of how one team began to plan their investigation.

Bridge Test

Our Team's Planning Meeting

Notes

1. We know the weight of the cars is a force.
2. The force of the cars pushes down on the bridge.
3. How can we use the cup to push or pull down on the bridge?
4. Where will we put the cup?
5. How will we add the pennies?

6

A Bridge Building

⏱ 45 minutes
👥 pairs

Prep and Planning Tips

Direct students to cut a straw in thirds and practice taping the ends together to form a triangle. Explain that this form is called a truss, a very strong construction unit. Tell students they can use triangles and straight straws but are not allowed to bundle straws together when making a truss bridge. Tell students to make sure there is a place in the middle of their bridge where a small paper cup can sit.

Expected Results

Students will observe that triangles are able to resist greater forces than straight straws but that, by combining them, they can span the 25 cm.

B Stress Test

⏱ 20 minutes
👥 pairs

Prep and Planning Tips

See the Planning for Inquiry page for more information.

Science Notebook

Students can use the Science Notebook as a model for designing their own investigation. Guide students to consider placing the cup in the center of their bridge before adding pennies one by one. When either the cup falls off or the bridge collapses, students can count the number of pennies used.

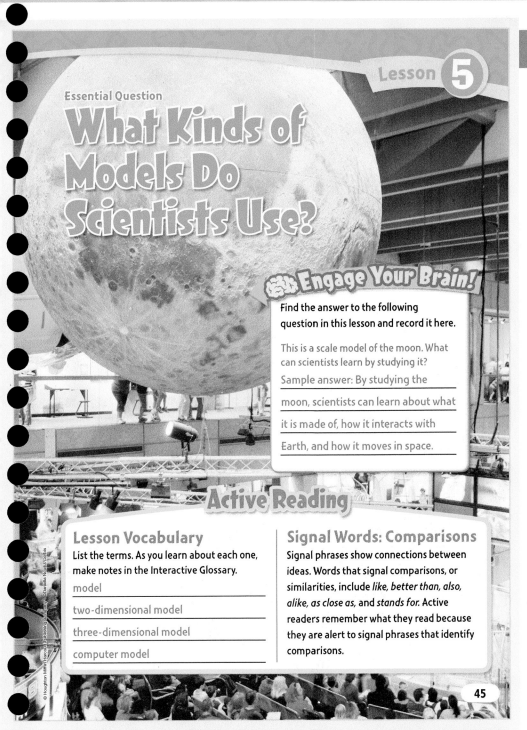

Essential Question

What Kinds of Models Do Scientists Use?

Lesson 5

Engage Your Brain!

Find the answer to the following question in this lesson and record it here.

This is a scale model of the moon. What can scientists learn by studying it?

Sample answer: By studying the

moon, scientists can learn about what

it is made of, how it interacts with

Earth, and how it moves in space.

Active Reading

Lesson Vocabulary

List the terms. As you learn about each one, make notes in the Interactive Glossary.

model

two-dimensional model

three-dimensional model

computer model

Signal Words: Comparisons

Signal phrases show connections between ideas. Words that signal comparisons, or similarities, include *like, better than, also, alike, as close as,* and *stands for.* Active readers remember what they read because they are alert to signal phrases that identify comparisons.

45

Go Digital

An interactive digital lesson is available in Online Resources. It is suitable for individuals, small groups, or may be projected or used on an interactive white board.

---

1 Engage/Explore

Objectives

- Communicate that scientists use different types of models depending upon the subject they are studying.
- Identify differences between examples of models, such as a picture, replica, and animation.
- Determine that technology has helped scientists make more accurate models.

Engage Your Brain!

Guide students to think about what they have learned from looking at model cars, model airplanes, or other kinds of scale models. Tell students that scale models can help people study large objects. Remind students to record their final answer to the question when they find it on the second page of this lesson.

Active Reading   Annotations

Remind students that active readers "make texts their own" by annotating them with notes and marks that help with comprehension. Encourage students to use pencil, not pen, to make annotations as they read. The goal of annotation is to help students remember what they have read.

Vocabulary and Interactive Glossary

Remind students to find and list the yellow highlighted terms from the lesson. As they proceed through the lesson and learn about the terms, they can add notes, drawings, or sentences in the extra spaces provided in the Interactive Glossary.

2 Explain

Generate Ideas

Brainstorm with students some possible answers to the question in the introductory paragraph: **But what is a model in science?** Sample answers: something you build, something you make with a computer

After students have completed the second through fourth pages of this lesson, have them return to their list and refine it.

Active Reading

Remind students that active readers annotate, or mark up, text to benefit their own recollection of the information presented. Though students may star different sentences, it is important they are able to offer a reasonable explanation for their annotation.

Develop Science Concepts

Point out that models are used to explain hard-to-understand ideas in a simpler way.

Invite students to describe a mental model. **What is your mental model for how the sun, Earth, and moon work as a system?** Sample answer: Earth circles around the sun, and the moon circles around Earth.

What two-dimensional models can you find in this book? Students should be able to find labeled diagrams, tables, maps, and photo/art combinations that model objects or processes.

Two-dimensional model of the solar system

Models and Science

Native Americans had mental models for the sun, moon, and planets. Several tribes in North America tell stories of the beginning of time, when Earth did not exist. All of the animals applied mud to the shell of a turtle. Earth was born when the mud became thick and large on the turtle's back.

46

English Language Learners

Compare Attributes of Models Make an attribute chart of mental, two-dimensional, three-dimensional, and computer models. Compare these attributes: mind picture, length, width, height, on a screen. Then, show students a world map and a globe. Discuss which is two-dimensional and which is three-dimensional. Compare and contrast these models. Ask students how these models are different from mental and computer models.

Make a Two-dimensional Model!

Good models are as close to the real thing as possible. Draw a floor plan of a room in your home. Show the doorways and windows. Show the objects that sit on the floor. Add labels. Be as accurate as you can!

Answers will vary. Ask students to describe their models to ensure accuracy.

A toy car. A doll's house. A person who shows off clothes on a runway. These are all models. But what is a model in science?

Active Reading As you read these two pages, draw a star next to what you think is the most important sentence. Be ready to explain why.

Scientists make models to investigate questions and explain conclusions. In science, a **model** represents something real that is too big, too small, or has too many parts to investigate directly. For example, our solar system is too big to see all the parts at once. So, scientists make models of the solar system. They use models to investigate the motion and positions of planets and moons. They can use the models to predict when a comet or asteroid will pass close to Earth.

Models can take many forms. A *mental model* is a picture you create in your mind. One good thing about this kind of model is that you always have it with you! A **two-dimensional model** has length and width. It can be a drawing, a diagram, or a map.

47

Differentiation — Leveled Questions

Extra Support

Show students a map of their state or other region. **What does this two-dimensional model show?** Sample answer: It shows the shape of our state.

Challenge

Explain that many people form mental models of mathematical ideas. **What is your mental model of a year? How do you visualize a whole year in your mind?** Sample answer: I see it as a circle divided into 12 months.

Develop Science Vocabulary

model Have students look around the room and find examples of models. Point out that the word *model* can be a verb or a noun. Invite students to use both forms of *model* in a sentence.

two-dimensional model Explain that *dimensional* means a measure in one direction. Models that are two-dimensional have both length and width.

Develop Inquiry Skills

USE MODELS To help students better understand the nature of models and how they change, have them draw the floor plan of a room in their homes from memory. Discuss how they are using a mental model to create a two-dimensional model.

Explain to students that scientists change and improve their models as they learn more about an object, a system, or a process. Allow students to take their floor plans home, gather more information, and refine them.

How would using a tape measure or ruler affect your two-dimensional model? Sample answer: Measuring could make it more exact.

Notebook ▸ Summarize Ideas

Direct students to think about the main idea on these two pages. Ask if their idea about what a science model is has changed since reading this section. Have them summarize the main idea orally and in writing.

2 Explain (continued)

 **Generate Ideas**

Have students read the introductory paragraph. Ask: **When or where might you have an experience like this?** Sample answers: at a planetarium, science museum, playing a video game, on the NASA website

Active Reading

Remind students that authors compare and contrast events, objects, and ideas when pointing out ways these things are alike and different. Active readers remember similarities and differences because they focus on events, objects, and ideas being compared.

Develop Science Concepts

Point out that many toys, in addition to model trains, are themselves three-dimensional models. Have students work in groups to brainstorm lists of such models. Then, allow them to share and compare their lists. Sample list: model sailboats, toy cars and trucks, stuffed animals, dolls, toy kitchen sets

What kinds of toys are used to build three-dimensional models? Sample answers: plastic interlocking block sets, wooden block sets, log cabin sets, model airplane sets, origami kits

Help students understand computer models by viewing and discussing a computer simulation game. You could also ask students to explore any of a number of NASA websites, where they will have many opportunities to identify and explore computer models.

In 2006, scientists of the International Astonomical Union (IAU) voted to define a planet as "a body that orbits the sun, has sufficient mass to attain and retain a roughly spherical shape, and is sufficiently large to 'sweep' its orbit of lesser objects." As a result of this definition, Pluto was reclassified as a "dwarf planet," because it does not meet the third criterion.

Other Models Scientists Use

Do the Math!
Use Fractions

You plan to make a model of the solar system. You make the tiniest ball of clay you can for Mercury. The ball is 4 mm across. If Mercury were that size, the chart shows how big all the other objects in your model would be.

Object	Diameter (mm)
Sun	1,100
Mercury	4
Venus	9
Earth	10
Mars	5
Jupiter	110
Saturn	92
Uranus	37
Neptune	36

1. What fraction tells how the size of Mars compares to Earth?
   Mars is $^5/_{10}$ or $^1/_2$ the size of Earth.

2. Which object is about $^1/_4$ the diameter of Neptune?
   Venus

3. Which object is about $^1/_9$ the diameter of Saturn?
   Earth

48

 Differentiation — Leveled Questions

Extra Support

What kind of model can you walk around to see different parts of it? a three-dimensional model

Challenge

Three-dimensional models can show the inside as well as the outside of objects. What three-dimensional models show the inside an object? Sample answers: a human body model, models of car engines

You see thousands of stars in the night sky. You point to a very bright star. Suddenly, you are zooming through space. As you get closer, the star gets bigger and brighter. Your trip isn't real, but it feels like it is. It's another kind of model!

Active Reading As you read these two pages, draw boxes around a clue word or phrase that signal things are being compared.

Three-Dimensional Models

The more a model is like the real thing, the better it is. If the object you want to model has length, width, and height, a **three-dimensional model** is useful. Such a model can show the positions of planets, moons, and the sun better than a two-dimensional model can.

If you want to compare sizes and distances in a model, then you make a *scale model*. The scale tells how much smaller or bigger the model is than the real thing. For example, a model railroad may have a scale of 1 to 48. This means each one inch on the model stands for 48 inches on the real train.

Computer Models

What if you want to understand how asteroids move through the solar system? You'd use a computer model. A **computer model** is a computer program that models an event or object. Some computer models make you feel like you are moving through the solar system!

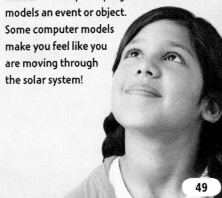

49

Math Connection

Solve an Area Problem
Have students decide where the biggest place in their classroom is to project a model of the solar system. Allow them to form teams to plan how to solve the problem.

Provide metric tools for measuring and instruction in calculating area if requested. After solving the problem, have the teams present their conclusions.

Develop Science Vocabulary

three-dimensional model Remind students that dimensional means a measure in one direction. Models that are three-dimensional have length, width, and height. Demonstrate how three-dimensional models can be viewed from all sides and from above and below.

computer model Explain to students that computer models can work like two-dimensional or three-dimensional models.

Do the Math!

Use Fractions

Guide students to understand that the table shows size relationships between the sun and the planets. To solve each problem, students will have to find the fraction of a group.

1. Have students draw 10 dots in a row and circle five of them. Ask: **What fraction of 10 is 5?**

2. Students can draw 36 dots, circle four equal groups, and then find the model planet that has a diameter equal to one group.

3. Suggest that students use mental math to estimate the answer to 92 divided by 9.

Notebook ▸ Summarize Ideas

Have students look again at the photos of two kinds of models in this section. Invite them to think about what they see and then summarize the main idea orally or in writing.

2 Explain (continued)

Notebook ▶ Generate Ideas

Ask students to explain how previewing the heads and pictures can help them answer the question in the introductory paragraph before reading the text: **How can models save lives?** Record their ideas on the board and allow them to revise their responses after reading these two pages.

Develop Science Concepts

Help students understand the concept of real-time data—information that is delivered as soon as it is collected. There are many sources of real-time data on the Internet, including weather data from land-based weather stations around the world, satellite images, ocean wave data from buoys, traffic maps, and webcams of wildlife.

Explain that many of the lines showing the borders of countries and states on maps are imaginary or are not visible from space. They have been added to the photo to make the model easier to understand.

The eye of a hurricane is a small area near the center of the hurricane around which clouds spiral. **Where is the eye of the hurricane in this computer model?** partly over the ocean and partly over southeastern Florida

Why It Matters

Weather Models Save Lives

Dangerous weather can happen suddenly. Hurricanes, tornadoes, floods, and winter storms can harm people, pets, and homes. How can models save lives?

FLORIDA

Data from Space

Satellites circle Earth 24 hours each day. Images and other weather data are beamed back to Earth. It's called *real-time* data because scientists see the pictures almost as soon as they are taken. In this image, a hurricane sits along the coast of Florida. The colors are not real. Scientists choose them to show differences in wind speeds, heights of clouds, and other factors.

Using Models

Meteorologists use satellite data to make computer models of weather. They model hurricanes, tornadoes, and thunderstorms. The models are used to predict how and where storms will get started.

50

English Language Learners

Understand Words as Nouns or Verbs Call students' attention to the paragraph under the heading "Using Models." Note the use of *model* and *models* in these sentences. Explain that in the first and third sentences, *models* is a noun, or naming word. In the second sentence, however, *model* is a verb. Say: What do weather scientists do? They *model* hurricanes, tornadoes, and thunderstorms. Elicit other examples using *model* as a noun or verb.

This weather model shows the height of the clouds of a storm.

Getting the Word Out

Weather reporters also use models. They make two-dimensional maps for TV and Internet viewers to see. The maps can change to show how fast and where bad weather will be.

What Can We Do?

You can use models to help your family be prepared for dangerous weather. Draw a diagram of your home in your Science Notebook. Label the exits. Does your family have a safe place to meet in an emergency? Where is it?

Sample answer: If there's a fire in our house, our meeting place is in the backyard by the shed. If it's stormy, we meet in the hallway because it doesn't have any windows.

How can your model help you in an emergency?

Answers will vary. Sample answer: The model shows everyone where to meet so that we all have the same information.

51

Develop Science Concepts

Help students understand that weather scientists develop models that can predict how, when, and where storms form. They can also be used to predict how fast a storm will move and in what direction.

Develop Inquiry Skills

USE MODELS To help students better understand weather models, have them interpret weather maps found on the Internet or in a printed newspaper. Direct them to write a summary of the weather represented by the map.

When students draw a diagram of their home and neighborhood, have them write street names and list the phone number and name of someone to contact out of your area.

Have students add to their diagrams the locations of emergency supplies.

 Notebook ▸ ## Summarize Ideas

Have students think about the diagram they drew and the weather models scientists use and revise their answer to the question in the introductory paragraph, **How can models save lives?** Sample answer: An emergency diagram can save family members' lives if there is a storm, and the models scientists use can warn people to get ready for the storm.

Writing Connection

Write Persuasive Text Direct students to develop a script for a public service announcement (PSA) that will urge citizens to pay attention to weather models and make their own storm emergency plans. Have students practice reading their PSAs and then edit the scripts to make them less than one minute long. Allow students to record audio files that could be played periodically on the school's public-address system in the event that there is an emergency.

3 Extend/Evaluate

Sum It Up!

- Direct students to cover the answer key before trying to fill in the detail boxes. Afterward they can use the Answer Key to check and revise their answers.

- Suggest to students that they read the summary carefully for clues regarding what to fill in the boxes.

- To answer items 1 and 2, suggest students look back at the fourth and fifth pages of this lesson.

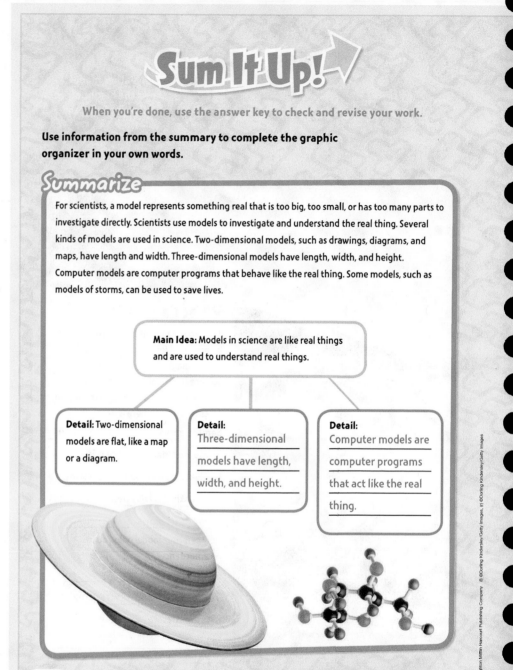

Sum It Up!

When you're done, use the answer key to check and revise your work.

Use information from the summary to complete the graphic organizer in your own words.

Summarize

For scientists, a model represents something real that is too big, too small, or has too many parts to investigate directly. Scientists use models to investigate and understand the real thing. Several kinds of models are used in science. Two-dimensional models, such as drawings, diagrams, and maps, have length and width. Three-dimensional models have length, width, and height. Computer models are computer programs that behave like the real thing. Some models, such as models of storms, can be used to save lives.

Main Idea: Models in science are like real things and are used to understand real things.

Detail: Two-dimensional models are flat, like a map or a diagram.

Detail: Three-dimensional models have length, width, and height.

Detail: Computer models are computer programs that act like the real thing.

Answer Key: 1. Three-dimensional models have length, width, and height. 2. Computer models are computer programs that act like the real thing.

52

© Houghton Mifflin Harcourt Publishing Company (f) ©Dorling Kindersley/Getty Images, (r) ©Dorling Kindersley/Getty Images

Brain Check

Lesson **5**

Name _____

Word Play

1 Use the words in the box to complete the puzzle.

Word box:
computer model*
mental model
scale model
two-dimensional model*
three-dimensional model*
real-time model*
satellite
weather

*Key Lesson Vocabulary

Crossword answers:

Across (row 1): ²MENTALMODEL (with ¹C down and ³T down)
²MODEL, ⁵S
⁶WEATHER
⁷TWODIMENSIONALMODEL
⁹SATELLITE

Down words: COMPUTERMODEL, THREEDIMENSIONALMODEL, SCALEMODEL, REALTIME

Across

2. A type of model that is in your head
4. Something that represents the real thing
6. These kinds of models can save lives
7. A type of model that has length and width
9. A device that sends weather images back to Earth

Down

1. A type of model made with a computer program
3. A type of model that has length, width, and height
5. In this type of model, a measurement on the model stands for a measurement on the real thing
8. Data that scientists can see as soon as it is collected

53

Answer Strategies

Word Play

1. Make sure students understand that the two-word terms in the crossword puzzle will not include the space or hyphen between the words. If students need help, suggest that they find the places in the lesson where the terms are defined or discussed.

Assessment

Scoring Guide

You may wish to use this suggested scoring guide for the Brain Check.

Item	Points
1	45 (5 points each)
2	20
3	15
4	10
5	10
Total	100

Lesson Quiz

See Assessment Guide, p. AG 5.

3 Extend/Evaluate (continued)

Answer Strategies

Apply Concepts

2. Help students understand that lightning strikes can be deadly and destructive. Ask how the models scientists make to understand lightning could be used.

3. Point out to students that flash floods can turn streets into rivers and that storm water can cause erosion and damage to structures.

4. Help students understand that scientists create traffic models that can give real-time data as well as those that show traffic patterns over long periods of time.

5. Have students think about small three-dimensional models of playground equipment that they could move around.

 **Take It Home**

Suggest to students that they work with a family member to create a portfolio of models and classify them as two-dimensional, three-dimensional, or computer models.

Apply Concepts

Tell how making or using each model below could help people.

2 A model to show where lightning is likely to strike

Sample answer: It could help people

decide where not to stand in a storm.

_____

_____

3 A model to show where water flows during a storm

Sample answer: It could help people stay

away from places that will flood or

decide where to build a house.

4 A model to show how traffic moves in a city

Sample answer: It could help people decide where to place signs and

traffic lights.

5 A model to show equipment for a new playground

Sample answer: It could help people decide which pieces of equipment to

buy and where to put them.

 Take It Home! Many kids' toys are models of real things. Challenge your family to find such toys at home, in ads, or where you shop. Ask yourself: How is this toy like the real thing? How is it different?

54

Make Connections

Art Connection

Model the Figure in Action

- Provide chenille sticks, and have students combine and twist them into three-dimensional models showing the human body in motion: jumping, running, swinging a baseball bat, dancing.

- Discuss how the sticks can be used to make a drawing-like model in two-dimensions, or a sculpture-like model in three-dimensions. Allow students to mount their works on cardboard and display them.

Challenging

Health and Physical Education Connection

Model the Human Body

Lead a discussion of how body organs work together, for example how muscles and bones support and move the body. Make research materials available, and suggest students draw and label an example of two body parts working together. Possible examples: arm bones and muscles, knee joints, heart and blood vessels, eyes and brain, teeth and stomach.

Average

Language Arts Connection

Draw a Map and Write Directions

- Direct students to use mental models to write directions explaining how to get from one place in their community or school to another. Remind students to include cardinal directions (N, S, E, and W), landmarks, and distances. Then, have them draw maps (two-dimensional models) that visually represent their directions.

- Have students exchange directions and maps and peer edit.

Challenging

Math Connection

Make Nets

- Review with students the names of three-dimensional geometric figures such as cubes, pyramids, cylinders, and prisms.

- Discuss *nets*. A net is a two-dimensional shape that can be cut out and folded to create a three-dimensional shape.

- Provide students with graph paper and rulers, and challenge them to create nets that can be used to construct a three-dimensional object.

Guided Inquiry

 FLIPCHART P. 7

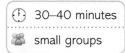
⏱ 30–40 minutes

👥 small groups

Students follow the directions on the Flipchart. The accompanying Lesson inquiry pages in the Student Edition provide scaffolding for guided inquiry.

How Can You Model a School?

There are many types of models: mental models, two-dimensional, three-dimensional, and computer models. In this activity, you'll model a part of your school in two ways.

Materials
drawing paper
graph paper
tape measure
cardboard boxes
computer drawing or
  modeling program

1 With a team, choose a part of your school to model. It may be a single room, a floor, or a whole building.

2 Next, choose two types of models to make. Get permission from your teacher to carry out your plans.

3 With your team, choose the materials you will use. Make any measurements you need, and record them carefully.

4 Make the two models, and compare them to those of other teams.

Inquiry Skills Focus Formulate or Use Models, Measure, and Communicate

Objectives

• Measure the classroom using metric tools such as tape measures and meter sticks.

• Construct a model of the classroom.

• Compare the models made and note differences, based on spatial awareness or measurements made.

Prep and Planning Tips

See the Planning for Inquiry page for more information.

• You may want to have students gather measurement data one day and create their models the following day.

• If a team chooses to make a mental model, tell them they need to write directions for others to use the same mental model.

Expected Results

Students will find that they can communicate some kinds of information more easily with a particular kind of model.

1   Engage/Explore

Attention Grabber

Bring an unusual or humorous model to school to share with the class: a model ship, a model railroad car, a snow globe, a model skyscraper, a model airplane. Discuss what it represents. Then, ask students **How is the model the same as the real thing?** Sample answers: color, shape, many of the same parts **How is it different than the real thing?** size, how it works

Preview Activity

Before beginning the investigation, have students review the directions on the Inquiry Flipchart and the accompanying Student Edition response pages. Then, have them complete the response pages as they follow directions on the Flipchart.

Inquiry Flipchart page 7

Name _____

Essential Question

How Can You Model a School?

Set a Purpose

What inquiry skills will you practice in this investigation?

measuring, using models

_____

_____

Think About the Procedure

How will you decide what part of your school to model?

Students may talk about the time needed

to model a part or a whole. They may

mention time constraints or the limits of

their measurement tools.

How will you choose the two types of models?

Students may mention time constraints,

the available materials and supplies, or

personal preferences.

_____

Record Your Observations

Identify the part of your school you modeled.

Answers will vary. Verify that the area

modeled by the students is accurately

described.

_____

Identify the two types of models you made and describe them.

Sample answer: I made a two-dimensional

model and a three-dimensional model. For

the two-dimensional model, I used graph

paper to make my model to scale. I built a

diorama for the three-dimensional model.

_____

_____

55

Guide the Investigation

Develop Inquiry Skills

FORMULATE OR USE MODELS When choosing the types of models they will make, have students consider whether the colors they use are important and how each type of model can include color information.

MEASURE Allow students to practice using the tape measure to understand the scale, the units, and how to record measurements accurately. Suggest that, regardless of the end model they plan to make, a rough sketch of the school or a part of the school can be used for recording measurements.

Have team members check one another's work when they transfer measurements from their sketch or notes to the final model.

COMMUNICATE Point out to students that models are one way scientists communicate the results of investigations to others. **How does the kind of audience affect the kind of model needed?** Sample answer: If the audience is young children, a simple model might be better than a complicated one.

Go Digital

A virtual lab experience is available with the Online Resources for this program.

How Can You Make a Model?

2   Explain

Develop Inquiry Skills

DRAW CONCLUSIONS When deciding what they learned about their school, have the students show that information on their models.

ANALYZE AND EXTEND Discuss students' responses to the items.

1. Explain to students that scientists compare their results and discuss the reasons for differences. Then scientists decide if an investigation should be changed or repeated.

2. Ask students to share the "mistakes" they made and how they had to change or correct their model as they worked on it.

3. Remind students that one inaccurate measurement is enough to make a model not look correct or work properly.

4. **What will engineers do if they find that their model does not work as they expected?** Sample answer: They will either build it in a different way or give up on it and try something completely different.

3   Extend/Evaluate

5. Have students consider manufacturing processes, such as how a car is made, and places around the world they might like to visit some day, such as the pyramids in Egypt or the Great Wall of China.

6. Invite students to share the questions they would like to ask about making models. Discuss with them how they could find the answers to their questions.

Assessment

Lesson Quiz
See Assessment Guide, p. AG 6.

Draw Conclusions

What was something you learned about your school from making the models?

Sample answer: All of the classrooms are equal in size.

Analyze and Extend

1. Why is it helpful to compare results with others?

to check if our measurements were correct

2. What was the hardest part of making the models? Explain.

Sample answer: deciding how big to make them, because you might run out of materials

3. Why is it important to be accurate when making your measurements?

A model should be an accurate representation of an object or process. If the measurements aren't accurate, the model will not be accurate or useful.

4. Why is it important for engineers to make and try out models before making a real building or bridge?

Sample answer: They can save time and money by working out the plans with a model. They can also test the model to see if the building or bridge will be safe.

5. What other things or places would you like to learn about by making a model? Explain why.

Sample answers: a boat, a submarine, a skyscraper; to see how they work

6. What other questions would you like to ask about making models?

Sample answer: How do scientists make models of very small things they cannot see?

Differentiated Inquiry

Average

Make a Mental Model of the Solar System

- Write on the board My Very Educated Mother Just Sent Us Nine Pizzas. Have students underline the first letter of each word and show how they represent the names and correct order of the planets in our solar system. Explain that this is called a mnemonic device—a kind of mental model that helps people picture the solar system. Note that Pluto has been reclassified as a dwarf planet.

- Next, have students work in pairs to develop their own mnemonic device for remembering the planets and share them with the class.

Average

Model the Inside of a Volcano

- Have students research and model the structure of the inside of a volcano. Emphasize that this will not be a baking soda and vinegar model.

- Allow time for students to complete Internet or library research.

- Guide students to develop cross-sectional models by drawing, painting, or using modeling clay. Have them title and label the parts of the model.

Average

Explore Computer Simulations

- Explain that computer simulations are a kind of working model, which is able to perform some or all of the functions of the real object or process.

- Make available some of the simulation software available in your school or on the Internet. After students try one, have them write reviews that describe what the model does and how the user can make changes and see the results.

Challenging

Make a Large-Scale Model

- Explain that a scale model is often smaller than the original, but it can sometimes be bigger (such as models of cells and atoms). Challenge students to make a large-scale model of a small part of a living thing, such as a leaf.

- Have students lay a tree leaf on a piece of graph paper and trace its outline.

- Challenge students to draw a larger version of the leaf by changing each small box on the grid to a larger square. For example, if they have $\frac{1}{4}$ inch graph paper, have students make a new grid with one-inch squares. They can then use the outline on the small grid as a pattern for redrawing it on the larger grid.

- Have students do research to identify parts of a leaf and label them on the large-scale model.

Enduring Understandings

Revisit the Big Idea and Essential Questions

Big Idea Scientists answer questions about the world around us by carrying out careful investigations.

To explore the Big Idea, post the term *investigation,* and invite students to use what they have learned in the unit to brainstorm methods and processes scientists use to do investigations. Prompt students as needed to ensure they recall the following methods and processes:

- Observe
- Ask questions
- Hypothesize
- Plan and conduct experiments
- Make and use models

- Use variables
- Infer
- Compare
- Predict
- Draw conclusions
- Gather data

- Use measurement tools, such as microscopes, spring scales, and pan balances
- Record and analyze data
- Communicate results

Essential Questions

Post the Essential Questions and use the following prompts to guide a discussion.

Lesson/Essential Question	Prompts
L1 What Do Scientists Do?	• Tell what scientists do.
L2 What Skills Do Scientists Use?	• Name or demonstrate three skills scientists use.
L3 How Do Scientists Collect and Use Data?	• Give two examples of how scientists collect data.
L4 Why Do Scientists Compare Results?	• Give two reasons why a scientist would want to compare results with other scientists.
L5 What Kinds of Models Do Scientists Use?	• Describe the different kinds of models a scientist may make or use.
L6 How Can You Model a School?	• Explain why a scientist might decide to make a model.

Notebook **Science Notebook**

You may use the following strategies after students complete the unit or after each lesson.

- Have students review and edit the answers to Essential Questions they drafted at the beginning of the unit. Suggest they cross out sentences or ideas that are unnecessary or inappropriate.
- Have students add sentences or ideas that reflect their new understandings. Invite them to refer to their textbook as needed. Tell students they may paraphrase information from the textbook but may not copy it word for word.
- Allow time for students to make a final draft of their answers and proofread their draft to correct any spelling, grammar, or punctuation errors.

Science Notebook

Essential Questions	Answers
What Do Scientists Do?	
What Skills Do Scientists Use?	
How Do Scientists Collect and Use Data?	
Why Do Scientists Compare Results?	
What Kinds of Models Do Scientists Use?	
How Can You Model a School?	

Unit 1 Review

Name _____

Vocabulary Review

Use the terms in the box to complete the sentences.

> inference
> investigation
> observation
> pan balance
> spring scale

1. When people collect information by using their five senses,

   they make a(n) ___observation___.

2. A tool used to measure the mass of an object

   is a(n) ___pan balance___.

3. When people ask questions, make observations, and
   use other methods to gather data about an event or

   object, they are doing a(n) ___investigation___.

4. Someone who makes a statement that explains an

   observation is making a(n) ___inference___.

5. If you want to measure the pull of a force, such as
   the force of gravity, you would use a tool called

   a(n) ___spring scale___.

Science Concepts

Fill in the letter of the choice that best answers the question.

6. Amira wants to compare close-up views
   of different bird feathers. Which tool
   should she use?

   (A) measuring cup

   (B) meterstick

   (C) microscope

   (D) pan balance

7. Camilla is studying minerals in different
   types of rocks. Which of the following
   would **not** help Camilla obtain data about
   a rock?

   (A) measuring the volume of the rock

   (B) inferring that the rock is millions of
   years old

   (C) testing the effect of dripping vinegar
   onto the rock

   (D) making observations of the rock's
   minerals

Item Analysis

Items	Depth of Knowledge	Cognitive Complexity
1–5	1	Low
6	2	Moderate
7	4	High

Unit Review

Answer Key

Vocabulary Review (5 points each)

1. **observation** People make observations
   when they collect information using their
   five senses. If necessary, have students
   review the section on communicating in
   Lesson 1.

2. **pan balance** Review with students how
   to measure the mass of an object. Have
   them review the use of science tools in
   Lesson 3.

3. **investigation** Scientists and others
   investigate, or do an investigation, when
   they ask questions, make observations,
   and gather data. Have students review the
   steps in an investigation in Lesson 1.

4. **inference** Have students look back at the
   section on inference in Lesson 2 and give
   examples of other inferences they can
   make by looking at the sky.

5. **spring scale** Scientists use spring scales
   to measure the amount of force acting on
   an object. Direct students to Lesson 3 to
   review common tools used in science.

Science Concepts (5 points each)

6. **C** A microscope allows the viewer to
   observe small objects in more detail. Have
   students give examples of objects they
   would like to observe under a microscope.

7. **B** Inferring the age of the rock will not
   help Camilla learn about minerals in rock.
   After reviewing Lesson 2, have volunteers
   explain the difference between observing
   and inferring.

Assessment

**Unit 1 Test and Performance
Assessment**

See Assessment Guide,
pp. AG 7–AG 13, for Unit Test and
Performance Task with Long Option
rubric.

Unit Review continued

Answer Key

Science Concepts (5 points each)

8. **D** The model shows that the length of the room (9 m) is greater than the height of the room (3 m). Refer students to Lesson 6 to review an inquiry that involves making a model.

9. **C** You didn't observe Julia hurting her arm, but observing the ice pack on her arm enables you to infer that she hurt her arm. Direct students to review Lesson 2 on inferring and other science skills.

10. **C** Because Diego came to the conclusion that a location with bright sunlight is best for the plant, he must have observed that the plant kept in sunlight grew better than the plant kept in shade. Review Lesson 2 and have a volunteer tell when in an investigation a scientist might draw conclusions.

11. **A** After making and recording observations, she must decide what the results mean and draw a conclusion. Review Lesson 2 and have students tell why a scientist draws conclusions after conducting an experiment.

12. **B** To test a hypothesis, scientists can conduct an experiment. They ask questions and gather materials before they conduct an experiment. They draw conclusions after they conduct an experiment. If necessary, have students review Lessons 1 and 2.

13. **C** If the scientist's experiment does not support his hypothesis, he should make and test a different hypothesis. Have students explain why a scientist should not forget the experiment or try to make up supporting evidence for a hypothesis.

---

8. Junichi looks at this 2-D model of a classroom on a computer screen that uses perspective so it appears as a 3-D model.

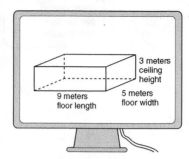

3 meters ceiling height
9 meters floor length
5 meters floor width

Junichi wants to know if the classroom is longer than it is tall. How can he use evidence from this model to answer the question?

- (A) He can look at the length of the floor.
- (B) He can look at the height of the ceiling.
- (C) He can compare the length and the width.
- (D) He can compare the length and the ceiling height.

9. During gym class, Julia had an ice pack on one arm. You think she must have hurt her arm. What scientific skill did you use?

- (A) communicating
- (B) comparing
- (C) inferring
- (D) measuring

10. Diego has been observing how well one type of plant grows in different locations. He concludes that a location with bright sunlight is best for the plant. Which of the following could be a reason for his conclusion?

- (A) His friend told him that all plants need bright sunlight to grow.
- (B) Plants that he kept in shade grew better than plants that he kept in sunlight.
- (C) Plants that he kept in shade did not grow as well as plants that he kept in sunlight.
- (D) He thinks that the plants he kept in sunlight would have grown better with more water.

11. A scientist is using a scientific method. She studies a table of data she has collected and recorded. What does the scientist do next?

- (A) She draws a conclusion.
- (B) She makes a hypothesis.
- (C) She conducts an experiment.
- (D) She studies the results one more time.

12. Scientists state a hypothesis for each experiment. What is one way that scientists can test a hypothesis?

- (A) asking questions
- (B) conducting an experiment
- (C) drawing conclusions
- (D) gathering materials

© Houghton Mifflin Harcourt Publishing Company   (border) ©NDisk/Age Fotostock

---

Item Analysis *(continued)*

Items	Depth of Knowledge	Cognitive Complexity
8–9	2	Moderate
10	3	Moderate
11	1	Low
12–13	2	Moderate

13. A scientist has spent a year conducting an experiment. He concludes that evidence from his experiment does not support his hypothesis. What should the scientist do next?

Ⓐ Forget this experiment and choose a new problem.

Ⓑ Try to make up evidence that supports his hypothesis.

Ⓒ Look at the evidence and see if he can make a new hypothesis.

Ⓓ Look at the information and find a different way to organize his results.

14. Gia hypothesizes that hot water will cause a sugar cube to dissolve faster than cold water will. She investigates by filling three cups: one with hot water, one with cold water, and one with ice water. She drops a sugar cube in each cup. Which observation will help Gia decide whether her hypothesis is correct?

Ⓐ which cup the sugar cube dissolves in first

Ⓑ the time it takes for two sugar cubes to dissolve

Ⓒ changes in water temperature from start to finish

Ⓓ changes in the size of the sugar cube in cold water

15. The local news station asks viewers to measure the amount of rain that falls in their neighborhoods. Four measurements are shown below.

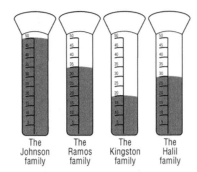

The Johnson family   The Ramos family   The Kingston family   The Halil family

Which family measures the most rain?

Ⓐ Halil family

Ⓑ Johnson family

Ⓒ Kingston family

Ⓓ Ramos family

16. Seiji wonders why flowers will not grow in his garden. What part of the inquiry process does this represent?

Ⓐ asking a question

Ⓑ conducting an investigation

Ⓒ drawing a conclusion

Ⓓ making a prediction

Item Analysis (continued)

Items	Depth of Knowledge	Cognitive Complexity
14	2	Moderate
15	1	Low
16	2	Moderate

Unit Review continued

Answer Key

Science Concepts (5 points each)

14. A Gia is trying to determine whether water temperature affects how quickly a sugar cube dissolves, so she must determine in which temperature of water the sugar cube dissolved first. Have students refer to Lesson 2, and ask volunteers to explain why it is important to control variables in an experiment.

15. B The rain gauge that is the fullest measured the most rainfall. Have students review "Recording and Displaying Data" in Lesson 3, and ask volunteers to explain how the illustration is used to answer the question.

16. A When a person observes an event and wonders why it happens, he or she is asking a question. Have students review Lesson 1, tell what step asking a question would be in an inquiry process, and explain their answers.

Short Option Performance Assessment

Task

Write a Job Description
Have students think about the work that different kinds of scientists do. Tell them to write a paragraph that describes the skills possessed by one kind of scientist, such as a chemist, zoologist, meteorologist, astronomer, physicist, or geologist.

Rubric

Preparation To serve as a basis for writing, you may wish to provide students with print source material that you have found or compiled or with digital content. If necessary, discuss this material as a group before students begin writing.

Scoring Rubric—Performance Indicators

____ Summarizes or gives examples of types of research conducted by the chosen scientist.

____ Describes skills that are of particular importance in the chosen field.

____ Uses appropriate and accurate details that present a clear picture of the chosen field.

Observations and Rubric Scores

3   2   1   0

Unit Review *continued*

Answer Key

Apply Inquiry and Review the Big Idea

(7 points)

17. See student page for sample answer.

To reinforce this concept, let students provide one another with a scenario such as this: "You see a football in a tree. What can you infer happened?" Have another student tell what he or she infers.

(6 points)

18. See student page for sample answers.

Remind students that they make observations based on their senses. Ask why they cannot say that they observe that the leaf is green. If necessary, have students review measuring in Lesson 4.

(7 points)

19. See student page for sample answer.

Elicit from students why it is important for Rachel to have the ramp be the same height and length during both trials.

UNIT 1

Apply Inquiry and Review the Big Idea

Write the answers to these questions.

17. Luis fed his cat in the kitchen. These pictures show what Luis saw as he left the kitchen and then what he saw when he returned.

Luis figured out that the cat jumped on the table and knocked the mitt onto the floor. What inquiry skill did Luis use? Give a reason for your answer.

Sample answer: Luis inferred. He did not actually see the cat knock the mitt to the

floor, but he reasoned this was the most likely cause of the mitt falling to the floor.

18. Write three observations about this leaf.

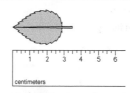

My Observations

a. Sample answer: The leaf is about 3.5 centimeters long.

b. Sample answer: The leaf has jagged edges.

c. Sample answer: The leaf has one point.

19. Rachel wonders if a heavy ball rolls down a ramp faster than a light ball. Describe an investigation she could do to find out.

Sample answer: Rachel could use a stopwatch to time how long it takes a heavy

ball to roll down a ramp and then how long it takes a light ball to roll down the

same ramp.

60   Unit 1

Item Analysis

Items	Depth of Knowledge	Cognitive Complexity
17	3	High
18	3	Moderate
19	4	High

UNIT 2 The Engineering Process

Big Idea and Essential Questions

This Unit was designed to focus on this Big Idea and Essential Questions.

Big Idea

Engineers use a process to design products and processes that solve human problems.

Essential Questions

L1 **What Is an Engineering Design Process?**

L2 **How Can You Design a Solution to a Problem?**

L3 **What Is Technology?**

L4 **How Do We Use Technology?**

Take It Home!
A School-Home Connection letter is provided in Online Resources.

 Professional Development

Houghton Mifflin Harcourt and **NSTA,** the **National Science Teachers Association,** have partnered to provide customized professional development resources for teachers using *ScienceFusion*.

The Professional Development Resources include:

- Do-it-yourself resources, where you can study at your own pace
- Live and archived online seminars
- Journal articles, many of which include lesson plans
- Fee-based eBooks, eBook chapters, online short courses, symposia, and conferences

   Access to the **NSTA Learning Center** is provided in the *ScienceFusion* Online Resources.

National Science Teachers Association

The **NSTA** Learning Center

Unit Planning

Options for Instruction

Two parallel paths meet the unit objectives, with a strong Inquiry strand woven into each. Follow the Print Path, the Digital Path, or your customized combination of print, digital, and inquiry.

	LESSON 1	LESSON 2	LESSON 3
Essential Questions	**What Is an Engineering Design Process?**	☑ **Guided Inquiry** **How Can You Design a Solution to a Problem?**	**What Is Technology?**
Print Path	☐ **Student Edition** pp. 63–76 • What Is Engineering? • What Is the Design Process? • Design You Can Use • Are We Done Yet?	☐ **Student Edition** pp. 77–78 • Scaffolding for Inquiry	☐ **Student Edition** pp. 79–92 • Tools Rule! • What Is Technology? • Technological Systems • The Good and the Bad of It • Out with the Old
Hands-On Inquiry	**Inquiry Flipchart** p. 8 **Design a Solution to a Problem** ☐ Directed Inquiry **Build a Prototype** ☐ Independent Inquiry	**Inquiry Flipchart** p. 9 **How Can You Design a Solution to a Problem?** ☐ Guided Inquiry	**Inquiry Flipchart** p. 10 **Goals, Inputs, and Outputs** ☐ Directed Inquiry **All Systems Go!** ☐ Independent Inquiry
Digital Path	☐ **Digital Lesson** Online Resources Interactive presentation of lesson content	☐ **Virtual Lab** Online Resources Interactive scaffolded inquiry	☐ **Digital Lesson** Online Resources Interactive presentation of lesson content

✓ Guided Inquiry

How Do We Use Technology?

OTHER UNIT FEATURES

👥 **People in Science, p. 95**

💻 **Video-based Project,**
It's a Bird! It's a Plane!

🔵 **Online Resources**

Teacher Notes

☐ **Student Edition**
pp. 93–94
• Scaffolding for Inquiry

Inquiry Flipchart
p. 11

How Do We Use
Technology?
☐ Guided Inquiry

☐ **Virtual Lab**
Online Resources
Interactive scaffolded inquiry

Unit Assessment

Formative Assessment
Sum It Up! and Brain Check
Student Edition, end of each lesson

Summative Assessment
Lesson Quizzes
Assessment Guide,
pp. AG 14–AG 17

Unit 2 Review
Student Edition, pp. 97–100

Unit 2 Test
Assessment Guide,
pp. AG 18–AG 22

Performance Assessment
SHORT OPTION: Teacher
Edition, p. 99
LONG OPTION: Assessment
Guide, pp. AG 23–AG 24

RTI ▶ **Response to Intervention**

RTI Strategies p. 61I

🔵 Online Assessment
Test-taking and automatic scoring
Banks of items from which to
build tests

Planning for Inquiry

Use the following preview of Inquiry Activities and Lessons to gather and manage the materials needed for each lesson.

Activity	Inquiry and Design Process Skills Focus	Materials	Prep Tips, Troubleshooting, and Expected Results
Lesson 1 DIRECTED INQUIRY Flipchart **p. 8** **A Design a Solution to a Problem** OBJECTIVE Follow directions for an investigation to design a device that will solve a problem. 🕐 30–40 minutes 👥 small groups	• Plan and Conduct a Simple Investigation • Infer • Draw Conclusions	• pencil • paper • colored pencils or markers (optional) • reference materials (optional)	**Prep Tips** You may wish to lead a brainstorming session to help students come up with problems to solve before they start the activity, or else have them design a solution to the problem shown on the Flipchart page. **Troubleshooting** Provide a variety of materials. Discuss the idea of inventions and patents. **Expected Results** Results will vary, depending on the problems students choose to solve. While students' designs may be whimsical, or even fantastical, they should address a clearly defined problem and provide a specific solution for it.
INDEPENDENT INQUIRY Flipchart **p. 8** **B Build a Prototype** OBJECTIVE Plan and conduct an investigation to build and test a prototype. 🕐 20–30 minutes 👥 small groups	• Hypothesize • Draw Conclusions • Experiment	• various materials as requested by students • Science Notebook	**Prep Tips** Before students begin the investigation, discuss which materials they will use. Prepare an area in which each group can work on and test their prototype. Be prepared for students to revise their designs as they test their prototypes, which may lead to students needing additional materials. **Expected Results** Students will build and test a prototype. During the testing process, they will probably have to modify their original designs.

Additional teaching support for all inquiry activities is available in **Online Resources**.

Notebook **Science Notebook Strategies**
- Lists of Kit-Supplied Materials
- Meeting Individual Needs
- Investigate More—Extensions and Variations and More!

Activity	Inquiry and Design Process Skills Focus	Materials	Prep Tips, Troubleshooting, and Expected Results
Lesson 2 GUIDED INQUIRY **Flipchart** p. 9 Student Edition pp. 77–78 **How Can You Design a Solution to a Problem?** OBJECTIVES • Design an apparatus that gently absorbs the force of motion. • Build and test prototypes based on their designs. ⏰ 45 minutes 👥 small groups	• Experiment • Predict	• egg • gallon freezer bag • various other materials, such as cotton, fabric, packing foam, yarn, newspaper, tissue boxes, plastic bags, bubble wrap	**Prep Tips** Begin gathering materials two weeks prior to the activity. Boil the eggs prior to the activity. Locate an area to be used for testing. **Caution!** Some students may be allergic to eggs. Give these students a different task to perform. **Troubleshooting** You may need to break the activity into two sections to allow students time to gather the materials they need between the design phase and the building phase. You may wish to schedule additional sessions of redesigning, building, and testing, during which students can improve their designs. **Expected Results** Students may or may not succeed in protecting the egg, but they will learn about the processes involved in designing, building, and testing a piece of equipment.

Go Digital! Virtual Lab

How Can You Design a Solution to a Problem?
Key Inquiry Skills: Plan and Conduct Simple Investigations, Control Variables, Measure
Students design parachutes with minimal material that allow the safe delivery of cargo.

Planning for Inquiry (continued)

Activity	Inquiry and Design Process Skills Focus	Materials	Prep Tips, Troubleshooting, and Expected Results
Lesson 3 DIRECTED INQUIRY Flipchart p. 10 **A Goals, Inputs, and Outputs** **OBJECTIVE** Follow directions to make a device that lifts a piece of candy. ⏱ 30–40 minutes 👥 small groups	• Plan and Conduct a Simple Investigation • Infer • Draw Conclusions	• cardboard strip, 20 cm x 6 cm (1 per group) • shoebox (1 per group) • masking tape • dominoes (10 per group) • shower curtain ring (1 per group) • ruler • string (1 1-meter length per group) • small piece of wrapped candy (1 per group) • marble (1 per group)	**Prep Tips** Prepare an area to test the activity. You may wish to set up the tables and the shoeboxes ahead of time. Cut the 20 cm x 6 cm cardboard strips and the 1-meter lengths of string. **Troubleshooting** Step 1: Tell students that one end of the ramp should be taped to the top of the shoebox, and the other end should be taped about 12 inches from the edge of the desk. Step 2: The dominoes need to be spaced evenly so that a chain reaction occurs when they fall. Step 4: Tape the loose end of the string to the last domino. **Expected Results** The marble should have rolled down the ramp and knocked over the dominoes in a chain reaction. When the last domino falls from the desk, it should lift the candy on the string pulley.
INDEPENDENT INQUIRY Flipchart p. 10 **B All Systems Go!** **OBJECTIVE** Plan and conduct an investigation to observe and improve an emergency system. ⏱ 20–30 minutes 👥 individuals	• Observe • Draw Conclusions	• Science Notebook • art supplies (optional)	**Prep Tips** Prior to doing this activity, have students study their school emergency system, noting the alarms, signs, public announcements, and procedures for everyone to follow during emergency situations. Suggest that students take their Science Notebooks with them on a guided walk of the school so that they can record their observations. They may want to sketch maps to use for reference later. **Troubleshooting** Encourage students to compartmentalize steps to take for various types of emergencies such as alarms to sound, routes to take, and so on. **Expected Results** Results will vary depending on the setting. Be sure students understand that school supervisors have spent a lot of time designing and making adjustments to the school emergency system in order for it to work well. Have students record any suggestions they have for improving the system in their Science Noteboooks. Remind students that there are often good reasons why seemingly inefficient systems operate as they do. These reasons may not be obvious if the observer doesn't know all the details.

Activity	Inquiry and Design Process Skills Focus	Materials	Prep Tips, Troubleshooting, and Expected Results
Lesson 4 INQUIRY **GUIDED INQUIRY** Flipchart p. 11 Student Edition pp. 93–94 **How Do We Use Technology?** **OBJECTIVES** • Identify design criteria. • Evaluate solutions to a problem. • Test a model using a unit of measurement. ⏱ 20–30 minutes 👥 small groups	• Formulate and Use Models • Infer • Draw Conclusions	• string (2 150-cm lengths per group) • books (4 per group) • spring scale • marbles (5 per group) • jar lid (1 per group) • cubes (at least 3 per group)	**Prep Tips** You may wish to cut 150-cm lengths of string and tie the books in advance of the activity. The number and size of marbles needed will depend on the size of the lip of the jar lid. **Caution!** Be sure that students take proper caution with the book on the spring scale. **Troubleshooting** Review with students how to operate a spring scale. Invite them to probe the scale by pulling on the hook with their fingers. They should note that the scale's gauge indicates the amount of force being applied. Coach students to tie the books both lengthwise and widthwise, and tightly enough so that the string will hold the books together as they are dragged. Be aware of any variations in the texture of surfaces on which students work. **Expected Results** Students will find that it takes more force (as measured by the spring scale) to pull the books across the bare table than it takes to pull them with the lid and marbles beneath them. They should conclude that the marbles reduce the resistance from friction. By substituting cubes for some of the marbles, students should conclude that the spherical shape of the marbles is the reason they made the books move more easily. The average force needed to move the books with marbles and cubes should fall between the average force needed for marbles alone and that needed for no marbles at all.

Go Digital! Virtual Lab

How Do We Use Technology?
Key Inquiry Skills: Measure, Predict, Plan and Conduct Simple Investigations
Students examine and attempt to improve a device used to help counteract the force of friction.

Differentiated Instruction

Customize and Extend

You can extend and customize science instruction for your students using the following resources.

Leveled Readers

The **Science & Engineering Leveled Readers** can be used to provide additional nonfiction reading practice in the subject area of Unit 2.

ON-LEVEL This Reader reinforces unit concepts. It includes student response activities for your students.

EXTRA SUPPORT This Reader shares title, illustrations, vocabulary, and concepts with the On-Level Reader. However, the text is linguistically accommodated to provide simplified sentence structures and comprehension aids. It also includes response activities.

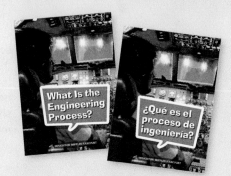

ENRICHMENT This high-interest nonfiction Reader enriches and extends unit concepts. It reinforces some of the unit vocabulary, includes *stretch vocabulary*, and includes response activities.

TEACHER GUIDE

The accompanying **Teacher Guide** provides teaching strategies and support for using all the Readers, as well as English and Spanish worksheets that focus on vocabulary development. A correlation to the Disciplinary Core Ideas of the Next Generation Science Standards is included.

 DIGITAL VERSIONS

All of these Leveled Readers are available online. They are also available in an innovative and engaging format for touchscreen mobile devices. Contact your HMH Sales Representative for more information.

RTI Response to Intervention

Response to Intervention is a process for identifying and supporting students who are not making expected progress toward essential learning goals.

The following *ScienceFusion* components have the flexibility to be used to provide Core Classroom Instruction (Tier 1), strategic intervention (Tier 2), and intensive intervention (Tier 3).		
Component	**Location**	**Strategies and Benefits**
Student Edition, Active Reading prompts Sum It Up!, Brain Check	Active Reading throughout each lesson, Sum it Up! and Brain Check at the end of each lesson	Student responses can be used as screening tools to assess whether intervention is needed.
Assessment Guide, Lesson Quizzes	pp. AG 14–AG 17	Student responses can be used as screening tools to assess whether intervention is needed.
Inquiry Flipcharts	Inquiry Flipchart pp. 8, 10	Directed Inquiry for students who learn best through directed or teacher-led hands-on activities.
Teacher Edition, Unit Review Answer Strategies	TE pp. 97–100	Suggestions for intervention, guidance, and remediation for each review question.
Leveled Readers	TE p. 61H	Content support for students not meeting the learning needs during core classroom instruction.
Leveled Readers, Teacher Guides and Vocabulary Worksheets	TE p. 61H	Direct instruction with small groups of students needing additional content at various readability levels.
Extra Support for Vocabulary and Concepts (online worksheets)	Online Resources	Support for individualized instruction with practice in essential content.
Online Student Edition with Audio	Online Resources	Provides learners with multiple-modality access to science concepts and information.
Interactive Digital Lessons and Virtual Labs	Online Resources	Provides individualized learning experiences. Lessons make content accessible through simulations, animations, videos, audio, and integrated assessment.

Differentiated Instruction

English Language Learners

Choose from these instructional strategies to meet the needs of English language learners. Suggestions are provided for adapting the activity for three proficiency levels. Point-of-use strategies also appear within unit lessons.

☑ Unit Vocabulary

Lesson 1	Lesson 3
engineering	tool
design	technology
prototype	

Vocabulary Cards are provided in Online Resources.

Vocabulary Activity

Complete a Crossword Puzzle

Make a crossword puzzle for the five vocabulary terms. Clues for the terms can be provided in different ways. Examples:

• Show a picture or drawing for each term.
• Write a description for each term.

Beginning	Intermediate	Advanced
Write the terms on the board. Fill in some of the letters for the terms in the crossword puzzle. Present clues by drawing, showing, or pointing to a picture for each term. Have students guess the term. Assist them in writing the term in the puzzle. As students write each term in the puzzle, cross it off on the board.	Present clues by describing each term aloud. For example, *This thing helps people shape or build something.* (tool) Have students guess the term. Ask students to say one more thing about the term (e.g. *A shovel is a tool for the garden.*) Have them write the term in the puzzle.	Write the terms and where they go in the puzzle (e.g. #1 Across) on index cards. Put students into groups. Students should take turns drawing a card and describing the term as others guess. Then students should write the term in the puzzle.

☑ Model Concepts

The Design Process

Remind students that there are five steps in the design process. Have students work in pairs. Provide pairs with a graphic organizer (similar to the one in their book) showing five numbered boxes with arrows. Students will identify the steps in the design process and discuss them.

Beginning	Intermediate	Advanced
Provide students with five key words or phrases to copy into each box. For example, *build prototype, test prototype, problem*, etc. Have students decide which words or phrases belong in each box. Assist them in filling in the boxes. Then ask **What is Step 1? What is Step 2?** and so on.	Have students fill in the boxes with the five steps of the design process, using phrases or short sentences. For example, *There is a problem*. Have student discuss the process using sequence words such as *first, second, next, then,* and *finally*.	Have students fill in the boxes with the five steps of the design process. Tell students to use complete sentences. Have students ask each other questions about the process. For example, *What happens first? What happens after _____? What happens last?*

☑ Model Inquiry Skills

Hypothesize and Draw Conclusions

Students will hypothesize and draw conclusions as they complete the Inquiry Lesson, *How Can You Design a Solution to a Problem?*

Beginning	Intermediate	Advanced
Ask students to predict, or hypothesize, what they think will happen to their egg. Write *break* and *not break* on the board and have pairs check their predictions. Then assist them in drawing conclusions after testing their prototype in Step 3. Ask: **Did the egg break? Why (not)?** Elicit reasons from students that support the results. Ask: **What do you need to change?** Allow students to respond with single words or phrases.	Provide students with sentence frames for them to use as they predict what will happen to their egg and then draw conclusions after testing their prototype in Step 3. For example: *I think the egg will _____ because _____. The egg broke/did not break because _____.* If necessary, have students share what they need to do to improve their prototype. Provide the frames: *We need to _____. We should _____.*	Have students discuss what they think will happen to their egg. Place pairs into groups of four and have each pair ask the other pair questions, such as *Do you think your egg will break? What do you think will happen to your egg? Why?* After testing their prototype in step 3, have pairs share their conclusions with others. Require students to use complete sentences as they explain their conclusions and propose how they will improve their prototypes.

The Engineering Process

I Wonder Why

Use the images and the question to stimulate interest in the unit topic. Ask students how they think objects such as the ancient tools shown might be used. Point out the inset photo and explain that scientists use technology such as microscopes and hand lenses to enhance their ability to see details. Discuss with students what ancient tools may have in common with modern-day tools.

Here's Why

Have students turn the page and read the response to the question. You may wish to share the following background with students.

More About...

Ancient Tools

All tools are designed to help people meet a need. Tools such as this spear point helped ancient hunters meet their need for food. The leather-wrapped shaft is called an atlatl. The shaft of the spear fits into a cup on the end of the atlatl. The thrower holds the atlatl at the leather grip and moves the arm forward, similar to the way a baseball is thrown. The spear is flung forward as the cup swings over the thrower's shoulder. The atlatl allows the thrower to achieve spear velocities of about 150 km/h.

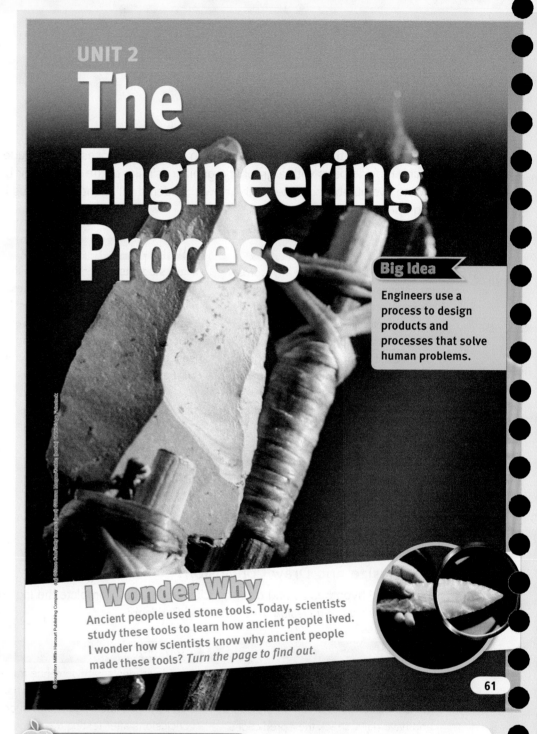

UNIT 2

The Engineering Process

Big Idea

Engineers use a process to design products and processes that solve human problems.

I Wonder Why

Ancient people used stone tools. Today, scientists study these tools to learn how ancient people lived. I wonder how scientists know why ancient people made these tools? *Turn the page to find out.*

61

🍎 **Professional Development**   **Science Background**

Use the keywords to access

- Professional Development from **The NSTA Learning Center**
- **SciLinks** for additional online content appropriate for students and teachers
- Teacher Science Background in the back of this Teacher Edition and in the Planning Guide

Keywords

engineering and technology
engineering design process

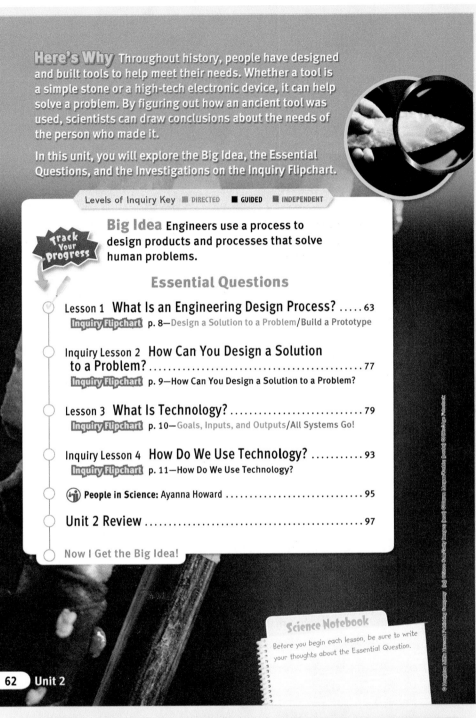

Here's Why Throughout history, people have designed and built tools to help meet their needs. Whether a tool is a simple stone or a high-tech electronic device, it can help solve a problem. By figuring out how an ancient tool was used, scientists can draw conclusions about the needs of the person who made it.

In this unit, you will explore the Big Idea, the Essential Questions, and the Investigations on the Inquiry Flipchart.

Levels of Inquiry Key ▪ DIRECTED ▪ GUIDED ▪ INDEPENDENT

Track Your Progress

Big Idea Engineers use a process to design products and processes that solve human problems.

Essential Questions

Now I Get the Big Idea!

Science Notebook
Before you begin each lesson, be sure to write your thoughts about the Essential Question.

Go Digital

For a complete digital curriculum and resources that provide full coverage of the objectives for this unit, see the Online Resources for this program.

Big Idea and Essential Questions

Big Idea Engineers use a process to design products and processes that solve human problems.

Post the Unit Big Idea on the board. Have students read the Essential Questions, which are also the titles of the lessons in this unit.

- Discuss how the Essential Questions can help them focus on the Big Idea.

- Have students read the Big Idea statement. The statement describes the main science concept they will be learning.

- Have students predict other ideas that will be taught in the lessons based on the titles, or have them give examples of pictures they expect to see.

Once they have completed all the lessons, they should have a better understanding of the Big Idea.

Essential Questions You may use the following Science Notebook strategy for working with the Essential Questions before students begin the unit or lessons in the unit.

- Strategies for revisiting the Big Idea and Essential Questions are provided in Enduring Understandings on page 97A.

Notebook Science Notebook

- Have students copy the Essential Questions into their Science Notebooks. Suggest they leave writing lines between questions.

- Ask students to write responses to the Essential Questions. Urge students not to worry about whether their responses are correct. They should expect their ideas to change as they work in the unit. Comment that students will be able to review and revise their answers to the Essential Questions at the end of the unit.

- Tips and strategies for using Science Notebooks are provided throughout this unit, in the Planning Guide, and in Online Resources.

Options for Inquiry

FLIPCHART P. 8

Students can conduct these optional investigations at any time before, during, or in response to the lesson in the Student Edition.

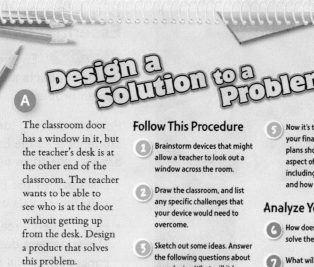

A — Design a Solution to a Problem

The classroom door has a window in it, but the teacher's desk is at the other end of the classroom. The teacher wants to be able to see who is at the door without getting up from the desk. Design a product that solves this problem.

Materials
pencil and paper
colored pencils or markers (optional)
reference materials (optional)

Follow This Procedure

1. Brainstorm devices that might allow a teacher to look out a window across the room.

2. Draw the classroom, and list any specific challenges that your device would need to overcome.

3. Sketch out some ideas. Answer the following questions about your device: What will it be made of? How many parts will it have? If you can't answer a question right away, jot it down and come back to it later.

4. When you have answered all of your questions and made your decisions, your design is done.

5. Now it's time to draw up your final plans. These plans should show every aspect of your product, including measurements and how it will be built.

Analyze Your Results

6. How does your product solve the problem?

7. What will your product be made of? Why did you make that decision?

8. What if the window were also too high to see out of? Is there a way to modify your device to solve this problem as well?

B — Build a Prototype

Now you're going to build and test a prototype of your product. Using the materials you listed in your design, build and test your prototype. As you are building, record any additional materials you had to add. Also describe any modifications that you have to make in order to make your device work. Test your device and record your observations.

Here is an example of how one student began to plan his or her investigation.

Science Notebook

Questions	Answers
1. Which materials do I need?	
2. What additional materials did I add?	
3. What changes did I have to make to the original design?	
4. Does the device work as predicted?	

8

Directed Inquiry

A Design a Solution to a Problem

⏱ 30–40 minutes
👥 small groups

Prep and Planning Tips

You may want to lead a brainstorming session, before starting the activity, to help students identify the problems that would need to be solved. Have a variety of materials available to students including lenses, clay, tape, and cardboard tubes.

Expected Results

While students' designs may be whimsical, or even fantastical, they should address a clearly defined problem and provide a specific solution for it.

Independent Inquiry

B Build a Prototype

⏱ 20–30 minutes
👥 small groups

Prep and Planning Tips

See the Planning for Inquiry page for more information. Discuss with students what materials they will use before allowing them to start.

Science Notebook

Students can use the Science Notebook as a model for designing their own investigation. If students have completed the lesson in the Student Edition, encourage them to consider the material in it as they plan their prototypes.

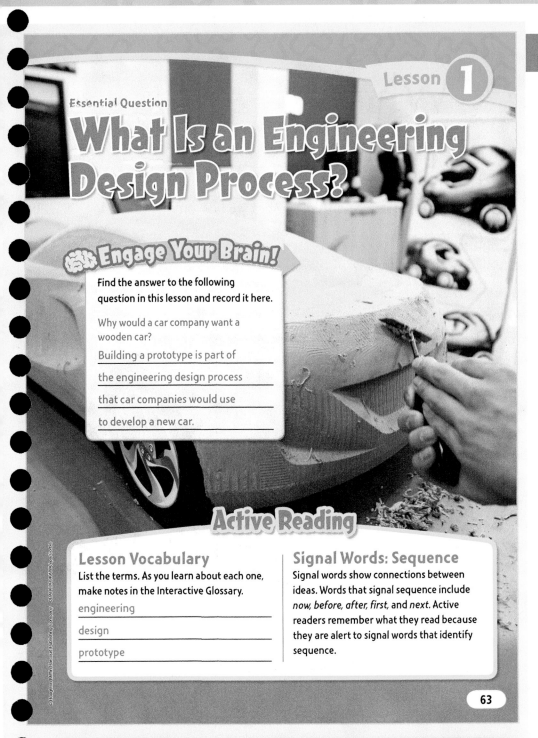

Essential Question

What Is an Engineering Design Process?

Lesson 1

Engage Your Brain!

Find the answer to the following question in this lesson and record it here.

Why would a car company want a wooden car?

Building a prototype is part of the engineering design process that car companies would use to develop a new car.

Active Reading

Lesson Vocabulary

List the terms. As you learn about each one, make notes in the Interactive Glossary.

engineering

design

prototype

Signal Words: Sequence

Signal words show connections between ideas. Words that signal sequence include *now, before, after, first,* and *next.* Active readers remember what they read because they are alert to signal words that identify sequence.

63

Go Digital

An interactive digital lesson is available in Online Resources. It is suitable for individuals, small groups, or may be projected or used on an interactive white board.

Objectives

• Describe how to use the design process to create a solution to a problem.

Engage Your Brain!

Have students brainstorm answers to the question "Why would a car company want a wooden car?" Discuss what steps they think might be involved in the process of designing a new car. Be sure they understand you're talking about planning a brand-new model, not simply building or manufacturing a car.

Remind students to record their final answer to the question, when they find it, on the fifth page of this lesson.

Active Reading Annotations

Remind students that active readers "make texts their own" by annotating them with notes and marks that help with comprehension. Encourage students to use pencil, not pen, to make annotations and to feel free to change their annotations as they read. The goal of annotation is to help students remember what they have read.

Vocabulary and Interactive Glossary

Remind students to find and list the yellow highlighted terms from the lesson. As they proceed through the lesson and learn about the terms, they should add notes, drawings, or sentences in the extra spaces provided in the Interactive Glossary.

2 Explain

 Generate Ideas

Ask students to brainstorm answers to these two questions: **How is engineering different from science? How are they related?** Write students' responses on the board. When you have completed the rest of this lesson, return to these answers. Have students correct any inaccuracies they can find.

Active Reading

Remind students that detail sentences give examples, features, characteristics, or facts about a topic. Active readers stay focused on the topic when they ask, What fact or information does this sentence add to the topic?

Develop Science Concepts

The definition of *engineering* given on these pages uses the word *practical*. Be sure students understand that, as it is used here, *practical* is the opposite of *theoretical*.

This distinction between practical and theoretical provides a useful way to distinguish between the scientist and the engineer.

Provide students with this example: a scientist might figure out how to split the nucleus of atoms to release energy. An engineer might use that knowledge to build an energy generating station that changes nuclear energy into electrical energy.

Be sure students understand there can be a lot of overlap between the two fields. Scientists can design and build practical equipment, and engineers do make scientific discoveries. In fact, the first devices that used nuclear energy were designed and built by scientists and engineers working closely together.

What Is ENGINEERING?

From the food we eat and the clothes we wear, to the cars we drive and the phones we talk on, science is at work in our lives every day.

Active Reading As you read the next page, circle the main idea of the text, and put brackets [ ] around each detail sentence.

Electrical engineers use their knowledge of physics to build things like this robot.

64

Knowledge of math and geology allows surveyors to make maps of Earth.

This biomedical engineer uses his knowledge of biology to make glass eyes.

Look around. Many of the things you see are products of engineering. **Engineering** is the use of scientific and mathematical principles to develop something practical. Some engineers use biology. Others use geology, chemistry, or physics.

Engineers use this knowledge to create something new. It might be a product, a system, or a process for doing things. Whatever it is, it's practical. People use it. Engineers develop things that people use.

▶ In the space below, draw a picture of something you can see around you that was probably designed by an engineer.

Students may draw desks, microscopes, computers, and lights.

65

Develop Science Vocabulary

engineering For hundreds of years, the word *engine* simply meant any kind of mechanical device. (For example, Eli Whitney's cotton engine, or cotton "gin," was cranked by hand.) So, an engineer was someone who designed and built mechanical devices.

Develop Inquiry Skills

COMPARE Tell students to suppose they want to buy a water bottle to take with them when they go hiking. In the store are two bottles. One is a squeezable plastic bottle with a flip top. The other is made of composite material and guaranteed to keep the water cold for at least eight hours. **Which bottle was probably designed by an engineer?** both bottles were designed by engineers.

Point out that both bottles help us meet the same practical need—to store and transport water. However, each one was designed to meet these goals in a slightly different way.

Interpret Visuals

Explain that engineering is not a modern invention. You may wish to share with students drawings of Leonardo DaVinci's robot. Ask students to describe the robot's driving mechanism (levers, pulleys, and cables) and how it functioned. Have students compare DaVinci's robot with the electromechanical robot shown on the facing page.

Notebook ▶ Summarize Ideas

Direct students to summarize the main idea orally or in writing.

2 Explain (continued)

 Generate Ideas

Tell students to suppose they are engineers who have been hired to design a new air conditioning system for the school. Ask them to brainstorm questions they would have to ask and have answered before they could start work. Write some of the questions on the board and return to them after you have finished this section.

Active Reading

Remind students that signal words show connections between ideas. Words that signal sequence include *on* (a day or date), *now*, *before*, *after*, *first*, and *next*. Active readers remember what they read because they are alert to signal words.

Develop Science Concepts

Give students scenarios so they can practice thinking like engineers. Have them suppose they are going to build a bridge across a river. Ask: **Which materials would you use?** Students may suggest materials such as steel, concrete, wood, or stone. Explain that an important part of the engineering design process is to carefully identify the problem. Ask students to explain how their choice of material would change if it were used to build a footbridge or a railroad bridge. Explain that engineers ask many questions before beginning to think about the materials they might use in a project.

Explain to students that engineers need to know what they are designing in order to know if their model meets their design criteria. If it doesn't, they have to make changes to their design.

What Is the DESIGN PROCESS?

It has been said that necessity is the mother of invention. But once you find a need, how do you build your invention? That's the design process!

Active Reading As you read these two pages, draw boxes around clue words or phrases that signal a sequence or order.

What is design? **Design** means to conceive something and prepare the plans and drawings for it to be built. Engineers use the design process to develop new technology, but anyone can follow the design process.

From basic to complex, skateboards have changed over time.

66

English Language Learners

Multiple-Meaning Words
Some words have more than one meaning. Explain that the word *solution* can mean "a mixture in which all its parts are evenly mixed," as in the air we breathe; or "a way to solve a problem," as in a solution to a problem. In this lesson, *solution* means a "way to solve a problem." Ask students to use reference materials to find and record at least three common words that have multiple meanings. (bright, power, current)

The design process starts with identifying a need or a problem. Next, you brainstorm and write down ideas on how to plan and build a potential solution. Once you have some options, select a solution to try. Usually, engineers test possible solutions using a prototype.

A prototype is an original or test model on which a real product is based. If the prototype works, then the real product is made. Usually, after testing a prototype, improvements have to be made. The prototype is then tested again. Finally, a finished product is made.

Design Process Steps

- Find a problem
- Plan and build
- Test and improve
- Redesign
- Communicate

Even something seemingly simple takes a lot of thought, planning, testing, and improvement.

How was it improved?

Look at the skateboards. Describe two design features that have been improved over time.

Sample answer: Wooden boards have

been replaced with plastic; Metal

wheels have been replaced with rubber

wheels; The single board was replaced

with two movable parts

67

Differentiation—Leveled Questions

Extra Support

What is the first step in the engineering design process? clearly defining a problem that needs to be solved

Challenge

Why did plastic boards replace wooden ones on skateboards? Sample answer: Plastic is more durable than wood.

Develop Science Vocabulary

design *Design* comes from the Latin word *designare*, meaning "mark out" or "devise." Explain to students that *devise* means "invent" or "plan out in the mind."

prototype *Prototype* comes from the Greek word *prototypos*, meaning "original" or "primitive." Explain to students that the prefix *proto–* means "first."

Develop Inquiry Skills

COMPARE Direct students' attention to the photos of the skateboards. Have students write captions about how each version differs from the previous one. Then, have student volunteers read their captions aloud.

How does the second skateboard differ from the first? The board is lighter, thinner, and smoother, and the wheel attachment is less bulky.

How does the last skateboard differ from the previous two? Sample answers: The board now has a curved-up edge; the wheels are different. The shape and material of the board has changed.

How do these changes improve the way the skateboard works? Sample answer: The shape of the board and the footpads make it more comfortable and easier for the skater to grip. The material is less bulky and more responsive.

Notebook ▸ Summarize Ideas

Have students think about the steps of the design process that were used to redesign the skateboard. Have them summarize the main idea orally or in writing.

2 Explain (continued)

 Generate Ideas

With students, preview the images on these two pages. Ask students how the images might provide a clue as to what they will read about.

Active Reading

Remind students that active readers annotate, or mark up, text to benefit their own recollection of the information presented. Explain that annotations may vary, that there are often several correct answers, and that it is important to be able to offer a reasonable explanation for an annotation.

Develop Science Concepts

Review this sequence with students: The first stages of the design process take place in the engineer's mind. Next, the ideas get worked out on paper. Then, the engineer builds a prototype.

Refer students back to the photo of the wooden model car in the Lesson Opener. **Does this prototype move like a car?** No. **Does it do work like a car?** No. **Then what is the purpose of building it?** Sample answer: to judge the size, proportions, and styling of the design

Remind students that steps of the design process include planning and building a model, and then testing and improving that model. Have students identify the steps of the design process discussed on these pages.

Design YOU CAN USE

Look around you at all the things you use every day. Do you have ideas about improving them?

Active Reading As you read these two pages, find and underline the meaning of the word *prototype*.

Who Needs It?

The first step in any design process is identifying a need or problem. Is there a chore that could be easier, a tool that could work much better, a car that could go faster or be safer? Often, the design process begins with the phrase "What if?"

Prototype!

A prototype is a test version of a design. To build a prototype, a person has to have plans. Early sketches give a rough idea. More detailed drawings provide exact measurements for every piece. Keeping good records and drawings helps to make sure that the prototype can be replicated.

This skateboard turns fairly well. But what if it could go around curves even better?

68

 Math Connection

Rename Fractions The plans for a new game console show that the controllers will be $5\frac{9}{16}$ inches long, $3\frac{12}{16}$ inches wide, and $\frac{8}{16}$ inch thick. How would you express these measurements in simplest form? (answer: $5\frac{9}{16}$ inches; $3\frac{3}{4}$ inches; $\frac{1}{2}$ inch)

Details

Draw a blueprint of a school supply, favorite toy, or tool. Label its parts and include exact measurements.

Students' pictures will vary, but should include detailed measurements of their chosen object.

Sketches and detailed drawings are an important step in planning a product.

Every part of a product can become an opportunity for a design change.

wheel

trucks

deck

69

Develop Inquiry Skills

OBSERVE Remind students of the sequence you described earlier: in the engineer's mind, worked out on paper, prototype.

Where is the "worked out on paper" stage shown on these pages? in the sketches and in the detailed drawings, or plans

How are the sketches different from the plans? Sample answer: The sketches are quick drawings; they are not necessarily to scale; they contain questions that the engineer will answer later. The plans are carefully drawn; they are to scale; they are marked with all relevant measurements.

Interpret Visuals

Have students carefully examine the sketch and plans for the skateboard prototype. Ask: **What is the main purpose of these images?** Sample answer: to help the engineer work out ideas and answer questions about the physical characteristics of the new design.

Notebook **Summarize Ideas**

Have students think about the prototype process. Have them identify situations in which they may need to build a prototype. Encourage students to summarize their ideas and present them to the class orally or in writing.

Differentiation—Leveled Questions

Extra Support

Which part of the skateboard could be redesigned? Sample answer: All the parts of the skateboard could be redesigned.

Challenge

Why is it important to be able to replicate a prototype? Sample answer: so more than one person can make it

2 Explain (continued)

Notebook **Generate Ideas**

Read the introductory paragraph aloud. Then, discuss with students what steps might come after the testing of the prototype. Write some of their suggestions on the board and return to them after you have finished this section.

Active Reading

Remind students that signal words show connections between ideas. Words and phrases that signal contrasts include *unlike*, *different from*, *but*, and *on the other hand*. Active readers remember what they read because they are alert to signal words.

Develop Science Concepts

Tell students about a hypothetical first-grade class. Every Monday, the class is given ten new spelling words for the week. They are tested on these words on Monday. They review the words several times during the week and are tested again on Friday. **What is the purpose of Friday's spelling test?** Sample answer: to determine whether the students know how to spell the words **What is the purpose of Monday's spelling test?** Sample answer: to help students see which words they already know how to spell and which they need to study

Explain that prototype testing is like Monday's spelling test. Its purpose is to let the engineer know what aspects of the design work and what aspects need improvement.

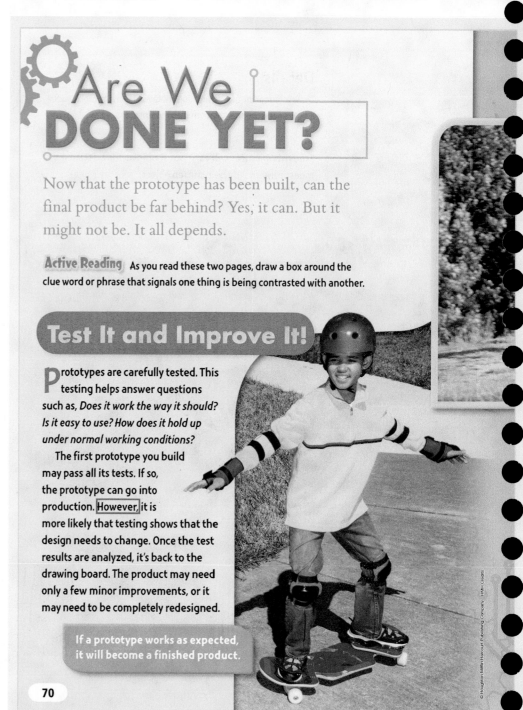

Are We DONE YET?

Now that the prototype has been built, can the final product be far behind? Yes, it can. But it might not be. It all depends.

Active Reading As you read these two pages, draw a box around the clue word or phrase that signals one thing is being contrasted with another.

Test It and Improve It!

Prototypes are carefully tested. This testing helps answer questions such as, *Does it work the way it should? Is it easy to use? How does it hold up under normal working conditions?*

The first prototype you build may pass all its tests. If so, the prototype can go into production. However, it is more likely that testing shows that the design needs to change. Once the test results are analyzed, it's back to the drawing board. The product may need only a few minor improvements, or it may need to be completely redesigned.

If a prototype works as expected, it will become a finished product.

70

English Language Learners

Practice Cause and Effect

Drop a pencil on the floor. Help students see that what happened *(the pencil fell)* is the effect. Why it happened *(you dropped it)* is the cause. Have them start a two-column chart labeled *Cause* and *Effect*. Give them a cause *(in the rain without an umbrella)* and ask them to write the effect *(get wet)*. Give an effect *(failed the test)* and ask for the cause *(didn't study)*. Relate the process of cause and effect to the prototype evaluation process.

Redesign and Share

When a prototype fails to meet a design goal, it may be redesigned. Redesign takes advantage of all work done before. Good design features are kept, and those that fail are discarded.

When the final working prototype is done, team members communicate the design. Sketches, blueprints, and test data and analysis are shared. Often, the product details are recorded in a legal document called a *patent*.

Sometimes, one prototype leads to ideas for others.

Spin Off!

Imagine a normal bicycle. Now think of three ways it could be modified to work better in different environments. Sample answer: It could have fatter tires for offroading. It could float and have tires with paddles. It could have an aerodynamic windshield for going really fast.

New ideas keep the engineering design process constantly moving forward.

71

Writing Connection

Informational Text Have students write the results of the testing of the prototype of a new product of their choice. If they wish, their reports may include visuals, such as graphs. However the information is conveyed, students' reports should provide all the information that engineers would need to refine the design of their product.

Develop Inquiry Skills

COMMUNICATE Suppose we've been hired by an engineering firm to test their prototype of a new ballpoint pen. We try to use the prototype, but it doesn't write. We can't simply tell the engineers, "It doesn't write," because that doesn't give them enough information to fix the problem. **What other information should we give them?** Sample answers: how hard we pressed down on the pen; what type of paper we tried to write on; what the temperature was in the room

What information can we give them about their design even though the prototype doesn't work? Sample answers: how light or heavy the pen feels; how comfortable it is to hold and use; how attractive or unattractive the color and shape are; whether it's likely to roll off the desk

Interpret Visuals

Remind students of what they've read about non-working prototypes. **Why might you build a prototype that doesn't actually do anything?** to judge the size, proportions, and styling of the design

Direct students' attention to the photos on these pages. **How does the skateboard design for a beginner differ from that for a professional racer?** The beginner skateboard is designed for comfort, safety, and ease of use. The professional skateboard is designed to perform quickly in specific conditions.

Notebook ▸ Summarize Ideas

Have students think about the main idea on these pages. Ask if their ideas about the engineering design process have changed since they read this section. Have them summarize the main idea orally or in writing.

3 Extend/Evaluate

Sum It Up!

- Have students read through the summary in its entirety before trying to break it up into steps. You may wish to point out the sequence of the boxes before they begin.

- If students are unsure of any answers, refer them back to the appropriate page(s) in the lesson.

- Encourage students to complete all the items before they check the Answer Key.

- If students have trouble with any of the answers on this page, be sure to review the relevant concepts before allowing students to move on to the Brain Check.

- After students have used the Answer Key to check their answers, tell them to revise any incorrect answers on the page. This will allow them to use the Sum It Up! page as a study aid when they prepare for tests.

When you're done, use the answer key to check and revise your work.

Use information in the summary to complete the graphic organizer.

Summarize

The first step in the design process is to identify a need or a problem to be solved. The next step is to plan and build a prototype. Brainstorming ideas and drawing detailed sketches of potential solutions are important parts of this step. The third step is to test and improve a prototype. After testing, a prototype might need to be redesigned and tested again. A prototype that meets all its design goals is ready for production. The final step in the design process is to communicate to others the details of a working prototype.

1 The design process starts with identifying a need or problem to be solved _____.

3 The third step is to _____ test and improve _____ the prototype. _____

5 The final step in the design process is to communicate _____.

2 The second step in the design process is to plan and build a prototype. _____

4 After testing, a _____ prototype might need to be redesigned and tested again. _____

Answer Key: 1. problem to be solved **2.** The second step in the design process is to plan and build a prototype. **3.** The third step is to test and improve the prototype. **4.** After testing, a prototype might need to be redesigned and tested again. **5.** communicate

72

Word Play

Name _____

1 Use the clues to help you write the correct word in each row. Some boxes have been filled in for you.

A. To conceive something and prepare plans to build it

B. The use of scientific and mathematical principles to develop something practical

C. A prototype may undergo many rounds of this.

D. Engineers have to be familiar with these principles.

E. The answer to a problem

F. A test version of something

G. Is identified during the first step in the design process

H. What comes after sketches, plans, and the prototype?

I. Something that people will use is described as this.

J. Engineers have to be familiar with these principles.

			D	E	S	I	G	N	
E	N	G	I	N	E	E	R	I	N	G
			T	E	S	T	I	N	G
	S	C	I	E	N	T	I	F	I	C
		S	O	L	U	T	I	O	N
P	R	O	T	O	T	Y	P	E
P	R	O	B	L	E	M
P	R	O	D	U	C	T
P	R	A	C	T	I	C	A	L
M	A	T	H	E	M	A	T	I	C	A	L

73

Answer Strategies

Word Play

1. If necessary, have students refer back to pages in the lesson where the topic is discussed. As they leaf back through the lesson, they should look for words or visuals that relate to the clue in question. As a challenge activity, have students prepare a series of game show questions based on these words.

Assessment

Suggested Scoring Guide

You may wish to use this suggested scoring guide for the Brain Check.

Item	Points
1	20 (2 points per item)
2	12
3	15
4	15
5	15
6	8
7	15
Total	100

Lesson Quiz
See Assessment Guide, p. AG 14.

3 Extend/Evaluate (continued)

Answer Strategies

Apply Concepts

2. Make certain students can identify each visual. If not, allow them to flip back through the pages of the lesson until they find the picture in question. If necessary, review the stages of the engineering design process as described in this lesson.

3. Lead a brief discussion on the purpose of a prototype. Ask students why engineers might build a prototype and what they hope to learn from it. Ask them to describe an aspect of a prototype that is not important, such as the prototype's appearance.

4. Ask students to describe what might happen if a safety problem were found in a product after tens of thousands of people had bought it.

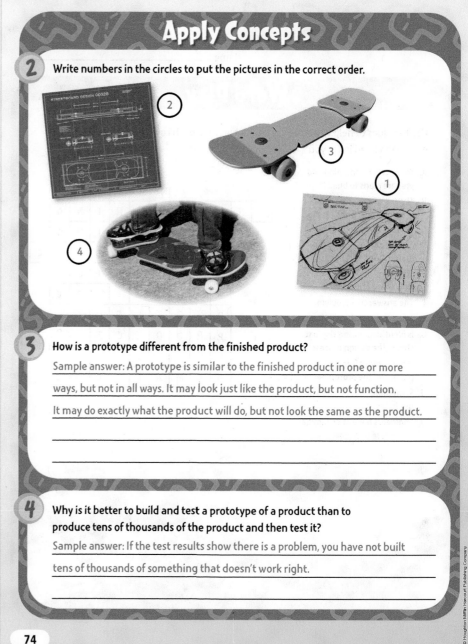

Apply Concepts

2 Write numbers in the circles to put the pictures in the correct order.

3 How is a prototype different from the finished product?

Sample answer: A prototype is similar to the finished product in one or more ways, but not in all ways. It may look just like the product, but not function. It may do exactly what the product will do, but not look the same as the product.

4 Why is it better to build and test a prototype of a product than to produce tens of thousands of the product and then test it?

Sample answer: If the test results show there is a problem, you have not built tens of thousands of something that doesn't work right.

74

5

The owner of a safety apparel company asks an engineer to "design a better helmet for skateboarders." How would you improve this instruction?

Sample answer: Our current skateboard helmets make skaters' heads too hot. We need a new helmet that is lightweight and just as strong, but cooler to wear.

_____

_____

_____

6

Which job is more likely to be done by an engineer? Why?

Developing a new material that will be used to make the outer covering of vitamin capsules	Determining how vitamins are absorbed into the bloodstream

Sample answer: The first job is more likely. Engineers make things that people use, and the new material is something that people will use.

_____

_____

_____

_____

75

Answer Strategies

Apply Concepts

5. Briefly discuss the importance of defining the problem to be solved as clearly as possible.

6. Remind students of the difference between practical and theoretical. Review the similarities and differences between the jobs of scientists and those of engineers.

3 Extend/Evaluate (continued)

Answer Strategies

Apply Concepts

7. Have a student volunteer read the question aloud. On the board, note each detail given about the new dishwasher. For each one, ask students what the engineers and designers might want to make sure of before they decide they are ready to manufacture the machine.

Take It Home!

See *ScienceSaurus®* for more information about science and engineering. *ScienceSaurus* is a "mini-encyclopedia" students can use to find out more about unit topics. It contains numerous resources including concise content summaries, an almanac, many tables, charts, and graphs, history of science, and a glossary.

---

7 The engineers at an appliance company have developed a new dishwasher. It looks very different from previous models. The controls look different and work differently. The part of the machine that heats the water has been completely redesigned. Now that the plans are completed, should the company start producing thousands of these dishwashers? Why or why not?

Sample answer: No. They need to build and test prototypes first. They need to see if people like the new look. They need to find out if the controls are easy to use. They need to make sure the controls and the water heater work the way they are supposed to work.

Take It Home!

See *ScienceSaurus®* for more information about science and engineering.

76

Make Connections

Easy

Math Connection

Scale Down a Drawing

Tell students that a new DVD player will measure 20 cm by 24 cm by 4 cm. In the plans for building the prototype, the drawings are one-half the size of the actual machine. How big are the drawings? (10 cm by 12 cm by 2 cm)

Average

Writing Connection

Write a Letter to a Company

Have students think of a product they have used recently that they think could be improved. Tell them to write a letter to the manufacturer of the product describing how they think the product could be improved. Letters should be polite and follow business letter format.

Average

Art Connection

Draw Up Plans for a Prototype

Tell students they are going to draw the plans for the prototype of a product. It could be a product they already use, an existing product they would like to modify, or something brand new. Drawings should be to scale and contain all relevant measurements.

Challenging

Social Studies Connection

Research the Development of Television

Many technological developments are the culmination of the work of many different engineers, often working separately on different projects and at different points in time. Have students research the development of television. Even the original, tiny, black and white television system had many inventors, while developments such as color TV and HD have added many more to the mix. Tell students to report back to the class on different innovations that led to TV and how they came about.

Guided Inquiry

FLIPCHART P. 9

🕐 45 minutes

👥 small groups

Students follow the directions on the Inquiry Flipchart. The accompanying Lesson Inquiry pages in the Student Edition provide scaffolding for guided inquiry responses.

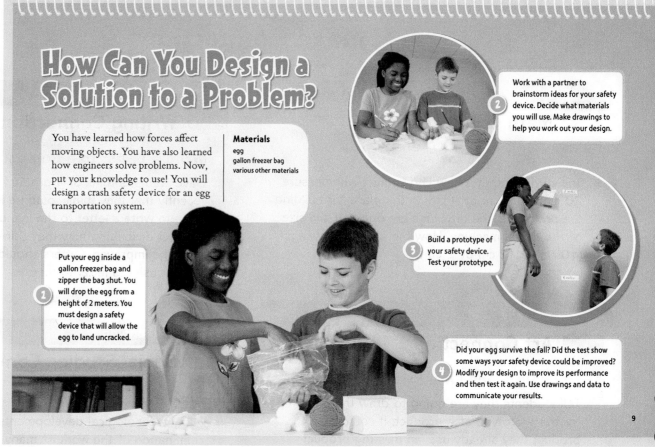

How Can You Design a Solution to a Problem?

You have learned how forces affect moving objects. You have also learned how engineers solve problems. Now, put your knowledge to use! You will design a crash safety device for an egg transportation system.

Materials
egg
gallon freezer bag
various other materials

1 Put your egg inside a gallon freezer bag and zipper the bag shut. You will drop the egg from a height of 2 meters. You must design a safety device that will allow the egg to land uncracked.

2 Work with a partner to brainstorm ideas for your safety device. Decide what materials you will use. Make drawings to help you work out your design.

3 Build a prototype of your safety device. Test your prototype.

4 Did your egg survive the fall? Did the test show some ways your safety device could be improved? Modify your design to improve its performance and then test it again. Use drawings and data to communicate your results.

9

Inquiry Skills Focus Experiment, Predict

Objectives

• Design an apparatus that gently absorbs the force of motion.

• Build and test prototypes based on their designs.

Prep and Planning Tips

See the Planning for Inquiry page for more information.

• You may need to break the activity into two sections to allow students time to gather the materials they need between the design phase and the building phase.

• You may choose to schedule additional sessions of redesign, building, and testing, during which students can improve their designs.

Expected Results

Students may or may not succeed in protecting the egg. But they will learn about the processes involved in designing, building, and testing a piece of equipment.

1 Engage/Explore

Attention Grabber

Place an egg inside a zippered plastic bag. Hold it approximately 2 meters above the ground—stand on a chair if you need to, but place the chair where students can see the floor in front of it. Drop the bag containing the egg.

Discuss with students things that you might have done in order to prevent the egg from breaking when it hit the ground.

Preview Activity

Before beginning the investigation, have students review the directions on the Inquiry Flipchart and the accompanying Student Edition response pages. Then, have them complete the response pages as they follow directions on the Inquiry Flipchart

Inquiry Flipchart page 9

Lesson 2 INQUIRY

Name _____

Essential Question

How Can You Design a Solution to a Problem?

Set a Purpose

What do you think you will learn from this experiment?

Possible answer: How to absorb the forces

created by dropping something from a

height of 2 meters

_____

Think About the Procedure

How will the equipment you design be similar to safety belts and airbags in a car?

Possible answer: Both protect something

from the forces that are created when a

moving object stops very quickly.

_____

_____

_____

_____

Why is it a good idea to make sure the plastic bag is tightly sealed before you test your prototype?

Possible answer: To prevent having to clean

up a mess if the prototype is not successful.

_____

Record Your Data

In the space below, draw a table to record the materials you used in your prototype and your observations from each test.

Students should draw a table that lists the test number, prototype materials, and result observations.

© Houghton Mifflin Harcourt Publishing Company

77

Guide the Investigation

Develop Inquiry Skills

PREDICT Point out to students that while this is an engineering exercise, it does have elements similar to those in the more standard type of experiment. For example, they are going to have to predict how their devices will handle the forces involved in being dropped and hitting the floor.

What causes the egg to break when it's dropped? the force of hitting the floor **Where does that force come from?** the energy of motion that comes from the egg falling

Explain that students' devices will have to absorb or redirect that force. Before they can consider their designs to be complete, they will need to predict how well the proposed device will perform that function. **How will you test that prediction?** by building the device, putting an egg in it, and dropping it

GATHER AND RECORD DATA Discuss with students how they will record their results. They will need to note whether the egg survived the fall, and describe the severity of the damage. If the egg did not survive, they may want to note possible reasons their design failed, as well as ideas for improving it.

Go Digital

A virtual lab experience is available with the Online Resources for this program.

2 Explain

Develop Inquiry Skills

DRAW CONCLUSIONS Once students know whether their devices work, encourage them to examine the used equipment to determine whether the various parts performed as intended.

ANALYZE AND EXTEND Discuss students' responses to the items.

1. Help students examine the various parts of their devices. If one part was supposed to hold the egg in place, did it? If one structure was supposed to collapse in order to absorb the force of impact, did it?

2. Students whose devices did not work can use their answers to the previous question to help determine how to improve their designs. Students whose devices successfully protected the egg may still want to improve their designs, either from a functionality standpoint, an appearance standpoint, or both.

3. Set up a time for students to share the results of their tests with the class.

4. Review the definition of a prototype and its purpose. Help students understand the difference between design and prototype.

3 Extend/Evaluate

5. Accept reasonable answers. Some students' questions may focus on dropping eggs as they did in this inquiry. Other students may ask questions about actual safety equipment or other real-life examples of forces and transportation.

Assessment

Lesson Quiz
See Assessment Guide, p. AG 15.

Draw Conclusions

What conclusions can you draw as a result of your test observations?

Answers will vary depending on students' designs. Students should recognize that all tests provide useful information, even if the prototype doesn't work as planned.

Analyze and Extend

1. Was your design successful? Why or why not?

Answers will vary depending on whether the egg broke. If the egg did not break, the design was successful.

2. Based on your results, how could you improve your design? Describe and draw the changes you would make to your prototype.

Answers will vary depending on students' results. Students may want to add more cushioning, add a parachute, and so on. Students should draw their design below.

3. Were there any aspects of someone else's design you might incorporate into your design?

Answers will vary depending on students' designs.

4. What is the difference between a successful design and a successful prototype?

Sample answer: A successful prototype follows the design plan and provides feedback about the design. A design is successful only when it actually solves a given problem or meets a need.

5. Think of other questions you would like to ask about forces and transportation.

Sample answer: I wonder if I could build something that would make an egg bounce back up after it was dropped.

78

Differentiated Inquiry

Easy

Catch an Egg

Have students design a device for safely catching an egg that is tossed lightly to them. As with the dropped egg, this egg should also be placed in a zippered bag before it is tossed.

Average

Analyze the Fall

- Have students repeat this inquiry. This time, have them record the impact of their device using a video or movie camera. (A camera with high-speed capability, if available, would be ideal.)

- Then, have students prepare a brief report describing exactly what happened to the various parts of their device and to the egg during the course of the impact.

Average

Raise the Bar

- Have students design the same type of device as they did in this inquiry activity. The new device must be able to protect an egg when dropped from a second-story window.

- If your school building is not two stories tall, discuss with students other locations where they can test their devices.

Challenging

Broken But Not Smashed

- Have students design a device that will break, but not smash, an egg. After the device is used, the shell should be intact enough to be disposed of properly, and the egg itself should be able to be cooked.

- After reviewing the designs, you may choose to have some students proceed to the prototype phase.

Options for Inquiry

FLIPCHART P. 10

Students can conduct these optional investigations at any time before, during, or in response to the lesson in the Student Edition.

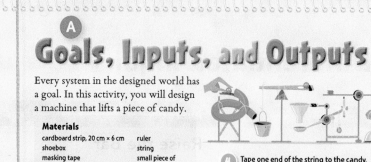

Goals, Inputs, and Outputs

Every system in the designed world has a goal. In this activity, you will design a machine that lifts a piece of candy.

Materials

cardboard strip, 20 cm × 6 cm	ruler
shoebox	string
masking tape	small piece of
dominoes	wrapped candy
shower curtain ring	marble

Follow This Procedure

1. Fold the cardboard in half lengthwise to make a V-shaped ramp. Tape one end to the top of an upside down shoebox on a desk. Tape the other end to the desk.

2. At the bottom of the ramp, stand up 10 dominoes in a row with the last one at the very edge of the desk.

3. Tape the shower curtain ring to the end of the ruler. Set the other end of the ruler under a stack of books on a second desk 30 cm from the dominoes. The end of the ruler with the loop should stick out over the floor.

4. Tape one end of the string to the candy. Set the candy on the floor below the ruler. Thread the loose end of the string through the loop above. Carefully tape it to the domino on the ledge of the table. Be sure there is no slack in your string.

5. Push the marble off of the shoebox and down the ramp.

Analyze Your Results

6. What happened to the piece of candy?

7. How was this machine able to meet its goal?

8. What are the inputs and outputs of the system you built?

9. Hypothesize what you could do to make this system work better.

All Systems GO!

Some systems don't work as well as planned. Others work, but could be made better. At school, you participate in regular emergency drills. These drills are a part of a system whose goal is to keep you safe in case of an emergency. Exits signs, flashing lights, and loud alarms are all part of this system. The teachers, school administrators, and you are another part. Study and evaluate how the emergency system in your school works. What are some events that may trigger the system? Does everyone know where to go, and when? Suggest improvements to the system.

Here is an example of how one student organized her data.

Science Notebook

Goal: Evaluate your school emergency drills.

How it works now

How it could work better

What part of the system to change

10

Directed Inquiry

A Goals, Inputs, and Outputs

🕐 30–40 minutes
👥 small groups

Prep and Planning Tips

Prepare an area to test the activity.

Step 1: Cut the 20 cm x 6 cm cardboard strips and the 1-meter lengths of string.

Step 2: Tell students that one end of the ramp should be taped to the top edge of the shoe box, and the other end of the ramp should be taped about 30 cm (12 in.) from the edge of the desk.

Step 3: The dominoes have to be spaced evenly so that a chain reaction occurs when they fall.

Step 4: Be sure the string is taut when this step is complete.

Expected Results

Students will identify the goal (lifting the candy), the input (setting the marble in motion), and the output (the lifted candy) in a system. The marble should have rolled down the ramp and knocked over the dominoes. When the last domino falls from the desk, it should lift the candy on the string pulley.

Independent Inquiry

B All Systems GO!

🕐 20–30 minutes
👥 individuals

Prep and Planning Tips

Prior to doing this activity, go over an event that may trigger a school evacuation. Discuss evacuation procedures with students. If possible, conduct a mock emergency drill. Have students observe the signs, alarms, evacuation routes to safe gathering areas, and the role of school staff during an emergency drill. Have paper, markers, and other materials available for students who wish to make a display that details their suggested improvements.

Science Notebook

Students can use the Science Notebook page shown on the Flipchart as a model for evaluating emergency procedures. Encourage students to compartmentalize steps, such as sounding alarms, steps to take for various types of situations, routes to take, and so on.

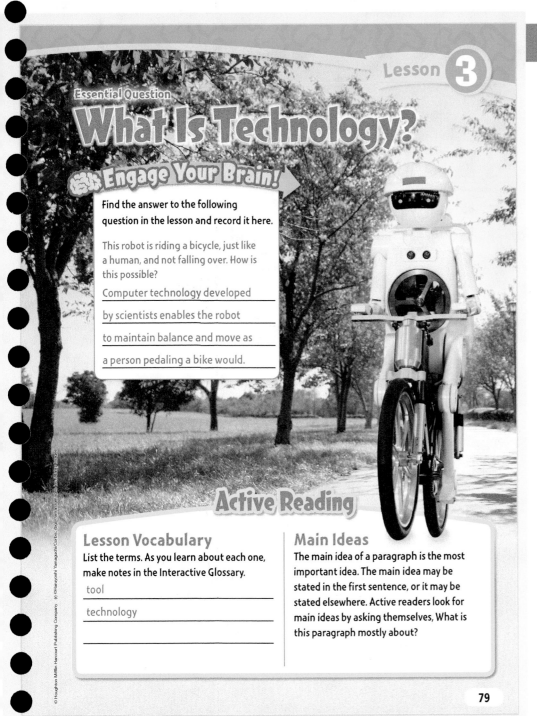

Lesson 3

Essential Question
What Is Technology?

Engage Your Brain!

Find the answer to the following question in the lesson and record it here.

This robot is riding a bicycle, just like a human, and not falling over. How is this possible?

Computer technology developed

by scientists enables the robot

to maintain balance and move as

a person pedaling a bike would.

Active Reading

Lesson Vocabulary
List the terms. As you learn about each one, make notes in the Interactive Glossary.

tool

technology

Main Ideas
The main idea of a paragraph is the most important idea. The main idea may be stated in the first sentence, or it may be stated elsewhere. Active readers look for main ideas by asking themselves, What is this paragraph mostly about?

79

Go Digital

An interactive digital lesson is available in the Online Resources. It is suitable for individuals, small groups, or may be projected or used on an interactive white board.

Objectives
- Identify examples of tools that help people produce, shape, or build things.
- Identify needs that technology helps us meet.
- Identify technological products, processes, and systems.
- Describe how technology has changed your community.
- Identify the benefits and risks of using technology.

Engage Your Brain!

Lead students in a discussion of how a robot can ride a bicycle and not fall over. Tell them the robot has a simple computer as a "brain." Guide the discussion by asking, **What skills are needed to ride a bike? Would it be easy or hard to build a robot that could ride a bike?** Record students' answers on the board. Remind them to record their answer to the question when they find it on the spread titled "Technological Systems."

Active Reading Annotations

Remind students that active readers "make texts their own" by annotating them with notes and marks that help with comprehension. Encourage students to use pencil, not pen, to make annotations and to feel free to change their annotations as they read. The goal of annotation is to help students remember what they have read.

Vocabulary and Interactive Glossary

Remind students to find and list the yellow highlighted terms from the lesson. As they proceed through the lesson and learn about the terms, they should add notes, drawings, or sentences in the extra spaces provided in the Interactive Glossary.

2 Explain

Notebook ▸ Generate Ideas

Read aloud the introductory copy beneath the head "Tools Rule!" Ask students to name the tools they currently have within arm's reach. Encourage students to examine the photos on these pages, and invite them to name and describe the purpose of each tool shown.

Active Reading

Remind students that text may describe one or more solutions to a problem. When multiple solutions are described, active readers mark each solution with an *S* to help them stay focused on the way information is organized and remember it more accurately.

Develop Science Concepts

Explain that tools help people solve problems and accomplish many daily tasks. At home, tools help us keep clean, organize our clothes, and repair things when they break. Ask: **What tools have you used today?** Sample answers: I used a spoon, a toaster, and a stapler.

What problems did each of those tools solve? The spoon helped me eat my cereal, the toaster helped me prepare my breakfast, and the stapler helped me attach my homework papers together.

As students complete the Problem Solved! Interactivity on the facing page, have them consider the information in each row separately. Point out that they are to make up their own problem and the tool that solves it in the last row. Students may wish to use one of the problems/tools identified above as a response.

Grappler

A bulldozer and a shovel serve the same purpose. However, because of a bulldozer's size, it can move huge amounts of material much more quickly than a shovel can.

TOOLS RULE!

Look in your desk. Do you see pens and pencils? Scissors? A ruler? All of these things are tools.

Active Reading As you read these two pages, put brackets [ ] around the sentences that describe a problem. Underline the sentences that describe the solution.

[**P**lanting a vegetable garden? <u>You'll need a shovel, a rake, and a spade.</u> All these items are tools. A **tool** is anything that helps people shape, build, or produce things to meet their needs.

Your family's toolbox probably contains a hammer and screwdrivers. Construction workers have similar tools that do the same jobs, only on a larger scale. Instead of hammering nails by hand, construction workers use tools that quickly drive nails into wood with the push of a button. Their tools are sized and powered differently to meet different needs.

80

Differentiation — Leveled Questions

Extra Support

When would construction workers use smaller tools? They would use small tools for smaller tasks. Their large tools would not work for tasks such as putting a door on its hinges or painting a room's corners.

Challenge

Which tools would construction workers need to build a sky-scraper that they probably would not need to build a single-story house? large cranes, rivet guns, welders, jackhammers

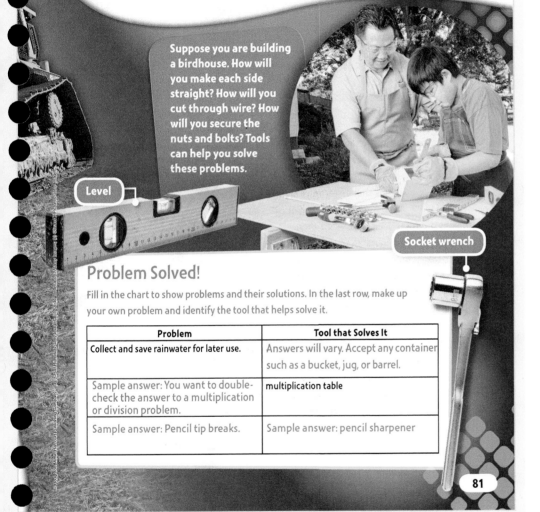

Some tools are designed to do one task. You use a pen to write a note to a friend. You keep your science notes organized in a notebook. You talk to your grandmother on the phone. What if you had one tool that could do all these tasks? A smartphone is a tool that can help you send a message, organize information, *and* talk to people.

A smartphone, like all tools, is an example of technology. **Technology** is any designed system, product, or process that people use to solve problems. Technology doesn't have to be complex. The pencil you write with and the cell phone you text with are both technology. Technology changes as the needs of people change.

Suppose you are building a birdhouse. How will you make each side straight? How will you cut through wire? How will you secure the nuts and bolts? Tools can help you solve these problems.

Level

Socket wrench

Problem Solved!

Fill in the chart to show problems and their solutions. In the last row, make up your own problem and identify the tool that helps solve it.

Problem	Tool that Solves It
Collect and save rainwater for later use.	Answers will vary. Accept any container such as a bucket, jug, or barrel.
Sample answer: You want to double-check the answer to a multiplication or division problem.	multiplication table
Sample answer: Pencil tip breaks.	Sample answer: pencil sharpener

81

Differentiation — Leveled Questions

Extra Support
What are some examples of technology that you have used today? Sample answers: Pencils and pens, computer, buses and cars; almost everything in our modern life can be classified as technology.

Challenge
What are some additional things that technology has enabled phones to do? Sample answers: take pictures, store messages (voice mail), access the Internet

Develop Inquiry Skills

SEQUENCE List on the board the following items in random order: vinyl record, 8-track tape, audiocassette, compact disc (CD), MP3 player. Describe the items as necessary, or display photographs. Have students use the descriptions and photos to order the items from oldest to most recent. vinly record, 8-track tape, audiocassette, CD, MP3 Reinforce that technology changes over time.

Interpret Visuals

Draw attention to the photos of the child and tools on this page. **Which tools could the child use to build the birdhouse, and how would the tools be used?** The ruler could be used to measure the length of the side pieces; the saw could be used to make the boards the proper lengths. **What are some tools not shown that could be helpful?** a hammer, a power saw, a paintbrush

Develop Science Vocabulary

tools Ask students to name a tool and describe all of the things they could use it for. For example, a screwdriver could be used to tighten or loosen a screw. It could also be used to pry open the lid of a paint can.

technology Technology involves all the ways that people modify the world around them to meet their needs or to solve practical problems. Ask students to point out examples of technologies they see in the lesson.

Notebook Summarize Ideas

Have students revisit the photos and Interactivity on these two pages, and remind them of the opening discussion. Have students use this information to state the overall concepts of the lesson either orally or in writing.

2 Explain (continued)

Notebook ✎ Generate Ideas

Ask students to brainstorm additional examples of ways in which technology contributes to entertainment and leisure activities, such as DVDs and DVD players, cable and satellite TV, and the Internet. Ask students to name some activities, such as reading books, listening to the radio, or going out to the movies, that may have declined because of these technologies. Guide a discussion on similarities between the older pastimes and newer ones. Point out that earlier leisure activities were also the result of technology.

Active Reading

Remind students that some text segments state information essential to understanding a topic. Active readers identify and focus on those segments as a way to deepen their understanding of the topic.

Develop Science Concepts

Explain that because technology is anything that helps people meet their needs, there can be many kinds of technology. Ask: **What are some needs technology help us meet?** Sample answer: transportation, food, shelter, health, and entertainment Emphasize that technology is not a modern invention and that most technology does not require electricity. Ask: What are some technological products in our classroom a student from 100 years ago would recognize? Sample answer: blackboard, chalk, books, desks, and chairs Explain that many modern technology products have not changed very much. People from a hundred years ago would likely recognize most of what the girl pictured on this page is wearing. However, they will not recognize the remote video controller in her hands or understand how it works.

WHAT IS TECHNOLOGY?

Vending machines, televisions, and video games are examples of technology products you know—but there are more. Technology is all around you.

Active Reading As you read this page, underline technology products. On the next page, circle the paragraph that describes examples of a technology process.

A video game is the end product of a technology process. Programming a video game involves technology you can't hold in the palm of your hand.

You've learned that technology is any designed system, product, or process. A *technology product* is anything designed to meet a need or desire. Some people think that electronics are the only type of technology product. However, most technology products do not use electricity!

This book, the desk it is on, and the backpack you use to take it home are all technology products. Your bike and the sidewalk you ride it on are technology products, too. Technology products can be very large or very small. They can be a single thing like a stone brick or made of many things put together. Some technology products, such as medicine, are made to keep us healthy. Others, such as construction tools, are made to shape the world around us. We also invent technology products just to have fun.

▶ Circle three examples of technology in this photo. Sample answers shown.

82

Writing Connection

Write a Narrative Have students use online encyclopedias and nonfiction books from the school library to find out more about the evolution of video games, from the arcade games of the 1970s to the home and online game systems of today. Instruct them to use their new knowledge to write a first-person one-page narrative of that evolution from the point of view of an early video arcade character.

The way a product is made is also a form of technology. A *technology process* is a series of steps used to achieve a goal or make a product. The steps in a technology process are like the steps in a scientific investigation. They are carefully designed for doing something a certain way.

Many things you do are a technology process. You follow a series of steps to make gelatin dessert, tie your shoelaces, and add music to your MP3 player. If you have ever played baseball, you are familiar with its rules. The rules of a game are a technology process.

Safety gear and clothing are types of technology that help baseball players perform. The bleachers and the backstop are types of technology that let spectators watch safely.

Play Ball

The ballpark, scoreboard, rules, and baseball equipment are all examples of technology. How can technology help deliver the game's events to people who aren't at the ballpark?

Sample answer: Technology enables people to watch games on TV, over the Internet, or listen on the radio.

83

Interpret Visuals

Draw attention to the baseball setting on this page. Ask: **What specific examples of technology shown here are related to baseball?** Invite students to identify additional objects not mentioned in the captions, such as the batting helmet, or objects they have seen when at a baseball park, such as the netting that protects spectators or the public-address system. As students prepare to complete the Interactivity, have them make a list of different types of technology they use to either watch, hear, or read about a sporting event.

Develop Inquiry Skills

DRAW CONCLUSIONS **Is it possible to have a technology product without a technology process? Explain.** No, a technology product is always the result of a technology process. You need to figure out how to make the product before it can be made.

 Notebook ▶ **Summarize Ideas**

Ask students to state the main ideas presented on these two pages, framing their comments in terms of technology products and technology processes. Underscore the fact that there are many kinds of technology, some simple and some very complex. Remind students that technology continues to evolve. Then have them briefly summarize the lesson thus far orally or in writing.

Math Connection

Solve a Problem Point out that the proper use of technology often involves precise measurements of length, distance, time, and so on. Explain that there are options when measuring distances; the best unit often depends on the purpose of the measurement.

To emphasize this idea, share that a baseball diamond is actually a square that measures 90 feet on each side. Have students calculate that distance in yards (30) and inches (1,080). Ask them which measurement they think is easiest to use, and why.

2 Explain (continued)

 Notebook **Generate Ideas**

Introduce the concept of technological systems by pointing to an artificial light source in the room and inviting students to name its parts. **Where does the energy for this light come from?** It is carried by wires from the generating station where the electricity is produced. Brainstorm other examples of technology products that are parts of larger connected groups. Take notes of students' observations on the board and refer to these notes throughout the lesson to support concepts in the text.

Active Reading

Remind students that detail words give examples, features, characteristics, or facts about a topic. Active readers stay focused on the topic when they ask, What fact or information does this word add to the topic?

Develop Science Concepts

To help students grasp the connection between technology processes and a designed system, ask: **What kind of process was used to develop the systems shown here?** a technology process; Technology is not only devices that solve problems, but also processes. Devices and processes together make up designed systems. **Name a job in a transportation system that could probably not be done by a tool, robot, or computer.** Sample answer: It would probably take a human to make sure that all of the other parts of the system were working smoothly. **Why would a human supervisor be considered a part of a designed system?** Human beings play a role in most designed systems. A supervisor generally makes sure that the parts of a system are working together effectively and makes changes if they are not.

In this factory, there are tools, robots, computers, and people. They all make up a system.

TECHNOLOGICAL SYSTEMS

The next time you ride in a car, look at how many parts it has. It took many tools and hundreds of steps to produce this technology.

Active Reading As you read this page, underline the sentence that describes what makes a designed system.

Groups of things that work together to achieve a goal make up a *system*. Tools, parts, and processes that work together form a *designed system.* Designed systems help us travel and ship goods. They help us communicate and grow our foods.

You are a part of many designed systems. Whether you ride the bus or walk to school, you are a part of a transportation system. This system is made up of the sidewalks, roads, and traffic signs. It also includes the cars, buses, planes, and trains that move people and materials from place to place.

Designed systems help us shape the world around us. When you ride around your town, you might see cars, roadways, buildings, or farm fields. All these things make up the *designed world*. The designed world is the part of your community that is designed and built by people.

Many designed systems work together in the designed world. For example, the agricultural system produces the food that we need. Ships, trains, and trucks in the transportation system carry food where it is needed.

84

English Language Learners

Verbs Versus Modifiers Write *design* and *designed* on the board. Explain that *design* is a verb that means "to plan how to build"; *designed* is the past tense of *design*. *Designed* is also a modifier meaning "something that was planned." Share these sentences, and have students repeat: *I will design (plan how to build) a house. I just designed (planned how to build) a house. My designed (something that was planned) house will be energy efficient.* Encourage partners to use both words in a conversation.

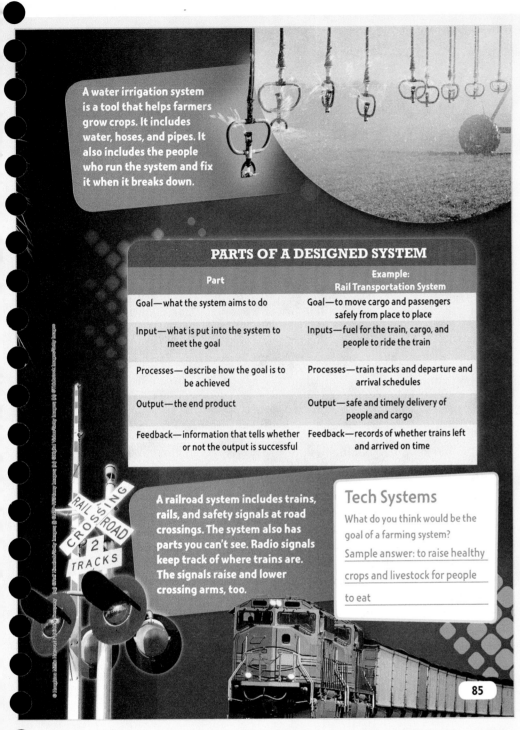

A water irrigation system is a tool that helps farmers grow crops. It includes water, hoses, and pipes. It also includes the people who run the system and fix it when it breaks down.

PARTS OF A DESIGNED SYSTEM

Part	Example: Rail Transportation System
Goal—what the system aims to do	Goal—to move cargo and passengers safely from place to place
Input—what is put into the system to meet the goal	Inputs—fuel for the train, cargo, and people to ride the train
Processes—describe how the goal is to be achieved	Processes—train tracks and departure and arrival schedules
Output—the end product	Output—safe and timely delivery of people and cargo
Feedback—information that tells whether or not the output is successful	Feedback—records of whether trains left and arrived on time

A railroad system includes trains, rails, and safety signals at road crossings. The system also has parts you can't see. Radio signals keep track of where trains are. The signals raise and lower crossing arms, too.

Tech Systems

What do you think would be the goal of a farming system?

Sample answer: to raise healthy crops and livestock for people to eat

85

Interpret Visuals

Help students analyze the information about the water irrigation system and the parts of a designed system. Ask: **Is the irrigation system a designed system? Explain your answer.** Yes, it is a designed system. The goal is to transport water to the crops. Water and energy are inputs in this system. The system's processes include the way the system is built and the irrigation schedules for the fields. Delivering enough water for the crops is the system's output. Feedback includes records of whether the crops get the right amount of water. **What does this technology system keep people from having to do?** It keeps them from having to transport water using simpler technologies, such as carrying it in buckets or transporting it with trucks.

Develop Inquiry Skills

USE MODELS **What would a diagram of a designed system probably look like? Explain your answer.** Sample answer: A diagram of a designed system would probably look like a web of interconnected parts. Many parts work together in a designed system.

What might be in the center of such a web as the engineers initially design the system? the goal of the system Have students consider the importance of a goal as they complete the Interactivity.

 Summarize Ideas

Write *technology product, technology process,* and *designed system* on the board. Invite students to state connections between any two of the terms. Illustrate these connections using arrows. Then write the term *designed world* below the first three terms, and review its definition. Have students summarize this discussion orally or in writing.

Differentiation — Leveled Questions

Extra Support

What is another example of a designed system that transports something? Sample answers: a town's electrical system (transports electricity); the Internet (transports information and communication)

Challenge

What are some other systems that a rail transportation system depends on? a construction system to build it, a maintenance system to keep it in working order, a system of engineers to study and improve it

2 Explain (continued)

Notebook ▶ Generate Ideas

Ask students to consider the usefulness of cell phones. **Cell phones with texting abilities make it easy to communicate. What new problems does this technology cause?** They can be a distraction from studying, they can cause accidents if used while driving or walking. Record responses, and point out that these responses are an example of feedback. Stress the importance of feedback in the growth of technology. Feedback allows technology to change with changing needs.

Active Reading

Remind students that informational text contains many facts. Active readers process informational text with deliberate speed that enables them to focus on and retain the facts presented. Underlining facts helps active readers focus more readily.

Develop Science Concepts

Why do people want different kinds of light bulbs? Sample answers: Different kinds of light are best for different situations; some people are interested in energy efficiency. **Do all light bulbs serve a practical purpose?** Bulbs used to provide light in dark areas serve a practical use. Some other bulbs, such as those used in holiday lights, are decorative but do not provide enough light to be of practical use.

Develop Inquiry Skills

PREDICT **How might future technology improve LED and CFL bulbs?** Sample answers: by finding ways to make them consume even less energy; by finding cheaper materials to use in producing LED bulbs; by finding safer materials to substitute for the hazardous substances in CFL bulbs

THE GOOD AND THE BAD OF IT

Compact fluorescent lights (CFLs) and light emitting diodes (LEDs) use less energy than incandescent bulbs. However, CFLs contain mercury, which can be hazardous if the bulbs break open, and LEDs are more expensive than regular light bulbs.

A light bulb that can save you $100 a year? What's the catch?

Active Reading As you read this page, draw a box around the main idea.

Technology is constantly changing. Anyone can invent or improve a technology product or process. It takes new ideas and knowledge for technology to change. The goal of any new technology is to better meet people's needs. However, new technology can also bring new risks.

Changes in technology often involve making things safer, quicker, easier, or cheaper. For example, people once used candles and lanterns to light their homes.

These things helped people see at night, but they could also cause fires. Electricity and incandescent light bulbs helped solve this problem, but this technology also has its risks.

We burn coal to generate electricity. When coal burns, harmful ash and gases are produced. The potential harm these substances can cause leads to negative feedback. Such feedback helps people think of ways to improve technology.

86

Writing Connection

Write a Summary Have students write three examples of technological drawbacks that are identified on this page. Instruct them to make a question for each example that must be answered to resolve the drawback. Have them conclude the exercise by using what they have written to address the question "Why do we use technology even though it is sometimes harmful?"

Sometimes the problems with technology are caused by the way people use technology. For instance, pesticides are helpful technology products. They are used to protect people, crops, and farm animals from harmful organisms. However, when used incorrectly, they can contaminate the soil, the water, and the air. Living things exposed to pesticides by accident can get sick and die.

Airplanes can transport a lot of people at one time. However, they burn a lot of fuel and release pollution into the atmosphere. Engineers redesign airplanes to improve their performance.

Do the Math!
Interpret a Table

Use the data in the table to answer the questions below.

Light Bulb Cost Comparisons		
	60-Watt Equivalent CFL	60-Watt Equivalent Eco-Incandescent
Cost of bulb	$3.00	$1.50
Bulb life	2500 days (about 7 years)	500 days (about 1.4 years)
Energy cost per year	$2.40	$7.00
Total cost over 7 years	$19.80	$56.50

1. How much more is the total cost of incandescent bulbs than a CFL?
$56.50 - $19.80 = $36.70

2. How much would your yearly energy cost be if you had 20 CFL bulbs in your home?
20 x $2.40 = $48.00

3. Which bulb lasts longer?
The CFL bulb lasts longer than the incandescent light bulb.

87

Interpret Visuals

Draw attention to the photos of the airplane and its engine on this page. Ask: **Before airplanes were invented, in what other ways did people travel long distances?** by train, ship, car, horse, and covered wagon **Are these ways of travel better or worse than flying?** Answers will vary. Sample answers: They were worse because they were slower. Some were better because they were more comfortable. **What are some examples of new problems caused by the invention of airplanes?** Sample answers: easier spread of contagious diseases, air and noise pollution, possible accidents

Do the Math!

Interpret a Table

Point out to students that the cost of two things cannot always be compared by simply looking at their prices. Ask what information the table provides and what they can conclude from that information. Tell students they will have to decide what computations to perform in order to answer the questions below the table. After they have done the computations, have students look at their answers and decide whether they make sense.

Notebook ▸ **Summarize Ideas**

Direct students to think about the technology processes described on these pages. Have them summarize, orally or in writing, the connections between technology growth, new problems, and further technology growth.

2 Explain (continued)

 Generate Ideas

Draw attention to the photos on these two pages. Ask students to describe each one. Read the photo captions aloud, or have students do so. Point out that some of the possible drawbacks of technology are not directly measurable, having to do with how we live our everyday lives. Ask students for their thoughts on this and write their responses on the board.

Develop Inquiry Skills

INFER In today's society, technology products are frequently and rapidly updated. Mention that technology products, such as electronics, are often discarded not because they don't work, but because better versions of the products are invented. **What problem is caused by discarded electronics?** Sample answer: additional waste and hazardous materials in landfills **What technologies might be developed to help solve the problems caused by discarded electronics?** Sample answers: technologies to neutralize hazardous substances, technologies to recycle parts of outdated electronic equipment

Why It Matters

OUT WITH THE OLD

Computers, cell phones, and flat-screen TVs are fun and useful. But like all technology, electronic gadgets have drawbacks.

Electronic technology seems to change at the blink of an eye. New electronic devices rapidly replace old ones. People benefit from new or improved electronic devices, but they also bring new problems.

Not long ago, most televisions and computer monitors were large, bulky things. New technology has made these large devices a thing of the past. They have been replaced by thin, lightweight flat screens.

But what do we do with old electronics? Some are taken apart and recycled; however, like the devices shown on this page, most end up in landfills. At landfills, electronics may release harmful chemicals into the environment.

Many electronic devices contain lead. Lead can be harmful to people and other organisms in the environment.

88

 Differentiation — Leveled Questions

Extra Support

How might computer technology affect health? Sample answers: negative: discourages exercising, causes eye strain; positive: exercise machines use computer technology; information on healthy habits and lifestyles is online

Challenge

What problems can voice-recognition technology for computers help solve? Sample answer: Speaking to a computer instead of operating it manually can help reduce injuries caused by the repeated motion of typing.

Electronics are helpful communication, work, and entertainment tools. They can also be a distraction. Some people spend a lot of time playing video games or on the Internet. They send text messages or listen to MP3 players while they are with other people. Some might even operate electronics while driving and cause a safety hazard for themselves and others.

People can solve these problems. They can set limits on computer and game time. They can put the phone away and pay attention to people and driving. These are ways to be responsible with technology.

▶ On the chart below, fill in the pros and cons of each electronic technology. Some examples have been provided for you.

	Pros	Cons
Television	can be educational; can provide breaking news quickly	can be a distraction; take time away from other activities
Smartphones	gives people instant access to communication with other and to information	can take time away from doing other activities or being social; can cause drivers to be a hazard
Video games	fun; can be social when played with others	can be a distraction; take time away from other activities; can cause inactivity

89

Differentiation — Leveled Questions

Extra Support
How can computers be used to help people be more social? Sample answers: Families can enjoy home entertainment together, families can use e-mail to keep in contact across long distances.

Challenge
How does technology make the world "a smaller place"? By making it easier to meet and interact with people with common interests, technology can build understanding among people throughout the world.

Interpret Visuals

Draw attention to the photo and Interactivity on this page. Ask students to describe the photo. Family members are all together, each using his or her own technology. **Are the members of this family spending time together? Explain your answer.** The family is physically together, but each member is involved in an activity that separates him or her from the others. **What kinds of technologies do you use at home?** Sample answers: TV, computer, game systems, music systems, DVD players **Do these products help your family socialize with one another, or do the products distract family members from one another?** Answers will vary. Underscore the idea that too much use of some technology products can isolate people from each other. Brainstorm other possible "pros" and "cons" before having students complete the chart.

Develop Inquiry Skills

DRAW CONCLUSIONS **What are some positive things that result from the negative aspects of technology?** Students should understand that the negative aspects of technology provide room for improvement and progress.

Notebook ▶ Summarize Ideas

Guide a discussion that recaps the ideas in this section and ties them to ideas and concepts in earlier sections of this lesson. Have students write a short paragraph summarizing three new things they learned in this lesson.

3 Extend/Evaluate

Sum It Up!

- Suggest that struggling students work together in teams.

- Encourage students to write notes that might be helpful on this page. They may find it useful to write the page numbers of where they found the answers to some questions. This will allow them to quickly locate information when they are reviewing.

- Review the structure of the graphic organizer. Make sure students understand that the three lower boxes are components of the overarching idea in the top box.

- Some students may have trouble completing the Summarize section correctly. You can assist these students by giving them a choice of two terms to fill in each blank. This will help them choose. Once they have completed the paragraph correctly, have them complete it again without the word choices.

- Remind students to use the Answer Key to check their answers. Tell students to correct the answers they got wrong by writing a new response.

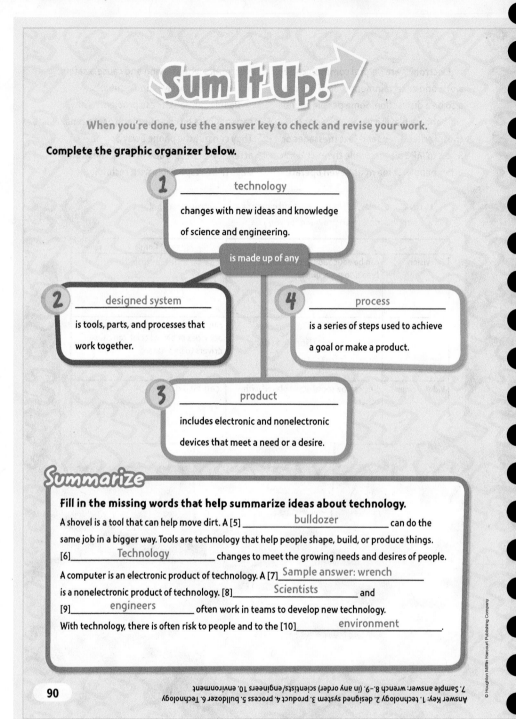

Sum It Up!

When you're done, use the answer key to check and revise your work.

Complete the graphic organizer below.

1. _____technology_____ changes with new ideas and knowledge of science and engineering.

is made up of any

2. _____designed system_____ is tools, parts, and processes that work together.

4. _____process_____ is a series of steps used to achieve a goal or make a product.

3. _____product_____ includes electronic and nonelectronic devices that meet a need or a desire.

Summarize

Fill in the missing words that help summarize ideas about technology.

A shovel is a tool that can help move dirt. A [5] _____bulldozer_____ can do the same job in a bigger way. Tools are technology that help people shape, build, or produce things. [6] _____Technology_____ changes to meet the growing needs and desires of people. A computer is an electronic product of technology. A [7] _____Sample answer: wrench_____ is a nonelectronic product of technology. [8] _____Scientists_____ and [9] _____engineers_____ often work in teams to develop new technology. With technology, there is often risk to people and to the [10] _____environment_____.

Answer Key: 1. technology **2.** designed system **3.** product **4.** process **5.** bulldozer **6.** Technology **7.** Sample answer: wrench **8.–9.** (in any order) scientists/engineers **10.** environment

© Houghton Mifflin Harcourt Publishing Company

90

 **Brain Check**

Name _____

Word Play

1 Use the clues below to fill in the words of the puzzle.

1. Any designed system, product, or process

2. Anything that helps people shape, build, or produce things to meet their needs

3. Tools, parts, and processes that work together

4. Things that are made to meet a need

5. The end product or service of a system

6. Anything that is put into a system to meet a goal

7. Information that tells whether or not the output is successful

8. This is made up of all products of technology

9. A series of steps that result in a product

designed world	
feedback	input
process	products
output	system
technology*	tool*

* Key Lesson Vocabulary

1. T E C H N O L O G Y
2. T O O L
3. S Y S T E M
4. P R O D U C T S
5. O U T P U T
6. I N P U T
7. F E E D B A C K
8. D E S I G N E D   W O R L D
9. P R O C E S S

Read down the squares with red borders. The word will answer the question below.

Murata Boy is a bicycling robot. He can ride forward, backward, and stop without falling over. Where does he get the ability to do it?

C O M P U T E R S

© Houghton Mifflin Harcourt Publishing Company

91

Answer Strategies

Word Play

1. Encourage students to first read through the definitions before they begin to enter the answers into the puzzle. If students are struggling, tell them that the words they choose should enable the word *computers* to be spelled vertically in the puzzle. Have students work in pairs if they run into trouble coming up with the answers on their own.

Assessment

Suggested Scoring Guide

You may wish to use this suggested guide for the Brain Check.

Item	Points
1	54 (6 points each)
2	11
3	11
4	24 (8 points each)
Total	100

Lesson Quiz

See Assessment Guide, p. AG 16.

3 Extend/Evaluate (continued)

Answer Strategies

Apply Concepts

2. Refer students to the section entitled "Technological Systems." Remind them how the irrigation system and the railroad system fulfill the definition of *technological system*.

3. Revisit class discussion about the section "The Good and the Bad of It" so that students can summarize the risks and benefits related to airplane travel. Be sure they understand which aspect of the discussion is considered a risk and which one is a benefit.

4. Suggest that students make a two-column chart in which they list the benefits of each of these technologies in one column, and the problems associated with each in the second column. They can then record one of the problems they have identified on the student page.

Take It Home!

Suggest that students do a "walk-around" of their kitchen with a family member, and record the names of the tools they find there. They can then work with the family member to describe the uses of each tool. Encourage students to think of several ways different tools could be used.

Apply Concepts

Passenger jets can transport people quickly from one place to another. Modern computer electronics help pilots fly these planes.

2 Describe two technological systems that are related to airplanes.

Sample answer: The plane is part of the air transportation system. It was built in a factory system.

3 What are some of the risks of global airline travel? What are some of the benefits?

Sample answer: Some risks are air pollution and the possibility of crashes. Some benefits are people being able to get places faster.

4 Write a problem associated with each example of electronic technology.

1. Compact fluorescent light bulbs	2. Video games	3. Cell phones
They contain mercury, which can be hazardous.	People can spend too much time playing them.	People who text while driving put themselves and others at risk.

Take It Home! Work with a family member to make a list of tools found in your kitchen. Sort the items in your list into simple and complex tools. Share your work with your class. Explain how you categorized the items in your list.

92

Make Connections

Easy

Art Connection

How Technology Evolves

Have students use an encyclopedia or the Internet to research Thomas Edison's invention of the phonograph. Ask them to draw an illustration of the first "cylinder" records. Using that illustration as the first in a series of illustrations, ask students to make a timeline to show the history of recordings, from cylinder records to the MP3 players of today. Direct students to label each device with its name and the year it was invented.

Average

Social Studies Connection

Government and Technology

Have students use an encyclopedia or the Internet to research and write a two- or three-paragraph description of how the government has embraced technological advances to help it carry out its duties (administration of government programs, electronic voting machines, administration of the postal service, law enforcement, and so on). Instruct students to contrast the methods used in the past with newer methods.

Easy

Writing Connection

A Letter to the Future

Ask students to write a two- or three-paragraph letter to an imaginary friend in the future, describing the use of technology in their everyday life. Instruct students to include specific examples of technology products and processes that affect them each day. Students should also describe how those technologies might change in the future.

Challenging

Health and Physical Education Connection

Gymnasiums Then and Now

Have students use an encyclopedia or the Internet to research and write a four-paragraph report describing how the technology of exercise equipment has changed in the last century. Students can compare a typical gymnasium of the early 1900s to today's typical gym. Remind students to include the invention of devices that monitor heart rate and blood pressure during exercise.

Guided Inquiry

FLIPCHART P. 11

⏱ 20–30 minutes

👥 small groups

Students follow the directions on the Flipchart. The accompanying Lesson Inquiry pages in the Student Edition provide scaffolding for guided inquiry.

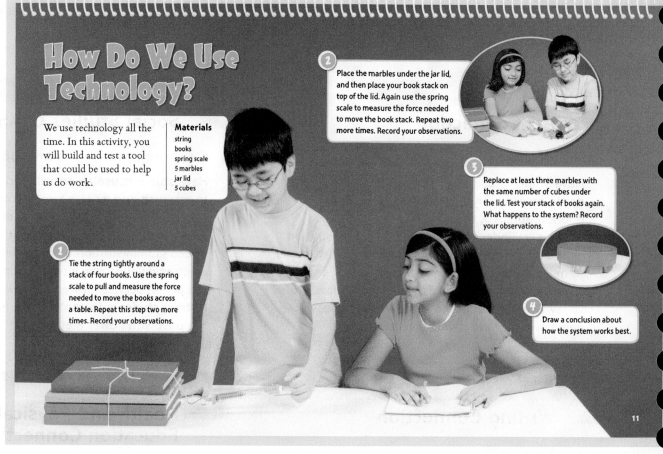

How Do We Use Technology?

We use technology all the time. In this activity, you will build and test a tool that could be used to help us do work.

Materials
string
books
spring scale
5 marbles
jar lid
5 cubes

1 Tie the string tightly around a stack of four books. Use the spring scale to pull and measure the force needed to move the books across a table. Repeat this step two more times. Record your observations.

2 Place the marbles under the jar lid, and then place your book stack on top of the lid. Again use the spring scale to measure the force needed to move the book stack. Repeat two more times. Record your observations.

3 Replace at least three marbles with the same number of cubes under the lid. Test your stack of books again. What happens to the system? Record your observations.

4 Draw a conclusion about how the system works best.

11

Inquiry Skills Focus Formulate and Use Models, Infer, Draw Conclusions

Objectives

- Identify design criteria.
- Evaluate solutions to a problem.
- Test a model using a unit of measurement.

Prep and Planning Tips

See the Planning for Inquiry page for more information.

- You may want to cut 150 cm lengths of string in advance.
- Review with students how to operate a spring scale.

Expected Results

The average force needed to move the books with marbles and cubes should fall between the average force needed for marbles alone and that needed for no marbles at all.

1 Engage/Explore

Attention Grabber

Have volunteers describe how they have helped to move heavy boxes or pieces of furniture. Discuss ways that they may have made moving easier. Some students may have seen someone use a wheeled cart or other device as an aid in moving a heavy load. Students may have also used or seen advertised slick disks that are placed under the legs of furniture as an aid to moving it across carpeting. Have students speculate as to what all of these aids have in common.

Preview Activity

Before beginning the investigation, have students review the directions on the Inquiry Flipchart and the accompanying Student Edition response pages. Then have them complete the response pages as they follow the directions on the Flipchart.

Inquiry Flipchart page 11

Name_____

Essential Question

How Do We Use Technology?

Set a Purpose

What do you think you will learn from this activity?

Sample answer: I will learn how we

use technology to solve a problem.

Think About the Procedure

What does the spring scale measure?

The spring scale measures force.

Why is it a good idea to repeat each trial in Steps 1 and 2 three times?

Accept any answer that suggests

that repeating each trial at least three

times would yield more accurate data.

_____

What is being modeled when some of the marbles are replaced with cubes?

Sample answer: The cubes help us model

wear on the marbles.

_____

Record Your Data

Record your observations for Trials 1–3 in the space below. Answers will vary. Check students' work for accuracy.

	Measured Force (N)		
Trial	Bare table	Marbles	Marbles and cubes
1			
2			
3			
Average			

Draw Conclusions

Calculate the average force needed to move the book stack in each setup. Show your work and record your answers in the table above.

93

---

1 Engage/Explore (continued)

Guide the Investigation

Develop Inquiry Skills

FORMULATE AND USE MODELS **What tools did you combine and use in this investigation?** spring scale, marbles, cubes, string, jar lid **Why were these tools used in this investigation?** to measure how much force it takes to overcome friction under different conditions

IDENTIFY DESIGN CRITERIA **Which design made it easier to move the books?** It was easier to move the books using the marbles.

PROBLEM AND SOLUTION **What problem did this investigation address?** Sample answer: how to more easily move heavy objects **How did the tool you made make it easier to move the books?** Reducing the amount of friction reduced the amount of force needed to move the books. **What are some everyday things that demonstrate the same principle as the use of marbles?** wheels, ball bearings

GATHER AND RECORD DATA Explain that the spring scale has a minimum and a maximum force range it can measure. If the force needed to pull the books is greater than the scale can measure, students should note this in the appropriate place on the "Record Your Data" table. If necessary, review with students the concept of numerical averages and how to compute them.

Go Digital

A virtual lab experience is available with the Online Resources for this program.

2 Explain

Develop Inquiry Skills

DRAW CONCLUSIONS Ask students to describe how the tool helped them use less force to move the books.

ANALYZE AND EXTEND Discuss students' responses to the items.

1. Point out that many tools are constructed from simpler tools. For example, cars are tools for transportation, but many smaller tools (wheels, steering wheel, gas pedal) are used for specific purposes within cars.

2. Reinforce that spherical objects reduce friction because the shape provides less resistance than objects with flat surfaces.

3. Draw a sample bar graph on the board, but do not label the axes. Put the bars in an order other than the one dictated by the student observation table. Invite students to identify which bar represents each setup.

4. Accept reasonable answers. Students will likely suggest chipping and wear as ways that a round object might become more angular.

3 Extend/Evaluate

5. Remind students of the example of a shovel and a bulldozer. Invite them to picture some larger objects, such as a boulder, and what they might use to move those objects.

Draw Conclusions (continued)

Which problem did the tool you built help solve?

Sample answer: The tool helped us use less force to move a stack of books.

Which setup required the greatest amount of force to move the book stack? Why?

Answers will vary. The bare table setup should take the greatest amount of force to move. There is nothing between the books and the table to ease motion. (Some students may identify friction as a force that prevents motion.)

Analyze and Extend

1. **Which products of technology did you use to build your tool?**

Answers will vary. Students may identify the string, spring scale, jar lids, and marbles as products of technology.

2. **What other objects could you have used in place of marbles?**

Sample answer: I could have used steel ball bearings, rubber balls, jawbreakers, anything round and all the same size. I could have sprinkled powder under the books.

94

3. **In the space below, draw a bar graph to show the average force needed to move the book stack in each setup.**

Check students' work.

4. **What could cause the marbles to become more like cubes?**

Answers will vary. Students may suggest that rubbing between the marbles may cause them to chip. Over time, they could become more angular, like cubes.

5. **How could you redesign this tool to move larger things?**

Answers will vary. Check students' answers for accuracy.

Differentiated Inquiry

Easy

Add Slight Incline

- Ask students to make a prediction about the amount of force needed to drag an object up an incline.

- Have them repeat steps 1 and 2 of the inquiry, but on a slight incline instead of a level surface.

- Ask students whether their prediction was correct. Ask why it takes more force to move an object up an incline than over a flat surface. Sample answer: Gravity increases as a factor when something is lifted upward.

Average

Use More Marbles

- Provide students with six jar lids and a similarly increased number of marbles.

- Have them repeat steps 1 and 2 of the inquiry, using one "coaster," then three, then five, then six. Perform the experiment on a hard, flat surface.

- Ask students to make a generalization based on their observations. Sample answer: More marbles make it easier to move an object, but only to a point.

Easy

Friction Requires More Force

- Ask students to make a prediction about the amount of force needed to drag an object across carpet.

- Have them repeat steps 1 and 2 of the inquiry, but on a carpet, rug, or other rough fabric instead of a smooth surface.

- Ask students whether their prediction was correct. Ask why it takes more force to move an object across a carpet than over a smooth surface. Sample answer: There is more friction to overcome on a rough surface.

Challenging

Steeper Incline

- Ask students to repeat steps 1 and 2 of the inquiry on progressively steeper inclines—ten degrees, 20 degrees, 30 degrees, and 45 degrees.

- Have them chart their averages on a line graph, connecting the points.

- Ask them to make a generalization about force, resistance, and gravity, based on their results and graph. Sample answer: The steeper the incline, the more resistance gravity gives to an object being moved.

People in Science

Objectives

- Describe the role of scientists.
- Describe that scientists come from all backgrounds.
- Determine the role of technology in the work of scientists.

Notebook ▸ Generate Ideas

Write the word *roboticist* on the board, and ask students to help you analyze it. Explain that the suffix *-ist* can mean a member of a profession. Most students will recognize the base word *robot*.

Background

- Ayanna Howard was born in 1972 and grew up near Los Angeles, California.
- When Ayanna Howard was 12 years old, she was inspired by a television show called The Bionic Woman, whose main character had robot limbs that gave her superhuman powers. Ayanna still likes to watch science fiction films today.
- Dr. Howard worked at NASA while she was a college student and as a professional for 12 years, from 1993 to 2005, on robotics projects. After leaving NASA, she went to work for the Georgia Institute of Technology, one of the top science universities in the United States. There she founded her own robotics laboratory and teaches courses on robotics to engineering students.
- In 2009, Dr. Howard received a Golden Torch Award from the National Society of Black Engineers.

People in Science

8 Things YOU SHOULD KNOW ABOUT Ayanna Howard

1 Dr. Ayanna Howard is a roboticist. She designs and builds robots.

2 Dr. Howard is making robots that will make decisions without the help of people.

3 To get a robot to make decisions on its own, Dr. Howard must teach the robot how to think.

4 Dr. Howard uses computer programs to teach robots. She observes the robots. Then she changes her computer programs to get better results.

5 Dr. Howard studies how robots can help explore outer space and unsafe places on Earth.

6 Dr. Howard taught a robot called SmartNav to move around things in its path. This robot could explore the surface of Mars.

7 Scientists want to understand why the ice in Antarctica is melting. Dr. Howard's SnoMote robots can safely gather data on the cracking ice sheets.

8 Dr. Howard has won numerous awards in engineering, innovation, and education.

95

© Houghton Mifflin Harcourt Publishing Company   (bkgd) ©Sharon Dujulio/Alamy; (tc) ©Corbis; (tc) ©Getty Images/PhotoDisc

Writing Connection

Interview Questions: Ask students to suppose that Ayanna Howard could come to speak to their class. Have them brainstorm the kinds of questions they would ask her about her life and work. Hold a class discussion to evaluate the questions. Then, have each student write his or her final list of interview questions and practice asking the questions orally in front of the class or with a partner.

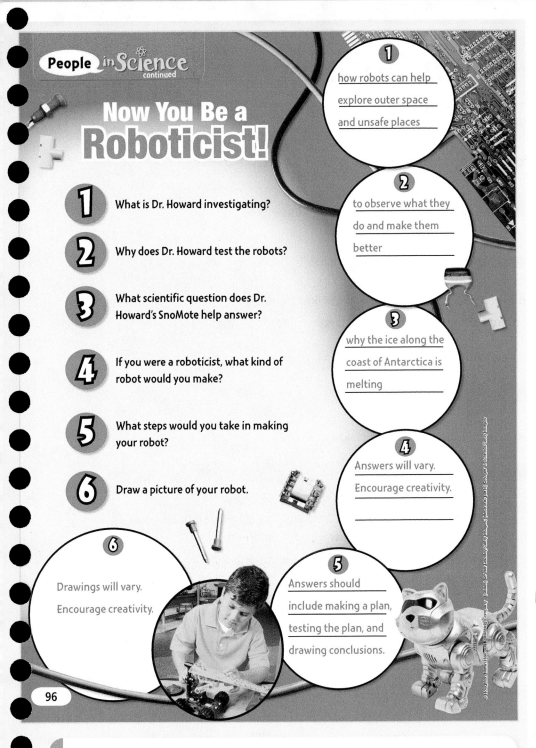

Now You Be a Roboticist!

1 What is Dr. Howard investigating?

2 Why does Dr. Howard test the robots?

3 What scientific question does Dr. Howard's SnoMote help answer?

4 If you were a roboticist, what kind of robot would you make?

5 What steps would you take in making your robot?

6 Draw a picture of your robot.

1 how robots can help explore outer space and unsafe places

2 to observe what they do and make them better

3 why the ice along the coast of Antarctica is melting

4 Answers will vary. Encourage creativity.

5 Answers should include making a plan, testing the plan, and drawing conclusions.

6 Drawings will vary. Encourage creativity.

96

Science in History

Robots have been imagined for hundreds of years, but they could not be invented until the development of small electronics systems and computers in the 1950s. Explain that robots are programmable machines that can do certain tasks on their own and seem to think and act in some ways like humans. For example, Ayanna Howard's SnoMotes can move around uneven ice and snow and collect temperature data and other data automatically.

Develop Science Concepts

Which tool does Ayanna Howard use to program robots? a computer

Direct students to the photo of the Antarctic ice shelf. **What problems would scientists have working on the edge of this ice?** Sample answers: It would be very cold; the ice could break; there might be dangerous animals in the water; it is hard to get there; it would be hard to find a safe place where the scientists would sleep at night.

Develop Inquiry Skills

How could a team of SnoMotes help solve these problems? Sample answer: If the robots collect the data, the scientists don't have to be in danger or get too cold or be away from home so long.

Review science skills with students before answering the questions on this page.

If students need guidance with question 4, suggest they brainstorm some tasks that are impossible or difficult for humans to do.

Encourage students to label their drawings of a robot.

Notebook ▸ ## Summarize Ideas

Direct students to state orally or in writing the main ideas of this feature, including what Ayanna Howard does, some details about her background, and which tools she uses in her work.

Enduring Understandings
Revisit the Big Idea and Essential Questions

Big Idea Engineers use a process to design products and processes that solve human problems.

To explore the Big Idea, post vocabulary terms from the unit on the board. Challenge students to find and explain different ways vocabulary term pairs are connected. Possible answers:

- *Engineering* and *design* are connected because engineers use the design process to produce products that offer solutions to problems.
- *Design* and *prototype* are connected because every design has a prototype, or first model.
- *Technology* and *tool* are connected because improved technology often results in better tools that help people meet their needs.

Essential Questions

Post the Essential Questions and use the following prompts to guide a discussion.

Lesson/Essential Question	Prompts
L1 What Is an Engineering Design Process?	• Describe the engineering process.
L2 How Can You Design a Solution to a Problem?	• Explain the steps you followed to design a solution to the problem of how to cushion an egg.
L3 What Is Technology?	• List some examples of technology, and identify the needs that each example helps people meet.
L4 How Do We Use Technology?	• Explain how technology can help us move an object from one place to another more easily.

Notebook ▸ Science Notebook

You may use the following strategies after students complete the unit or after each lesson.

- Have students review and edit the answers to Essential Questions they drafted at the beginning of the unit. Suggest they cross out sentences or ideas that are unnecessary or inappropriate.
- Have students write three questions about the unit which they would like to answer in their Science Notebooks. Challenge students to research and report on the answers they find for "extra credit." Remind them to list sources they consult and to document the notes they take in their Science Notebooks. Allow time for students to share their questions and what they have learned with the class.

Science Notebook

Essential Questions	Answers
What Is an Engineering Design Process?	
How Can You Design a Solution to a Problem?	
What Is Technology?	
How Do We Use Technology?	

Unit 2 Review

Name _____

Vocabulary Review

Use the terms in the box to complete the sentences.

> design
> designed system
> engineering
> process
> prototype
> technology
> technology product
> tool

1. Anything that is made to meet a need or desire is

   a(n) __technology product__.

2. To conceive of something and prepare the plans and drawings

   for it to be built is __design__.

3. A designed system, product, or process that people use to solve

   problems is called __technology__.

4. A series of steps used to achieve a goal or make a product is

   called a(n) __process__.

5. The use of scientific and mathematical principles to develop

   something practical is called __engineering__.

6. An original or test model on which a real product is based is

   called a __prototype__.

7. Tools, parts, and processes that work together form

   a(n) __designed system__.

8. Anything that helps people shape, build, or produce things

   to meet their needs is called a __tool__.

Item Analysis

Items	Depth of Knowledge	Cognitive Complexity
1–8	1	Low

Unit Review

Answer Key

Vocabulary Review (5 points each)

1. **technology product** Remind students that technology products are not just things that run on electricity. All of the objects we use in daily life are products of technology.

2. **design** Have volunteers give examples of when they have made designs before making something.

3. **technology** Remind students that it is not just the final outcome that is technology, but also the systems and processes that are used to make the product.

4. **process** Discuss any TV shows students may have seen in which the process for making a type of food, such as peanut butter, is shown. Reinforce that the steps shown are a process, and that process is technology.

5. **engineering** Have students study the photos and reread the captions in "What is Engineering?" in Lesson 1.

6. **prototype** Return to the idea of design introduced in question 2. Elicit from students that the first model resulting from the design is a prototype. Suggest that students identify which of the skateboards might have been an early prototype in Lesson 1.

7. **designed system** Provide examples of familiar designed systems, such as our system of highways. Have students reread the section entitled "Technological Systems" in Lesson 3.

8. **tool** Remind students that many of the objects in their desks are tools that help them communicate ideas or measure objects.

Assessment

Unit 2 Test and Performance Assessment

See Assessment Guide, pp. AG 18–AG 24, for Unit Test and Performance Task with Long Option rubric.

Unit Review *continued*

Answer Key

Science Concepts (4 points each)

9. **D** Refer students to text under "Test It and Improve It!" in the "Are We Done Yet?" section of Lesson 1. Remind students that many designs must go through several rounds of improvements before they meet the need.

10. **C** Have students review the photos and captions in "What is Engineering?" in Lesson 1.

11. **D** Point out that the computer is a tool that provides access to the designed system we call the Internet.

12. **B** Review the steps of the design process presented in Lesson 1 in the section titled "What Is the Design Process?"

13. **A** Refer students to "What is Technology?" in Lesson 3. If necessary, revisit the definition of *technology product*.

14. **D** Refer students to "Are We Done Yet?" in Lesson 1 and the appropriate text in Lesson 2. If necessary, revisit the steps of the design process.

15. **D** Compare testing a prototype multiple times with running multiple trials in a science experiment. Both actions provide more reliable sets of data. Remind students that they ran multiple trials as they designed and tested the book mover in Lesson 4.

16. **B** Refer students to the definition of a tool in "Tools Rule!" in Lesson 3. Remind them that tools do not need to be "high tech" in order to be considered technology.

17. **C** Refer students to "Are We Done Yet?" in Lesson 1. Point out that continued testing provides more information that can help refine designs and produce a usable product.

Science Concepts

Fill in the letter of the choice that best answers the question.

9. A group of researchers is working on a way to make winter coats warmer. The first coat the researchers design is not very warm. What should they do?

   (A) They should try again without using tools.

   (B) They should find a different designed system.

   (C) They should continue their work without using technology.

   (D) They should examine their test data for ways to improve the coat's design.

10. Sylvia works for a car company. She uses her knowledge of math and science to design dashboards that make it easier to operate cars. What is Sylvia's profession?

    (A) analyst

    (B) biologist

    (C) engineer

    (D) geologist

11. Marco is using this object to help him find information for a report.

    Which statement best describes this object?

    (A) It is a technology process.

    (B) It is an engineer.

    (C) It is a prototype.

    (D) It is a tool.

12. Researchers want to build a new type of spaceship for transporting astronauts to the moon. What should they do **first**?

    (A) They should test the prototype.

    (B) They should plan a prototype.

    (C) They should build a model.

    (D) They should evaluate how the prototype worked.

13. Bulldozers, measuring cups, pencils, and hammers are all examples of tools. What else can be said about all of them?

    (A) They are all technology products.

    (B) They are all in the prototype stage.

    (C) They all release harmful gases into the atmosphere.

    (D) They all require power sources other than their users.

14. New solutions to problems often begin with a "What if?" question. Which "What if?" question might an engineer ask after seeing the electrical energy station shown below?

    (A) What if we burned trees instead of coal?

    (B) What if we could find even more coal to burn?

    (C) What if we all threw away all of our electrical appliances?

    (D) What if we could burn coal to make electricity without polluting the air?

Item Analysis *(continued)*

Items	Depth of Knowledge	Cognitive Complexity
9–10	2	Moderate
11	2	Low
12–14	3	Moderate
15	3	High
16	2	Low

Name _____

15. Angie tested a reflector that she hopes will make bicycles safer. Although her first test went well, she repeated the test three more times. Which of these statements is **true**?

(A) She skipped the step of asking "What if?"

(B) She wasted her time by repeating the same test.

(C) She obtained unreliable data, because there were more chances for mistakes.

(D) She obtained more accurate data than if she had only tested the reflector once.

16. You probably use the tools shown below every day.

Which statement about these tools is **true**?

(A) They cost about the same to produce.

(B) They are both examples of technology.

(C) They are examples of identical technology.

(D) They are each designed for many different tasks.

17. Sometimes, a prototype tests poorly or fails completely. What should be done when that happens?

(A) The prototype should be abandoned.

(B) A second prototype should be built.

(C) The prototype should be modified, with the good parts of it kept.

(D) The prototype should be examined to see if it has other uses.

18. A fuel-efficient automobile is an example of a designed system. What is an example of feedback for such an automobile?

(A) safe arrival at the destination

(B) fuel for the car and the roads on which it will travel

(C) data on how much fuel the car used to travel 100 km

(D) to move a family of four 100 km using only 2 liters of gasoline

19. Long ago, there were few roads. Now there are many roads. How has a system of roads changed most communities?

(A) People can easily get from one place to another.

(B) People live closer to where they work and drive less.

(C) People travel less and rarely see family members that live far away.

(D) Use of fossil fuels has decreased with the increase in roads and highways.

Unit 2   99

© Houghton Mifflin Harcourt Publishing Company   (border) ©RCdesc/Age Fotostock

Item Analysis *(continued)*

Items	Depth of Knowledge	Cognitive Complexity
17	3	High
18–19	3	Moderate

Unit Review *continued*

Science Concepts (4 points each)

18. **C** Direct students to review the table in Lesson 3 in which the parts of a designed system are detailed. Have students compare each answer choice to the information in the chart and identify to which part each refers.

19. **A** Refer students to "The Good and the Bad of It" in Lesson 3. Remind them that technology carries risks even as it improves lives or meets a need. Have volunteers list other examples of technology and how they have changed your community.

Short Option Performance Assessment

Task

A Quieter Pencil
Every day, pencils are dropped on the floor, causing distracting noise. Tell students that their task is to design a pencil that, when dropped, will make little or no noise. Have students consider how they would carry out all the steps of the design process in order to develop their product. Students will then make a poster that describes all of their steps.

Rubric

Preparation Provide art supplies for students to make their posters. As an alternative, students can make computer slideshows in order to present their product and the process they would follow to develop it.

Scoring Rubric—Performance Indicators

____ Lists all the steps of the design process.

____ Details how the product would be developed using these steps.

____ Presents the steps he or she would follow in either a poster or computer slideshow format.

Observations and Rubric Scores

3   2   1   0

Unit Review *continued*

Answer Key

Apply Inquiry and Review the Big Idea

(8 points each)

20. See student page for sample answers.

Refer students to the components of a designed system detailed in Lesson 3. Suggest they make a table similar to the one shown, leaving the second column blank. They can then analyze the solar panel system, and add specifics of the goal, inputs, processes, outputs, and feedback to column 2.

21. See student page for sample answers.

Refer students to the design process as detailed in Lesson 1. Suggest that they write out all of the steps, along with descriptions of the goal of each step. They can then more easily identify why keeping good notes is important, why the engineer should build a prototype, and the step that should occur after prototype testing.

Apply Inquiry and Review the Big Idea

Write the answers to these questions.

20. This picture shows solar cells on the roof of a house. These cells take solar energy and convert it into electricity that appliances in the house need to function.

a. How is this an example of a designed system?

Sample answer: A designed system is any group of tools and processes people put together to solve a problem. The solar cells are connected to the home's electrical system and its electrical appliances.

b. Identify the goal, input, output, and feedback of this system.

Sample answer: Goal: use solar energy to generate electricity; input: planning, material, cost, and solar energy; output: electrical energy; feedback: reduced use of commercial electricity.

21. An engineer follows the design process to improve soccer shoes. First, he studies shoes on the market and reads about what people have to say about them. Then, he starts to design his prototype.

a. Why is it important for the engineer to keep good notes during the design process?

Sample answer: It is important to keep good notes so the design can be duplicated.

b. Why should the engineer build a prototype of the shoes?

Sample answer: It is important to build a prototype to test and identify problems before the final design goes into production.

c. Describe a part of the design process the engineer should do **after** testing the prototype.

Sample answer: The engineer should evaluate the design and modify it if necessary. Any redesigned prototype should also be evaluated through a series of repeated tests until it meets the design criteria. The final design solution should be presented using graphs or drawings so others can replicate the work.

100   Unit 2

Item Analysis *(continued)*

Items	Depth of Knowledge	Cognitive Complexity
20	4	High
21	3	High

UNIT 3 Plants and Animals

Big Idea and Essential Questions

This Unit was designed to focus on this Big Idea and Essential Questions.

Take It Home! A School-Home Connection letter is provided in Online Resources.

Big Idea

Living things are adapted for survival in their environment.

Essential Questions

L1 **What Are Some Plant Structures?**

L2 **How Do Plants Reproduce?**

L3 **How Can We Observe a Plant's Life Cycle?**

L4 **How Do Animals Reproduce?**

L5 **How Are Living Things Adapted to Their Environment?**

L6 **Why Do Bird Beaks Differ?**

Professional Development

Houghton Mifflin Harcourt and **NSTA,** the **National Science Teachers Association,** have partnered to provide customized professional development resources for teachers using *ScienceFusion*.

The Professional Development Resources include:

- Do-it-yourself resources, where you can study at your own pace
- Live and archived online seminars
- Journal articles, many of which include lesson plans
- Fee-based eBooks, eBook chapters, online short courses, symposia, and conferences

  Access to The NSTA Learning Center is provided in the *ScienceFusion* Online Resources.

National Science Teachers Association

The **NSTA** Learning Center

Unit Planning

Options for Instruction

Two parallel paths meet the unit objectives, with a strong Inquiry strand
woven into each. Follow the Print Path, the Digital Path, or your customized
combination of print, digital, and inquiry.

Essential Questions	LESSON 1	LESSON 2	LESSON 3
	What Are Some Plant Structures?	**How Do Plants Reproduce?**	☑ **Guided Inquiry** **How Can We Observe a Plant's Life Cycle?**

Print Path

☐ **Student Edition** pp. 103–114 • Types of Plants • Using the Tubes • Lots of Leaves • Plants Make Food	☐ **Student Edition** pp. 117–132 • How Does a Garden Grow? • Flowers and Cones • The Power of Pollen • Seeds on the Move • Other Ways Plants Grow	☐ **Student Edition** pp. 133–134 • Scaffolding for Inquiry

Hands-On Inquiry

Inquiry Flipchart p. 12 **What Pulls the Water Up?** ☐ Directed Inquiry **Neighborhood Plants** ☐ Independent Inquiry	**Inquiry Flipchart** p. 14 **Finding Out About Flowers** ☐ Directed Inquiry **What's Cooking?** ☐ Independent Inquiry	**Inquiry Flipchart** p. 15 **How Can We Observe a Plant's Life Cycle?** ☐ Guided Inquiry

Digital Path

☐ **Digital Lesson** Online Resources Interactive presentation of lesson content	☐ **Digital Lesson** Online Resources Interactive presentation of lesson content	☐ **Virtual Lab** Online Resources Interactive scaffolded inquiry

LESSON 4	LESSON 5	LESSON 6	OTHER UNIT FEATURES

LESSON 4

How Do Animals Reproduce?

LESSON 5

How Are Living Things Adapted to Their Environment?

LESSON 6

✓ Guided Inquiry

Why Do Bird Beaks Differ?

Careers in Science, p. 149

S.T.E.M. Engineering and Technology, pp. 115–116B

Video-based Project, Alligators Up Close

Online Resources

☐ **Student Edition**
pp. 135–148
- Life in Full Circle
- Bringing Up Baby
- Growing Up
- My, How You've Changed!
- Saving the Sea Turtles

☐ **Student Edition**
pp. 151–164
- Life on the Blue Planet
- Who Is Out on a Limb?
- Who Can Go with the Flow?
- Who Can Take the Heat?
- Who Can Take the Cold?

☐ **Student Edition**
pp. 165–166
- Scaffolding for Inquiry

Unit Assessment

Formative Assessment
Sum It Up! and Brain Check
Student Edition, end of each lesson

Summative Assessment
Lesson Quizzes
Assessment Guide,
pp. AG 25–AG 30

Unit 3 Review
Student Edition, pp. 167–170

Unit 3 Test
Assessment Guide,
pp. AG 31–AG 35

Performance Assessment
SHORT OPTION: Teacher
Edition, p. 169
LONG OPTION: Assessment
Guide, pp. AG 36–AG 37

Inquiry Flipchart
p. 16

Breeding Brine Shrimp
☐ Directed Inquiry

Can Waxworms Stand the Heat?
☐ Independent Inquiry

Inquiry Flipchart
p. 17

Cold as Ice
☐ Directed Inquiry

Putting a Foot Down
☐ Independent Inquiry

Inquiry Flipchart
p. 18

Why Do Bird Beaks Differ?
☐ Guided Inquiry

RTI ▶ **Response to Intervention**

RTI Strategies p. 101K

Online Assessment
Test-taking and automatic scoring
Banks of items from which to build tests

☐ **Digital Lesson**
Online Resources

Interactive presentation of lesson content

☐ **Digital Lesson**
Online Resources

Interactive presentation of lesson content

☐ **Virtual Lab**
Online Resources

Interactive scaffolded inquiry

Planning for Inquiry

Use the following preview of Inquiry Activities and Lessons to gather and manage the materials needed for each lesson.

Activity	Inquiry and Design Process Skills Focus	Materials	Prep Tips, Troubleshooting, and Expected Results
Lesson 1 — DIRECTED INQUIRY Flipchart p.12 **A What Pulls the Water Up?** OBJECTIVE Follow directions for an investigation to determine how water moves through vascular plants. ⏱ 15 minutes each day for 2 days 👥 pairs	• Observe • Compare • Draw Conclusions	• 1 stalk of celery with leaves • 1 large plastic cup • water • blue or red food coloring • paper towels	**Prep Tips** Keep the celery dry prior to the activity. Keep the celery overnight in a cool place, such as a refrigerator or cooler with ice. Do not store the celery in water beforehand. Just before the activity, cut 2–3 cm off the base of the stalks, which will encourage the celery to draw in water. Cover work surfaces with newspaper, and provide paper towels or sponges for cleanup. **Caution!** Students who have food allergies or intolerances may be sensitive to celery and food colorings. Have these students work with a partner. Students should notify you immediately of any spills, which can make surfaces slippery and cause falls. Have students wash their hands after this activity. Caution students to be careful with the food coloring as it can stain whatever it contacts. **Troubleshooting** You may wish to make a control for the experiment by placing a stalk of prepared celery in a cup of clear water. Students can compare their results to this control **Expected Results** Celery is a vascular plant. Water moves up through the tubes to the plant's stem and leaves. Students will observe that the leaves turned color. They should also see some color in the tubes of the freshly-cut celery stalks.
INDEPENDENT INQUIRY Flipchart p.12 **B Neighborhood Plants** OBJECTIVE Plan and conduct an investigation to describe and draw three local plants. ⏱ 30–40 minutes 👥 individuals	• Gather, Record, Display or Interpret Data	• plants • Science Notebook	**Prep Tips** If time permits and you have plants around your school to observe, plan to take students outside for observations. If students are to find plants on their own, tell them to be sure to search with a trusted adult. **Troubleshooting** Before students begin this activity, show them pictures of plants and have them identify the plant parts. As an alternative, point out the parts of a classroom plant or one you bring from home. **Caution!** Remind students not to touch the plants they observe. Many plants are poisonous or have sharp edges or thorns that will damage the skin. Pulling a plant from the ground will kill the plant. **Expected Results** Students will describe and draw the parts of three plants, including stems, leaves, flowers, and possibly roots.

Additional teaching support for all inquiry activities is available in **Online Resources.**

Notebook **Science Notebook Strategies**
- Lists of Kit-Supplied Materials
- Meeting Individual Needs
- Investigate More—Extensions and Variations and More!

Activity	Inquiry and Design Process Skills Focus	Materials	Prep Tips, Troubleshooting, and Expected Results
S.T.E.M. **Engineering and Technology** Flipchart p.13 **Make a Process: Planting and Caring for a Garden** OBJECTIVE • Use the five steps of the design process to plan and care for a garden. • Apply scientific knowledge of the needs of plants. ⏱ 25–30 minutes 👤 individuals	DESIGN PROCESS STEPS 1 Find a Problem 2 Plan and Build 3 Test and Improve 4 Redesign 5 Communicate	• gardening books • seed catalogs • various materials for making models • Science Notebook	**Prep Tips** Provide students with any research materials they need to learn more about garden planning. Gardening books and seed catalogs may be helpful. You may wish to compile a list of websites that students can refer to for information. Gather any materials students will need and set them out in workstations around the room. **Caution!** Remind students to wash their hands after handling soil. **Expected Results** Students should be able to plan and design a garden, as well as devise a schedule for the garden's care.
Lesson ② DIRECTED INQUIRY Flipchart p.14 **Ⓐ Finding Out About Flowers** OBJECTIVE Follow directions for an investigation to identify parts of a real flower. ⏱ 15–20 minutes 👤 individuals	• Observe • Gather, Record, Display or Interpret Data	• 1 flower, such as a lily • hand lens • colored pencils	**Prep Tips** Review with students the use of a hand lens for close observations. Also review basic flower structure. Write the words *petals, sepals, stamens, anthers,* and *pistils* on the board. Keep flowers for the activity in a cool place and watered prior to use. **Caution!** Some students may have allergies to pollen. These students should not participate and may be given a diagram of a flower without its labels to use instead. Direct students to wash their hands at the conclusion of this activity. **Expected Results** Students should be able to identify the flower's main parts, including the petals, sepals, stamens, anthers, and pistils.
INDEPENDENT INQUIRY Flipchart p.14 **Ⓑ What's Cooking?** OBJECTIVE Plan and conduct online research to determine which foods come from plants. ⏱ 20–30 minutes 👤 individuals	• Gather, Record, Display or Interpret Data • Draw Conclusions	• Science Notebook • research materials	**Prep Tips** Before students begin their lists, write some common ingredients on the board, such as flour, sugar, salt, vinegar, and yeast. Discuss with students where each item comes from and how it is made. **Troubleshooting** Model the entire process of the activity for students. **Expected Results** Students will find that most of the ingredients in familiar foods come from plants. They may also find that a typical food item contains many more ingredients than they thought.

Planning for Inquiry **101E**

Planning for Inquiry (continued)

Activity	Inquiry and Design Process Skills Focus	Materials	Prep Tips, Troubleshooting, and Expected Results
Lesson ③ INQUIRY GUIDED INQUIRY **Flipchart** p.15 **Student Edition** pp.133–134 **How Can We Observe a Plant's Life Cycle?** **OBJECTIVES** • Compare how fast different types of seeds germinate. • Observe a developing plant embryo. ⏱ 25 minutes for initial setup; 5 minutes per day for two weeks to make and record observations pairs or small groups	• Observe • Gather, Record, Display or Interpret Data • Draw Conclusions	• clear plastic bag • masking tape (class use) • marker (class use) • 2 paper towels • 1 bean seed • 1 gourd seed • 1 sunflower seed • water	**Prep Tips** Find a location where the seeds can be placed and receive natural light and not be disturbed. Be sure that students understand the importance of recording observations for this activity. Have extra paper towels available for cleanup. Make one completed bag as a sample to show students how their bags should look when finished. **Caution!** Have students notify you immediately of any spills. Water can make surfaces slippery and cause falls. Have students wash their hands after the activity. **Troubleshooting** Students will need to be patient when placing the seeds along the side of the bag. The paper towels should fill the bag enough so that the seeds can stay in place along the side of the bag. If seeds will not stay in place, have students add another damp paper towel to the bag. Warn students against giving their seeds too much water. Seeds exposed to too much water may rot instead of germinate. (You may want to set up a seed bag this way to show them what happens.) Direct students to wring out the paper towels so there aren't pools of water in the bottoms of the bags. Have students note any observations at each step to help monitor the progress of their seeds. If a group's seeds do not germinate, pair them up with another group so that the first group can still make observations and record data. **Expected Results** Students will observe that seeds from different plants germinate at different rates. Have students include additional observations for the seeds that germinate fastest, such as the direction the roots and shoots grow and the color of the different plant parts.

Go Digital! Virtual Lab

How Can We Observe a Plant's Life Cycle?

Key Inquiry Skills: Plan and Conduct a Simple Investigation, Control Variables, Record Data, Infer

Students plant and monitor seeds of four different vegetables to determine their typical germination times.

Additional teaching support for all inquiry activities is available in Online Resources.

Activity	Inquiry and Design Process Skills Focus	Materials	Prep Tips, Troubleshooting, and Expected Results
Lesson 4 DIRECTED INQUIRY Flipchart p. 16 **A Breeding Brine Shrimp** OBJECTIVE Follow directions for an investigation to observe an animal's life cycle. ⏱ 15 minutes the first day; 5 minutes each day for 2 weeks 👥 small groups	• Observe • Compare • Measure • Gather, Record, Display or Interpret Data	• brine shrimp kit (1 per group or 1 for the class) • hand lens • Science Notebook	**Prep Tips** You may wish to only use a single brine shrimp kit for the whole class and have all students observe the same kit. Set aside 5 minutes each day for two weeks for students to observe the brine shrimp and record their changes. Brine shrimp are sensitive to poor water quality, so plan to change the water during the course of this activity. **Caution!** Students should wash their hands after handling brine shrimp eggs. **Troubleshooting** If no brine shrimp hatch after 72 hours, you will need to start again with different eggs. When brine shrimp first hatch, they are very small (about the size of a period), so students will need hand lenses to observe them. Remind students to continue to feed the shrimp throughout the investigation. You may wish to keep the shrimp as "pets" once the investigation is complete. **Expected Results** Results will depend on the species of brine shrimp used. Many brine shrimp complete their entire life cycle in four weeks or less.
INDEPENDENT INQUIRY Flipchart p. 16 **B Can Waxworms Stand the Heat?** OBJECTIVE Plan and conduct an investigation to determine how temperature can affect the life cycle of a wax moth. ⏱ 30–45 minutes 👥 small groups	• Plan and Conduct a Simple Investigation • Observe • Compare • Gather, Record, Display or Interpret Data	• wax moth caterpillars • food • 3 jars with lids (per group) • forceps • lamp with incandescent bulb • refrigerator or other cool (not freezing) environment	**Prep Tips** Gather a wide assortment of resources and information about the wax moth. Remind students to handle the waxworms safely and humanely at all times. Provide small jars with lids that you have pre-punched with small holes (the waxworms will climb the walls of the jar and escape from large air holes). Food for the waxworms is a mixture of glycerin, sugar, hot water, and oat baby cereal. Several recipes for waxworm food are available on the Internet. Be sure to have information and follow the proper care and handling of the waxworms. **Caution!** Tell students to wash their hands after working with the waxworms. Tell students to keep the jars closed. **Troubleshooting** Help students brainstorm supplies they will need for their investigations. They will also need to identify a cool environment in which to place the worms. Help students determine ways to keep all variables constant except for temperature. **Expected Results** Waxworms develop fastest at temperatures from 28–34 °C (82–93 °F). Therefore, students should discover that the waxworms kept under an incandescent lamp (or at room temperature) develop faster than those kept in a refrigerator.

Planning for Inquiry (continued)

Activity	Inquiry and Design Process Skills Focus	Materials	Prep Tips, Troubleshooting, and Expected Results
Lesson 5 **DIRECTED INQUIRY** **Flipchart** p.17 **A Cold as Ice** **OBJECTIVE** Follow directions for an investigation to find out why animals that live in cold habitats have thick layers of fat and fur. 🕐 20–30 minutes 👥 small groups	• Compare • Infer • Draw Conclusions	• faux fur fabric (1 piece per group) • shortening • plastic gloves (2 per group) • 2 plastic bags (per group) • ice • water • bowl • thermometer • timer	**Prep Tips** If time is short, you may want to prepare the fur-lined bag and the shortening-filled bag before class. Have paper towels or sponges on hand for cleanup. You may wish to cover surfaces with paper towels or newspaper to absorb spills. **Caution!** Have students notify you immediately of any spills. Water can make surfaces slippery and cause falls. **Troubleshooting** Have students make a data table to record the three temperature readings. The data tables should have a separate column for each temperature reading. Students may also measure change in temperature over time. Shortening can be very messy. Remind students to dispose of the bag of shortening and the glove that was in the bag of shortening as soon as they finish the activity. As an option, seal the shortening in two snack-sized zipper plastic bags, and have students sandwich the gloved thermometer between the sealed bags for the activity. **Expected Results** Students will find that the temperature inside the bag with the faux fur and shortening will change the least. The temperature inside the glove without a fur pouch will change the most.
INDEPENDENT INQUIRY **Flipchart** p.17 **B Putting a Foot Down** **OBJECTIVE** Plan and conduct an investigation of how an animal's feet are adapted to the animal's environment. 🕐 30–60 minutes 👥 individuals	• Formulate or Use Models • Infer • Draw Conclusions	• Science Notebook • various materials for making models	**Prep Tips** Before students start, show them pictures of different animals' feet. Tell students the type of environment each animal lives in, and have them discuss how the feet of each animal help it move around its environment. Point out different foot adaptations for living in trees, walking on sand, walking on snow, and so on. **Troubleshooting** Some animals can live in various habitats. Tell students to design their model foot for use in the kind of habitat shown in the photographs. **Expected Results** Students will observe, draw, and model a foot of one of the animals shown in the lesson. Animals and habitats include: Arctic fox: tundra; zebra: semi-arid grasslands; mountain goat: mountainous regions; ostrich: grasslands; prairie dog: shortgrass prairies; sloth: rainforests; horned lizard: deserts; jackrabbit: deserts; Arctic hare: tundra; emperor penguin: pack ice and oceans; and pond turtle: marshes, streams, rivers, ponds, and lakes.

Additional teaching support for all inquiry activities is available in Online Resources.

Activity	Inquiry and Design Process Skills Focus	Materials	Prep Tips, Troubleshooting, and Expected Results
Lesson INQUIRY 6 GUIDED INQUIRY Flipchart p. 18 Student Edition pp.165–166 **Why Do Bird Beaks Differ?** OBJECTIVES • Describe the variations that can be observed in different types of bird beaks. • Identify which tool works best for which food. • Relate different bird beaks to different types of food. • Explain why some birds are better suited to a certain habitat than other birds are. ⏱ 30–40 minutes 👥 small groups	• Infer • Experiment	• chopsticks (2 per group) • dropper • large pliers • needle-nose pliers • slotted spoon • forceps • shredded lettuce in a bowl of water • juice in a graduated cylinder • rice in plastic foam • gummy worms in sand • sunflower seeds • walnuts (1 per group)	**Prep Tips** Demonstrate how to use the tools safely. Discuss how the shapes of the tools are related to the shapes of the bird beaks. You may want to show students pictures of birds with various beak shapes, and have the students match the tools with the beaks. **Caution!** Students with food allergies should not handle nuts or seeds. Students should not share straws. Remind students not to eat any of the foods used in this activity. Have students notify you immediately of any spills. Water can make surfaces slippery and cause falls. Direct students to wash their hands after this activity. **Troubleshooting** Step 1: Students need to see how each tool works for themselves after being shown how to properly operate each one. Step 2: Be sure that students think about how a bird might use each tool. **Expected Results** Students will likely find that the dropper is best for the juice, the slotted spoon is best for lettuce, the forceps are best for the rice, the chopsticks are best for the gummy worms, the needle-nose pliers are best for sunflower seeds, and the large pliers are best for the walnut.

Go Digital! Virtual Lab

Why Do Bird Beaks Differ?
Key Inquiry Skills: Observe, Experiment, Infer, Predict
Students examine the beaks of several different types of birds and associate the shape of the beak with the type of food the bird eats.

Differentiated Instruction
Customize and Extend

You can extend and customize science instruction for your students using the following resources.

Leveled Readers

The **Science & Engineering Leveled Readers** can be used to provide additional nonfiction reading practice in the subject area of Unit 3.

ON-LEVEL This Reader reinforces unit concepts. It includes student response activities for your students.

EXTRA SUPPORT This Reader shares title, illustrations, vocabulary, and concepts with the On-Level Reader. However, the text is linguistically accommodated to provide simplified sentence structures and comprehension aids. It also includes response activities.

ENRICHMENT This high-interest nonfiction Reader enriches and extends unit concepts. It reinforces some of the unit vocabulary, includes *stretch vocabulary*, and includes response activities.

TEACHER GUIDE
The accompanying **Teacher Guide** provides teaching strategies and support for using all the Readers, as well as English and Spanish worksheets that focus on vocabulary development. A correlation to the Disciplinary Core Ideas of the Next Generation Science Standards is included.

DIGITAL VERSIONS

All of these Leveled Readers are available online. They are also available in an innovative and engaging format for touchscreen mobile devices. Contact your HMH Sales Representative for more information.

RTI Response to Intervention

Response to Intervention is a process for identifying and supporting students who are not making expected progress toward essential learning goals.

The following *ScienceFusion* components have the flexibility to be used to provide Core Classroom Instruction (Tier 1), strategic intervention (Tier 2), and intensive intervention (Tier 3).		
Component	**Location**	**Strategies and Benefits**
Student Edition, Active Reading prompts, Sum It Up!, Brain Check	Active Reading throughout each lesson, Sum It Up! and Brain Check at the end of each lesson	Student responses can be used as screening tools to assess whether intervention is needed.
Assessment Guide, Lesson Quizzes	pp. AG 25–AG 30	Student responses can be used as screening tools to assess whether intervention is needed.
Inquiry Flipcharts	Inquiry Flipchart pp. 12, 14, 16, 17	Directed Inquiry for students who learn best through directed or teacher-led hands-on activities.
Teacher Edition, Unit Review Answer Strategies	TE pp. 167–170	Suggestions for intervention, guidance, and remediation for each review question.
Leveled Readers	TE p. 101J	Content support for students not meeting the learning needs during core classroom instruction.
Leveled Readers, Teacher Guides and Vocabulary Worksheets	TE p. 101J	Direct instruction with small groups of students needing additional content at various readability levels.
Extra Support for Vocabulary and Concepts (online worksheets)	Online Resources	Support for individualized instruction with practice in essential content.
Online Student Edition with Audio	Online Resources	Provides learners with multiple-modality access to science concepts and information.
Interactive Digital Lessons and Virtual Labs	Online Resources	Provides individualized learning experiences. Lessons make content accessible through simulations, animations, videos, audio, and integrated assessment.

Differentiated Instruction
English Language Learners

Choose from these instructional strategies to meet the needs of English language learners. Suggestions are provided for adapting the activity for three proficiency levels. Point-of-use strategies also appear within unit lessons.

☑ Unit Vocabulary

Lesson 1	Lesson 2	Lesson 4	Lesson 5
root	germination	complete metamorphosis	environment
stem	maturity	incomplete metamorphosis	adaptation
leaf	fertilization		physical adaptation
photosynthesis	pollination	nymph	behavioral adaptation
chlorophyll	spore		instinct

Vocabulary Cards are provided in Online Resources.

Vocabulary Activity
Describe It

Organize the class into small groups. Give each group a stack of cards with the vocabulary terms. Have students play a game in which they describe a term to their group as others guess. For example: This is the term for the process plants use to make food. (photosynthesis) The first student to guess the term gets a point. The student with the most points wins. Allow students to describe the terms in different ways as suggested below.

Beginning	Intermediate	Advanced
Have students take turns drawing a card. Students may point to images in their book or draw pictures that represent the term. For example, when describing complete metamorphosis, students could point to the correct life cycle diagram in Lesson 4.	Have students take turns drawing a card. Provide students with sentence frames to help them describe the terms. For example: *This is the part of the plant that _____.* Or, *In this process, _____.* Students may draw pictures to support their descriptions.	Have students take turns drawing a card. The student who drew the card shares a sentence that describes the part. The student continues providing descriptive statements until a team member guesses the term. For example: *This is a part of a plant. It moves water from the roots to the leaves. It moves food from the leaves to the roots.* Team members guess after each statement until *stem* is guessed.

✔ Model Concepts

How Plants Reproduce

Remind students that wind, water, and animals carry pollen from plant to plant. These same agents help spread the plant seeds after they form. Provide pairs of students with two large sheets of paper attached in a book-like fashion on which they can make giant Science Notebook pages for display in the classroom. Have on hand scissors, discarded nature magazines, glue, and colored pencils or markers.

Beginning	Intermediate	Advanced
Provide pairs with picture-based sources, such as magazines or picture books. Ask them to find or draw pictures that show how wind, water, and animals help spread the seeds of plants. Provide assistance with labeling the pictures. Have students display their pages in the room.	Ask students to draw pictures or use images from other sources to show pollination by wind, water, and animals. Have students add an appropriate title to each page. Require students to label or caption each illustration with a word, phrase, or short sentence. Have students present their pages to the class.	Ask students to draw pictures or use images from other sources to make their pages. Have them write sentences describing pollination or seed dispersal by wind, water, and animals. Have students imagine they are teachers and use their pages to teach the concepts to the class.

✔ Model Inquiry Skills

Observe and Infer

Organize the class into small groups. Provide each group with pictures of various animals in their natural environments. Pictures should clearly show the animals' physical features or actions. Ask students to choose several animals, identify the animals' adaptations, and infer how the adaptations help the animals survive.

Beginning	Intermediate	Advanced
Have students circle the adaptations they see in the pictures. Provide a chart with the headings: *Adaptation* and *How It Helps*. Have students draw the adaptation in the first column (e.g., wings) and how it helps the animal in the second (e.g., a bird flying). Assist students in writing one- or two-word labels in the chart.	Have students label each animal's adaptations and then infer how the adaptations help with survival. Provide sentence frames for students to discuss the adaptations. For example: *A(n) _____ uses its _____ to _____. A(n) _____ has a _____ for _____.* Have students present their ideas to the class.	Have students discuss the animals' adaptations and how they help with survival. Ask students to imagine they are an animal and write clues about their adaptations. For example: *In winter, my fur changes to white so I can hide in the snow. I have large hind feet for walking on the snow.* Students should write clues for several animals and then read their clues as others guess.

Plants and Animals

I Wonder Why

Use the images and the question to stimulate interest in the unit topic. Help students identify the insect in the larger photo. Explain that the insect's body shape is an adaptation that helps keep it safe from predators. Point out how many of this insect's body parts, includings its legs, antennae, and abdomen, look like leaves. Suggest that students think about how leaves look when the winds blows as they consider the I Wonder Why.

Here's Why

Have students turn the page and read the response to the question. You may wish to share the following background with students.

More About...

Surviving Predators

The members of the family Phylliidae are found from South Asia through Southeast Asia to Australia. Known as leaf insects, or walking leaves, they are related to walking sticks. These insects mimic leaves so well that many species appear to have bite marks and brown spots along edges of their bodies. The swaying motion that is part of their walk further fools predators into thinking that these insects are leaves blowing in the wind.

UNIT 3

Plants and Animals

Big Idea

Living things are adapted for survival in their environment.

I Wonder Why

This insect looks like a leaf. When it walks, it rocks back and forth. Why? *Turn the page to find out.*

101

Professional Development **Science Background**

Use the keywords to access

- Professional Development from **The NSTA Learning Center**
- **SciLinks** for additional online content appropriate for students and teachers
- Teacher Science Background in the back of this Teacher Edition and in the Planning Guide

Keywords

animals

plants

SCiLINKS®
THE WORLD'S A CLICK AWAY

Here's Why This bug is a walking leaf. It mimics leaves to hide from predators. It rocks back and forth when it walks, which makes it look like a leaf blowing in the wind—a bird won't think this bug is food!

In this unit, you will explore the Big Idea, the Essential Questions, and the Investigations on the Inquiry Flipchart.

Levels of Inquiry Key ■ DIRECTED ■ GUIDED ■ INDEPENDENT

Track Your Progress

Big Idea Living things are adapted for survival in their environment.

Essential Questions

Now I Get the Big Idea!

Science Notebook
Before you begin each lesson, be sure to write your thoughts about the Essential Question.

Go Digital

For a complete digital curriculum and resources that provide full coverage of the objectives for this unit, see the Online Resources for this program.

Big Idea and Essential Questions

Big Idea Living things are adapted for survival in their environment.

Post the Unit Big Idea on the board. Have students read the Essential Questions, which are also the titles of the lessons in this unit.

- Discuss how the Essential Questions can help them focus on the Big Idea.

- Have students read the Big Idea statement. The statement describes the main science concept they will be learning.

- Have students predict other ideas that will be taught in the lessons based on the titles, or have them give examples of pictures they expect to see.

Once they have completed all the lessons, they should have a better understanding of the Big Idea.

Essential Questions You may use the following Science Notebook strategy for working with the Essential Questions before students begin the unit or lessons in the unit.

- Strategies for revisiting the Big Idea and Essential Questions are provided in Enduring Understandings on page 167A.

Notebook **Science Notebook**

- Have students copy the Essential Questions into their Science Notebooks. Suggest they leave writing lines between questions.

- Ask students to write responses to the Essential Questions. Urge students not to worry about whether their responses are correct. They should expect their ideas to change as they work in the unit. Comment that students will be able to review and revise their answers to the Essential Questions at the end of the unit.

- Tips and strategies for using Science Notebooks are provided throughout this unit, in the Planning Guide, and in Online Resources.

Options for Inquiry

FLIPCHART P. 12

Students can conduct these optional investigations at any time before, during, or in response to the lesson in the Student Edition.

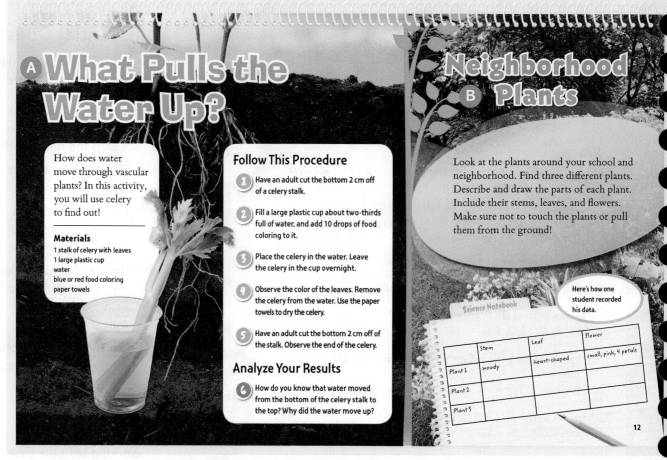

A What Pulls the Water Up?

How does water move through vascular plants? In this activity, you will use celery to find out!

Materials
1 stalk of celery with leaves
1 large plastic cup
water
blue or red food coloring
paper towels

Follow This Procedure

1. Have an adult cut the bottom 2 cm off of a celery stalk.
2. Fill a large plastic cup about two-thirds full of water, and add 10 drops of food coloring to it.
3. Place the celery in the water. Leave the celery in the cup overnight.
4. Observe the color of the leaves. Remove the celery from the water. Use the paper towels to dry the celery.
5. Have an adult cut the bottom 2 cm off of the stalk. Observe the end of the celery.

Analyze Your Results

6. How do you know that water moved from the bottom of the celery stalk to the top? Why did the water move up?

B Neighborhood Plants

Look at the plants around your school and neighborhood. Find three different plants. Describe and draw the parts of each plant. Include their stems, leaves, and flowers. Make sure not to touch the plants or pull them from the ground!

Here's how one student recorded his data.

Science Notebook

	Stem	Leaf	Flower
Plant 1	woody	heart-shaped	small, pink, 4 petals
Plant 2			
Plant 3			

12

Directed Inquiry

A What Pulls the Water Up?

⏱ 15 minutes per day, for two days

👥 pairs

Prep and Planning Tips

- Keep the celery dry (do not store it in water) prior to the activity. Keep the celery overnight in a cool place, such as a refrigerator or a cooler with ice.

- Just before the activity, cut 2–3 cm off of the base of each celery stalk to encourage it to draw water into its stem and tubes.

- Cover work surfaces with newspaper and provide paper towels or sponges for cleanup.

- White carnations or the wildflower Queen Anne's Lace can be substituted for celery stalks.

Caution! Students who have food allergies or intolerances may be sensitive to celery and food colorings. Have these students work with a partner.

Expected Results

Students will observe that the leaves turned color. They should also see some color in the tubes of the freshly-cut celery stalks.

Independent Inquiry

B Neighborhood Plants

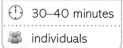

⏱ 30–40 minutes

👤 individuals

Prep and Planning Tips

See the Planning for Inquiry page for more information. Prior to the activity, have students identify the parts of a classroom plant.

Science Notebook

Students can use the sample Science Notebook page as a model for recording their observations. Encourage students to describe the plants as completely as possible, including shapes and sizes. Students may want to take rulers along with their Notebooks and take approximate measurements of each plant's height, leaf size, and so on, without touching the plant. Encourage students to make sketches of the plants they examine.

Lesson 1

Essential Question
What Are Some Plant Structures?

Engage Your Brain!

Find the answer to the following question in this lesson and record it here.

How does the stem of this tree differ from the stems of other plants?

This tree has a single woody stem.

This tree's stem is larger than the

stems of most plants.

Active Reading

Lesson Vocabulary
List the terms. As you learn about each one, make notes in the Interactive Glossary.

root   photosynthesis

stem   chlorophyll

leaf

Main Idea and Details
Detail sentences give more information about a main idea. The information may be examples, features, characteristics, or facts. Active readers stay focused when they ask, What fact or information does this sentence add to the main idea?

103

Go Digital
An interactive digital lesson is available in Online Resources. It is suitable for individuals, small groups, or may be projected or used on an interactive white board.

Objectives
- Describe the structures of typical plants.
- Describe the process of photosynthesis.

Engage Your Brain!
Ask students to think about the stems of common plants and describe their characteristics. Then have them describe the characteristics of a tree for comparison. Remind students to record their final answer to the question when they find it on the fourth page of this lesson.

Active Reading Annotations
Remind students that active readers "make texts their own" by annotating them with notes and marks that help with comprehension. Encourage students to use pencil, not pen, to make annotations and to feel free to change their annotations as they read. The goal of annotation is to help students remember what they have read.

Vocabulary and Interactive Glossary

Remind students to find and list the yellow highlighted terms from the lesson. As they proceed through the lesson and learn about the terms, they should add notes, pictures, or sentences in the extra spaces in the Interactive Glossary.

2 Explain

Notebook ▸ Generate Ideas

Ask students to think about the plants they are familiar with that grow in their neighborhood. Have them name and list some of these plants. Lead the class in a discussion in which they identify the differences in some of these plants. For example, what makes a plant a tree, and how are trees different from flowers? Accept all ideas and encourage students to think about their examples as they read these pages.

Active Reading

Remind students that authors compare and contrast events, objects, and ideas when they point out ways they are alike and different. Active readers remember similarities and differences because they focus on the events, objects, and ideas being compared.

Develop Inquiry Skills

COMPARE **How do the sizes of vascular and nonvascular plants compare?** The rose plant, a vascular plant, is much bigger and taller than the moss plant, a nonvascular plant. **What explains this difference?** The tubes allow water to be carried over a distance. The rose plant can grow larger because it can get water from the soil to all parts of the plant.

Types of Plants

How many plants can you name? Rosebushes, maple trees, cacti, ferns, and mosses are just a few examples. Scientists have identified more than 310,000 types of plants on Earth! How do scientists group all of them?

Active Reading As you read these two pages, circle the two types of plants that are being compared each time they appear.

Scientists classify plants into two groups: (nonvascular plants) and (vascular plants.) (Nonvascular plants) are the simplest types of plants that grow on land. These small plants grow close to the ground and soak up water and minerals like a sponge. Some parts of (nonvascular plants) look like structures on (vascular plants,) but the functions are different. For example, (nonvascular plants) have parts that look like roots, but the parts don't take in water. Instead they help anchor the (nonvascular plant) in the ground. (Nonvascular plants) don't have stems or leaves, either. Instead they have a stalk on which leaflike structures grow.

Mosses are (nonvascular plants.) Most types of moss grow to a height of less than 10 cm.

104

Differentiation — Leveled Questions

Extra Support

What structures do vascular plants have? Roots, stems, and leaves. Do nonvascular plants also have roots and leaves? Explain. No. They have structures that look similar but are not true leaves and roots.

Challenge

Why are the structures on nonvascular plants not considered true roots, stems, and leaves? They are not made of vascular parts. For example, rootlike parts only anchor plants in the soil, they do not take in water.

Vascular plants, such as this rosebush, have roots, stems, and leaves. Water and nutrients taken in by the roots move through the stem to the leaves in tubes. The tube system also moves food from the leaves to other parts of the plant.

Most plants that you see every day are vascular plants. Vascular plants have a system of tubes that carry water and nutrients through the plant. These tubes run through the plant's roots, stems, and leaves. Roots take in water and minerals and also anchor the plant in the ground. Stems hold up the plant's leaves, which make food for the plant.

All plants that produce flowers, such as rosebushes and magnolia trees, are vascular plants. Flowers are reproductive structures, but not all vascular plants have flowers. Some vascular plants such as pine trees, produce reproductive structures called cones.

Do the Math!
Work with Fractions

About $\frac{1}{10}$ of the 310,000 known types of plants are nonvascular. The remaining $\frac{9}{10}$ are vascular plants. Use this information, and two different colors, to color in and label the circle below.

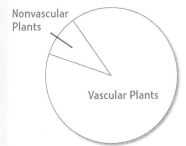

Nonvascular Plants

Vascular Plants

105

Develop Science Concepts

How is a vascular system useful? It is made up of tubes that can carry water and nutrients long distances.

What are some examples of ways that people use tubes to move water? Drinking straws, hoses, and pipes in homes are some examples.

How does using tubes change the way water can be used? Sample answer: Tubes allow water to be used over longer distances and to be distributed to different places.

Do the Math!
Work with Fractions

Point out that the circle is like a pie. The entire circle represents all the known types of plants. After students read about the number of vascular and nonvascular plants, direct them to make the connection between the $\frac{9}{10}$ in the reading and the large portion of the circle. Repeat for $\frac{1}{10}$. Students should now be able to color and label the sections of the graph correctly.

Notebook ▶ Summarize Ideas

Instruct students to compare and contrast nonvascular and vascular plants. Encourage them to use lists or a table format to see the similarities and differences side by side.

Differentiation — Leveled Questions

Extra Support

Why are nonvascular plants shorter than vascular plants? Nonvascular plants soak up water from the ground like a sponge. Because they don't have vascular tubes to move water throughout the plant, they cannot grow as tall.

Challenge

Compare and contrast the function of a stem in vascular and nonvascular plants. In vascular plants, the stem holds up the plant and carries water from the roots to the leaves. In nonvascular plants, the stalk only holds up the plant.

© Houghton Mifflin Harcourt Publishing Company (bg) ©Bob Jacobson/Corbis; (l) ©Russell Illig/Getty Images

2 Explain (continued)

 Generate Ideas

Draw a picture on the board of an idealized vascular plant. Include roots, stems, and leaves in the picture. Have a volunteer come to the board and draw lines where he or she thinks there are tubes in the plant. Discuss what these tubes might do.

Active Reading

Remind students that the main idea may be stated in the first sentence, or it may be stated elsewhere. To find a main idea, active readers ask, What is this paragraph mostly about?

Develop Science Concepts

On the board, make a two-column chart with the headings *Plant Parts* and *Functions*. After students read these pages and study the pictures and captions, call on volunteers to identify the plant parts.

Which type of plant has roots and stems? a vascular plant

What is the function of a plant's roots? The roots absorb water and minerals from the soil and help anchor the plant in the soil.

What does the stem do? The stem supports the plant and carries water and nutrients to different parts of the plant.

Why are these structures important to all parts of a plant? They carry water, minerals, and sugars to all parts of the plant.

Using the Tubes

What type of tool do you use to drink juice in a pouch? A straw, of course! Vascular plants have tubes that work like straws to move water, minerals, and sugars through the plant.

Active Reading As you read this page, draw two lines under the main idea.

Vascular plants have structures called roots. Roots are usually underground and absorb water and minerals from soil. If you have ever helped weed a garden, you know that roots also help anchor a plant in the soil. There are two main types of roots—fibrous roots and taproots.

Fibrous roots are thin, branching roots that grow close to the surface. Grasses and most trees have fibrous roots.

Taproots are thick, strong roots that grow deep in the soil. Some plants use taproots to store food. When you eat a carrot or a beet, you are eating a taproot!

106

© Houghton Mifflin Harcourt Publishing Company (bg) ©Bob Jacobson/Corbis

English Language Learners

Understand the Functions of Plant Structures Have students make flashcards of the different plant structures. On one side of the card, students should write a description of the function. On the other side of the card, have them write the structure that performs the function. Students can make several cards for each structure. For example, one card for *roots* can describe "takes in water" while another card describes "anchors the plant in the soil." Allow pairs to practice with the cards.

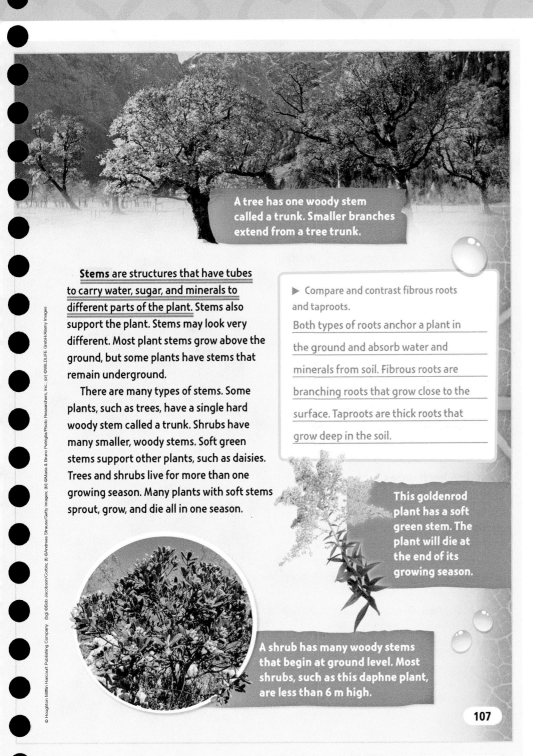

A tree has one woody stem called a trunk. Smaller branches extend from a tree trunk.

Stems are structures that have tubes to carry water, sugar, and minerals to different parts of the plant. Stems also support the plant. Stems may look very different. Most plant stems grow above the ground, but some plants have stems that remain underground.

There are many types of stems. Some plants, such as trees, have a single hard woody stem called a trunk. Shrubs have many smaller, woody stems. Soft green stems support other plants, such as daisies. Trees and shrubs live for more than one growing season. Many plants with soft stems sprout, grow, and die all in one season.

► Compare and contrast fibrous roots and taproots.

Both types of roots anchor a plant in the ground and absorb water and minerals from soil. Fibrous roots are branching roots that grow close to the surface. Taproots are thick roots that grow deep in the soil.

This goldenrod plant has a soft green stem. The plant will die at the end of its growing season.

A shrub has many woody stems that begin at ground level. Most shrubs, such as this daphne plant, are less than 6 m high.

107

© Houghton Mifflin Harcourt Publishing Company (bg) ©Bob Jacobson/Corbis; (t) ©Andreas Strauss/Getty Images; (b) ©Maria & Bruno Petriglia/Photo Researchers, Inc.; (cr) ©WILDLIFE GmbH/Alamy Images

Writing Connection

Write a Poem Invite students to write a poem about a plant. Their poem should include descriptions of the different parts and functions of a plant.

Encourage students to be creative. For example, they might write their poems from the viewpoint of a plant talking about its structures.

Develop Science Vocabulary

roots Remind students that roots have more than one function. They anchor the plant in the ground, and they absorb water and minerals from the soil. Ask students to point out the roots on each picture of a plant on these pages.

stems Students will likely be familiar with this plant part. Remind them that the stem not only supports the plant but also carries water, sugar, and minerals throughout the plant. Ask students to point out the stems on each picture of a plant on these pages.

⁄⁄ Misconception Alert ⁄⁄

Many students will think of stems only in terms of green stems that support a flower. Ask: **Are tree trunks and branches considered to be stems?** Students should be able to correctly answer that these are woody stems.

Interpret Visuals

Direct students to look at the two root systems shown on the facing page. Ask them where they have seen roots that look like these. For example, the carrots we eat are taproots. If students have helped an adult family member pull weeds, they may have experienced the difficulty of pulling a plant with fibrous roots such as those on grasses. Ask students to use these visuals to make their comparisons and contrasts as they complete the Interactivity.

Notebook ► **Summarize Ideas**

Return to the picture of the vascular plant you made on the board. Ask if students would change anything about the tubes that were added to the picture. Suggest that they make a similar picture in their Science Notebooks.

2 Explain (continued)

 Notebook **Generate Ideas**

Ask students to look at the pictures on these pages before they read. Have them generate questions that they have about leaves or the pictures. Write their questions on the board and revisit them after students have finished reading these pages.

Active Reading

Remind students that informational text contains many facts. Active readers process informational text with deliberate speed that enables them to focus on and retain the facts presented. Underlining facts helps active readers focus more readily.

Develop Science Concepts

Direct students to the picture of the maple leaf. **Does this leaf come from a vascular plant or a nonvascular plant? How do you know?** It comes from a vascular plant. Only vascular plants have true leaves.

Why are veins important to a plant? Veins carry water and nutrients from one part of the plant to another. Veins also fill with water and help support leaves.

Develop Science Vocabulary

leaves Remind students that leaves grow out from the stem and are the site of food production in the plant. Display a variety of leaves for students to examine, and allow them to make rubbings of the leaves in their Science Notebooks. Point out that the dark lines that show up in the rubbings are the tubes that move water, food, and minerals throughout the leaf and connect with tubes in the stem.

Lots of Leaves

Leaves can be long, short, wide, narrow, smooth, rough, shiny, or dull. Some leaves even have fuzzy surfaces!

Active Reading As you read the paragraph on this page, underline two facts about leaves.
Sample answers shown.

Leaves are another part of vascular plants. **Leaves** are plant parts that use sunlight to produce sugar for the plant's food. While leaves may have the same function, leaves come in many shapes and sizes. Some plants, such as water lilies, have round leaves. On other plants, such as redbud trees, the leaves are heart-shaped. Grasses have leaves that are long and narrow. Leaves can even be triangular, as they are on a gentian sage plant.

heart-shaped

▶ Scientists often use leaf shape to identify plants. Label each leaf shape.

Vascular plants, such as maple trees, have leaves with veins.

108

 Math Connection

Calculate Numbers of Plants Tell students that in a field of plants, half of the plants have long, thin leaves and the other half have round leaves. If a scientist goes through the field and counts a total of 350 plants, how many of the plants have long, thin leaves?

Answer: $350 \div 2 = 175$ plants with long, thin leaves.

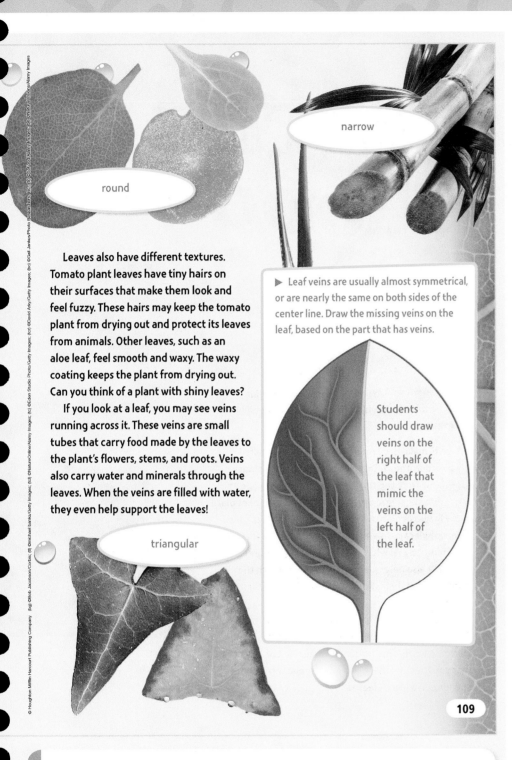

round

narrow

Leaves also have different textures. Tomato plant leaves have tiny hairs on their surfaces that make them look and feel fuzzy. These hairs may keep the tomato plant from drying out and protect its leaves from animals. Other leaves, such as an aloe leaf, feel smooth and waxy. The waxy coating keeps the plant from drying out. Can you think of a plant with shiny leaves?

If you look at a leaf, you may see veins running across it. These veins are small tubes that carry food made by the leaves to the plant's flowers, stems, and roots. Veins also carry water and minerals through the leaves. When the veins are filled with water, they even help support the leaves!

▶ Leaf veins are usually almost symmetrical, or are nearly the same on both sides of the center line. Draw the missing veins on the leaf, based on the part that has veins.

Students should draw veins on the right half of the leaf that mimic the veins on the left half of the leaf.

triangular

109

Develop Science Concepts

Before students complete the leaf identification interactivity, draw a word web on the board. Write *leaf* in the center circle and surround it with three to five smaller circles. Have volunteers go to the board and draw a differently shaped leaf in each smaller circle. When all of the smaller circles are filled, ask: **What do all of these leaves have in common?** They all use sunlight to produce sugar for the plant's food. They all have veins to transport water, minerals, and sugars to the different plant parts.

Interpret Visuals

Before students complete the Interactivity on the student page, point out the veins in all of the leaves shown on this page. Have students look especially at the drawing of the maple leaf on the facing page, which more clearly shows the veins. If you have actual leaves in the classroom, demonstrate that if you fold the leaf along its center line, the veins are almost identical on each side of the fold. As students complete the Interactivity, encourage them to branch the vascular lines out as far as possible. Point out that vascular tubes go into every part of the leaf. They simply become very small as they continue to branch and are less obvious.

Notebook ▶ **Summarize Ideas**

Review the questions that students had as they began this section. Then, to summarize the ideas from these pages, have students make word webs with the word *leaves* in the central circle. Allow them to include as much information as they feel necessary and organize it in the way they feel is appropriate.

English Language Learners

Understanding Irregular Plurals: Leaf and Leaves

Words with irregular plural forms may confuse some students. Have students write the word pair *leaf/leaves*. Have them circle the word part that changes when the plural is formed. Then, on the board, write a sentence using the word *leaf*. Have students rewrite the sentence, changing the word to plural. Have students read both sentences aloud, emphasizing the difference between *leaf* and *leaves*.

2 Explain (continued)

Notebook ▶ Generate Ideas

Encourage students to discuss the importance of food for all living things. Invite students to compare and contrast the variety of ways people and animals get food. Use this discussion to introduce students to the methods plants use to make food.

Active Reading

Remind students that some text segments state information essential to understanding a topic. Active readers identify and focus on these text segments as a way to deepen their understanding of the topic.

Develop Science Vocabulary

photosynthesis Write the term on the board and draw a line to break it in halves. Show students that the first part of the word *photo* refers to light, much the way a photograph captures light. The second part *synthesis* means to make something. Together, the word means "to make something out of light."

chlorophyll Ask students to explain how chlorophyll is important to making food. Students should understand that chlorophyll is the substance that captures light energy for photosynthesis.

Develop Science Concepts

What would happen if you removed all the leaves from a plant? The plant would die, because it could not make enough food for energy through photosynthesis. Explain that other green leaf parts also contain chlorophyll but not enough to keep the plant alive. You can further test students' understanding of photosynthesis by asking what would happen to a plant placed in the dark for a long period of time. Students should understand that plants use light energy to produce sugars for food.

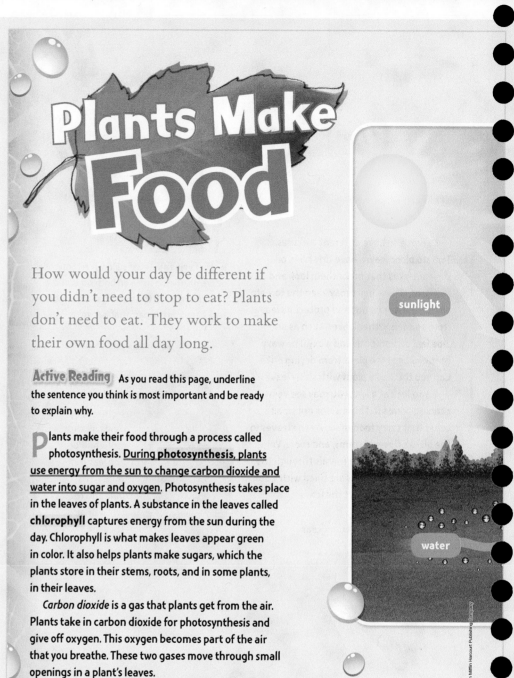

Plants Make Food

How would your day be different if you didn't need to stop to eat? Plants don't need to eat. They work to make their own food all day long.

Active Reading As you read this page, underline the sentence you think is most important and be ready to explain why.

Plants make their food through a process called photosynthesis. During **photosynthesis**, plants use energy from the sun to change carbon dioxide and water into sugar and oxygen. Photosynthesis takes place in the leaves of plants. A substance in the leaves called **chlorophyll** captures energy from the sun during the day. Chlorophyll is what makes leaves appear green in color. It also helps plants make sugars, which the plants store in their stems, roots, and in some plants, in their leaves.

Carbon dioxide is a gas that plants get from the air. Plants take in carbon dioxide for photosynthesis and give off oxygen. This oxygen becomes part of the air that you breathe. These two gases move through small openings in a plant's leaves.

110

 ### Differentiation — Leveled Questions

Extra Support

Ask students to draw a plant showing the stem and leaves. Have students use a green crayon or marker to show where chlorophyll is found in plants.

Challenge

What does it mean if a plant's leaves start to turn yellow? Something is wrong with the plant. It could be age, too much or too little light, water or heat, or a number of other ailments.

food

oxygen

carbon dioxide

The Ins and Outs of Photosynthesis

Fill in the blanks to show what happens during photosynthesis.
Some of the words are filled in for you.

Sunlight + ___Carbon dioxide___ + ___Water___ yields ___Food or Sugar___ + Oxygen

© Houghton Mifflin Harcourt Publishing Company

111

Develop Science Concepts

Have students take a few minutes to closely examine the diagram on this page. To help them interpret the diagram, ask the following questions.

What does a plant need to carry out photosynthesis? carbon dioxide, water, sunlight

What does a plant give off to its surroundings during photosynthesis? oxygen

What does a plant make during photosynthesis? sugar

After students answer these questions, direct them to complete the Interactivity at the bottom of the page.

⚡ Misconception Alert !

Some students may think that the sugars made by plants during photosynthesis are only used by animals and other organisms. Remind students that plants do not eat and, therefore, must make their own food. From this, they should understand that the plant itself also uses these sugars for food.

Notebook ▸ Summarize Ideas

Ask students to summarize the process of photosynthesis, including what is needed for the process to happen, the substance in the leaves that captures the sun's energy, and the products of this process. Invite students to summarize their ideas verbally or in writing.

Writing Connection

Write a Picture Book Have students write a picture book to share with first-grade students describing how plants make food. Remind students that since their intended audience is beginning readers, they should use few words to explain the process.

Encourage students to outline the steps of the process, and label their illustrations. After they complete their books, schedule time with a first-grade class and have students read their books aloud to the younger students.

3 Extend/Evaluate

Sum It Up!

- As students read over the descriptions and examine the images, encourage them to review the lesson to locate any information that is unfamiliar to them.

- Encourage students to make any notes that might be helpful on this page. They may find it useful to write the page numbers of where they found the answers to some questions. This will allow them to locate information quickly when they are reviewing.

- Some students may have trouble with the Summarize section. Assist these students by giving them a choice of two terms to complete each blank. After they have completed the paragraph correctly, have them complete it again without the word choices.

- Remind students to use the Answer Key to check their answers. Tell students to correct the answers they got wrong by writing a new response.

- Suggest that students who are struggling work together in pairs or small groups.

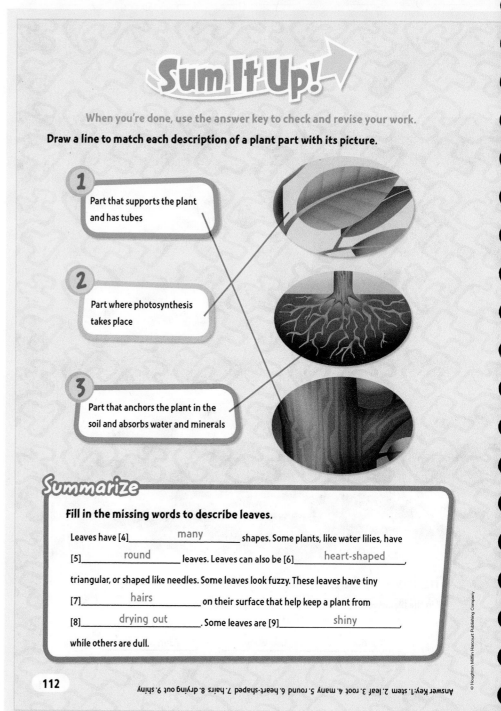

Sum It Up!

When you're done, use the answer key to check and revise your work.

Draw a line to match each description of a plant part with its picture.

1. Part that supports the plant and has tubes

2. Part where photosynthesis takes place

3. Part that anchors the plant in the soil and absorbs water and minerals

Summarize

Fill in the missing words to describe leaves.

Leaves have [4] _____many_____ shapes. Some plants, like water lilies, have [5] _____round_____ leaves. Leaves can also be [6] _____heart-shaped_____, triangular, or shaped like needles. Some leaves look fuzzy. These leaves have tiny [7] _____hairs_____ on their surface that help keep a plant from [8] _____drying out_____. Some leaves are [9] _____shiny_____, while others are dull.

Answer Key: 1. stem 2. leaf 3. root 4. many 5. round 6. heart-shaped 7. hairs 8. drying out 9. shiny

© Houghton Mifflin Harcourt Publishing Company

 **Brain Check**

Name _____

Word Play

1 Use the words in the box to complete each sentence. Then use the circled letters to answer the question below.

photosynthesis*	chlorophyll*	**flowers**	root*
veins	**vascular**	leaf*	stems*

*Key Lesson Vocabulary

The process of changing carbon dioxide and water into sugar and oxygen using energy from sunlight is p h o t o s y (n) t h e s i s.

Plants may have hard woody or soft green (s) t e m s.

Plants with tubes that move water, minerals, and sugar are called v a s c (u) l (a) r plants.

The part of the plant that absorbs water and minerals is the (r) o o t.

All plants that produce f (l) o w e r s are examples of vascular plants.

The part of the plant where food is made is the l e (a) f.

The lines in a leaf that contain tubes are called (v) e i (n) s.

The substance in leaves that captures sunlight is called (c) h l o r (o) p h y l l.

Mosses are examples of which type of plant?

n o n v a s c u l a r

113

Answer Strategies

Word Play

1. Encourage students to first review the terms and define them either by thinking of a definition or by writing notes next to the terms. Then, when they read through the incomplete sentences, they will be prepared to select the best option. Have students find the definitions of any terms they are unfamiliar with by reviewing the lesson.

Assessment

Suggested Scoring Guide
You may wish to use this suggested scoring guide for the Brain Check.

Item	Points
1	63 (7 points each)
2	12
3	25
Total	100

Lesson Quiz
See Assessment Guide, p. AG 25.

© Houghton Mifflin Harcourt Publishing Company

3 Extend/Evaluate (continued)

Answer Strategies

Apply Concepts

2. Refer students to the first two pages of the lesson where vascular and nonvascular plants are defined. Review the examples of the different types of plants along with the definitions. Then help students organize this information into a contrast format. Remind students that contrasting two items means to point out their differences.

3. Make sure that students are familiar with vascular tubes and their function. Check their diagrams to ensure that they have accurately depicted how vascular tubes run throughout the plant from roots through stems and into leaves. Students' diagrams and/or descriptions should indicate that materials flow in both directions through the plant: water and minerals flow from the roots to the leaves through the tubes, and food moves from the leaves to the rest of the plant through the tubes.

 Take It Home!

See *ScienceSaurus*® for more information about characteristics of living things. *ScienceSaurus* is a "mini-encyclopedia" students can use to find out more about unit topics. It contains numerous resources including concise content summaries, an almanac, many tables, charts, and graphs, history of science, and a glossary.

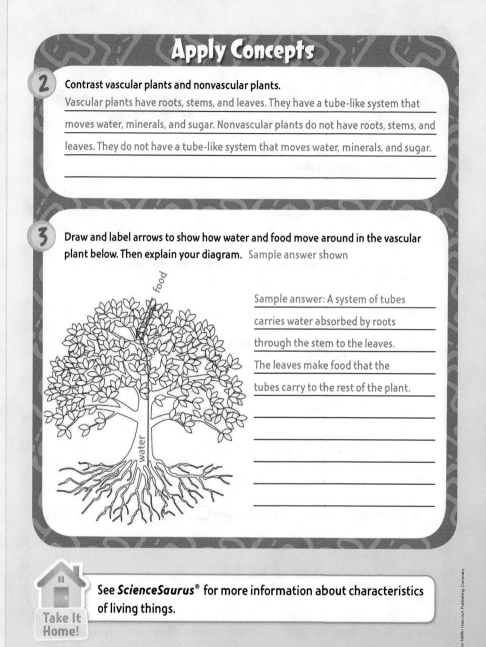

Apply Concepts

2. Contrast vascular plants and nonvascular plants.

Vascular plants have roots, stems, and leaves. They have a tube-like system that moves water, minerals, and sugar. Nonvascular plants do not have roots, stems, and leaves. They do not have a tube-like system that moves water, minerals, and sugar.

3. Draw and label arrows to show how water and food move around in the vascular plant below. Then explain your diagram. Sample answer shown

food

water

Sample answer: A system of tubes carries water absorbed by roots through the stem to the leaves. The leaves make food that the tubes carry to the rest of the plant.

Take It Home! See *ScienceSaurus*® for more information about characteristics of living things.

114

Make Connections

Art Connection

Picturing Plant Structures

Ask students to make an artistic piece that depicts a plant. Encourage them to be creative and use paint, pencils, clay, or whatever medium they wish. Remind them that their piece should illustrate at least two different plant structures or represent a plant function.

Average

Writing Connection

A Day Without Plants

Plants are an important part of our daily lives. Invite each student to think about one way that plants are essential to him or her. Ask students to write an account of a day in their life in which this plant and product did not exist.

Average

Health and Physical Education Connection

Classify Food by Plant Structures

Tell students that most of the food they eat comes from plants. Have students identify ten different foods they have eaten recently that come from plants, and list these foods. Then ask them to define which plant structures produce the foods. Have them organize the foods into these categories: fruits, stems, roots, leaves.

Challenging

Social Studies Connection

Chlorophyll and Changing Leaf Colors

Ask the class to describe the season of fall. Students should include descriptions of leaves changing color and falling to the ground. Explain that these changes are due to changing levels of chlorophyll in the leaves. Challenge students to find out how chlorophyll causes these changes. Students can present their findings as a poster or computer slide show.

S.T.E.M.

Engineering and Technology

Objectives

- Identify problems that an irrigation system can help solve.
- Compare past and present types of irrigation systems.
- Identify technology that resulted in improved irrigation systems.

Notebook ▶ Generate Ideas

Ask students to discuss what they know about how large amounts of water might be delivered to a crop or field that is far from a water source. Have them brainstorm their own ideas as they look at the photos on this page.

Background

- Irrigation is the name given to the human-made process of supplying soil with the water that it needs to grow crops, flower and vegetable gardens, and other landscaping plants.

- The idea of using irrigation to supplement insufficient rainfall dates back to the ancient Egyptians, who built canals to connect natural water sources to crops. Today's water irrigation systems are sophisticated and use modern technologies to pump groundwater and reservoir water long distances. Millions of acres of agricultural land worldwide have been equipped with permanent irrigation structures to deal with large volumes of crops.

- Drip irrigation and sprinkler systems are popular methods for delivering water uniformly over large areas. Subirrigation uses methods to artificially raise the water table to moisten soil below a plant's roots.

S.T.E.M.
Engineering & Technology

How It Works:
Water Irrigation System

A water irrigation system moves water to where it is needed. This water may come from rivers, lakes, or wells. Pumps and valves control the movement of water into and through the system. Farmers use a control panel to determine how much and how quickly water moves through a field.

pipe and drip pipes

center pivot gear

system control panel

"A" frame

pump and check valve

wheel

Troubleshooting

Find and circle the pump on the diagram. What would happen to the irrigation system if the pump stopped working?

Sample answer: Without the pump, water would not flow from the wells or holding tanks through the pipes. The irrigation system would stop working because it relies on all of its parts to work properly.

115

S.T.E.M.
continued

Show How It Works

People use irrigation systems to water their vegetable gardens at home.
Look at the picture of a backyard irrigation system. Label its parts.
Then answer the questions.

faucet

sprinkler

hose

Name some parts of the irrigation system not shown in the diagram.

Sample answer: Students may identify the home's plumbing, the water utility

meter, and the people who turn the water on and off.

Identify some problems with this irrigation system. Then, describe how you would solve them.

Sample answer: Problem: The hose is leaking where it connects to the faucet. Solution:

Tighten the fitting/add or replace a rubber washer. Problem: Too much water is coming

out of the sprinkler head closest to the faucet. Solution: Replace sprinkler head.

Build On It!

Rise to the engineering design challenge—complete **Make a Process:
Planting and Caring for a Garden** on the Inquiry Flipchart.

116

Build On It!

In **Make a Process: Planting
and Caring for a Garden**, the
design challenge associated with
this lesson, students use the steps
of the engineering design process
to build their own irrigation
system. See the pages that follow.

Other opportunities to apply the
design process appear throughout
the *Inquiry Flipchart.*

Develop S.T.E.M. Concepts

DESIGN CRITERIA Explain that irrigation
can be as simple as using a watering can to
bring water to a garden or as complex as using
motors to move water through piping systems.
Remind students that when engineers begin
a project, they think about the problem and
the obstacles that must be overcome. They
identify the project's design criteria, which are
the outcomes that would make their new tool,
product, process, or system a success. **Why
would using watering cans for a large crop
field not be an efficient way to meet watering needs?** Sample answer: It would take too
long. **What design criteria must a watering
system for a large crop field meet to be
successful?** It must distribute water evenly
over a large area.

As students complete the Troubleshooting
Interactivity, emphasize how the parts of a
system work together. Remind them that all
parts of a system must be functioning in
order for the system to work properly.

Develop Inquiry Skills

COMMUNICATE Invite students to summarize
the process shown on the photo of the home
irrigation system. Have them orally explain the
steps that the water goes through as it moves
through the system.

USE MODELS **If you were to make a model
of an irrigation system that could water
two gardens at once, how would you
modify the system shown here?** Sample
answer: I would use a valve that split the water
between two garden hoses and delivered the
water to different places.

Notebook ▸ Summarize Ideas

Use the Interactivity on the second page of
the feature as an opportunity to stress that
all parts of a system must function together.
Have students summarize this idea, either
orally or in writing.

S.T.E.M.
Engineering **&** Technology

Make a Process: Planting and Caring for a Garden

Planning is important to any project. It is especially true when planting a garden. Before the first seed is planted, you need to think ahead.

All plants share some basic needs, but their seeds might germinate under different conditions. To plan a garden, you need to learn about seeds, plant care, and what will grow in your local environment.

It is important to think about your design and know what to expect. As you do this research, you will come up with a process to help you design your garden.

DESIGN PROCESS STEPS

What to Do

1. Research types of gardens. Pick one garden type and decide where to plant it.

2. Find out which types of seeds would be best to plant in your local environment.

3. In your Science Notebook, make a diagram of your garden's layout.

4. Use available materials to construct a model of your design.

5. Write a process that describes how you will care for the different seeds, seedlings, and plants that will grow in your garden. What types of resources will you need? How will you get these resources?

6. Make up a schedule to care for your garden. Include daily, weekly, and monthly tasks.

Keep a record of your work in your Science Notebook.

13

Objectives

- Use the five steps of the design process to plan and care for a garden.

- Apply scientific knowledge of the needs of plants.

Prep and Planning Tips

- Provide students with any research materials they may need to learn more about garden planning. Gardening books and seed catalogs may be helpful. You may wish to compile a list of webpages that students can refer to for information.

- Gather any materials students will need, and set them out in workstations around the room.

Caution! Remind students to wash their hands after handling soil.

Expected Results

Students should be able to plan and design a garden, as well as devise a schedule for the garden's care.

1 Engage/Explore

Attention Grabber

Display pictures of seedlings just beginning to sprout from the ground, and then show pictures of fully mature summer gardens. Explain that the gardens were planted by people to add beauty or to provide fruits or vegetables to eat. Elicit from students what kind of garden they would like to grow if they could. Explain that in this activity, students will plan and design a garden and arrange a schedule for its care.

Preview Activity

Before beginning the activity, have students review the directions on the Engineering and Technology Flipchart page. You may wish to have students review the lesson on the engineering design process earlier in this program.

Guide the Activity

Develop Inquiry Skills

COMPARE Remind students of the complex irrigation system shown in their texts. Reiterate that they are going to devise a system for watering a home garden. **How is this system different from the one used to irrigate the large farm field?** Sample answer: The larger system uses many more pipes and valves and is controlled by a computer. My garden system will be less complex.

COMPARE **How is your garden different from the large farm field? How will this affect your irrigation system?** Sample answer: The larger system irrigates only one crop, which has specific water needs. My system will need to be modified to supply water to a variety of crops, and each of those crops may have different water needs.

Strategies for Success

Be sure that students indicate what kinds of seeds they would like to plant in their gardens and research what soil, sunlight, and watering conditions those seeds require. Encourage students to group seeds that have similar light and watering needs to make caring for the garden easier.

Explain to students that the placement of a garden is a major consideration when deciding what to plant. South-facing gardens tend to receive the most direct sunlight, while north-facing gardens tend to receive the least. Shade-loving plants grow best in north-facing gardens.

Notebook → Science Notebook

During the Activity As students sketch their designs, remind them to determine how much space they will leave between plants. Explain that seed packets or catalogs contain information about how large a plant will grow and the spacing it requires. Suggest that they include this information on their sketches.

Remind students that they also need to devise a process for caring for the plants once the garden is planted. Encourage them to list the actions they will take and the materials they will need to keep the plants healthy. Remind them to consider where they will get these materials, as well.

2 Explain

Develop the Engineering Design Process

2. PLAN AND BUILD As students begin to build their models, ask guiding questions to help them with their design. **What problem does the grouping you have**

suggested solve? Sample answer: It keeps the plants that need the same amount of light and water together. **How have you accommodated the different heights of plants?** Sample answer: The taller plants will be planted to the north of the shorter plants so that they do not block sunlight from the shorter plants.

4. REDESIGN Before students redesign their gardens, have them communicate with each other about problems they had with their designs. Knowing what worked or didn't work for others may help them complete the redesign process.

3 Extend/Evaluate

Quick Check

Discuss with students what they learned as they went through the design process. Ask students which resources they were most concerned about obtaining for their gardens.

Ask students to discuss any difficulties they had or solutions they devised while planning and building their models and writing their care plan.

Notebook → Science Notebook

After the Activity Students should get full credit for researching, completing a garden design, and making a care plan. They should receive partial credit for completing some of the tasks, and should not receive any credit for not completing any of the tasks.

Michael DiSpezio's
Tips & Tricks

Tour a Garden If possible, escort students on an exploratory field trip through a local garden or greenhouse. Have them observe and take notes on planting and layout strategies.

Make a Model If time allows, supply students with clean soil, a shallow pan, and art materials for constructing a scale model of their design. Also investigate the opportunity to plant a garden on school grounds.

Options for Inquiry

FLIPCHART P. 14

Students can conduct these optional investigations at any time before, during, or in response to the lesson in the Student Edition.

Finding Out About (A) Flowers

You've seen a drawing of a flower and its parts. Now let's see if you can identify the parts of a real flower.

Materials
1 flower, such as a lily
hand lens
colored pencils

Follow This Procedure

1. Use the hand lens to closely observe your flower.
2. Find and identify all of its parts.
3. Make a drawing of your flower. Label all of the parts.

Analyze Your Results

4. Which part of the flower makes pollen? Which part of the flower can produce seeds?

(B) What's Cooking?

Most of the food you eat comes from plants. List all of the ingredients for your favorite meal in a table. In the second column of the table, write whether the ingredients come from a plant. If they do come from a plant, find out which plant. Choose one of the plants, and research where and how the plant is grown. Make a short fact sheet about the plant, and present it to your class.

Science Notebook

Here is an example of one student's chart.

Ingredient	From a Plant?	Which Plant?
flour		
salt		
sugar		
yeast		
raisins		

Directed Inquiry

(A) Finding Out About Flowers

⏱ 15–20 minutes
👥 individuals

Prep and Planning Tips

Some flowers students might examine include daffodils, gladioluses, lilies, and tulips. Do not use flowers such as daisies, roses, and irises, because their structures can be difficult to identify.

While students are examining their flowers, you may wish to display a labeled diagram of a flower, which shows its major parts.

Caution! Some students may have allergies to pollen. These students should not participate and may be given a diagram of a flower without its labels to use, instead.

Expected Results

Students should be able to identify the flower's main parts, including the petals, sepals, stamens, anthers, and pistils.

Independent Inquiry

(B) What's Cooking?

⏱ 20–30 minutes
👥 individuals

Prep and Planning Tips

Before students find their recipes, you may want to list some common ingredients on the board, such as flour, sugar, salt, and vinegar. Review each item and discuss with students where that item comes from and how it is made. For example, tell students that flour comes from wheat plants. Grains of wheat are harvested and then ground up into flour.

Science Notebook

Students can use the Science Notebook as an example of how to organize their notes. If time allows, consider having students bring in their prepared recipes along with their plant fact sheets.

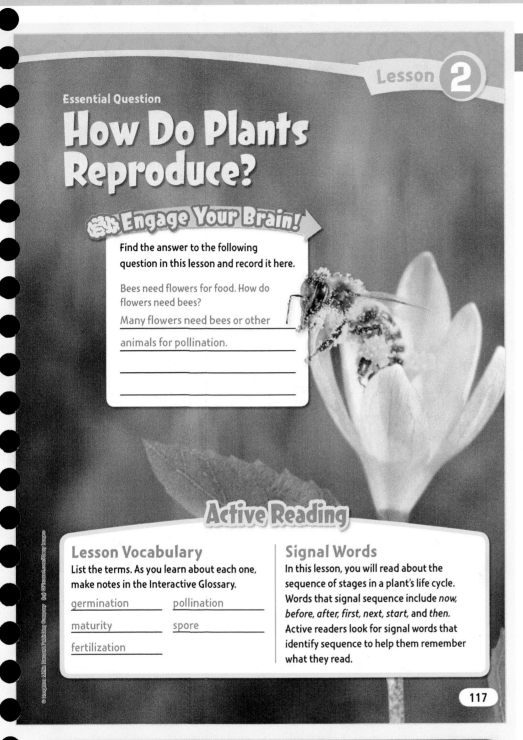

Essential Question
How Do Plants Reproduce?

Engage Your Brain!

Find the answer to the following question in this lesson and record it here.

Bees need flowers for food. How do flowers need bees?

Many flowers need bees or other

animals for pollination.

Active Reading

Lesson Vocabulary

List the terms. As you learn about each one, make notes in the Interactive Glossary.

germination   pollination

maturity   spore

fertilization

Signal Words

In this lesson, you will read about the sequence of stages in a plant's life cycle. Words that signal sequence include *now, before, after, first, next, start,* and *then.* Active readers look for signal words that identify sequence to help them remember what they read.

117

Go Digital

An interactive digital lesson is available in Online Resources. It is suitable for individuals, small groups, or may be projected or used on an interactive white board.

Seed production

Some plants produce seeds in flowers, while others produce seeds in cones. Click each label to learn more about how plants make seeds.

Objectives

- Recognize that all seed-plant life cycles include germination, maturity, reproduction, and death.
- Identify the stages in the life cycle of a flowering plant.
- Identify the stages in the life cycle of a nonflowering, seed-bearing plant (such as a conifer).
- Describe the role of pollination in the sexual reproduction of seed plants.
- Describe ways that plants are pollinated.
- Describe reproduction in seedless plants.

Engage Your Brain!

Encourage students to study the photograph on this page as they brainstorm answers to the question, "How do flowers need bees?" **What is the bee's body covered with as it climbs out of the flower?** pollen Suggest that students keep this picture in mind as they study this lesson.

Remind students to record their final answer to the question when they find it on the sixth page of this lesson.

Active Reading Annotations

Remind students that active readers "make texts their own" by annotating them with notes and marks that help with comprehension. Encourage students to use pencil, not pen, to make annotations and to feel free to change their annotations as they read. The goal of annotation is to help students remember what they have read.

Vocabulary and Interactive Glossary

Remind students to find and list the yellow highlighted terms from the lesson. As they learn about the terms, they should add notes, drawings, or sentences in the extra spaces in the Interactive Glossary.

2 Explain

Notebook **Generate Ideas**

Read the main heading on this page aloud, and have students think about how plants in a garden grow. Ask students to brainstorm different ways that plants change as they grow and mature.

Active Reading

Remind students that sequence, or order, is important in text that describes the development of an idea or the steps in a process. Active readers stay focused on sequence when they mark the transition from one stage of an idea or step in a process to another.

Develop Science Vocabulary

germination Show students a picture of a germinating seed or bring an actual germinating seed to class. Have students point to the part of the diagram on this page that shows seed germination.

maturity Show students various sets of images of young plants and animals and their adult counterparts. Have students point out which of the two images shows a mature organism. Discuss with students how they knew which organism was mature and which organism was still immature.

How Does a Garden Grow?

Think of some of the plants you saw on your way to school today. You might have seen trees, grasses, flowers, or even weeds. Where did all of these plants come from?

Active Reading As you read the next page, circle the signal words that show the sequence in which a plant grows.

Radish Life Cycle

A seed, such as this radish seed, contains the embryo of a plant.

When a seed sprouts during a process known as germination, the embryo in the seed begins to grow.

As the plant continues to grow, it gets larger. It also gets more roots.

When a plant grows to its full size, it reaches maturity. Mature plants make seeds that can grow into new plants.

118

Differentiation — Leveled Questions

Extra Support
Starting from a seed, what is the order of a plant's life cycle? The seed germinates. The plant grows. It makes new seeds.

Challenge
What do you think takes place last in a plant's life cycle? The plant eventually dies.

When a plant grows, it goes through a series of set stages. The series of stages that a living thing goes through as it develops is called a *life cycle*. It is important for people to understand plant life cycles, because most of the food we eat comes from plants.

Most plants grow from seeds. First, a seed is placed in soil, so it can sprout. Next, the plant grows until it reaches maturity. A mature plant may grow flowers or cones. Then these structures make more seeds. You will learn about flowers and cones on the next pages.

Lima Bean Life Cycle

Place the pictures in the correct sequence to show the life cycle of a lima bean plant. Write a number next to each picture. Start with the seed.

1. Lima Bean Seeds — *Phaseolus lunatus*
3.
4.
2.

119

Interpret Visuals

Read through the sequence of events that occur in the life cycle of a radish plant. Tell students that a radish is a flowering plant. Its life cycle is different from the life cycle of nonflowering plants, such as mosses, ferns, and pines.

During which stage of a plant's life cycle does the seed begin to grow into a plant? during germination

During which stage of a plant's life cycle does a plant make new seeds? during maturity

⚡ Misconception Alert ⚡

Students may think of lima beans as vegetables. However, beans, along with many other foods we label as vegetables (tomatoes, peppers, cucumbers), are actually fruits. In scientific terms, a fruit develops from a flower and contains a seed or seeds.

Develop Inquiry Skills

COMMUNICATE Ask students to name some fruits they have eaten and have them describe any seeds they may have found. Point out that seeds come in many sizes. For example, the seeds in a tomato or a radish are small compared with the seed in an avocado or a peach. Tell students that they will learn more about different seed types later in this lesson.

 Math Connection

Solve a Problem Have students solve the following word problem:

A young tree has just sprouted. If the tree grows $\frac{1}{2}$ ft every year, what will be the tree's age when it is 18 feet tall? (36 years)

As an extension, you may want to have students investigate the growth rates of some plants. Then have students write their own word problems based on the growth rates they investigated. Have students solve each other's word problems.

Notebook ▸ Summarize Ideas

Instruct students to complete the Lima Bean Life Cycle activity on this page to make sure they understand this plant's life cycle. Have them compare the life cycle of a lima bean with that of a radish. Have them summarize the main idea orally or in writing.

2 Explain (continued)

Notebook Generate Ideas

Have students scan over the images on these two pages. Ask students to list some plants they have seen with flowers as well as some plants they have seen with cones.

Active Reading

Remind students that informational text contains many facts. Active readers process informational text with deliberate speed, which enables them to focus on and retain the facts presented. Underlining and circling facts helps active readers focus more readily.

Develop Science Vocabulary

fertilization Write *sperm + egg* on the board. Explain that for fertilization to occur, a sperm must join with an egg. Tell students that this is true for both plants and animals.

Develop Science Concepts

What do flowers and cones have in common? Both flowers and cones are used by different types of plants for reproduction.

What must take place before a seed can develop? A sperm cell must join with an egg cell inside a flower or cone.

Which part of a flower makes sperm cells? anther

Which part of a flower makes egg cells? pistil

Flowers and Cones

There are about 310,000 types of plants. Almost 90% of them produce seeds. How do plants produce seeds?

Active Reading As you read this page, underline the names of male plant parts and circle the names of female plant parts.

Flowers and cones are reproductive structures that make seeds. They produce sex cells. Sex cells are used during *sexual reproduction*. Male sex cells are called sperm, and female sex cells are called eggs. **Fertilization** is the process of a sperm and an egg cell joining together. A fertilized egg grows into an embryo inside a seed.

About 1,000 types of plants produce seeds in cones. In plants with cones, sperm are made in male cones and eggs are made in female cones.

Most plants produce seeds in structures called flowers. In plants with flowers, grains of pollen, produced in parts called anthers, contain the sperm. Eggs are made in a structure called a pistil. Many flowers have both anthers and a pistil. As you can see in the picture, flowers have many other parts as well.

Petals are the outer parts of a flower.

The male organ is the stamen [STAY•muhn]. It consists of a thin stalk topped by a saclike anther, which produces pollen.

The female organ is the pistil [PIS•tuhl]. Its rounded base contains eggs.

120

Writing Connection

Letter To help students connect their knowledge of flowers and cones to the world around them, have them write a one-page friendly letter describing the flowers and cones they see on the plants near their home.

Remind students of the parts of a friendly letter: a greeting, a body, and a closing. They should use in their letters the parts of the flowers and cones they have read about.

Most cone-bearing plants are trees. Pines, spruces, and cycads [SY•kadz] are all cone-bearing plants.

A female pine cone makes egg cells.

A male pine cone makes sperm cells.

Plant Parts

Add labels to the flower.

- pistil
- anther
- petal
- stamen
- stem

121

Interpret Visuals

Have students examine the diagram of a flower's parts. Then show students various pictures of flowers. Have students identify the different flower parts that are visible in the pictures. After examining the various pictures of flowers, have students complete the labeling activity on this page.

As an extension, allow students to design their own flowers. You may have students make fantasy flowers out of construction paper, cloth, or other craft materials. The flowers can have any petal shape and be of any size and color. They must, however, contain all the structures shown in the flower diagram on this page.

Develop Inquiry Skills

OBSERVE Bring in several cones to class. Have students examine the cones' structure. Encourage students to compare the cones to flowers and their structures.

Notebook ▶ **Summarize Ideas**

Organize students into small groups. Direct students to quiz each other on the different parts of a flower and the functions of those parts. Have them summarize the main idea orally or in writing.

Differentiation — Leveled Questions

Extra Support

How are flowers and cones similar? They both serve the same function—to make seeds for a plant.

Challenge

What advantage might there be to having male and female parts in the same flower? Sample answer: The pollen would not have to travel from one flower to another.

2 Explain (continued)

Notebook ▶ Generate Ideas

Tell students that they will now be learning more about how fertilization occurs in flowers. Before students read the text, ask them to brainstorm different ways they think pollen could move from an anther to a pistil.

Active Reading

Remind students that active readers annotate, or mark up, text to benefit their own recollection of the information presented. Though students may underline different sentences, it is important that they are able to offer a reasonable explanation for their annotations.

Develop Science Vocabulary

pollination On the board, draw a simple diagram of a flower. Include the flower's anthers and pistil. Draw a few pollen grains on an anther, and draw an arrow from the anther to the pistil. Beneath the diagram, write the word pollination. Instruct students to copy the diagram into their Science Notebooks. Then have students discuss what the diagram shows.

Develop Inquiry Skills

OBSERVE If possible, have students use hand lenses to observe the pollen on a flower's anthers. Point out how fine and powdery the pollen is. For students with allergies to pollen, show students a picture of a bee, bird, or bat with pollen on it.

Why is it important for pollen to be so fine and powdery? If pollen is fine and powdery, it can be blown by wind or picked up by the body parts of pollinators easily.

The Power of Pollen

In order for plant eggs to be fertilized, pollen has to move from the male parts to the female parts. How does the pollen get there?

Active Reading   Underline ways plants can be pollinated.

Plants reproduce through pollination. **Pollination** is the process of pollen moving from a male plant part to a female plant part. There are several ways this can happen. Sometimes wind can blow the pollen from one plant to another, which is how many grasses and trees are pollinated.

Other plants are pollinated by *pollinators*. Some bees, birds, butterflies, and other animals are pollinators. For example, a butterfly goes from flower to flower drinking nectar. At each flower, the pollen on the stamens rubs off on the butterfly. When the butterfly visits the next flower, the pollen may drop off and fall on the pistil. As a result, the flower will be pollinated.

Brightly colored flower petals attract pollinators.

122

Differentiation — Leveled Questions

Extra Support

How is fertilization related to pollination? For fertilization to occur, pollination, or the transfer of pollen to a pistil, must occur.

Challenge

Plants don't need nectar in order to grow or make seeds. Why do you think some plants make nectar? Some plants make nectar in order to attract pollinators. The pollinators use nectar as a food source.

Some water plants are pollinated by water. Flowing water carries the pollen from plant to plant.

Pollen Cloud

Do the Math!
Work with Fractions

Animals pollinate $\frac{3}{4}$ of seed-making plants. Wind and water pollinate the other $\frac{1}{4}$ of plants. Use this information to label the parts of the circle.

Students should mark three-fourths of the circle as "animal-pollinated." Students should mark one-fourth of the circle as "wind- or water-pollinated."

Wind blows pollen from male cones. The wind may carry the pollen to a female cone.

123

Develop Science Concepts

How does pollen get from one plant to another? Pollen may be blown by wind, carried by pollinators, or carried by flowing water.

Do the Math!

Work with Fractions

Before you have students complete this activity, point out to students that the entire circle represents all of the ways a plant can be pollinated.

After students read about pollination, direct them to make the connection between the $\frac{3}{4}$ in the reading and the large section in the circle. Repeat for $\frac{1}{4}$. Students should now be able to color and label the sections of the graph correctly.

Notebook ▶ Summarize Ideas

Instruct students to make a concept map that shows the three main ways a flower can be pollinated. Before students begin, you may want to display an example of a concept map. Tell students that the main concept on their maps should be, "How Plants Are Pollinated." There should be three supporting concepts attached to this main concept. Students can use their completed concept maps to help them summarize the main idea of these two pages orally or in writing.

English Language Learners

Understand Active and Passive Voice In the active voice, the subject performs an action. In the passive voice, the subject receives the action.

Scientists conducted an experiment. (*active*)

An experiment was conducted by scientists. (*passive*)

Have students change this sentence to the active voice: *Many water plants are pollinated by water.* (*Water pollinates many water plants.*)

2 Explain (continued)

Notebook ▸ Generate Ideas

Start a discussion by having students imagine a big field with several oak trees growing in different parts of it. Explain that oak trees—and their acorns—cannot move on their own. Have students brainstorm how acorns came to be at different parts of the field and grow into oak trees.

Active Reading

Remind students that informational text contains many facts. Active readers process informational text with deliberate speed, which enables them to focus on and retain the facts presented. Underlining facts helps active readers focus more readily.

Develop Inquiry Skills

INFER **Many plants grow seeds in large juicy berries and other kinds of fruits. Besides protecting the seeds that are forming inside them, what function might fruits serve?** Many animals eat fruit. When they do, they help spread the undigested seeds to new places where they may grow.

If time allows, ask students to name some of their favorite fruits. As students name the fruits, have them describe the seeds. If any student has ever tried to grow a plant from the seeds found in a fruit, have the student describe the experience to the rest of the class.

Seeds on the Move

Unlike most animals, plants cannot move around in their environment. So how can a plant's seeds be spread from place to place?

Active Reading As you read, underline three things that help seeds move from place to place.

Animals play a big role in moving plant seeds. The base of the pistil of flowers grows into a fruit that contains the flower's seeds. Think of the seeds in an apple or in a blackberry. When an animal eats these fruits, the seeds pass through the animal's body before being deposited elsewhere.

Other animals will find and bury seeds. Think of squirrels. Squirrels bury acorns so that they will have food in the winter. The squirrels will dig up and eat most of the acorns, but they may forget a few. These acorns will grow into new oak trees.

Seeds, such as burs, can also travel on an animal's body. Other kinds of seeds are very light. They can be carried by the wind. Still other seeds, including coconuts, float in water.

124

Some seeds are very light. They can be blown around by the wind.

Writing Connection

Write a Story Ask students to write a story from the point of view of a seed. The story should tell about the various experiences a seed might have in the course of being spread from one place to another. Direct students to end the story with the seed germinating in the place the seed was deposited. Encourage students to include illustrations with their stories.

Some seeds are covered in little hooks. These seeds are called burs. They can easily attach to fur or even to your socks!

▶ How are each of these seeds most likely spread from place to place?

Many animals eat fruit. This helps spread the seeds contained in fruit.

The fruit is eaten by animals, the burs are carried on animal fur, and the pine seeds are carried by wind.

125

Interpret Visuals

Direct students' attention to the photograph of the dandelion. Explain that the head of a dandelion may contain hundreds of seeds. Ask: **Have you ever blown air on the head of a dandelion? What happened?** Some students may indicate that when they blew on the dandelion, the seeds were carried off into the air.

Why can dandelion seeds be carried by wind? Dandelion seeds are very light and have structures like a parachute that enable the seeds to remain afloat in the air as the wind carries them away.

Next, have students examine the seeds shown in the Interactivity exercise. Before completing the activity, encourage students to point out the different structures they observe.

Develop Inquiry Skills

OBSERVE Bring in several types of seeds or pictures of seeds to class. Have students examine the seeds' structures. Students should use their observations to infer how the seeds are most likely dispersed.

Notebook ▶ Summarize Ideas

Instruct students to make a concept map showing three main ways seeds are dispersed, or spread. Tell students that the main concept on their maps should be, "How Seeds Are Spread." There should be three supporting concepts attached to this main concept.

After students complete their maps, compare them to the concept maps they made showing how flowers are pollinated. Discuss with students that plants rely on wind, flowing water, or animals to complete their life cycles. Have them summarize the main ideas of these pages orally or in writing.

English Language Learners

How Apostrophes Show Possession Explain *possession* as belonging: *plant's* stem (the stem belongs to the plant), *animal's* fur (the fur belongs to the animal). Show the placement of the apostrophe when added to plural nouns: *plants'* stems, *animals'* fur. Have students make a rule based on observation. Practice adding apostrophes to these nouns: boys' team; Jamal's shoes; Rita's and Joe's reports; the tree's leaves.

2 Explain (continued)

 Generate Ideas

Remind students that there are differences among plants that reproduce using seeds. Some plants produce seeds surrounded by a fruit, which develops from the flower. Other plants produce seeds in cones. On these two pages, students will learn about a third way that some plants reproduce.

Draw a concept map on the board with two top headings *Seeds* and *Spores*. Draw two lines under the "Seeds" head and label the lines *Flowers* and *Cones* respectively. Have students list some examples of plants that reproduce using flowers and cones. After students read these two pages, have them fill in examples of plants that grow from spores.

Active Reading

Remind students that words signaling a cause include *because* and *if*. Words signaling an effect include *so* and *thus*. Active readers remember what they read because they are alert to signal words.

Develop Science Vocabulary

spore Show students a fern frond with sori (singular *sorus*) on the underside of the frond. Explain that the structures they can see contain hundreds of individual spores. Use a reference book to show students pictures of spores being released from the sporangia.

Other Ways Plants Grow

Pine trees, beans, and sunflowers all grow from seeds. Other plants do not grow from seeds. These plants grow from structures called spores.

Active Reading As you read this page, draw one line under a cause. Draw two lines under its effect.

Have you ever looked at the underside of a fern leaf? You may have seen black or brown spots, like the ones in this picture. These spots are made up of pockets filled with spores.

A **spore** is a cell that can grow into a new plant when the conditions are right. Some plants, such as mosses and ferns, grow from spores instead of seeds. Plants that grow from spores have two distinct forms in their life cycles.

Spores are released when the structures that hold them break open. Wind carries the spores to new places. If a spore lands in a good spot, it will grow into a plant.

Spores are very tiny. They can be carried long distances by the wind.

126

 Differentiation — Leveled Questions

Extra Support

What are two ways plants make new plants? Plants make new plants using seeds; other plants grow from spores.

Challenge

What role does the size of spores have in plant reproduction? Spores are small enough that the wind carries them far to new places. This helps new plants grow in other areas, if conditions are right.

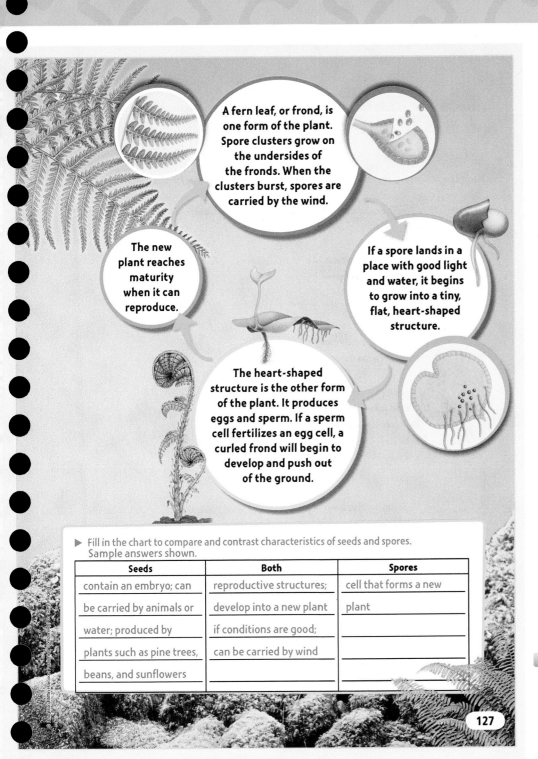

A fern leaf, or frond, is one form of the plant. Spore clusters grow on the undersides of the fronds. When the clusters burst, spores are carried by the wind.

The new plant reaches maturity when it can reproduce.

If a spore lands in a place with good light and water, it begins to grow into a tiny, flat, heart-shaped structure.

The heart-shaped structure is the other form of the plant. It produces eggs and sperm. If a sperm cell fertilizes an egg cell, a curled frond will begin to develop and push out of the ground.

▶ Fill in the chart to compare and contrast characteristics of seeds and spores. Sample answers shown.

Seeds	Both	Spores
contain an embryo; can be carried by animals or water; produced by plants such as pine trees, beans, and sunflowers	reproductive structures; develop into a new plant if conditions are good; can be carried by wind	cell that forms a new plant

127

Interpret Visuals

Review the diagram of the life cycle of a fern with students. Reinforce that in this plant, the sexual and asexual forms look very different.

What happens during the first form in a fern's life cycle? Spore clusters grow on the underside of the fronds. When the clusters burst, spores are carried away by the wind.

How are spores transported from one location to another? by the wind

What happens during the second form in a fern's life cycle? The plant produces eggs and sperm. If a sperm cell fertilizes an egg cell, the curled frond will begin to develop and push out of the ground.

Develop Inquiry Skills

COMPARE **How is the life cycle of a fern similar to the life cycle of a radish?** Both life cycles involve a plant reproducing when a sperm cell fertilizes an egg cell. Both life cycles involve a plant growing from a small structure into a larger plant.

How does the life cycle of a fern differ from the life cycle of a radish? A fern has two different forms. A fern grows from spores instead of seeds.

Notebook Summarize Ideas

Reinforce content by having students study the plant images and life cycle diagrams on these two pages. Invite them to think about the information in the visuals and then summarize the main idea orally or in writing. Encourage students to note at least one cause and effect in their summaries.

123 Math Connection

Multiply Multi-Digit Numbers
Have students solve the following word problem:

Suppose one leaf of a small fern has 8 spore clusters on its underside. If each spore cluster holds 200 spores, how many spores will be released from this one leaf? Write an equation showing your answer.

(1,600 spores will be released from this one leaf; $200 \times 8 = 1,600$)

3 Extend/Evaluate

Sum It Up!

- As students read over each statement, encourage them to underline the most important word or words in the statement. This strategy should help students find the correct image to match up with the statement.

- Students will likely benefit from reviewing illustrations and photographs in the lesson before working on this activity. You may wish to review the images as a class by having volunteers identify what each of the lesson's main images is illustrating.

- If students have trouble completing part of this exercise, have them review the lesson before continuing on to the Brain Check activities.

- Remind students to use the Answer Key to check their answers. Students should revise incorrect responses so they can use the Sum It Up! page to study for tests.

- Provide remediation for those students who need more instruction.

When you're done, use the answer key to check and revise your work.

Read the summary statements. Then match each statement with the correct image.

Summarize

<u>D</u>　1. When a seed germinates, the embryo in the seed grows.

A

<u>B</u>　2. The female organ of the flower is the pistil. The male organ of the flower is the stamen.

B

<u>E</u>　3. In order to make new seeds, flowers or cones need to be pollinated by animals, wind, or water.

C

<u>A</u>　4. Seeds can travel by water or wind, on an animal's body, or inside an animal's body.

D

<u>C</u>　5. Spores are stored in clusters on the underside of fern leaves.

E

128

Answer Key: 1. D 2. B 3. E 4. A 5. C

 **Brain Check** Lesson 2

Name _____

Word Play

1 Use the terms in the box to complete the puzzle.

Word box:
- cone
- cycle
- fertilization*
- flower
- germination*
- maturity*
- pollen
- pollination*
- seed
- spore*

*Key Lesson Vocabulary

Crossword answers:
- 3 Across: FERTILIZATION
- 4 Across: MATURITY
- 5 Across: SEED
- 6 Across: CYCLE
- 8 Across: POLLINATION
- 9 Across: SPORE
- 1 Down: GERMINATION
- 2 Down: POLLEN
- 6 Down: CONE
- 7 Down: FLOWER

Across

3. Which process happens when a sperm joins with an egg?

4. When a plant has grown enough to reproduce, it has reached which stage in its life cycle?

5. What forms when an egg within a pistil is fertilized?

6. All of the stages a plant goes through as it develops is called its life _____ .

8. Which process happens when pollen falls on a flower's pistil?

9. Which cell grows into a new plant, such as a fern or moss, if it lands in a spot with the right conditions?

Down

1. Which process happens when a small root and stem begin to grow out of a seed?

2. Which structures in seed-forming plants contain male sex cells?

6. Which structure do pine trees and spruce trees use to reproduce?

7. Which structure do rose bushes and apple trees use to reproduce?

129

© Houghton Mifflin Harcourt Publishing Company (t) ©Arco Images GmbH/Alamy Images

---

Answer Strategies

Word Play

1. If needed, have students refer back to the lesson page on which each term is defined or discussed.

As a challenge activity, ask students to construct their own crossword puzzles using the same or other relevant terms.

Assessment

Suggested Scoring Guide
You may wish to use this suggested scoring guide for the Brain Check.

Item	Points
1	30 (3 points each)
2	9
3	8
4	9
5	10
6	15
7	10
8	9
Total	100

Lesson Quiz
See Assessment Guide, p. AG 26.

3 Extend/Evaluate (continued)

Answer Strategies

Apply Concepts

2. Refer students to the first two pages of the lesson, where plant life cycles are discussed. Encourage students to use the diagram in their books as a guide to completing their own diagrams.

3. Before students answer this question, discuss how seeds form. Then have them examine the pictures and identify all of the plant structures shown. Tell students to circle the structures that can make seeds.

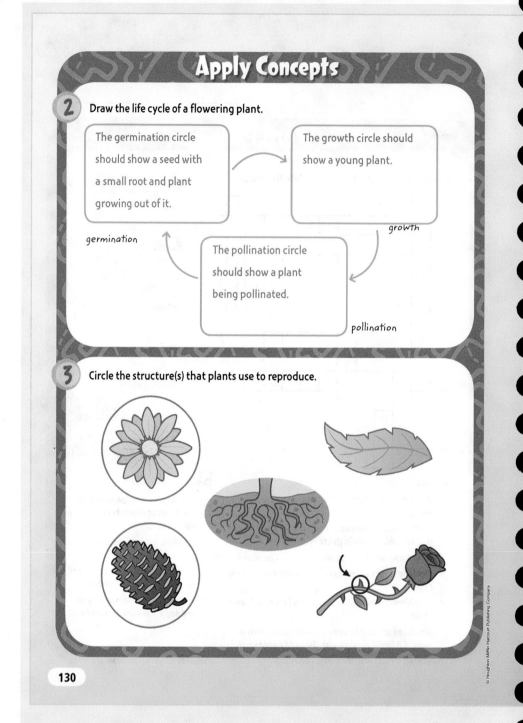

Apply Concepts

2 Draw the life cycle of a flowering plant.

The germination circle should show a seed with a small root and plant growing out of it.

germination

The growth circle should show a young plant.

growth

The pollination circle should show a plant being pollinated.

pollination

3 Circle the structure(s) that plants use to reproduce.

130

Name _____

4 List three ways a seed-forming plant can be pollinated.

1. by animals _____

_____

2. by wind _____

_____

3. by water _____

_____

5 Look at the seed shown here. How do you think this seed is spread? Explain your answer.

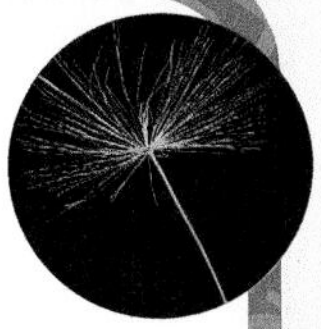

Sample answer: The seed is spread by wind. It has a structure that helps the wind pick up the seed and carry it away.

6 Draw a picture of a flower and label its parts.

Students' pictures should resemble the diagram of the flower shown in the lesson.

131

Answer Strategies

Apply Concepts

4. If students made a concept map about plant pollination, have them refer back to it as they answer this question. Alternatively, have students examine the images on the fifth and sixth pages of this lesson before completing the question.

5. Before having students answer this question, review the three main ways that seeds can be spread. If necessary, have students compare this photo to the photo of the dandelion shown earlier in the lesson.

6. Provide students with a list of the plant parts you expect them to include in their diagrams. You may wish to have them include some or all of the following flower parts: petals, sepals, stamens, anthers, and pistils.

3 Extend/Evaluate (continued)

Answer Strategies

Apply Concepts

7. Refer students back to the pages of the lesson where the terms fertilization and pollination are defined. Have a volunteer read the definitions aloud to the class before students attempt to answer this question.

8. Ask students to first identify what a pollinator does. Make sure students realize that pollinators transfer pollen from male plant parts to female plant parts. Remind students that they can circle more than one picture.

Take It Home!

Encourage students to draw pictures of some of the flowers or cones they saw on their walk. They can then share these pictures with their classmates.

---

7 Explain how pollination is different from fertilization in flowers. (Hint: Which needs to happen first—pollination or fertilization?)

Sample answer: During pollination, pollen lands on a flower's pistil. Sperm from the pollen move into the pistil to where the eggs are. Fertilization happens when a sperm joins with an egg.

8 Circle the pollinator(s) below.

Take It Home! With your family, go on a walk through your neighborhood or a local park. Locate plants that have flowers or cones. Examine the flowers or cones, and describe their structures to your family members.

132

Make Connections

Easy

Math Connection

Chart Plant Growth

Have students grow a young plant from a seed, such as a bean plant or a radish plant. Each day after the seed germinates, students should measure the plant's height. After two weeks, direct students to use the height data to construct a line plot.

Average

Art Connection

Design a Garden

Ask students to design a flower garden. Give students seed catalogs to help them determine which plants to put in their gardens. Guide students to select seeds or plants that are appropriate for the climate in your area. Have students use an online encyclopedia or nonfiction books from the school library to help them choose plants that require similar growing conditions. Students can then produce a drawing or a map of their planned gardens.

Challenging

Social Studies Connection

State Flower and Tree

Have students use an online encyclopedia or nonfiction books to research their state flower or tree. Students should make a poster or short slideshow about the plant. The poster or slideshow should give information about the plant's life cycle, how the plant is pollinated, how its seeds are spread, and how the plant is useful to people.

Challenging

Writing Connection

Plant Poems

Tell students to write a poem about their favorite plant. The poems may be serious or funny. The poems can take the form of ballad, haiku, limerick, sonnet, or free verse. Each poem should include information about the life cycle of the selected plant. Students who wish may read their poems to the class.

Guided Inquiry

FLIPCHART P. 15

⏱ 25 minutes for initial setup; 5 minutes per day for two weeks to make and record observations

👥 pairs

Students should follow the directions on the Flipchart. The accompanying Lesson Inquiry page in the Student Edition provides scaffolding for guided inquiry responses.

How Can We Observe a Plant's Life Cycle?

In this activity, you will compare the germination time of three types of seeds.

Materials
clear plastic bag   1 bean seed
masking tape   1 gourd seed
marker   1 sunflower seed
2 paper towels   water

1. Place a strip of tape across the bag about 6 cm from the bottom. Use the marker to label the tape from left to right with letters to represent each type of seed: B (bean), G (gourd), S (sunflower).

2. Wet two paper towels. Squeeze out the excess water, and fold the paper towels in half.

3. Stack the wet paper towels, and spread them in the bag.

4. Place each seed between the side of the bag and the paper towel. The seed should be next to its label and visible through the bag. Flatten the bag to remove all of the air, and seal the bag.

5. Tape the bag to a window. Check the paper towels once a day. Wet the paper towels as needed so they do not dry out.

6. Record observations of the germinating seeds every day until all three seeds have germinated.

15

Inquiry Skills Focus Observe, Draw Conclusions

Objectives

- Compare the rate of germination of different types of seeds.
- Observe a developing plant embryo.

Prep and Planning Tips

See the Planning for Inquiry page for more information.

- Find a location where the seeds can be placed and receive natural light and not be disturbed. Be sure that students understand the importance of recording observations for this activity.
- Have extra paper towels available for cleanup.
- Make one completed bag as a sample to show students how their bags should look when finished.

Expected Results

Students will observe that seeds from different plants germinate at different rates. Have students include additional observations for the seeds that germinate the fastest, such as the direction the roots and shoots grow and the colors of the different plant parts.

1 Engage/Explore

Attention Grabber

Display a potted plant or show a picture of one. Ask students to list the parts of the plant they can see (stem, leaves, perhaps flowers) and those they cannot see (roots). Refer students to the radish and lima bean life cycles in the lesson "How Do Plants Reproduce?" Ask: **Could we see what was happening to the seed as it germinated?** Discuss that this part of a plant's life cycle generally takes place underground. Tell students that in this investigation, they will get to see what happens underground.

Preview Activity

Before beginning the investigation, have students review the directions on the Inquiry Flipchart and the accompanying Student Edition response page. Then, have them complete the response page as they follow directions on the Flipchart.

Inquiry Flipchart page 15

Name _____

Essential Question

How Can We Observe a Plant's Life Cycle?

Set a Purpose
What will you learn from this experiment?
Sample answer: Seeds from different

plants have different germination times.

Think About the Procedure
What are the conditions that you will control, or try to make the same, for each seed?
Sample answer: the amount of light and

water each seed receives

Why is it important that each seed is exposed to the same conditions?
Sample answer: It is important to keep

the conditions the same because different

conditions could affect how quickly the

seeds germinate. If one seed has more

water or light than another seed, it may

germinate faster.

Record Your Data
In the space below, draw a table to record your observations.

Answers will vary based on the types of seeds and conditions selected. Check Students' tables for accuracy.

133

© Houghton Mifflin Harcourt Publishing Company

Go Digital
A virtual lab experience is available with the Online Resources for this program.

How Can We Observe a Plant's Life Cycle?

---

1 Engage/Explore (continued)

Guide the Investigation

Develop Inquiry Skills

IDENTIFY AND CONTROL VARIABLES
Identify which variables will remain the same in the activity. Variables that will remain the same include the size of the bag, the amount of water the seed and seedlings receive, the amount of light the seedlings receive, and the temperature.

What variable did you manipulate, or change, in this activity? the type of seed

What variable are you measuring? the rate at which each seed germinates

OBSERVE **What observations will you make about the seed and seedling as the activity continues?** I will observe the changes in the seed, such as when the root emerges and when the shoot emerges. I will observe changes in the height of the plant and the number of leaves produced.

GATHER AND RECORD DATA Discuss with students how they will construct a data table and then record their results.

Students' tables should contain four columns. The first column should identify the day on which they are making observations, and the remaining three columns should represent each seed type used in the experiment. Students should include rows for at least 12 days of observations. Students should record information about when the root emerges, when the shoot emerges, the growth of the roots and shoot, and the appearance and growth of leaves.

2 Explain

Develop Inquiry Skills

DRAW CONCLUSIONS Students should review their observations to determine their responses. Remind students that they have observed the first few stages of a plant life cycle and so should be able to identify which stages will follow.

ANALYZE AND EXTEND Discuss students' responses to the items.

1. Encourage students to think about the conditions that encourage seed germination and plant growth.

2. If necessary, review experimental design in Unit 1. Students should identify controlled and manipulated variables and how they will measure outcomes.

3. Remind students that plants need light to make food. Although the seeds germinate in the dark, continued growth is dependent on the presence of light.

4. Direct students to identify conditions that varied between the two sets of seeds. These variations should help explain any differences that students observed.

3 Extend/Evaluate

5. Accept all reasonable answers. Students might ask questions about factors needed for germination or how germination rates affect when farmers plant seeds.

Assessment

Lesson Quiz
See Assessment Guide, p. AG 27

Draw Conclusions

Which seed germinated the fastest? Which germinated the slowest?

Answers will vary based on the seeds used. Bean seeds may germinate faster than other types of seeds.

What would you expect to happen if you planted the germinated seeds in soil?

The seeds would continue to grow. They would grow roots, stems, and leaves. They would grow into mature plants.

Analyze and Extend

1. **Which factors do you think determine how fast a seed germinates?**

Sample answer: the type of plant it is, the amount of light or water the seed receives, the temperature of the soil

2. **Explain how you could test the effect of one of the factors you listed in Question 1 on the germination rate of seeds.**

Sample answer: I would take three seeds from the same type of plant. I would set up the experiment the same way as the one I just did except I would put one seed in the dark, one in low light conditions, and one in bright light. I would observe the germination rates of the three seeds.

134

3. **How do you think the plant would look if it was kept in the dark? How do you think the plant would look if it was kept in low light?**

If the plant was kept in the dark, I think it would not grow. If the plant was kept in low light conditions, I think it would be very small.

4. **Compare with a classmate the number of days it took for your seeds to germinate. Account for any differences and explain what you think happened.**

Sample answer: My gourd seed took 2 days longer to germinate than my classmate's, and my sunflower seed took 3 days longer to germinate. My seed may have taken longer to germinate because it got less sunlight.

5. **What other questions do you have about how seeds germinate?**

Sample answer: How closely can seeds be planted together and still germinate? How much water do plants need to germinate?

Differentiated Inquiry

Easy

Graph Plant Growth

- Encourage students to repeat the seed germination activity at home, using the type of seed that germinated fastest.
- From the time that the seed germinates, students should measure and record the height of the young plant each day.
- Students should then graph the data to show the overall rate of growth.

Average

Measure Germination Rates

- Encourage students to conduct the investigation that they described in the answer to Analyze and Extend question 2.
- Suggest that students work with the type of seed that germinated the fastest in the activity.
- Encourage students to identify which variables will remain constant and which variable they will manipulate. Students should make and record observations about the effect of the manipulated variable on the rate of germination.
- Ask students to summarize their experiment in the form of a written report.

Average

Graph Germination Rates

- Have students repeat the seed germination activity using three more bags. Each bag should contain the three different seeds using the same materials and procedure as before. Students should observe the seeds in each bag every day.
- Students can record in a data table when each seed germinates, then calculate the average germination time for each seed.
- Ask students to make a bar graph showing the average germination time, in days, for each type of seed, and compare this to their original results.

Challenging

Form and Test a Hypothesis

- Encourage students to research information about how the depth at which a seed is planted in soil can affect whether it germinates successfully.
- Have students form a hypothesis about how the depth at which a seed is planted affects its germination. Students should form their hypothesis about the type of seed that germinated fastest in the seed germination activity.
- Encourage students to design an experiment to test their hypothesis. Students should then carry out the experiment.
- Ask students to summarize their experiment in the form of an oral report supported with data tables and sketches.

Options for Inquiry

FLIPCHART P. 16

Students can conduct these optional investigations at any time before, during, or in response to the lesson in the Student Edition.

Breeding Brine Shrimp

My Kit

A Have you ever watched an animal go through its life cycle? In this activity, you'll get to see an animal hatch and become an adult in just a few weeks!

Materials
brine shrimp kit
hand lens

Follow This Procedure

1. Follow the instructions on your brine shrimp kit.

2. As your brine shrimp grow, examine them with a hand lens. Record how they change.

3. After two weeks, the brine shrimp should reach adult form. Draw what the adults look like.

Analyze Your Results

4. Use your observations to describe the life cycle of a brine shrimp.

Growing Up Fast

© Great things come in small packages

Can Waxworms Stand the Heat?

B The life cycles of animals can be affected by their environment. Develop a plan to investigate how temperature can affect the life cycle of a wax moth. Start by making a list of supplies you will need. For example, you'll need to obtain wax moth caterpillars (waxworms). You'll also need food and a container to house your caterpillars.

Science Notebook

Here's how one student started her investigation.

Hypothesis: Waxworms will develop fastest at room temperature.

Materials: waxworms, waxworm food, jars with holes in the lids, forceps, lamp

Steps:

1. Place several waxworms in each jar.

2. Put one jar on a counter, one jar in the refrigerator, and one jar under a lamp.

3. Each day, add an equal amount of food to the jars.

4. Observe the jars for several days.

16

Directed Inquiry

A Breeding Brine Shrimp

🕐 30–45 minutes
👥 small groups

Prep and Planning Tips

You may wish to only use a single brine shrimp kit for the whole class and have students all observe the same kit.

When brine shrimp first hatch, they are very small (about the size of a period), so students will need hand lenses to observe them.

Remind students to continue to feed the shrimp throughout the investigation. You may wish to keep the shrimp as "pets" once the investigation is complete.

Expected Results

Results will depend on the species of brine shrimp used. Many brine shrimp can complete their entire life cycle in four weeks or less.

Independent Inquiry

B Can Waxworms Stand the Heat?

🕐 30–45 minutes
👥 small groups

Prep and Planning Tips

See the Planning for Inquiry page for more information. Before students write their investigation plans, remind them to handle the worms safely and humanely at all times.

Science Notebook

Students can use the Science Notebook as a model for designing their own investigation. Encourage students to brainstorm different ways they could test how temperature affects waxworm development. Waxworms develop fastest at temperatures from 28–34 °C (82–93 °F). Therefore, students should discover that the waxworms kept under a lamp (or at room temperature) develop faster than those kept in a refrigerator.

Lesson 4

Essential Question

How Do Animals Reproduce?

Engage Your Brain!

Find the answer to the following question in this lesson and record it here.

How do you think these young egrets will change as they grow up?

Sample answer: They will grow larger, lose their fluffy down, and get a set of adult feathers.

Active Reading

Lesson Vocabulary

List the terms. As you learn about each one, make notes in the Interactive Glossary.

complete metamorphosis

incomplete metamorphosis

nymph

Sequence

Many ideas in this lesson are in a sequence, or order, that describes the steps in a process. Active readers stay focused on sequence when they go from one stage or step in a process to another.

135

Go Digital

An interactive digital lesson is available in Online Resources. It is suitable for individuals, small groups, or may be projected or used on an interactive white board.

Objectives

- Understand that some animals are born live, whereas other animals hatch from eggs.
- Understand that some animals go through metamorphosis as part of their life cycle.
- Compare and contrast complete metamorphosis and incomplete metamorphosis, and provide examples of animals that undergo each type.

Engage Your Brain!

Have students brainstorm answers to the question, "How do you think these young egrets will change as they grow up?" Suggest that they think about how animals they are familiar with change as the animals get older.

Remind them to record their final answer to the question when they find it on the second page of this lesson.

Active Reading   Annotations

Remind students that active readers "make texts their own" by annotating them with notes and marks that help with comprehension. Encourage students to use pencil, not pen, to make annotations and to feel free to change their annotations as they read. The goal of annotation is to help students remember what they have read.

Vocabulary and Interactive Glossary

Remind students to find and list the yellow highlighted terms from the lesson. As they proceed through the lesson and learn about the terms, they should add notes, drawings, or sentences in the extra spaces provided in the Interactive Glossary.

2 Explain

Notebook ▶ Generate Ideas

Remind students that a life cycle of an organism is all the changes that occur from the beginning of one generation to the beginning of another. Ask students how they think the life cycle of an animal would compare to that of a plant.

Active Reading

Explain that order is important in describing how something changes or how something is done. When order is important, active readers write numbers to help them remember the order in which things take place.

Interpret Visuals

Have students examine the diagram on this page.

For a baby bird, what is the first part of its life cycle? hatching from an egg

According to the diagram, what is the final stage of its life cycle? adulthood

How do you think a bird's life cycle differs from the life cycle of a dog? Unlike birds, dogs do not hatch from eggs.

How do you think a bird's life cycle is similar to the life cycle of a dog? Students will likely know that both birds and dogs grow and develop into adults and produce young.

Life in Full Circle

Like plants, animals have life cycles. Animals are born and then begin to grow up. When animals become adults, they may have young of their own. In this way, life continues to renew itself.

Active Reading As you read the next page, underline the description of each stage of an animal's life, and number the stages in the correct order.

When a bird reaches adulthood, it mates with another bird.

Over time, the bird grows. Soon it can live on its own.

After the eggs hatch, the parents feed the young birds.

After mating, a female bird lays eggs. Birds hatch from eggs.

136

Writing Connection

Write a Description Have students generate questions about the life cycles of various animals. Provide them with a list of references, such as websites, an online encyclopedia, or nonfiction books from the school library that they can use to answer their questions. After students do their research, have them write a short paragraph about each animal life cycle that they have researched. Tell students to make sure their paragraphs include answers to their questions.

Matching Game

Use the terms on the right to identify the correct life stages in each series of pictures.

Adult
Newborn
Youth

youth

adult

newborn

youth

newborn

adult

Most animals reproduce sexually. During sexual reproduction, sperm from a male joins an egg from a female. The fertilized egg can then develop into a new animal.

In some animals, such as many kinds of fish, eggs are fertilized outside of the female's body. In other animals, such as birds, eggs are fertilized inside the female's body. After the eggs are fertilized, birds lay the eggs. Bird parents then protect the

eggs until they have hatched.

After the young are born, they begin to grow and change. Over time, newborns develop into youths. Youths continue to develop until they grow into adults. Adult animals mate with one another to produce offspring. An animal's life cycle ends when the animal dies. However, the animal's offspring will likely have offspring of their own. In this way, the life cycle repeats again and again.

137

© Houghton Mifflin Harcourt Publishing Company (tl) ©Peter Arnold, Inc./Alamy; (tc) ©All Canada Photos/Alamy; (tr) ©Corbis; (cl) ©Comstock/Getty Images; (b) ©Mira/Alamy; (cr) ©Corbis

Math Connection

Make a Graph Tell students that a life cycle is not the same thing as a life span. A life span describes how long a plant or animal lives. Humans, for example, have an average life span of about 78 years. Also give students the following life-span information:

hummingbird—4 years;
tortoise—150 years;
mouse—2 years;
sugar maple tree—300 years.

Have students use the information to make a bar graph comparing the life spans of these animals.

⁄⁄ Misconception Alert ⁄⁄

Students may think that the animals inside eggs are fully formed from the start and are just waiting to hatch. Explain that eggs contain a yolk that nourishes a growing embryo after the egg is laid. A baby bird feeds off the yolk inside the egg as it grows and develops inside the egg. If possible, show students pictures showing the development of a baby bird inside the eggshell.

Develop Science Concepts

Discuss the different rates at which animals grow. Ask students to share any experiences they may have had watching an animal, such as a kitten or puppy, grow.

How is a young animal different from an adult? Students may say that young animals are smaller than adults and have colorings or structures that are different than adults. Other animals (such as crocodiles) look like miniature adults.

When is an animal considered an adult? Students may say that an animal is an adult when it is fully grown, when it can take care of itself without help from one or more parents, or when it is able to have offspring.

After answering these questions, have students do the Matching Game Interactivity on this page.

Notebook ▶ Summarize Ideas

Instruct students to make a life cycle drawing of an animal such as a turtle, cat, or horse. Have students compare and contrast their drawings. Ask if their ideas about the sequence of events in animal life cycles have changed since they read this section. Have them summarize the main idea orally or in writing.

2 Explain (continued)

Notebook ▶ Generate Ideas

Have students scan over the images on this page and the next. Ask students to point out the animals that they think get the most care from their parents. Have students explain their choices.

Active Reading

Remind students that authors may use examples to illustrate a concept, such as a specific animal to exemplify a category of animals. Active readers focus on these examples as a way to deepen their understanding of the concept and remember the most important characteristics.

Develop Inquiry Skills

OBSERVE Have students examine the picture of the hatching alligators and read the caption. **What visual clues in the picture tell you that an alligator's eggs are soft and leathery instead of hard and brittle?** Most students will be able to observe that the egg doesn't crack, it tears. Students may also observe that the egg seems flexible, unlike the eggs of birds.

Develop Science Concepts

Animals that feed their young milk are called mammals. What other animals do you know that feed their young milk? Sample answers: cows, dogs, goats, humans, mice, lions, and so on.

Bringing Up Baby

Like birds, many other animals hatch out of eggs. For example, most fish, reptiles, and spiders hatch from eggs. Other animals give birth to live young. Dogs, horses, and mice are all born this way.

Active Reading As you read these pages, draw a star next to the names of animals that hatch from eggs and a check mark next to the names of animals that are born live.

What happens after an animal is born? Some animals, such as turtles, are on their own as soon as they hatch from their eggs. Their parents do not help them. Other animals, such as penguins, give their young a great deal of care. They keep their young warm and fed until the young grow strong enough to take care of themselves.

Animals such as deer, bears, and rabbits take care of their young by feeding them milk. These animals may stay with their parents for months or years until they are able to live on their own.

Birds' eggshells are hard, but alligators and other reptiles have soft, leathery shells.

138

👥 Differentiation — Leveled Questions

Extra Support

Which animals spend more time caring for their young: turtles or kangaroos? Explain. Kangaroos spend more time caring for their young. A joey stays in its mother's pouch after it is born. Turtles are on their own when they hatch.

Challenge

A mother penguin lays only one or two eggs; a mother sea turtle may lay 100 eggs or more. Why do you think a sea turtle lays so many more eggs? A sea turtle doesn't take care of the young that hatch, while a penguin does.

▶ What are young kangaroos called?

joeys

Cats give birth to live young.
Young cats drink their mother's milk.

Do the Math!
Solve a Problem

Raccoons usually give birth to 3 to 5 young at one time. Raccoons give birth only once a year. Suppose a female raccoon lives 10 years. She is able to give birth for 9 of those years. How many offspring will she have?

She will have between 27 and 45

offspring.

When kangaroos are born, they are about the size of a dime. They then develop in their mother's pouch.

139

Do the Math!
Solve a Problem

Students may struggle with this word problem because there is a large amount of information provided. Assist struggling students step by step through the word problem by asking the following questions:

In the problem, for how many years does it say the raccoon is able to give birth?
9 years

How many times a year can she give birth?
once a year

How many offspring does she have every time she gives birth? 3 to 5

Should you use multiplication or division to solve this word problem? multiplication

Tell students that their answer will be a range instead of a single number. Ask: **What numbers will you multiply?** the number of babies she is able to have every time she gives birth by the number of times she will give birth

Summarize Ideas

Have students write sentences comparing and contrasting the life cycles of the following groups of organisms: turtles and penguins, cats and kangaroos, and bluebirds and deer. Afterwards, have students share their sentences with their classmates. Have them summarize the main idea orally or in writing. Be sure to correct any factual errors students have in their sentences.

English Language Learners

Understand Irregular Plurals
Remind students that most plurals are formed by adding a final *s* or *es*: dog/dogs, fox/foxes, book/books, class/classes. Some plurals, known as *irregular* plurals, change their spelling: mouse/mice, child/children, woman/mice, child/children, woman/ women, life/lives. Finally, some words are spelled the same for both singular and plural forms: deer, fish, shrimp. Have students write plurals for the following words: *man, girl, school, box, lunch, goose, foot, leaf,* and *dress.*

2 Explain (continued)

Notebook ▸ Generate Ideas

Have students share stories about when they or their younger brothers or sisters were younger. Then have students discuss how they or their siblings have changed since then.

Active Reading

Remind students that images and captions add information to the main text on the page. Active readers pause their reading to review the images and captions to determine how the information they provide deepens what is provided in the running text.

Interpret Visuals

Have students review the stages of the human life cycle shown on this page and the next page. **Which stage of the human life cycle are you in now?** childhood

Ask students to name people they know (family, friends, or celebrities) and to identify the life cycle stage they are in currently.

① When babies are born, they drink their mother's milk. They have no teeth, and they are not able to walk on their own.

② Babies grow into toddlers. Toddlers learn how to walk. They also start learning how to speak. Humans get their first set of teeth when they are toddlers.

Growing Up

Just like other animals, humans go through stages of development. After a human egg is fertilized, it grows inside the mother. After nine months, the baby is born. It takes many years for a human baby to grow into an adult. Study these pages to see all of the growth stages humans go through.

Active Reading Put a star next to the life stage that you are currently in.

③ As a child develops, the first set of teeth is replaced by permanent teeth. The child grows and develops many physical and mental skills.

140

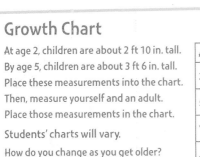

Growth Chart

At age 2, children are about 2 ft 10 in. tall.
By age 5, children are about 3 ft 6 in. tall.
Place these measurements into the chart.
Then, measure yourself and an adult.
Place those measurements in the chart.

Students' charts will vary.

How do you change as you get older?
You grow taller as you get older.

Age	Height
2	2 ft 10 in.
5	3 ft 6 in.
You	
Adult	

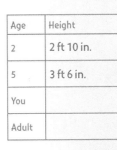

4 During the teenage years, boys and girls start looking more like adults. For example, boys start growing facial hair.

6 As an adult ages, they lose some of their physical abilities. The body changes in other ways, as well. For example, the hair turns gray.

5 During adulthood, people reach maturity. Often, adults marry and have children of their own.

141

Develop Science Concepts

What are some similarities and differences between the stages of human adulthood and childhood? Students may say that the body is still growing in the childhood stage, while in the adult stage, the body is fully grown and developed. In both stages, the body plan is basically the same.

For the Growth Chart interactivity, most students will find that they are taller than the five-year-old, but shorter than the adult.

As an extension, you may want to challenge students to compare the body proportions of people at different stages of life. Have students measure the height of a person's head, as well as their total height (you can use photographs for this activity). Show students how to use calculators to find the ratio between head height and total height (divide the head height by the total height). Then have students see how this ratio changes as a person gets older. Students should note that while a person's body height changes a great deal from childhood to adulthood, the size of their head only grows a small amount. Thus, children have larger heads in proportion to their bodies than adults do.

Notebook Summarize Ideas

Instruct students to make a chart that summarizes the stages of the human life cycle. The first column of the chart should list the name of the life cycle stage. The second column of the chart should have a description of that stage.

2 Explain (continued)

Notebook ▶ **Generate Ideas**

Have students examine the two life cycles shown on this page and the next. Then have students compare these life cycles to the life cycle of a bird shown on the first page of this lesson. Ask students to compare and contrast the features of all three of the illustrated life cycles.

Active Reading

Explain that a vocabulary word may be highlighted in a color. Active readers pay attention to highlighted words because their meaning is given in the same sentence or the next sentence.

Interpret Visuals

How many stages of development do butterflies and moths go through? four

What are the stages? The stages are egg, larva (caterpillar), pupa, and adult.

Develop Inquiry Skills

COMPARE **How does the life cycle of a butterfly compare to that of a grasshopper?** The butterfly has four main stages in its life cycle, while the grasshopper only has three. The butterfly stages are egg, larva, pupa, and adult. The grasshopper stages are egg, nymph, and adult.

My, How You've Changed!

A young frog, or tadpole, has a long tail and no legs. As it grows, its tail becomes shorter, and it begins to grow legs. An adult frog has no tail, but has legs. The young go through a series of changes known as *metamorphosis.*

▶ Write a caption for this photo of a butterfly breaking out of its chrysalis.
Sample answer: When a chrysalis opens, a fully-formed adult butterfly emerges.

Active Reading As you read the next page, underline the sentences that contain vocabulary terms.

Complete Metamorphosis

Egg

Butterflies go through complete metamorphosis. The larva of a butterfly is also called a caterpillar. The caterpillar grows into a pupa. Inside a chrysalis [KRIS•uh•lis], the pupa becomes an adult butterfly.

Larva

Adult

Pupa

142

Differentiation — Leveled Questions

Extra Support
What is the larval stage of a frog called? tadpole

Challenge
When aphids hatch, they look like tiny, wingless adults. What type of metamorphosis is this? How do you know? Aphids undergo incomplete metamorphosis because they resemble adults when they hatch as nymphs.

Incomplete Metamorphosis

Adult

Grasshoppers will molt five times before they reach the adult stage.

Grasshoppers go through incomplete metamorphosis. Young grasshoppers hatch as nymphs. A nymph grows and molts.

Nymph

Eggs

The female grasshopper lays eggs in the soil.

In many animals, the young look similar to the adults. But in other animals, the young look very different. In **complete metamorphosis** [met•uh•MAWR•fuh•sis], an animal goes through four different stages in its life cycle. The egg hatches into a *larva*. The larvae [LAR•vee] of many insects look like worms. A larva develops into a *pupa* [PYOO•puh]. The pupa of a moth is enclosed in a cocoon. While in the cocoon, the pupa develops into an adult moth. The adult splits its cocoon and flies out.

Some insects, such as dragonflies and termites, go through a different series of changes. In **incomplete metamorphosis**, an animal goes through three different stages in its life cycle. First, the animal hatches from the egg as a **nymph** [NIMF]. Nymphs look like tiny adults, but they don't have wings. As the nymph grows larger, it molts. Molting happens when an insect sheds its hard outer skeleton. After several moltings, the insect, which now has wings, reaches its adult stage.

143

Develop Science Vocabulary

complete metamorphosis Tell students that the word *metamorphosis* comes from the Greek words *meta*, which means "change," and *morph*, which means "form." In complete metamorphosis, the change is major. The adult form of the animal looks very different than the juvenile form.

incomplete metamorphosis **What is the difference between complete metamorphosis and incomplete metamorphosis?** During complete metamorphosis, the organism undergoes a complete change in body shape and characteristics at each stage of development. During incomplete metamorphosis, the organism does not undergo a complete change in body shape, but increases in size as it matures.

nymph Have students look at the image of the nymph on this page. **How is the nymph different from the adult grasshopper?** It is smaller, and its wings have not developed. **How is the nymph similar to the adult grasshopper?** It has basically the same shape or form.

Notebook ► Summarize Ideas

Draw a Venn diagram on the board. Write "complete metamorphosis" over one circle, "incomplete metamorphosis" over the second circle, and "both" over the area where the two circles intersect. Have students help you complete the Venn diagram. Have them summarize the differences and similarities between complete and incomplete metamorphosis orally or in writing.

English Language Learners

Understand that *ph* Makes the /f/ Sound Write the following words on the board, calling students' attention to the *ph* in each:

telephone, elephant, autograph, biography, nymph, metamorphosis

Have students practice saying the words out loud and listening to the sound the letters *ph* make. Explain that some words are not pronounced as they appear.

2 Explain (continued)

 Generate Ideas

Have students examine the pictures of the sea turtles on this page and the next. Encourage students to share what they have already learned about the life cycles of turtles.

Develop Science Concepts

Have students find out whether there are any endangered animals living in their area. If so, instruct students to find out more about the life cycles of these endangered animals. Then lead a discussion about how people could use information about the animals' life cycles to help increase the animal populations.

Develop Inquiry Skills

DRAW CONCLUSIONS **How might a captive-rearing program help more sea turtles survive?** Rearing the sea turtles in captivity keeps the sea turtles eggs safe from hunting, beach erosion, pollution, and predation until the turtles hatch and are ready to be released into the ocean.

Why It Matters

Saving the Sea Turtles

Some kinds of animals are endangered. That means there are not many of them left. Scientists study the life cycles of endangered animals to try to save them and help them increase their numbers.

Sea turtles are one example of an endangered animal. Hunting, pollution, and beach erosion have caused the number of sea turtles to go down. To help sea turtles, people have learned about the sea turtle's life cycle. They have used what they learned to rear sea turtles. The turtles are then released into the wild. Over time, scientists hope this will help increase the number of sea turtles.

To rear sea turtles, eggs are collected.

144

Interpret Visuals

According to the graph, about how many leatherback sea turtles were there in the eastern Pacific Ocean in 1989? about 1,500 leatherback sea turtles

According to the graph, about how many leatherback sea turtles were there in the eastern Pacific Ocean in 2009? 30 leatherback sea turtles

What are some things that have caused a decline in the number of leatherback sea turtles? hunting, pollution, and beach erosion

Mention other causes for the decline of the Pacific leatherback population, including loss of nesting habitat, confusion among hatchlings caused by beachfront lights, boating accidents, and predation of nests by animals.

If captive-rearing programs are successful, how do you think the graph will look if it is extended for another 20 years? As the sea turtle population gradually increases, the bars of the graph will get taller.

Why do you think the number of leatherback sea turtles was so low in the eastern Pacific Ocean in 2009? There is a pattern in the numbers. Some years there are fewer than the previous year, but within a year or two, the number of sea turtles goes up.

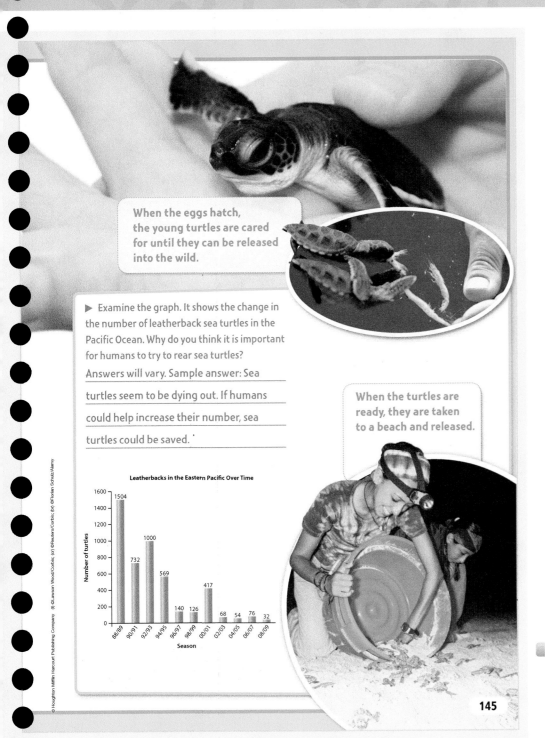

When the eggs hatch, the young turtles are cared for until they can be released into the wild.

▶ Examine the graph. It shows the change in the number of leatherback sea turtles in the Pacific Ocean. Why do you think it is important for humans to try to rear sea turtles?
Answers will vary. Sample answer: Sea turtles seem to be dying out. If humans could help increase their number, sea turtles could be saved.

When the turtles are ready, they are taken to a beach and released.

Leatherbacks in the Eastern Pacific Over Time

145

Notebook ▶ Summarize Ideas

Ask students to write a brief paragraph about things that they think people could do to help save the sea turtles. Have them summarize the main idea orally or in writing.

3 Extend/Evaluate

Sum It Up!

- Ask students to identify how the incorrect word in each statement is indicated. (It is shown in blue.) Explain to students that in order to make the statement correct, they need to replace the blue word or words with another word or words.

- Students will likely benefit from reviewing this lesson's vocabulary before working on this activity. You may wish to review the vocabulary as a class by having volunteers find the definition of each vocabulary term in their text and reading the definition aloud.

- If students have trouble completing part of this exercise, have them review the lesson before continuing on to the Brain Check activities.

- Remind students to use the Answer Key to check their answers. Students should revise incorrect responses so they can use the Sum It Up! page to study for tests.

- Provide remediation for those students who need more instruction.

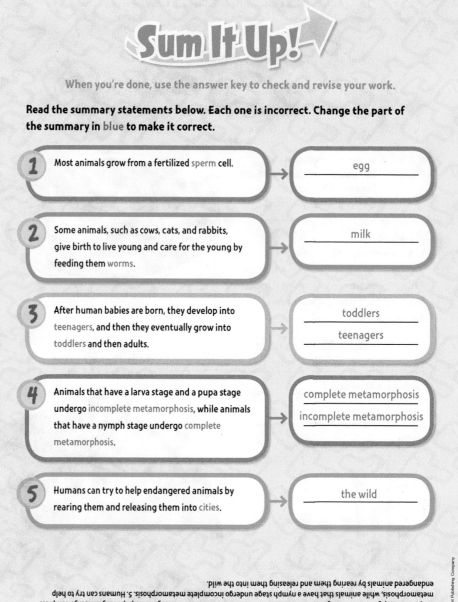

Sum It Up!

When you're done, use the answer key to check and revise your work.

Read the summary statements below. Each one is incorrect. Change the part of the summary in blue to make it correct.

1. Most animals grow from a fertilized sperm cell.
→ _____egg_____

2. Some animals, such as cows, cats, and rabbits, give birth to live young and care for the young by feeding them worms.
→ _____milk_____

3. After human babies are born, they develop into teenagers, and then they eventually grow into toddlers and then adults.
→ _____toddlers_____
_____teenagers_____

4. Animals that have a larva stage and a pupa stage undergo incomplete metamorphosis, while animals that have a nymph stage undergo complete metamorphosis.
→ _____complete metamorphosis_____
_____incomplete metamorphosis_____

5. Humans can try to help endangered animals by rearing them and releasing them into cities.
→ _____the wild_____

Answer Key: 1. Most animals grow from a fertilized egg cell. **2.** Animals such as cows, cats, and rabbits give birth to live young and care for the young by feeding them milk. **3.** After human babies are born, they develop into toddlers, and then they eventually grow into teenagers and then adults. **4.** Animals that have a larva stage and a pupa stage undergo complete metamorphosis, while animals that have a nymph stage undergo incomplete metamorphosis. **5.** Humans can try to help endangered animals by rearing them and releasing them into the wild.

146

Brain Check

Name _____

Word Play

1 Match the words to the correct picture.

E 1. metamorphosis

F 2. incomplete metamorphosis

A 3. larva

C 4. nymph

B 5. molt

D 6. pupa

Apply Concepts

2 Circle the animals that hatch from eggs.

147

Answer Strategies

Word Play

1. If necessary, have students refer back to the pages on which each term is defined or discussed. As a challenge activity, ask students to construct their own match-up game using the same and/or other relevant terms.

Apply Concepts

2. Go over each image with students and have them identify the illustrated animal. If students have difficulty with the exercise, have them go through the first four pages of the lesson and find animals similar to the animals illustrated here.

Assessment

Suggested Scoring Guide

You may wish to use this suggested scoring guide for the Brain Check.

Item	Points
1	20
2	20
3	20
4	20
5	20
Total	100

Lesson Quiz

See Assessment Guide, p. AG 84.

© Houghton Mifflin Harcourt Publishing Company

3 Extend/Evaluate (continued)

Answer Strategies

Apply Concepts

3. Before students answer this question, have them review the life cycle of the blue jay shown on the first page of this lesson. Ask: **What do blue jays and eagles have in common?** They are both birds.

4. If students struggle filling out the Venn diagram, have them review the illustrations of complete and incomplete metamorphosis in the lesson. Tell them to count the number of stages in each process.

5. Have students identify the animals shown in each illustration. If necessary, allow students to flip through the lesson and find information about the life cycles of each of these animals. Make sure students know that only one animal should be circled.

 Take It Home!

Students may enjoy comparing their own current photographs to those of their family members at the same age. Encourage students to compare and contrast how they look with their parents. This will prepare students for the next lesson.

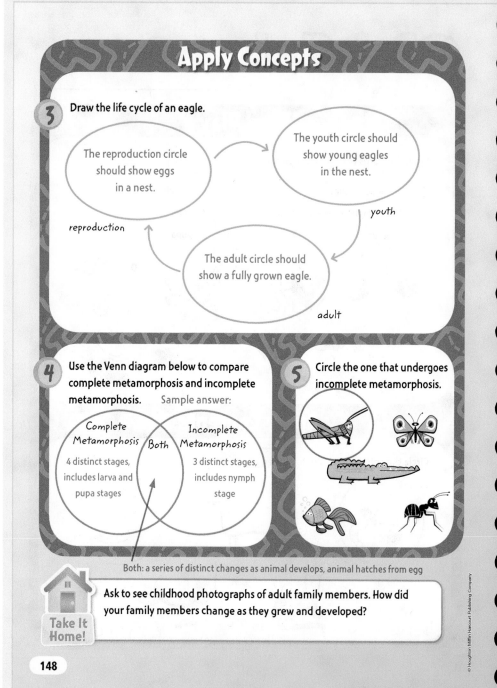

Apply Concepts

3 Draw the life cycle of an eagle.

The reproduction circle should show eggs in a nest.

reproduction

The youth circle should show young eagles in the nest.

youth

The adult circle should show a fully grown eagle.

adult

4 Use the Venn diagram below to compare complete metamorphosis and incomplete metamorphosis.   Sample answer:

Complete Metamorphosis — 4 distinct stages, includes larva and pupa stages

Both

Incomplete Metamorphosis — 3 distinct stages, includes nymph stage

Both: a series of distinct changes as animal develops, animal hatches from egg

5 Circle the one that undergoes incomplete metamorphosis.

Take It Home! Ask to see childhood photographs of adult family members. How did your family members change as they grew and developed?

148

Make Connections

Easy

Art Connection

Draw a Self Portrait

Ask students to draw a self portrait of themselves of what they think they'll look like when they are 40 years old. Underneath the portrait, students may write a brief description of what they think their life will be like when they are 40.

Average

Math Connection

Solve a Word Problem

Have students solve this word problem:
Amber was 90 cm tall when she was 2 years old. By the time Amber reached 12 years old, she was 170 cm tall. Assuming that Amber grew at the same rate each year, how many centimeters per year did Amber grow between the ages of 2 and 12? (170 cm − 90 cm = 80 cm ÷ 10 yr = 8 cm/yr)

Challenging

Health Connection

Make Life-Stage Care Manuals

People at different life stages have different needs. For example, babies should not eat the same foods as adolescents, and children need more sleep than adults. Have students choose a life stage and write a "care manual" that gives advice about how to stay healthy in that stage of life.

Challenging

Writing Connection

Write a Biography

Instruct students to write a short biography of a famous person, such as a former U.S. president. The biography should include such information as when the person was born, what their childhood was like, major accomplishments, and information about any children they might have had.

Careers in Science

Objectives

- Describe the role of scientists.
- Describe that scientists come from all backgrounds.
- Determine the role of technology in the work of scientists.

Notebook ▸ Generate Ideas

Tell students that on this page, they will learn about the study of animal behavior. Before reading the page, have students brainstorm different ways they could study how animals behave. As students think about this, have them also consider what technologies might be used in the study of animal behavior.

Background

- Animal behaviorists may study what causes animals to behave a certain way or how the behavior develops in the animal's lifetime. Some study the behaviors in one kind of animal, while others study one type of behavior in many kinds of animals.

- Animal behaviorists may use cameras and video recorders to observe their subject. They may study the recordings to find details or patterns they missed the first time they watched. They may also use computer programs to analyze movement or interpret sounds.

- An animal behaviorist may work to train animals to perform tasks that help humans. For example, guide dogs are trained to help the visually impaired with everyday tasks.

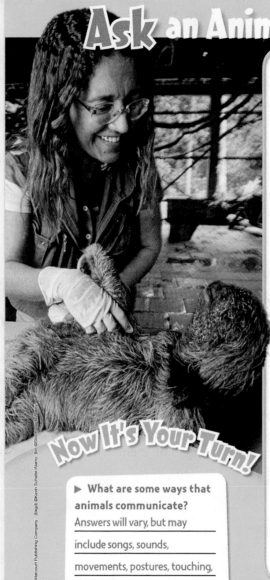

Ask an Animal Behaviorist

Careers in Science

Q. What is an animal behaviorist?

A. An animal behaviorist is a scientist. I study an animal's behavior, or how it responds to its environment. In other words, I research how animals act.

Q. Why do animals act the way they do?

A. Animals are born with some behaviors. These behaviors are called *instincts*. Birds migrate, or travel, when the seasons change. Ground squirrels hibernate during cold weather. Animals communicate using sounds or movements. These are all instincts.

Q. Do animal behaviors change as the animal grows?

A. Some animal behaviors are learned. These behaviors change with experience. In the wild, mothers teach their young to hunt. People train animals as pets, as performers, and as companions. Training animals takes time.

Now It's Your Turn!

▶ **What are some ways that animals communicate?**
Answers will vary, but may include songs, sounds, movements, postures, touching, and smells (pheromones).

© Houghton Mifflin Harcourt Publishing Company (bkgd) ©Kevin Schafer/Alamy; (br) ©StockShot/Alamy

149

Nature of Science

Many investigations of the natural world use controlled experiments, in which all conditions—except for the tested variable—are held constant. However, controlled experiments are not possible when studying animal behavior in the wild. Instead, scientists must conduct investigations based solely on observations. Some animal behaviorists use cameras attached to an animal to record the animal's perspective as it moves in its environment.

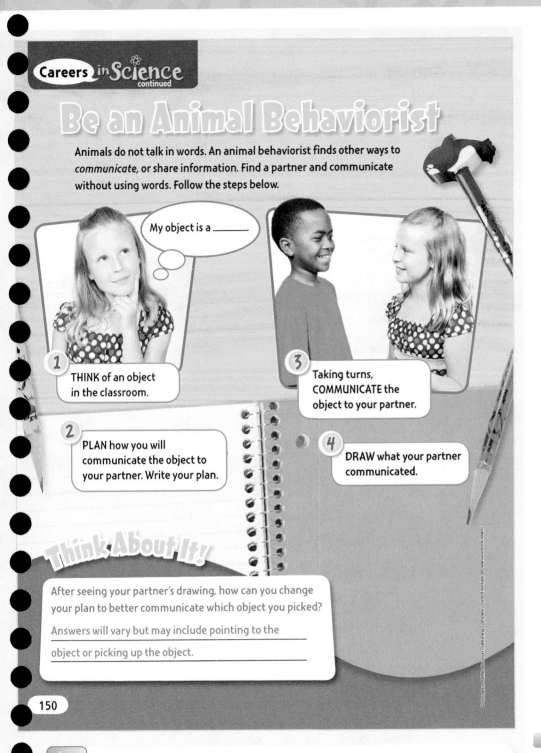

Careers in Science continued

Be an Animal Behaviorist

Animals do not talk in words. An animal behaviorist finds other ways to *communicate*, or share information. Find a partner and communicate without using words. Follow the steps below.

My object is a _____.

1 THINK of an object in the classroom.

2 PLAN how you will communicate the object to your partner. Write your plan.

3 Taking turns, COMMUNICATE the object to your partner.

4 DRAW what your partner communicated.

Think About It!

After seeing your partner's drawing, how can you change your plan to better communicate which object you picked?

Answers will vary but may include pointing to the object or picking up the object.

150

Writing Connection

Tell students that some people are born visually impaired or hearing impaired. Have students find out how such people are able to communicate with others. For example, students may research sign language or Braille. Have students write a one-page report detailing what they learned about these methods of communication.

Develop Science Concepts

After students complete the activity, lead them in a discussion about some ways that animals communicate.

Point out that many animals, including birds, dolphins, and elephants, communicate using sound. Animals may also communicate using visual cues. For example, bees indicate to each other where nectar can be found by performing a complex "dance."

Another way animals communicate is through smell. Some animals, such as ants and termites, release chemical signals called pheromones. The pheromones are used to mark the insects' territory and help the insects navigate. Other animals release pheromones to communicate readiness to mate.

Develop Inquiry Skills

OBSERVE Tell students that humans often communicate nonverbally. Show students videos or photos of different types of "body language." Or, students may reenact body language poses and facial gestures. For example, a person frowning with their arms crossed over their chest indicates an unwillingness to listen to new ideas. A person smiling and waving is communicating a greeting to another person. A person can indicate not knowing the answer to a question by shrugging the shoulders and raising their eyebrows.

Notebook ▸ Summarize Ideas

Have students write a brief statement that summarizes what they learned from this activity. Ask students to share their statements with the rest of the class. Students may then summarize the main idea orally or in writing.

Options for Inquiry

FLIPCHART P. 17

Students can conduct these optional investigations at any time before, during, or in response to the lesson in the Student Edition.

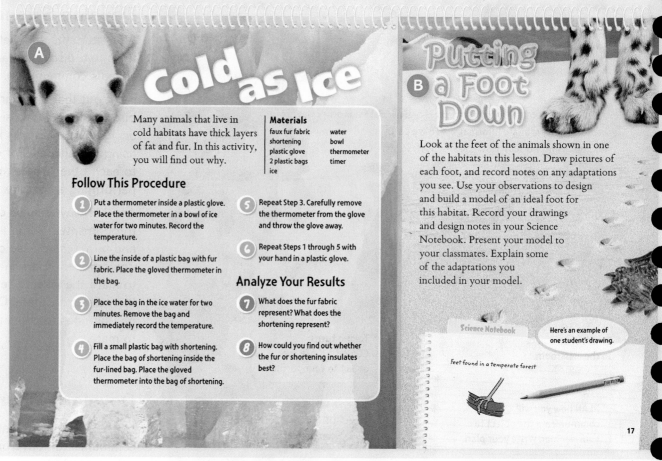

Cold as Ice

Many animals that live in cold habitats have thick layers of fat and fur. In this activity, you will find out why.

Materials
faux fur fabric · water
shortening · bowl
plastic glove · thermometer
2 plastic bags · timer
ice

Follow This Procedure

1. Put a thermometer inside a plastic glove. Place the thermometer in a bowl of ice water for two minutes. Record the temperature.

2. Line the inside of a plastic bag with fur fabric. Place the gloved thermometer in the bag.

3. Place the bag in the ice water for two minutes. Remove the bag and immediately record the temperature.

4. Fill a small plastic bag with shortening. Place the bag of shortening inside the fur-lined bag. Place the gloved thermometer into the bag of shortening.

5. Repeat Step 3. Carefully remove the thermometer from the glove and throw the glove away.

6. Repeat Steps 1 through 5 with your hand in a plastic glove.

Analyze Your Results

7. What does the fur fabric represent? What does the shortening represent?

8. How could you find out whether the fur or shortening insulates best?

Putting a Foot Down

Look at the feet of the animals shown in one of the habitats in this lesson. Draw pictures of each foot, and record notes on any adaptations you see. Use your observations to design and build a model of an ideal foot for this habitat. Record your drawings and design notes in your Science Notebook. Present your model to your classmates. Explain some of the adaptations you included in your model.

Science Notebook

Here's an example of one student's drawing.

Feet found in a temperate forest

17

Directed Inquiry

A Cold as Ice

 20–30 minutes
small groups

Prep and Planning Tips

If time is short, you may want to prepare the fur-lined bag and the shortening-filled bag before class.

Have students make a data table they can use to record the three temperature readings from the thermometer. The data tables should have a separate column for each temperature reading.

Students may also measure change in temperature over time. Have students check their thermometers every minute for 5 minutes to determine which insulator keeps their hands warm the longest.

Expected Results

Students will find that the temperature inside the bag with the faux fur and shortening will change the least. The temperature inside the glove that is not placed in a fur pouch will change the most.

Independent Inquiry

B Putting a Foot Down

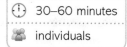 30–60 minutes
individuals

Prep and Planning Tips

Before students start this activity, show them pictures of different animals' feet. Tell students the type of environment each animal lives in, and have students discuss how the feet of each animal help the animal move around in its environment. Point out different foot adaptations for living in trees, walking on sand, walking on snow, and so on.

Science Notebook

Students can use the Science Notebook to help them understand how to use their observations of an animal to design a model. Encourage students to be creative in the type of craft supplies they use. They should try to make their models as realistic as possible.

Essential Question

How Are Living Things Adapted to Their Environment?

☺ Engage Your Brain!

Find the answer to the following question in this lesson and record it here.

How do the characteristics of this fox help it survive in its environment?
The fox's fur color allows it to blend in with its environment. Its short ears keep the fox from losing too much body heat. Its thick fur acts as insulation.

Active Reading

Lesson Vocabulary
List the terms. As you learn about each one, make notes in the Interactive Glossary.

environment   behavioral

adaptation   adaptation

physical   instinct

adaptation

Signal Words: Details
This lesson gives details about the types of adaptations that help plants and animals survive in different environments. Signal words, such as *for example, for instance,* and *like,* link main topics to added details. Active readers look for signal words that link a main topic to its details.

151

© Houghton Mifflin Harcourt Publishing Company ©Corbis

🖥 Go Digital

An interactive digital lesson is available in Online Resources. It is suitable for individuals, small groups, or may be projected or used as an interactive white board.

---

1 **Engage/Explore**

Objectives

- Define and explain the terms *environment* and *adaptation*.
- Define and explain physical and behavioral adaptations.
- Recognize physical and behavioral adaptations in plants and animals.

Engage Your Brain!

Encourage students to study the photograph, then have students brainstorm answers to the question, "How do the characteristics of this fox help it survive in its environment?" Suggest students think about the challenges an animal must face in the wild, such as predators and harsh weather.

Remind them to record their final answer to the question, when they find it, on the tenth page of this lesson.

Active Reading   Annotations

Remind students that active readers "make texts their own" by annotating them with notes and marks that help with comprehension. Encourage students to use pencil, not pen, to make annotations and to feel free to change their annotations as they read. The goal of annotation is to help students remember what they have read.

Vocabulary and Interactive Glossary

Remind students to find and list the yellow highlighted terms from the lesson. As they proceed through the lesson and learn about the terms, they should add notes, pictures, or sentences in the extra spaces in the Interactive Glossary.

2 Explain

Notebook > Generate Ideas

Have students brainstorm some of the different places where plants and animals live. Discuss with students how each of the environments they listed is similar to and different from one another.

Active Reading

Remind students that signal words show connections between ideas. *For example* and *For instance* signal examples of an idea. *Also* and *in fact* signal added facts. Active readers remember what they read because they are alert to signal words

Develop Science Vocabulary

environment Students have probably heard the word *environment* before. Ask students what they think the word means. Record some of their ideas on the board. Then, have students look up the word in the Glossary and compare their ideas with the actual definition.

Develop Inquiry Skills

COMPARE How are the two environments shown here different from one another? Students may point out that one environment is on flat land, while the other is in a mountainous area. One environment seems warm, while the other seems cold.

How are the environments similar? Students may notice that both environments seem relatively dry and have little plant life.

Life on the Blue Planet

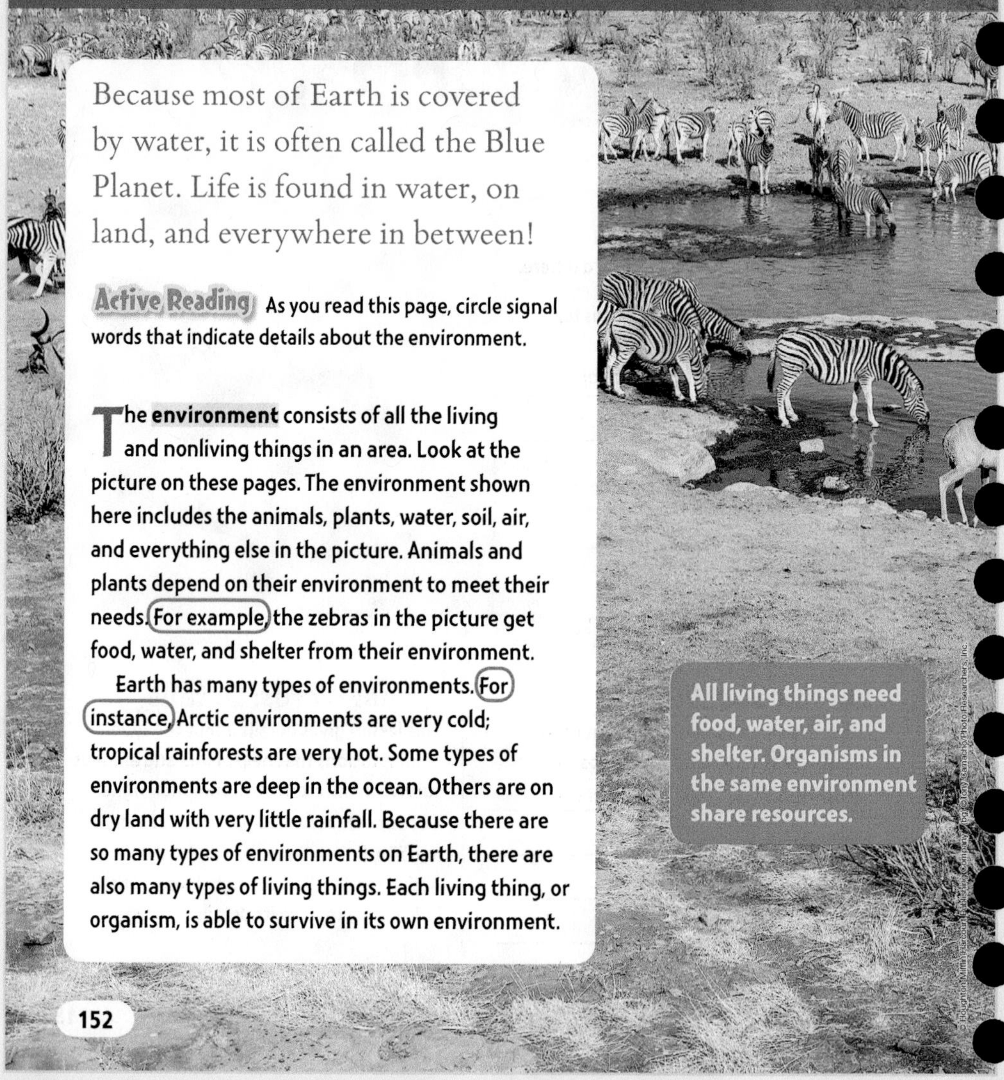

Because most of Earth is covered by water, it is often called the Blue Planet. Life is found in water, on land, and everywhere in between!

Active Reading As you read this page, circle signal words that indicate details about the environment.

The **environment** consists of all the living and nonliving things in an area. Look at the picture on these pages. The environment shown here includes the animals, plants, water, soil, air, and everything else in the picture. Animals and plants depend on their environment to meet their needs. For example, the zebras in the picture get food, water, and shelter from their environment.

Earth has many types of environments. For instance, Arctic environments are very cold; tropical rainforests are very hot. Some types of environments are deep in the ocean. Others are on dry land with very little rainfall. Because there are so many types of environments on Earth, there are also many types of living things. Each living thing, or organism, is able to survive in its own environment.

All living things need food, water, air, and shelter. Organisms in the same environment share resources.

152

Writing Connection

Write a Description Have students find a picture of another environment from around the world and write a brief description of the environment on a note card. Students should share their picture and description with the rest of the class. After comparing and contrasting each environment, you may wish to have students use the pictures and note cards to make a collage on one of the classroom's boards.

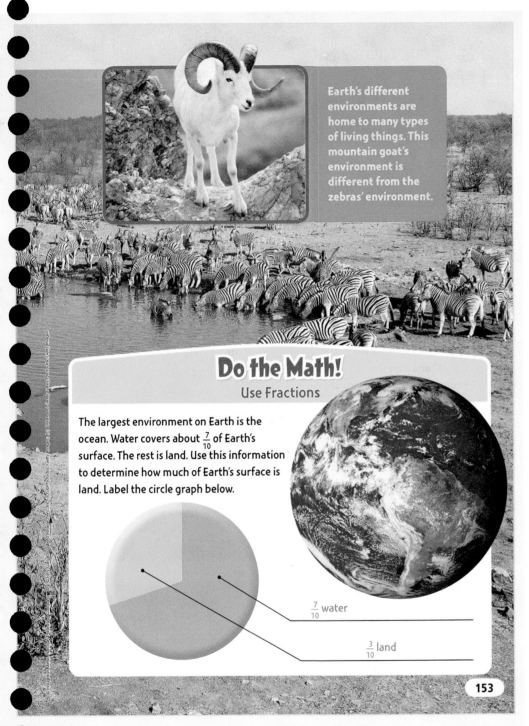

Earth's different environments are home to many types of living things. This mountain goat's environment is different from the zebras' environment.

Do the Math!
Use Fractions

The largest environment on Earth is the ocean. Water covers about $\frac{7}{10}$ of Earth's surface. The rest is land. Use this information to determine how much of Earth's surface is land. Label the circle graph below.

$\frac{7}{10}$ water

$\frac{3}{10}$ land

153

Math Connection

Fractions Tell students there are two main types of underwater environments: saltwater and freshwater environments. Saltwater environments are by far the most common, making up approximately $\frac{97}{100}$ of all the water on Earth. Have students use this information to calculate what portion of Earth's water is fresh water $\frac{3}{100}$. Then, have students draw and divide a circle to reflect this information.

Develop Science Concepts

What characteristics do you think an animal would have in order to survive in the savanna environment? Students may say an animal would need to run fast or fly in order to escape predators or have no fur or short fur in order to stay cool.

What characteristics do you think an animal would have in order to survive in a mountain environment? Students may say an animal would need to have strong, short legs in order to climb the mountain and stay stable. It would also need thick fur in order to stay warm.

Do the Math!

Use Fractions

Before students complete this activity, review the relationship between fractions and the sections of a circle graph. Draw a circle on the board and completely shade it in. Underneath the circle, write the fraction $\frac{1}{1}$. Then, draw another circle, but this time only shade in half the circle. Underneath this circle, write the fraction $\frac{1}{2}$.

Tell students that in the Do the Math activity, they will be working with other fractions. **How much of Earth's surface is covered in water?** $\frac{7}{10}$

How much of Earth's surface is covered by land? $\frac{3}{10}$

How big is $\frac{7}{10}$ compared to $\frac{3}{10}$? $\frac{7}{10}$ is more than twice as much as $\frac{3}{10}$.

Notebook ▶ Summarize Ideas

Instruct students to draw an environment different from the two shown on this page. The picture should include at least one animal that would be suited to living in that environment.

2 Explain (continued)

 Generate Ideas

Direct students' attention to the pictures of plants and animals on these two pages. Have students compare and contrast the plants and animals that live in a forest environment with the plants and animals that live in a grassland.

Active Reading

Remind students that a term may be highlighted. Active readers focus on highlighted terms because a definition is often provided at that point in the text.

Develop Science Vocabulary

adaptation Have a volunteer give the definition of adaptation. Then ask the following questions:

What adaptations does a fish have for living in the water? Sample answer: A fish has fins to swim and gills to breathe underwater.

What adaptations does a squirrel have for climbing a tree? Sample answer: A squirrel has sharp claws to help it climb a tree.

What adaptations does a frog have for jumping? Sample answer: A frog has long, powerful hind legs that help it jump.

physical adaptation After students have read the definition of the term physical adaptation, have them return to their answers to the previous questions about adaptations. Ask students:

Which of the examples you gave are examples of physical adaptations? All of the examples given above are physical adaptations.

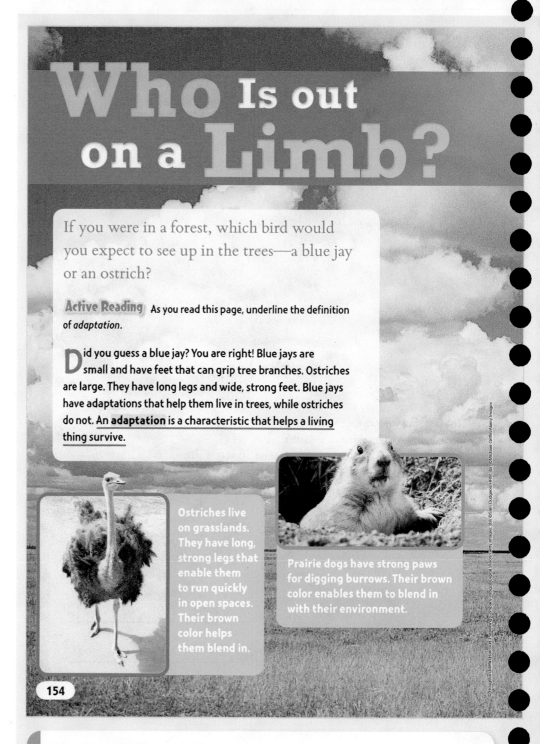

Who Is out on a Limb?

If you were in a forest, which bird would you expect to see up in the trees—a blue jay or an ostrich?

Active Reading As you read this page, underline the definition of *adaptation*.

Did you guess a blue jay? You are right! Blue jays are small and have feet that can grip tree branches. Ostriches are large. They have long legs and wide, strong feet. Blue jays have adaptations that help them live in trees, while ostriches do not. An **adaptation** is a characteristic that helps a living thing survive.

Ostriches live on grasslands. They have long, strong legs that enable them to run quickly in open spaces. Their brown color helps them blend in.

Prairie dogs have strong paws for digging burrows. Their brown color enables them to blend in with their environment.

154

English Language Learners

Understand Compound Words
Write *grassland* on the board and explain that compound words are made of two smaller words. Other examples include: *pathway*, *highway*, and *baseball*. Encourage students to provide examples of compound words. (*classroom*, *textbook*, *outdoors*) Challenge students to skim the remaining pages of the lesson for compound words. (*underground*, *underwater*)

A **physical adaptation** is an adaptation to a body part. Living things have different physical adaptations based on their specific environments. For example, plants and animals in open spaces have different physical adaptations than living things in forests.

In open spaces, grasses can bend in strong winds. Grassland animals have coverings to blend in with the grass. These animals may be able to run fast or have shovel-like paws for burrowing.

Living things in forests have physical adaptations to live in and around trees. Vines can climb up trees to reach sunlight they need. Many forest animals can grip branches.

This blue jay's curved feet help it grip small branches. Its wings enable it to fly from branch to branch.

This sloth's long claws help it to hang from tree branches for most of its life. A sloth can even sleep without letting go of the branch.

▶ Compare the prairie dog's grassland adaptations with the sloth's forest adaptations.

The prairie dog has strong

paws for digging and is light

brown to blend in with its

grassland environment.

The sloth has long claws for

hanging from tree branches.

_____

_____

155

Develop Science Concepts

What is the main difference between a grassland environment and a forest environment? A forest environment has various species of trees that shade the forest floor during the late spring and summer. A grassland environment consists of tall grasses.

How does this difference affect the adaptations of the animals living in each environment? The animals are adapted to make use of the available plants. For example, forest animals, such as the sloth, have long claws that help them hold onto tree branches. Blue jays also have claws that can grip tree branches. Grassland animals, such as ostriches and prairie dogs, blend in with the color of the grasses. They may also have long, strong legs to run fast (ostriches) or strong paws for burrowing (prairie dogs).

Interpret Visuals

Direct students' attention to the picture of the ostrich on the previous page.

Would the ostrich's adaptations be useful for living in a tree? Why or why not? No, the ostrich has wide feet that would not be able to grasp branches. Its large body size and long legs would make it difficult for the ostrich to climb into a tree and balance on the limbs.

Next, have students compare the pictures of the prairie dog and the sloth and answer the Interactivity on this page.

Notebook ▶ Summarize Ideas

To help students summarize information on these pages, have them make a two-column chart. In the first column, students should list adaptations that are helpful in a forest. In the second column, they should list adaptations that are helpful in a grassland. After students complete their lists, have them draw a line to connect any adaptations they listed that are helpful in both environments.

 Differentiation — Leveled Questions

Extra Support

Why do you find more vines growing in a forest than in a grassland? Forests have tall trees that vines can use as support to grow on. Vines must grow up trees in order to reach light.

Challenge

Ground squirrels live in grasslands. What adaptations do you think they would have to live in this environment? Grassland squirrels have claws for digging. Their fur helps them blend in with grasses instead of with tree bark.

2 Explain (continued)

📓 Notebook ▶ Generate Ideas

Ask students if they have ever spent time at a pond or lake. If so, have them describe the environment. Ask them to discuss the types of plants and animals they saw there. Then, have the class brainstorm how a pond or lake environment might be different from a stream environment.

Active Reading

Remind students that active readers annotate, or mark up, text to benefit their own recollection of the information presented. Though students may circle different words, it is important they are able to explain the thinking behind their annotations.

Develop Science Concepts

Work with students to model a riverbed. For example, you could shape sand in a sandbox to model a riverbed. Then, have students come up with ways to model how different plants will survive in flowing water. For example, you could use streamers to model plants like *Elodea*, straws to model weeds, and small plastic foam plates tied to strings to model water lilies. Place the plant models in the riverbed model. Then, use a hose to pour water down the river to see what happens to each of the plants placed in the riverbed.

Have students use their observations to discuss how a plant's shape can be an adaptation to its environment.

Who Can Go with the Flow?

Some living things swim upstream while others go with the flow. Which adaptations do living things need in different water environments?

Active Reading As you read the paragraph below, circle examples of fish physical adaptations.

Imagine you live in a constantly flowing stream of water. How could you stay in the same part of the stream without being carried away? Many fish that live in streams have (smooth bodies and strong tails.) These characteristics help fish swim against the current. Water plants have flexible stems that allow them to bend with the flow. Many water insects are able to hold on tightly to water plants. Other insects burrow into the soil at the bottom of the stream.

This fish has a smooth, streamlined body. Its body shape allows it to swim quickly in fast-moving water.

Elodea are very flexible plants, so flowing water is less likely to break them. If a piece of elodea is pulled off, though, the piece can sprout roots and start to grow in a new part of the stream.

156

English Language Learners

More on Compound Words
Review that compound words are made up of two smaller words. Challenge students to find at least three compound words on these pages. Words they might identify include *streamlined, catfish,* *cattails, upstream,* and *without.* Have partners choose one of these words and work together to define it based on the meaning of the two smaller words. Have them present their words and meanings to the class.

Plants in still water, such as ponds and lakes, have different adaptations. Some plants are tall and have strong stems, so they can grow above the water. Others, such as water lilies, float on the surface.

Animals that live in lakes and ponds are excellent swimmers. Many are adapted to living in deep water with little light. Catfish have whiskers that sense chemicals in the water to help them find food in the dark. Some birds wade at the shore and hunt. Their long, thin legs look like the cattails, so fish do not see them until it's too late.

Cattails grow in relatively still, shallow water, such as the water of a pond. Their stems are strong and stiff. Cattails can grow to more than 3 m tall.

Pond turtles are strong swimmers. They are also able to hold their breath for long periods of time. Their dark color allows them to stay hidden in dark, muddy water.

▶ Compare the elodea's adaptations with the cattail's adaptations. The elodea plants are flexible so flowing water can move over them easily. Cattails are tall and stiff so they can grow in the shallow water of a pond.

157

Interpret Visuals

Have students examine the turtle picture and caption.

Why would a pond turtle have a hard time living in a fast-moving stream? Pond turtles have short legs. Also, their bodies are not streamlined. Because of these two factors, pond turtles are slow swimmers. This would make it difficult for pond turtles to swim against the current in a fast-moving stream.

Develop Inquiry Skills

INFER **Do you think the same types of plants and animals that live in a pond or a lake could live in an ocean? Explain.** No, ponds and lakes are different types of environments from oceans. For example, an ocean is salt water, and most ponds and lakes are fresh water. In addition, an ocean is much larger and deeper than a pond or lake. For these reasons, the animals living in an ocean would need to have different adaptations from those animals living in a pond or lake.

Notebook ▶ ## Summarize Ideas

Have students make a two-column chart. In the first column, students should list adaptations that are helpful in a stream. In the second column, they should list adaptations that are helpful in a pond or lake environment. After students complete their lists, have them draw a line to connect any adaptations they listed that are helpful in both environments.

Differentiation — Leveled Questions

Extra Support

Why would a stiff plant not grow well in a fast-moving stream? The constantly flowing water would push against the rigid plant, likely causing it to snap in two.

Challenge

Would more plants and animals live in a fast-moving river or a slow-moving river? Explain. More plants and animals would likely live in the slow-moving river, because its slower water would be easier to cope with.

2 Explain (continued)

 Generate Ideas

Before students read the text, have them examine the pictures on these two pages. Ask them to describe a desert environment based on the photos.

Active Reading

Remind students that active readers annotate, or mark up, text to benefit their own recollection of the information presented. Though students may circle different words, it is important they are able to explain the thinking behind their annotations.

Interpret Visuals

Have students examine the three inset photos shown on these pages and read the captions that accompany them.

Why would it be important for a reptile to have adaptations that help keep water inside its body? An adaptation that helps conserve water will help the animal survive in the dry desert environment.

Why is staying cool an advantage for animals in the desert? This desert is very hot. If an animal cannot stay cool, it could become ill or die.

The cactus shown here has spines that help protect it from animals that might eat it. Why would a desert plant be more likely to have spines than a plant in an environment such as a rain forest? Unlike animals, plants can access water deep underground using their roots. Because water is so scarce in the desert, animals would likely try to eat a plant not just for food but also to get the water they need to survive.

Who Can Take the Heat?

Deserts are places that get very little rain. Some deserts are very hot. How do plants and animals live in such hot, dry places?

Active Reading As you read these two pages, circle the words or phrases that describe desert environments.

Desert plants and animals have physical adaptations that help them stay cool and conserve water. Many desert plants have waxy coatings on their stems to minimize water loss. Many of these plants have very long roots to reach water that is deep underground. Some desert plants have wide root systems that can absorb lots of water when it rains. Desert animals have physical adaptations to keep cool. Some have short, thin fur, or no fur at all.

Many reptiles live in deserts. This lizard's scales help it keep water inside its body.

Jackrabbits have large ears. Their ears release body heat and help the hares stay cool.

158

English Language Learners

Words Easily Confused
Review the following spellings and **pronunciations** with students.

DES·ert hot dry land

de·SERT to leave a place empty

des·SERT sweet food following a main meal

Ask students to read each of the following sentences aloud and then choose the correct definition.
We will have cake for dessert.
The Sahara is a desert in Africa.
At the first sign of trouble, the people will desert the village.

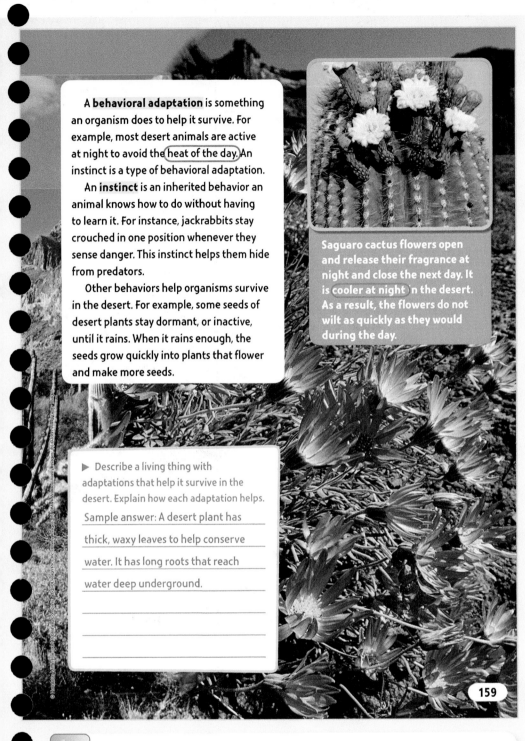

A **behavioral adaptation** is something an organism does to help it survive. For example, most desert animals are active at night to avoid the heat of the day. An instinct is a type of behavioral adaptation.

An **instinct** is an inherited behavior an animal knows how to do without having to learn it. For instance, jackrabbits stay crouched in one position whenever they sense danger. This instinct helps them hide from predators.

Other behaviors help organisms survive in the desert. For example, some seeds of desert plants stay dormant, or inactive, until it rains. When it rains enough, the seeds grow quickly into plants that flower and make more seeds.

Saguaro cactus flowers open and release their fragrance at night and close the next day. It is cooler at night in the desert. As a result, the flowers do not wilt as quickly as they would during the day.

▶ Describe a living thing with adaptations that help it survive in the desert. Explain how each adaptation helps.

Sample answer: A desert plant has

thick, waxy leaves to help conserve

water. It has long roots that reach

water deep underground.

159

Develop Science Vocabulary

behavioral adaptation Have a volunteer read the definition of behavioral adaptation aloud.

Compare and contrast a physical adaptation and a behavioral adaptation. Provide an example of each type of adaptation in a desert animal. Both types of adaptations help an animal survive in its environment. A physical adaptation is a body part, such as a jackrabbit's large ears. A behavioral adaptation is something an animal does, such as being active at night to avoid the heat of the day.

instinct After students have read the definition of instinct, ask them why an instinct helps an animal survive. Students should infer that if an animal knows how to do something without having to learn it, the animal may be able to react faster or recognize danger quicker.

Develop Science Concepts

Reinforce the differences between physical and behavioral adaptations. Draw a two-column chart on the board with the headings *Physical Adaptations* and *Behavioral Adaptations*. Organize the class into two teams. Have team 1 identify an adaptation described on these pages, such as the rabbit's large ears. Team 2 must tell you into which column to place that adaptation. For turn 2, teams switch roles. Continue until all of the adaptations described here are categorized.

Writing Connection

Write a Narrative Ask students to select a desert animal and write a story about that animal. The story should describe an event that happens during 24 hours in the life of the animal. Challenge students to write the story from the animal's point of view. Their stories should include details about the animal's physical and behavioral adaptations. Students should also include other desert animals as characters in the story and write dialogue. Encourage students to use descriptive details in their writing.

Notebook ▶ **Summarize Ideas**

Have students identify one of the organisms described on these pages and re-read the description of its adaptations. Suggest they underline the important details as they read. Have them use this information to complete the Interactivity on this page. Have volunteers share their descriptions with the class.

2 Explain (continued)

Generate Ideas

Draw on students' prior knowledge and ask them to describe Antarctica and the Arctic. Make a two-column chart on the board with column headings *Antarctica* and *The Arctic*, and record student responses. Encourage students to think about the location of each region, the climate of each region, and examples of animals that live in each region as they brainstorm answers.

Active Reading

Remind students that active readers annotate, or mark up, text to benefit their own recollection of the information presented. Though students may circle different words, it is important they are able to explain the thinking behind their annotations.

Interpret Visuals

Direct students' attention to the images of animals on these two pages.

Which behavioral adaptation is the Arctic hare displaying in the picture? It is sitting with its paws, tail, and ears tucked in to stay warm.

Which physical adaptations do penguins have that help them survive in Antarctica? They have a thick layer of fat to keep them warm. They have black feathers on their backs. The black feathers absorb heat from the sun, which helps keep the penguins warm.

Who Can Take the Cold?

Polar environments are very cold places. How do plants and animals survive in cold places such as Antarctica and the Arctic?

Active Reading As you read these pages, circle the words or phrases that describe polar environments.

Temperatures in Antarctica rarely get above freezing—even in summer! Plants and animals that live there have adaptations to live in extreme cold. Emperor penguins have a thick layer of fat—a physical adaptation that keeps them warm on land and in the water. To protect themselves from very cold winds, male penguins huddle together in large groups. The behavior is an instinct that helps male penguins and their newly hatched baby penguins keep warm.

The Antarctic pearlwort grows close to the ground in the warmer, wetter parts of Antarctica.

Black feathers on the backs of emperor penguins absorb heat from the sun, which helps them keep warm.

160

123 Math Connection

Compare Sizes Share that there are different species of penguins that live in the Antarctic region. Emperor penguins are 1.15 m (3.8 ft) in height. Chinstrap penguins are 68 cm (27 in) in height.

What is the difference in height between these two species of penguins? Students must convert meters to centimeters and then subtract. 1.15 m = 115 cm. 115 cm − 68 cm = 47 cm.

The Arctic has extremely cold winters and very short summers. Arctic animals have thick fur and a layer of fat to keep in body heat. Some Arctic animals are often white in the winter, which helps them blend in with the snow. These characteristics are physical adaptations. Arctic animals also have behavioral adaptations. For example, many Arctic animals live in dens dug into the ground or snow during very cold months.

Most Arctic plants have short roots because the ground there is frozen the majority of the year. These plants produce seeds during the short summer when the ground isn't frozen. Most Arctic plants grow close to the ground, which helps protect them from strong, cold Arctic winds.

This prairie crocus has fuzzy hairs that cover its flowers and seeds. The hairs protect the plant from wind and trap heat from the sun.

▶ Compare the adaptations that help the desert jackrabbit and the Arctic hare survive in their environments.

The jackrabbit's brown fur helps it

blend in with the desert environment.

Its large ears release body heat and

keep the rabbit cool. The Arctic hare's

white fur helps it blend into its snowy

surroundings. It sits with its paws, tail,

and ears tucked in to keep in body heat.

Arctic hares grow white fur in winter to blend in with the snow. They sit with their paws, tails, and ears tucked in to keep from losing body heat.

161

Differentiation — Leveled Questions

Extra Support
Why are most Arctic animals white in color? It helps them blend in with the snow, which makes it hard for predators to see them.

Challenge
Why do Arctic plants grow seeds quickly? Arctic summers are short. Seeds that grow quickly will germinate new plants before the weather turns too cold.

Develop Science Concepts

Provide students with books or other resources about Antarctica and the Arctic. Organize the class into two groups—Arctic and Antarctic. Have students in both groups identify organisms native to their given area. The organisms should be different from those shown here. Students should find pictures of the organisms and research some of the physical and behavioral adaptations that help them survive in their environment.

Instruct students to use their pictures and research to draw each organism and to write detailed captions about its adaptations. Assemble students' pictures into two collages—one about Antarctica and one about the Arctic. Give students time to study both collages. Afterwards, ask students to compare and contrast these two environments.

Develop Inquiry Skills

COMPARE After students compare the jackrabbit and the Arctic hare in the Interactivity, help students make a Venn diagram to compare and contrast the adaptations of desert plants with those of plants that live in cold regions. Students should conclude the following: Desert: waxy coating of stems, long roots; Cold regions: grow close to the ground, short roots, fuzzy hairs on flowers and seeds; Both: short life cycles

Notebook ▶ Summarize Ideas

Reinforce content by having students study the images on these two pages. Invite them to think about the information in the visuals and then summarize the main idea orally or in writing.

3 Extend/Evaluate

Sum It Up!

- Students will likely benefit from reviewing illustrations and photographs in the lesson before working on this activity. You may wish to review the images as a class by having volunteers identify what each of the lesson's main images illustrates.

- Have students read the instructions for each part of the Sum It Up! and to consider their answers carefully as they work through the activities.

- Students should review the definitions of the terms *physical adaptation* and *behavioral adaptation* before beginning Part II of this activity.

- If students have trouble completing part of this exercise, have them review the lesson before continuing on to the Brain Check activities.

- Remind students to use the Answer Key to check their answers. Students should revise incorrect answers so they can use the Sum It Up! page to study for tests.

- Provide remediation help for students who need more instruction.

When you're done, use the answer key to check and revise your work.

The outline below is a summary of the lesson. Complete the outline.

Summarize

I. Match each description to the living thing that has that adaptation.

A. flexible stem that bends in flowing water — Arctic hare

B. grows white fur in the winter — sloth

C. long claws to hang from tree branches — saguaro

D. flowers open at night when it's cooler — prairie dog

E. long claws for digging burrows — *Elodea*

II. Identify each adaptation described below as a physical adaptation or a behavioral adaptation.

A. An ostrich has long, strong legs. _____physical_____

B. An Arctic hare sits for hours to conserve heat. _____behavioral_____

C. A catfish has whiskers that sense chemicals in the water. _____physical_____

D. Male penguins huddle together to stay warm. _____behavioral_____

E. A fish has a smooth, streamlined body. _____physical_____

Answer Key: I. A. *Elodea* B. Arctic hare C. sloth D. saguaro E. prairie dog II. A. physical B. behavioral C. physical D. behavioral E. physical

162

 **Brain Check** Lesson **5**

Name _____

Word Play

1 Complete the crossword puzzle.

Across

4. Desert animals are active at night to avoid the heat. Which type of adaptation is this?

5. Which type of behavior does an animal know how to do without having to learn it?

Down

1. What are all of the living and nonliving things in an area called?

2. A blue jay's small, curved feet help it grip branches. Which type of adaptation is this?

3. What is a body part or behavior that helps a living thing survive called?

Crossword:

1. Down: E N V I R O N M E N T
2. Down: P H Y S I C A L
3. Down: A D A P T A T I O N
4. Across: B E H A V I O R A L
5. Across: I N S T I N C T

Apply Concepts

2 Draw a circle around the plant that would most likely live in a forest environment. On the line below, write an adaptation the plant has that helps it live in a forest.

Students should circle the vine.

Vines are flexible and able to climb up the trunks of trees to reach light.

163

Answer Strategies

Word Play

1. You may wish to make a list of the terms used in the puzzle for students. Terms include the following: environment, adaptation, physical, behavioral, and instinct. If needed, have students refer back to the lesson pages on which each term is defined. As a challenge activity, ask students to make riddles using these terms or other terms from the lesson. Have students take turns reading and guessing the riddles.

2. Refer students to the lesson pages where forest plants and animals are discussed. Encourage students to compare plants illustrated here with the plants shown on the lesson pages.

Assessment

Suggested Scoring Guide

You may wish to use this suggested scoring guide for the Brain Check.

Item	Points
1	30 (6 points per item)
2	15
3	20
4	15
5	20
Total	100

Lesson Quiz

See Assessment Guide, p. AG 29.

3 Extend/Evaluate (continued)

Answer Strategies

Apply Concepts

3. If students are having difficulty answering this question, have them start by listing adaptations that help an animal stay warm. Ask students to put a check mark next to any of the listed adaptations that snakes and lizards have. Most likely, students will not be able to check off many of the listed adaptations. Have them use this information to compose their answers.

4. If students are having difficulty answering this question, have them think about what adaptations forest animals have that they have already read about. Students can refer back to the third and fourth pages of the lesson to review information about forest environments.

5. If students are having trouble answering this question, ask them how long it took them to learn a skill such as writing. Have them consider how needing time to learn to hide from a predator might affect an animal's chance of survival.

🏠 Take It Home!

Encourage students to draw pictures of some of the plants and animals they saw on their walk. They can then share these pictures with their classmates.

---

3 Snakes and lizards are rarely found living near polar environments. Explain why.

Snakes and lizards do not have many physical adaptations for staying warm in cold environments. They do not have fur, and most do not have a thick layer of fat for insulation.

4

This spider monkey lives in the forest. What physical adaptations does it have that help it survive in this type of environment?

Its hands, feet, and tail are able to grip tree branches.

5 Why is it better for an animal to know how to hide from predators because of an instinct than to have to learn how to hide from them?

Sample answer: The animal may have yet to learn the behavior when it sees or meets a predator for the first time. If the ability to hide from a predator is an instinct, the animal will do this from the time it is born, which will increase its chances of survival.

Take It Home!

Take a walk with your family through your neighborhood or a local park. Look at different plants and animals, and point out the adaptations these plants or animals have to help them survive.

164

Make Connections

Easy

Art Connection

Comic Book

Tell students to think of an interesting or unique adaptation that a non-human animal has. For example, bats can find things in the dark using echolocation. Instruct students to draw a comic-book story about a superhero who has that adaptation and uses it to help people. If time allows, encourage students to share their comic books with each other.

Average

Math Connection

Measuring Length

Kangaroo rats are tiny rodents (about the size of a mouse) that live in the desert. They are named after kangaroos because they have powerful back legs that help them jump long distances to escape predators. In fact, kangaroo rats can leap 2.75 m in one bound! Have students measure and draw a line segment to show this length.

Average

Writing Connection

Environment Descriptions

Assign each student a different environment from around the world. Instruct students to research the environment and write a detailed description of what the environment is like and what kinds of plants and animals live there.

Challenging

Health Connection

Adaptations and Basic Needs

Explain to students that adaptations help a plant or animal meet its needs. Organize students into small groups. Each group should discuss the following questions: What does a human need to stay healthy? How do a human's adaptations help it meet these needs? Afterwards, have a representative from each group present an oral summary of the group's answers to these two questions.

Guided Inquiry

🕐 30–40 minutes

👥 small groups

Students should follow the directions on the Flipchart. The accompanying Lesson Inquiry pages in the Student Edition provide scaffolding for guided inquiry.

Why Do Bird Beaks Differ?

Birds have adapted to eat different kinds of food. Because of this, there are many different kinds of beaks. In this activity, you'll investigate which beaks work best for each kind of food.

Materials

chopsticks
dropper
large pliers
needle-nose pliers
slotted spoon
forceps

shredded lettuce in a bowl of water
juice in a graduated cylinder
rice in plastic foam
gummy worms in sand
sunflower seeds
walnuts

1 Look at the tools you will use to model beaks. Discuss how you use each tool and how each tool is different.

2 Next, place one of your food choices next to the beak that you think will work best to "eat" the food. **CAUTION:** Do not eat any of the foods in this investigation.

3 Try to "eat" each type of food using each of the different tools.

4 Record your observations.

A Word for the Wise
An **adaptation** is a trait that helps an organism survive.

18

Inquiry Skills Focus Infer

Objectives

• Describe the variations that can be observed in different types of bird beaks.

• Identify which tool works best for which food.

• Relate different bird beaks with different types of food.

• Explain why some birds are better suited to a certain habitat than other birds are.

Prep and Planning Tips

See the Planning for Inquiry page for more information.

• Demonstrate how to use the tools safely.

• Remind students not to eat any of the foods in this activity.

Expected Results

Students will likely find that the dropper is best for the juice, the slotted spoon is best for lettuce, the forceps are best for the rice, the chopsticks are best for the gummy worms, the needle-nose pliers are best for sunflower seeds, and the large pliers are best for the walnut.

---

1 Engage/Explore

Attention Grabber

Provide each student with a small bowl of soup, but give them forks instead of spoons to eat the soup with. Give students a minute to try to eat the soup using their forks. Then, pass out spoons and allow students to finish their soup with the spoons. Discuss with students which utensil was easier to eat the soup with. Tell students that in this lab, they will learn that just as some utensils are better for eating certain kinds of foods, some bird beaks are also better for eating certain kinds of foods.

Preview Activity

Before beginning the investigation, have students review the directions on the Inquiry Flipchart and the accompanying Student Edition response pages. Then, have them complete the response pages as they follow the directions on the Flipchart.

Inquiry Flipchart page 18

Name _____

Essential Question

Why Do Bird Beaks Differ?

Set a Purpose

Why do you think different birds have beaks with different shapes?

Sample answer: Different birds eat

different kinds of food.

_____

_____

Write a statement summarizing what you plan to investigate.

Sample answer: I plan to investigate how

different tools are easier or harder to use

to pick up different kinds of food.

_____

What will you be modeling in this investigation?

I will use tools as models for different

bird beaks.

_____

_____

Record Your Data

In the space below, make a table in which you record your observations.

Students should make tables in which they can record how easily they were able to "eat" each type of food using each of the beak models.

© Houghton Mifflin Harcourt Publishing Company

165

1 Engage/Explore (continued)

Guide the Investigation

Develop Inquiry Skills

INFER **Do other animals have mouths that are adapted to the foods they eat? What are some examples?** Students might describe sharp teeth for biting flesh, flat teeth for chewing plants, and mouths that are adapted for eating ants. Tell them that snakes have fangs that point backward to prevent prey from escaping.

Show students various pictures of birds eating. For each picture, have students infer how the bird's beak is helping the bird eat its food.

HYPOTHESIZE **Besides eating, how else do you think a bird might use its beak?** A bird may also use its beak to defend itself, feed its young, gather nest materials, build a nest, clean its feathers, and court mates.

GATHER AND RECORD DATA Discuss with students how they will make a table and then record their results.

At a minimum, students' data tables should have a row for each type of tool tested and a column for each type of food tested.

Go Digital

A virtual lab experience is available with the Online Resources for this program.

Why Do Bird Beaks Differ?

2 Explain

Develop Inquiry Skills

DRAW CONCLUSIONS Suppose a bird has a short, thick beak that is pointed, like that of a cardinal. Would this bird be better adapted to eating tough seeds, worms living in pond mud, or flower nectar? **Explain.** The bird would be best adapted to eating tough seeds because its short, thick beak would be powerful enough to crack the seeds open. The beak would probably be too short to dig around for worms living in mud or to get at the nectar found deep in a flower.

ANALYZE AND EXTEND Discuss students' responses to the items.

1. Tell students to rely on the observations they made during the investigation when answering this question. They should review their data table before answering.

2. When students are answering this question, ask them to think about the type of tool they would need to open a large, tough fruit.

3. If students are not sure about some beaks, have them start with the ones they are more sure about and then fill in the rest.

3 Extend/Evaluate

4. Tell students that when answering this question, they don't have to limit themselves to birds. They can think about any kind of animal that they would like to learn more about.

Assessment

Lesson Quiz
See Assessment Guide, p. AG 30.

Draw Conclusions

Did some beaks work for more than one kind of food? What might this suggest about the bird's ability to survive?

Sample answer: Yes, some beaks could be used for more than one type of food. Birds with this type of beak could eat several kinds of food and might survive if their food source changed.

Did one kind of beak work for eating all of the different foods?

Sample answer: No, there was no beak that could be used for all of the foods.

_____

_____

Analyze and Extend

1. Which bird's beak would be best for eating flower nectar? Which beaks would be best for picking insects out of wood and worms out of sand?

Students should conclude that the hummingbird beak would be best for flower nectar, the woodpecker beak would be best for picking insects out of wood, and the shorebird beak would be best for picking worms out of sand.

2. A toucan is a bird that eats very large, tough tropical fruit. What would you expect a toucan's beak to look like?

Sample answer: A toucan would probably have a very large, strong beak.

_____

3. Look at the bird beaks below. Tell which tool in the investigation was most similar to each of the beaks.

hummingbird
dropper

finch
small pliers

macaw
large pliers

shorebird
chopsticks

woodpecker
forceps

duck
slotted spoon

4. Think of other questions you would like to ask about how adaptations relate to the food an animal eats.

Students may want to know about adaptations for meat-eaters versus plant-eaters versus filter-feeders.

Differentiated Inquiry

Easy

Which Beaks?

- Have students make a table listing all of the tools they used during the investigation.
- Ask students to look through a reference book about birds.
- Students should find birds with beaks similar to the tools they used. Have students list the names of birds with those beak shapes in their tables and the diet the bird is described as having.

Average

Modeling Beak Shapes

- Have students look through a reference book about birds.
- Students should come up with ideas of tools they could use to model some of the types of bird beaks they see.
- Ask students to form a hypothesis and write an investigation plan to determine how one of the modeled beak shapes relates to food.

Easy

Are Teeth Like Beaks?

- Tell students that teeth, just like beaks, are adapted to the type of food an animal eats.
- Show students pictures of teeth from carnivores, such as lions and sharks; teeth from herbivores, such as deer, cows, elephants, and rodents; and teeth from omnivores such as bears, raccoons and humans.
- Discuss with students the similarities and differences between the different kinds of teeth.
- Discuss how each set of teeth is adapted for the animal's diet.

Challenging

Which Habitat?

- Have students look at several pictures of birds that show the birds out of context—not in their habitat.
- Tell students to examine the birds' beaks, feet, and other body features. Students should use their observations to try to infer what type of habitat the birds live in.
- Instruct students to record the bird names and their inferences in a table. Students should also record the reasons behind the conclusions they drew.
- Have students use Internet resources or reference books to check whether their inferences were correct.

Enduring Understandings
Revisit the Big Idea and Essential Questions

Big Idea Living things are adapted for survival in their environment.

To explore the Big Idea, challenge students to generate as many statements that support it as possible. Have students brainstorm in small groups. Then have groups compare their lists to those generated by other groups. Students should make a master list of statements, which can then be added to their Science Notebooks as a study sheet. Sample statements:

- If a characteristic helps an animal survive, it will likely pass that characteristic along to its young.
- Animals that live in similar environments often have similar characteristics.
- Animals that have fast legs can run away quickly and have a better chance of escaping a predator.

Essential Questions

Post the Essential Questions and use the following prompts to guide a discussion.

Lesson/Essential Question	Prompts
L1 What Are Some Plant Structures?	• List three plant structures and explain the function of each structure.
L2 How Do Plants Reproduce?	• Describe how plants reproduce.
L3 How Can We Observe a Plant's Life Cycle?	• Draw the stages in a seed plant's life cycle.
L4 How Do Animals Reproduce?	• Identify some animals that lay eggs and some that have young that are born alive.
L5 How Are Living Things Adapted to Their Environment?	• Describe differences between physical and behavioral adaptations, and give an example of each adaptation.
L6 Why Do Bird Beaks Differ?	• Demonstrate how birds use beaks for crushing seeds and for straining plants out of the water.

Notebook **Science Notebook**

You may use the following strategies after students complete the unit or after each lesson.

- Have students review and edit the answers to Essential Questions they drafted at the beginning of the unit. Suggest they cross out sentences or ideas that are unnecessary or inappropriate.
- Direct students to compare and contrast the ways in which plants and animals survive. Students should list their results in a Venn diagram with the heads *Plants, Animals,* and *Both.*

Science Notebook

Essential Questions	Answers
What Are Some Plant Structures?	
How Do Plants Reproduce?	
How Can We Observe a Plant's Life Cycle?	
How Do Animals Reproduce?	
How Are Living Things Adapted to Their Environment?	
Why Do Bird Beaks Differ?	

Unit 3 Review

Name _____

Vocabulary Review

Use the terms in the box to complete the sentences.

| adaptation |
| chlorophyll |
| environment |
| fertilization |
| incomplete |
| metamorphosis |
| photosynthesis |
| pollination |
| spore |

1. The process by which plants use energy from the sun to change carbon dioxide and water into sugar and oxygen is called ____photosynthesis____.

2. Animals that have three stages in their life cycles go through ____incomplete metamorphosis____.

3. A characteristic that helps an organism survive is a(n) ____adaptation____.

4. The substance in leaves that makes them appear green in color is ____chlorophyll____.

5. The process by which a sperm cell joins with an egg cell is called ____fertilization____.

6. A cell from a fern plant that can produce a new plant is called a ____spore____.

7. All of the living and nonliving things in an area make up an ____environment____.

8. The movement of sperm cells from the male part of a flower to the female part occurs through the process of ____pollination____.

© Houghton Mifflin Harcourt Publishing Company   (border) ©NG Iinc/Age Fotostock

Item Analysis

Items	Depth of Knowledge	Cognitive Complexity
1–8	1	Low

Unit Review

Answer Key

Vocabulary Review (2 points each)

1. **photosynthesis** Direct students to the information about how plants make food by photosynthesis in Lesson 1.

2. **incomplete metamorphosis** The three stages of incomplete metamorphosis are egg, nymph, and adult. Students can revisit animal development through metamorphosis in Lesson 4.

3. **adaptation** Students can review physical and behavioral adaptations in Lesson 5.

4. **chlorophyll** Plants use chlorophyll to capture the energy of sunlight. Students can review the section on how plants make food in Lesson 1.

5. **fertilization** Fertilization is needed for sexual reproduction. Students can review fertilization in plants by rereading "Flowers and Cones" in Lesson 2.

6. **spore** A spore can form a new plant when conditions are right. Students can review how some plants use spores for reproduction in Lesson 2.

7. **environment** Earth has many different types of environments, but each living thing is suited to life in a particular environment. Lesson 5 can be used to review Earth's varied environments.

8. **pollination** Reinforce the differences between pollination and fertilization. Fertilization is the joining of egg and sperm cells; pollination is the movement of sperm cells from the male part of the flower to the female part.

Assessment

Unit 3 Test and Performance Assessment

See Assessment Guide, pp. AG 31–AG 37, for Unit Test and Performance Task with Long Option rubric.

Unit Review *continued*

Answer Key

Science Concepts (4 points each)

9. **C** During photosynthesis, plants use energy from the sun to change carbon dioxide and water into sugar and oxygen. Students can review how plants make food by photosynthesis in Lesson 1.

10. **C** Direct students to Lesson 4 to review the stages of complete and incomplete metamorphosis.

11. **A** Help students analyze each of the choices shown. Students can review sexual reproduction of plants in Lesson 2.

12. **B** Have volunteers describe the attributes of the beak shown. It is short, and it has no hooks or points. Have students analyze the answer choices with this information in mind. Students can review in Lesson 5 how beak shape is adapted to getting food.

13. **C** Review the stages of the plant life cycle in Lesson 2. Point out that by the time the seed has formed, pollination and fertilization have already occurred.

14. **A** Remind students that insects pick up and transfer pollen as they feed. Students can review pollination and the methods by which it occurs in Lesson 2.

15. **C** Point out that the question states that the animal under discussion is an insect. Suggest students review the information on complete metamorphosis, and identify which stage is "wormlike."

16. **D** Point out that many animals use the sense of smell to locate food. Remind students that they themselves often can identify what is for lunch by the odors coming from the school's cafeteria.

Science Concepts

Fill in the letter of the choice that best answers the question.

9. Plants get the energy they need to live by changing substances into the sugars they use for food. Which two substances do plants change during photosynthesis to make food?
   - Ⓐ sugar and water
   - Ⓑ sugar and oxygen
   - Ⓒ carbon dioxide and water
   - Ⓓ carbon dioxide and oxygen

10. Which stage below is part of incomplete metamorphosis—but not of complete metamorphosis?
    - Ⓐ adult
    - Ⓑ egg
    - Ⓒ nymph
    - Ⓓ pupa

11. The bristlecone pine tree produces cones that are either male or female. In contrast, the fishpoison tree has flowers that contain both male and female parts. What can you infer about these two trees?
    - Ⓐ Both trees carry out sexual reproduction.
    - Ⓑ Both trees have incredibly long life cycles.
    - Ⓒ Both trees can disperse their seeds very far.
    - Ⓓ Both trees need insects to carry out pollination.

12. Examine the beak on the bird below.

For which type of feeding is the shape of this beak best suited?
    - Ⓐ tearing food
    - Ⓑ eating small seeds
    - Ⓒ getting flower nectar
    - Ⓓ digging insects from bark

13. The bald cypress tree produces seeds protected within cones. This type of tree is found in swampy areas where heavy rains produce floods. The flood waters help spread the cones throughout the swampy areas. What role do the flood waters play in the life cycle of the bald cypress tree?
    - Ⓐ pollination
    - Ⓑ fertilization
    - Ⓒ seed dispersal
    - Ⓓ removal of dead leaves

168 Unit 3

Item Analysis *(continued)*

Items	Depth of Knowledge	Cognitive Complexity
9	1	Low
10	2	Moderate
11–12	3	High
13–16	2	Moderate

Name _____

14. This picture shows a butterfly and bees visiting a flower to obtain nectar.

Which process are these insects helping the plant carry out?

Ⓐ pollination

Ⓑ germination

Ⓒ seed dispersal

Ⓓ photosynthesis

15. The caddis fly is an insect that can live in streams for months. When its body is more wormlike, this fly builds an underwater house from pebbles to protect it from predators. Which stage of metamorphosis is the fly in at this point?

Ⓐ egg

Ⓑ adult

Ⓒ larva

Ⓓ pupa

16. Sharks can smell very small amounts of substances in ocean water. What does this physical adaptation most likely help sharks do?

Ⓐ sense water temperature

Ⓑ find a place to lay eggs

Ⓒ find a safe place to hide

Ⓓ find food that is far away

17. Monarch butterflies migrate to warm places every winter. What is their migration an example of?

Ⓐ a trait   Ⓒ a characteristic

Ⓑ an instinct   Ⓓ a learned behavior

18. Sarai visits the local nature center. She sees a number of young animals. Which of the animals hatches from an egg?

Ⓐ a turtle   Ⓒ a dolphin

Ⓑ a cheetah   Ⓓ a bear

19. A mahogany tree produces seeds that look like the picture below.

Fan-like blades

Notice the blades on the surface of this seed. What role do these blades play in the life cycle of a mahogany tree?

Ⓐ protect the seed

Ⓑ end the plant's life cycle

Ⓒ store food for the seedling

Ⓓ help disperse the tree's seeds

20. Which of the following lists stages in the life cycle of a seed plant?

Ⓐ spore, reproduction, maturity

Ⓑ germination, maturity, reproduction

Ⓒ egg, larva, pupa, adult

Ⓓ germination, nymph, spore, death

Unit 3   169

© Houghton Mifflin Harcourt Publishing Company (border) ©NDisc/Age Fotostock

Item Analysis *(continued)*

Items	Depth of Knowledge	Cognitive Complexity
17–20	2	Moderate

Unit Review *continued*

Answer Key

Science Concepts (4 points each)

17. B Direct students to Lesson 5 to review the information on how instincts affect animal behavior.

18. A Remind students that different types of animals have different methods of reproduction. Mammals generally are born live. Reptiles generally hatch from eggs. Have students identify whether each answer choice is a reptile or a mammal.

19. D Offer examples of different ways that seeds are dispersed, such as by wind, by animals, by floating in water, or simply by falling from the plant.

20. B Students can review the life cycle of seed plants in Lesson 2.

Short Option Performance Assessment

Task

Draw Life Cycles
Have students draw the life cycle of a flowering plant. Then have students draw an animal life cycle. Students should then write one or two sentences comparing and contrasting the two life cycles.

Rubric

Preparation Provide students with art supplies.

Scoring Rubric—Performance Indicators

___ Correctly draws and labels the stages of a flowering plant's life cycle.

___ Correctly draws and labels the stages of an animal's life cycle.

___ Describes how the life cycles of the plant and animal are alike.

___ Describes how the life cycles of the plant and animal are different.

Observations and Rubric Scores

3   2   1   0

Unit Review *continued*

Answer Key

Apply Inquiry and Review the Big Idea

(12 points each)

21. See student page for sample answers.
Have four volunteers each identify one
plant part and describe its function.

22. See student page for sample answer.
Remind students that only one variable is
changed during a controlled experiment.
In this case, the only variable that should
change is the substrate on which the
seeds are germinated—soil or paper
towels. All other variables—the type and
number of seeds, the type of bag, the
amount of light and water—should be
constant between the two bags.

23. See student page for sample answers.
Help students identify the different
adaptations shown. Suggest that students
circle the adaptation they wish to write
about to help them focus their answer.

UNIT 3

Apply Inquiry and Review the Big Idea

Write the answers to these questions.

21. The illustration shows common structures of a flowering
plant. Identify each plant part, and describe its function.

Structure A: Stems provide support to the plant and
move water and minerals from one part
of the plant to another.

Structure B: Leaves use sunlight to produce food for
the plant.

Structure C: The flower is an organ of sexual
reproduction.

Structure D: Roots absorb water and minerals from soil and help anchor the plant in
the soil.

22. Sayana is testing where bean seeds germinate more quickly. She places several
bean seeds into two plastic bags—one containing moist soil and the other moist
paper towels. What does she need to do to make this a fair experiment?

Sample answer: Sayana needs to make sure each bag is in the same area and that each
bag receives the same amount of water and sunlight.

23. This picture shows organisms that live in a desert environment.
Choose one of the organisms. Identify one of its physical
adaptations, and describe how the adaptation helps the organism
live in a desert environment.

Answers will vary. Students may suggest that the rabbit's big
ears help it dissipate heat. They may suggest that the cactus's
thick stem helps it store water.

170 Unit 3

© Houghton Mifflin Harcourt Publishing Company (border) ©NDiac/Age Fotostock

---

Item Analysis *(continued)*

Items	Depth of Knowledge	Cognitive Complexity
21–22	2	Moderate
23	3	High

UNIT (4) Energy and Ecosystems

Big Idea and Essential Questions

This Unit was designed to focus on this Big Idea and Essential Questions.

Take It Home!
A School-Home
Connection letter
is provided in
Online Resources.

Big Idea

Ecosystems are made up of both living and nonliving parts that impact one another.

Essential Questions

L1 **What Are Populations, Habitats, and Niches?**

L2 **What Are Food Chains?**

L3 **How Can We Model a Food Web?**

L4 **What Are Natural Resources?**

L5 **How Do People Impact Ecosystems?**

L6 **How Do People Affect Their Environment?**

Professional Development

Houghton Mifflin Harcourt and **NSTA,** the **National Science Teachers Association,** have partnered to provide customized professional development resources for teachers using *ScienceFusion*.

The Professional Development Resources include:

- Do-it-yourself resources, where you can study at your own pace
- Live and archived online seminars
- Journal articles, many of which include lesson plans
- Fee-based eBooks, eBook chapters, online short courses, symposia, and conferences

  Access to The NSTA Learning Center is provided in the *ScienceFusion* Online Resources.

National Science Teachers Association

The **NSTA** Learning Center

Unit Planning

Options for Instruction

Two parallel paths meet the unit objectives, with a strong Inquiry strand woven into each. Follow the Print Path, the Digital Path, or your customized combination of print, digital, and inquiry.

Essential Questions	LESSON 1	LESSON 2	LESSON 3
			☑ Guided Inquiry
	What Are Populations, Habitats, and Niches?	What Are Food Chains?	How Can We Model a Food Web?

Print Path

	LESSON 1	LESSON 2	LESSON 3
	☐ Student Edition pp. 173–188 • Who Lives Where? • Nearby Neighbors • A Place of One's Own • Dinner Time! • Doing the Dirty Work	☐ Student Edition pp. 189–204 • Food Chains • You Are What You Eat • Hunt or Be Hunted • Food Webs • Changes in Food Webs	☐ Student Edition pp. 205–206 • Scaffolding for Inquiry

Hands-On Inquiry

	LESSON 1	LESSON 2	LESSON 3
	Inquiry Flipchart p. 19 **Bottle Ecosystems** ☐ Directed Inquiry **Wildlife Centers: Stepping Into the Wild** ☐ Independent Inquiry	Inquiry Flipchart p. 20 **Model a Food Web** ☐ Directed Inquiry **What Does It Eat?** ☐ Independent Inquiry	Inquiry Flipchart p. 21 **How Can We Model a Food Web?** ☐ Guided Inquiry

Digital Path

	LESSON 1	LESSON 2	LESSON 3
	☐ Digital Lesson Online Resources Interactive presentation of lesson content	☐ Digital Lesson Online Resources Interactive presentation of lesson content	☐ Virtual Lab Online Resources Interactive scaffolded inquiry

What Are Natural Resources?	**How Do People Impact Ecosystems?**	☑ **Guided Inquiry** **How Do People Affect Their Environment?**	👥 People in Science, p. 235 S.T.E.M. Engineering and Technology, pp. 237–238B 🖥 Video-based Project, Rainforest Habitats 🌐 Online Resources

☐ **Student Edition** pp. 207–220 • Resources You Can Rely On • Nonrenewable Resources • From Coast to Coast • Flowing Down Slope • Keeping It Clean	☐ **Student Edition** pp. 221–232 • The Natural Environment • Earth, the Global Store • People Change the Environment • Caring for Our Ecosystems	☐ **Student Edition** pp. 233–234 • Scaffolding for Inquiry	**Unit Assessment** **Formative Assessment** Sum It Up! and Brain Check Student Edition, end of each lesson
Inquiry Flipchart p. 22 **Recycle Resources Yourself** ☐ Directed Inquiry **Map It!** ☐ Independent Inquiry	**Inquiry Flipchart** p. 23 **How Does Water Pollution Affect Plants?** ☐ Directed Inquiry **All About Recycling** ☐ Independent Inquiry	**Inquiry Flipchart** p. 24 **How Do People Affect Their Environment?** ☐ Guided Inquiry	**Summative Assessment** Lesson Quizzes Assessment Guide, pp. AG 38–AG 43 **Unit 4 Review** Student Edition, pp. 239–242 **Unit 4 Test** Assessment Guide, pp. AG 44–AG 48 **Performance Assessment** SHORT OPTION: Teacher Edition, p. 241 LONG OPTION: Assessment Guide, pp. AG 49–AG 50

RTI **Response to Intervention**

RTI Strategies p. 171K

🌐 **Online Assessment**
Test-taking and automatic scoring
Banks of items from which to build tests

☐ **Digital Lesson** Online Resources Interactive presentation of lesson content	☐ **Digital Lesson** Online Resources Interactive presentation of lesson content	☐ **Virtual Lab** Online Resources Interactive scaffolded inquiry

Planning for Inquiry

Use the following preview of Inquiry Activities and Lessons to
gather and manage the materials needed for each lesson.

Activity	Inquiry and Design Process Skills Focus	Materials	Prep Tips, Troubleshooting, and Expected Results
Lesson 1 DIRECTED INQUIRY Flipchart p. 19 **A** **Bottle Ecosystems** **OBJECTIVE** Follow directions for an investigation to make a model of an ecosystem. ⏱ 25 minutes to set up ecosystem; 15 minutes per day for three days for observations 👥 small groups	• Observe • Use Models • Identify and Control Variables • Infer	• 2 empty 2-L plastic bottles • gravel • sand • soil • water • plastic spoon • several small plants • 16-oz spray trigger bottle • plastic wrap • safety goggles	**Prep Tips** Precut the tops off the 2-L bottles. Place masking tape around the top rim to cover any sharp edges. To save time, pre-measure portions of gravel, sand, and soil. Small plants may be purchased at a local nursery and can be divided before planting. Be sure to keep roots intact. Alternatively, you may wish to have students plant bean or grass seeds. Adjust activity time to allow for seeds to sprout. You may need to find a location outside the classroom for an adequate light source. **Caution!** Have students wear safety goggles. Have them notify you immediately of any spills. Water can make surfaces slippery and cause falls. Direct students to wash their hands following this activity. **Troubleshooting** Students can use the diagram on the Flipchart as a guide to assembling their terrariums. Have students gently tap the bottom of the container to help settle the gravel and sand before adding the soil layer. **Expected Results** Students will observe that plants need sunlight to grow and thrive.
INDEPENDENT INQUIRY Flipchart p. 19 **B** **Wildlife Centers: Stepping Into the Wild** **OBJECTIVE** Plan and conduct research on an organism's ecosystem and make a diorama that depicts that organism's ecosystem. ⏱ 30–60 minutes each day for three days 👥 small groups	• Gather, Record, Display or Interpret Data • Formulate or Use Models • Communicate	• a variety of reference resources • craft supplies, including construction paper, clay, craft sticks, markers, crayons, cloth, cotton balls, craft pipe cleaners • empty boxes • glue or tape • scissors	**Prep Tips** Gather a large assortment of reference materials. Try to have magazines, books, and other visuals that provide information on various ecosystems and wildlife. **Troubleshooting** Explain to students the types of exhibits found in a wildlife center or museum. To jump-start the student activity, have a class discussion about an ecosystem with which students might not be familiar. To ensure a variety of ecosystems are represented, make a class list that shows each group's chosen organism. You may wish to ask each group to choose a leader to present the diorama to the class. **Expected Results** Students will observe and model the parts of a particular organism's ecosystem. Students should be able to describe the organism, what it needs to live, and the parts of its ecosystem, including its community, population, habitat, and niche.

Activity	Inquiry and Design Process Skills Focus	Materials	Prep Tips, Troubleshooting, and Expected Results
Lesson 2 DIRECTED INQUIRY Flipchart p. 20 **A Model a Food Web** **OBJECTIVE** Follow directions for an investigation to make a mobile that models a food web. ⏱ 25 minutes 👥 small groups	• Formulate or Use Models • Gather, Record, Display or Interpret Data • Observe • Communicate	• magazines • scissors • construction paper or thin cardboard • different colored markers • glue • string or yarn	**Prep Tips** Identify websites that are best suited for this activity. Suggest students bring in old magazines from home. Students can cut out photos from the magazines, or they can download or draw pictures. Review the definitions of *producer*, *consumer*, and *decomposer* before students begin the activity. Begin a class discussion about a particular food web and the food chains within the web. Allot time for students to conduct research about a particular food web they will model. **Troubleshooting** Encourage students to place organisms from the top of the food web at the top of the mobile. Securing pictures to thicker construction paper or cardboard will help keep the pictures from curling and possibly tangling the food web. You may wish to have a larger piece of cardboard or construction paper for the top of the food web. Be sure students leave enough room on their mobiles to add labels of the organisms. **Expected Results** Student models will vary. A sample model might show a mobile of a pond food web. The living things in the food web would include birds, snakes, turtles, frogs, aquatic plants, small fish, and insects.
INDEPENDENT INQUIRY Flipchart p. 20 **B What Does It Eat?** **OBJECTIVE** Plan and conduct research, organize information, and display information about a food chain. ⏱ 35 minutes 👥 small groups	• Gather, Record, Display or Interpret Data • Communicate • Formulate or Use Models	• variety of materials of students' choice	**Prep Tips** Review how food chains and food webs are different and how each is useful. Students may use reference books or the Internet for their research. Explain to students they will be making a model of a food chain using materials of their choice. They can make a computer-based model using a software program, or they can use materials such as clay or paper to display their food chains. **Troubleshooting** Have students brainstorm different food chains, and list their ideas on the board. **Expected Results** Students will make a physical or computer model that depicts a food chain. Models should includes appropriate labels. Students should be able to communicate to others what their model represents and explain how energy flows through the food chain.

Planning for Inquiry (continued)

Activity	Inquiry and Design Process Skills Focus	Materials	Prep Tips, Troubleshooting, and Expected Results
Lesson INQUIRY 3 GUIDED INQUIRY **Flipchart** p.21 Student Edition pp. 205–206 **How Can We Model a Food Web?** OBJECTIVES • Investigate food webs. • Model a food web. ⊙ 35–40 minutes 👥 pairs	• Formulate or Use Models • Communicate • Gather and Record Data • Draw Conclusions	• shoebox • construction paper • discarded magazines • modeling clay • scissors • markers • glue stick • toothpicks • fishing line or other sturdy string (optional) • index cards	**Prep Tips** Review the definition of an ecosystem, habitat, and niche. Provide examples of each. Identify resources for research, including websites. You may wish to plan a trip to the library or set aside time for students to use Internet resources to research ecosystems. Ask students to bring in or have available shoeboxes or other boxes for each pair. You may wish to show an image or model representation of an ecosystem and discuss the food webs within that ecosystem. **Troubleshooting** Be sure students understand they will need to depict a food web in their ecosystem and to carefully research the niche of each organism in the ecosystem and how it fits into the food web. Tell students to take notes and make a drawing of the type of food web they will model. The shoebox will be the base of the diorama. After the box is turned sideways, students can draw or color parts of the ecosystem on the inside of the shoebox. Students can use clay, construction paper, and other materials to make replicas of plants, animals, and nonliving things in their ecosystems. Step 2: Students may find it easier to draw the picture on paper and glue it inside the box. Depending on the number of organisms depicted in the ecosystem, students may need more than one index card to write descriptions about their ecosystems. Some students may need to suspend objects in their dioramas to show objects in air or water. Use a pencil or paper clip point to make a small hole in the top of the diorama and feed the line or string through the hole. Knot the string on top of the box to secure it. **Expected Results** Student models should show both living and nonliving parts of the ecosystems. Living parts should include producers, consumers, and decomposers. Students should be able to explain the role of each organism in the food web.

 Go Digital! Virtual Lab

How Can We Model a Food Web?
Key Inquiry Skills: Use Models, Observe, Infer, Record Data, Graph
Students track populations in a model ecosystem to see how drought affects the members of a food web.

Additional teaching support for all inquiry activities is available in Online Resources.

Activity	Inquiry and Design Process Skills Focus	Materials	Prep Tips, Troubleshooting, and Expected Results
Lesson 4 DIRECTED INQUIRY Flipchart **p.22** **(A) Recycle Resources Yourself** **OBJECTIVE** Follow directions for an investigation to make recycled paper out of newspaper 🕐 20–30 minutes 👥 individuals	• Observe • Predict • Compare	• newspaper • large pan • flat board • blender • water • screen (must fit inside large pan) • large sponge (optional to absorb excess water and spills)	**Prep Tips** A 13 × 9 pan and a screen of the same size or bigger works well. If you use this size, 2 cups of water and 1 sheet of paper should be plenty. Pieces of screen can be purchased at a local hardware store. It will take from 12 to 48 hours for the paper to dry. **Caution!** Have students notify you immediately of any spills. Water can make surfaces slippery and cause falls. Follow manufacturer's safety precautions when using electrical appliances. Students should have an adult use the blender. When performing the activity, students should wear aprons to protect their clothing. **Troubleshooting** Paper should be torn into pieces small enough to fit easily into blender. Pour enough water in the blender to cover paper. Set blender to puree setting and run until there are no remaining large chunks. Step 4: Hold the screen over the pan until the water has stopped dripping. Then, place the screen within a section of newspaper for flattening. Step 5: Alternatively, place a layer of waxed paper over the pulp and use a small paint roller or rolling pin to gently press out the remaining water. Step 6: Let the pulp layer dry slightly before removing screen. **Expected Results** Students will have a rough sheet of paper after the pulp dries. Students should conclude that the homemade paper differs from notebook paper because it is thicker and less smooth.
INDEPENDENT INQUIRY Flipchart **p.22** **(B) Map It!** **OBJECTIVE** Plan and conduct research to identify local natural resources and make a map to show where those resources are located. 🕐 30–40 minutes 👥 individuals	• Observe • Plan and Conduct a Simple Investigation • Gather, Record, Display or Interpret Data • Communicate • Compare	• markers or crayons • paper • ruler (optional for straight edge or for scaling) • newspaper clippings • local map	**Prep Tips** Prior to the activity, ask students to observe and list things in their community such as bodies of water, farmland, local foliage, and gardens. Tell students to observe habitats and record what organisms in the habitats need to live. Remind students that things in the community, such as roads and buildings, likely are built with materials that utilize natural resources such as rock or trees. **Troubleshooting** Have available a local map, which students can use both as an example and as a way to locate some local natural resources. Students can use the diagram on the Flipchart as a guide in designing their own maps. **Expected Results** Students' maps should include natural resources in the community and should be accurately represented on the map. Maps can be a representation of part of the community. All maps should include symbols, labels, and a map key.

Planning for Inquiry (continued)

Activity	Inquiry and Design Process Skills Focus	Materials	Prep Tips, Troubleshooting, and Expected Results
Lesson 5 DIRECTED INQUIRY Flipchart **p. 23** **A How Does Water Pollution Affect Plants?** **OBJECTIVE** Follow directions for an investigation to determine how a plant is affected by water pollution. 🕐 25 minutes to set up plants; 10 minutes per day every third day for 10 days to record observations 👥 small groups	• Observe • Compare • Gather, Record, Display or Interpret Data • Communicate • Measure • Predict • Draw Conclusions • Identify and Control Variables	• 2 potted plants (both plants should be the same kind) • measuring cup (for water) • ruler (to measure height of plant) • teaspoon (to add vinegar to water) • water • marker • vinegar	**Prep Tips** Place plants in the classroom a few days prior to beginning the activity to ensure they are acclimated to classroom conditions. Put vinegar in small containers to avoid having students handle a large or glass container. To help students control variables, provide all groups with plants of the same variety, of nearly equal heights, and planted in similar containers. The control plant should be labeled A; the plant with the vinegar solution should be labeled B. **Caution!** Have students notify you immediately of any spills. Water can make surfaces slippery and cause falls. Direct students to wash their hands after this activity. Vinegar is an acid. Wear goggles and keep hands away from eyes. **Troubleshooting** Have students keep pairs of plants together to ensure that the amount of sunlight and temperature are the same for both plants. Step 2: ¼ to ½ cup of water may be enough depending upon plant size. Some subtle changes may be evident after 3 days. More significant changes can be noted after 6 days and 9 days in Step 5. **Expected Results** Students should find that Plant *A* thrived. Plant *B* likely stopped growing or lost leaves. Students should realize that the vinegar modeled acid rain. The activity showed how acid rain affects plants in the environment.
INDEPENDENT INQUIRY Flipchart **p. 23** **B All About Recycling** **OBJECTIVE** Plan, conduct research, and communicate about local recycling practices. 🕐 35 minutes for research; 20–25 minutes to make the brochure 👥 small groups	• Gather, Record, Display, or Interpret Data • Communicate	• heavy paper (brochure paper optional) • markers or crayons	**Prep Tips** You may wish to assign a different material for each group to research. Recyclable materials include plastics, different colored glass, cardboard, newspaper, aluminum cans, steel cans, magazines, office paper, and other items. **Troubleshooting** Students can use community resources, such as government agencies, to conduct their research on local recycling practices. If possible, find community websites that offer links to some of these agencies. Have available a few bi-fold or tri-fold brochures to give students an idea of what their brochure might look like. Students can use both sides of a sheet of paper or they can design two sheets of paper and glue them together before folding. **Expected Results** Students should produce a color brochure that outlines a recycling practice in the community. Information on brochures should include the type of material recycled, where it is recycled (and how it gets there), and uses for the recycled material.

Activity	Inquiry and Design Process Skills Focus	Materials	Prep Tips, Troubleshooting, and Expected Results
Lesson **INQUIRY 6** GUIDED INQUIRY **Flipchart** p. 24 Student Edition pp. 233–234 **How Do People Affect Their Environment?** OBJECTIVES • Observe and compare the rate of decay of different materials. • Record numerical data in a data table and descriptive data in sketches. • Understand that some environmental changes are beneficial and some are harmful. • Understand the affect that trash can have on the environment. ⏱ 15–20 minutes to set up; 5–10 mintues once a week for 3 weeks 👥 small groups	• Observe • Predict • Infer • Gather, Record, Display or Interpret Data • Compare	• apple core • banana peel • plastic spoon • plastic cup • soil • clean, empty soda can • large plastic bin • plastic disposable gloves	**Prep Tips** Prior to the activity ask students to bring in rinsed soda cans, plastic cups, and plastic ware. On the day of the activity you may wish to have a class snack of bananas and apples and use leftover items for the activity. Students can also bring leftover items from their lunches that day. Find a location where the bins can be left undisturbed for the duration of the activity. Pre-measure the amount of soil needed for the container you will be using. **Caution!** Direct students who will be handling soil to wear gloves. Check for allergies to latex before distributing gloves. Also have students wear aprons and goggles. Direct students to wash their hands after completing this activity. **Troubleshooting** Step 3: Cover the bin to keep out bugs and control odors. Place newspaper under the bin to catch dirt spills. **Expected Results** Students will find that even biodegradable items take a long time to decompose. Some items will never decompose.

 Go Digital! Virtual Lab

How Do People Affect Their Environment?
Key Inquiry Skills: Use Models, Compare, Record Data, Plan and Conduct Simple Investigations.
Students use a simple model to describe the rate at which different materials in a landfill decay over time.

Activity	Inquiry and Design Process Skills Focus	Materials	Prep Tips, Troubleshooting, and Expected Results
S.T.E.M. **Engineering and Technology** **Flipchart** p. 25 **Solve It: Getting Around a Dam** OBJECTIVES • Use the five steps of the design process to devise a way to help salmon swim around dams. • Understand the impact of dams on ecosystems. ⏱ 25–30 👥 individuals	 1 **Find a Problem** 2 Plan and Build 3 Test and Improve 4 **Redesign** 5 Communicate	• Materials to be chosen by students.	**Prep Tip** It may be easier for students to draw their designs on graph paper. Identify resources students can use to find out more about salmon behavior. **Expected Results** Students should be able to plan and draw a diagram for several kinds of structures that would allow salmon to migrate up ro down a damned river. They should also be able to list the advantages and disadvantages of each design, select the best one, and explain their design to a group.

Differentiated Instruction

Customize and Extend

You can extend and customize science instruction for your students using the following resources.

Leveled Readers

The **Science & Engineering Leveled Readers** can be used to provide additional nonfiction reading practice in the subject area of Unit 4.

ON-LEVEL This Reader reinforces unit concepts. It includes student response activities for your students.

EXTRA SUPPORT This Reader shares title, illustrations, vocabulary, and concepts with the On-Level Reader. However, the text is linguistically accommodated to provide simplified sentence structures and comprehension aids. It also includes response activities.

ENRICHMENT This high-interest nonfiction Reader enriches and extends unit concepts. It reinforces some of the unit vocabulary, includes *stretch vocabulary*, and includes response activities.

TEACHER GUIDE

The accompanying **Teacher Guide** provides teaching strategies and support for using all the Readers, as well as English and Spanish worksheets that focus on vocabulary development. A correlation to the Disciplinary Core Ideas of the Next Generation Science Standards is included.

DIGITAL VERSIONS

All of these Leveled Readers are available online. They are also available in an innovative and engaging format for touchscreen mobile devices. Contact your HMH Sales Representative for more information.

RTI Response to Intervention

Response to Intervention is a process for identifying and supporting students who are not making expected progress toward essential learning goals.

The following *ScienceFusion* components have the flexibility to be used to provide Core Classroom Instruction (Tier 1), strategic intervention (Tier 2), and intensive intervention (Tier 3).		
Component	**Location**	**Strategies and Benefits**
Student Edition, Active Reading prompts Sum It Up!, Brain Check	Active Reading throughout each lesson, Sum it Up! and Brain Check at the end of each lesson	Student responses can be used as screening tools to assess whether intervention is needed.
Assessment Guide, Lesson Quizzes	pp. AG 38–AG 43	Student responses can be used as screening tools to assess whether intervention is needed.
Inquiry Flipcharts	Inquiry Flipchart pp. 19, 20, 22, 23	Directed Inquiry for students who learn best through directed or teacher-led hands-on activities.
Teacher Edition, Unit Review Answer Strategies	TE pp. 239–242	Suggestions for intervention, guidance, and remediation for each review question.
Leveled Readers	TE p. 171J	Content support for students not meeting the learning needs during core classroom instruction.
Leveled Readers, Teacher Guides and Vocabulary Worksheets	TE p. 171J	Direct instruction with small groups of students needing additional content at various readability levels.
Extra Support for Vocabulary and Concepts (online worksheets)	Online Resources	Support for individualized instruction with practice in essential content.
Online Student Edition with Audio	Online Resources	Provides learners with multiple-modality access to science concepts and information.
Interactive Digital Lessons and Virtual Labs	Online Resources	Provides individualized learning experiences. Lessons make content accessible through simulations, animations, videos, audio, and integrated assessment.

Differentiated Instruction

English Language Learners

Choose from these instructional strategies to meet the needs of English language learners. Suggestions are provided for adapting the activity for three proficiency levels. Point-of-use strategies also appear within unit lessons.

☑ Unit Vocabulary

Lesson 1	Lesson 2	Lesson 4	Lesson 5
ecosystem	food chain	natural resource	pollution
community	herbivore	renewable resource	conservation
population	carnivore	nonrenewable resource	endangered species
habitat	omnivore		
niche	food web		
producer			
consumer			
decomposer			

Vocabulary Cards are provided in Online Resources.

Vocabulary Activity

Which One Is It?

Explain that non-examples can often give as much information about something as examples. Non-examples tell what something is *not*. Model an example/non-example for the class. For instance, say the word *red*. Hold up a red object and a blue object. Have students identify the example and the non-example. Continue with a term from the unit. For instance, say the term *renewable resource*, and show a wind turbine and a barrel of oil. When students are comfortable with the concept, organize them into small groups to carry out the activities.

Beginning	Intermediate	Advanced
Give each group a stack of note cards on which the vocabulary terms are written. Cards should also include an image that represents the term. Students take turns drawing a card, saying the vocabulary term, and presenting one example and one non-example (words or pictures in their books or ones they have drawn). For example, for *herbivore*, they may show or draw an elephant (example) and a lion (non-example). The first student to identify the example of the term gets a point. The student with the most points wins.	Give each group a stack of note cards on which the vocabulary terms are written. One student in the group orally presents a term, example, and non-example to group members. Students may also use pictures as needed. Provide sentence frames as an additional aid. *Which picture shows _____? Which picture shows a producer? Which is a _____, _____ or _____? Which is a producer, the grass or a dog?* The first student to identify the example gets a point. The student with the most points wins.	Have students make picture dictionaries for the terms by drawing or using images from magazines. Have students label each page with one term. Below the term, have them glue or draw a picture of an example and a non-example. Beneath each picture, they should write 2–3 sentences explaining their reasoning. Suggest they use a red crayon or marker to make the "no" symbol over the non-example. They can circle the example in green.

☑ Model Concepts

Using Natural Resources

Remind students that *natural resources* are materials found in nature that are used by living things. Elicit examples of natural resources, and discuss how people use them. Provide pairs of students with poster board on which they can make a poster about resource use to display in the classroom. Have scissors, discarded nature magazines, glue, and colored pencils or markers available and ready for students to use.

Beginning	Intermediate	Advanced
Provide magazines or picture books. Ask students to find or draw pictures that show natural resources and how we use them. Draw a two-column chart on the poster board with the heads *Natural Resource* and *How We Use It.* Students should place or draw pictures in the chart. Assist them in writing one- or two-word labels. Have students display their posters in the classroom.	Ask students to find or draw pictures that show natural resources and how we use them. Have students add a title to their poster. Students should label or caption the images with words, phrases, or simple sentences. Provide the sentence frame: *People use _____ to/ for _____.* Have students present their posters orally to the class.	Ask students to find or draw pictures that show natural resources and how we use them. Require students to write several sentences telling where these resources come from and several ways people use them. Have students present their posters to the class.

☑ Model Inquiry Skills

Observe, Predict, Infer

As students prepare to complete the Inquiry Lesson, *How Do People Affect Their Environment?,* ask them to think about what happens to trash they throw away. Where does it go? Define *landfill* as a place where trash is buried. Explain that the plastic container and the soil in the activity represent a landfill. Have students list examples of trash they throw out at home. Define the term *decompose* as to "break down" or "decay." Remind students that decomposers are organisms that break down dead plants and animals and return nutrients to the soil.

Beginning	Intermediate	Advanced
Define the inquiry skills and use them in context: *observe* means "watch something carefully;" *predict* means "guess what will happen before it happens;" and *infer* means "explain what you think happened based on what you already know." Ask how scientists use these skills.	Define and review the inquiry skills and terms. Explain that an *inference* (an untested conclusion based on your observations) is made when you use what you already know to explain your observations. (Example: Someone on the floor is crying. You can infer that the person fell and is hurt.) Ask students to discuss the Inquiry and tell what they observed, predicted, and inferred about the decomposition of various materials.	Define and review the inquiry skills and terms. Have students give examples of how scientists' observations and predictions help people. (Example: The discovery that pollution harms coral reefs is a warning to people to control pollution before the reefs are damaged further.) As scientists, have students discuss the observations, predictions, and inferences they make in the Inquiry and make a list of solutions to trash disposal.

Energy and Ecosystems

I Wonder Why

Use the images and the question to stimulate interest in the unit topic. Ask students how cars get energy. Remind them that living things need "fuel" too. Invite them to share any ideas they may have about energy and living things.

Here's Why

Have students turn the page and read the response to the question. You may wish to share the following background with students.

More About...

Coral Reefs

Coral reefs are made of the remnants of hundreds of coral skeletons cemented together. Colonies of living coral grow on top of these skeletons. Corals themselves are classified as animals, and are related to jellyfish and anemones. Worldwide, about 500 million people depend on coral reefs for food and or income from fishing, building materials, and tourism. About 30 million people actually live on the tops of reefs that form islands called atolls.

Even though all of the world's shallow-water coral reefs total less than 0.015 percent of the ocean, the reefs harbor more than one-quarter of the ocean's biodiversity. Coral reefs are known as "the rain forests of the sea."

UNIT 4

Energy and Ecosystems

Big Idea

Ecosystems are made up of both living and nonliving parts that impact one another.

I Wonder Why

Why are these living things able to move and grow? How do they get their energy? *Turn the page to find out.*

171

🍎 **Professional Development** **Science Background**

Use the keywords to access

- Professional Development from **The NSTA Learning Center**
- SciLinks for additional online content appropriate for students and teachers
- Teacher Science Background in the back of this Teacher Edition and in the Planning Guide

Keywords

ecosystems
food chains
food webs

SciLINKS
THE WORLD'S A CLICK AWAY

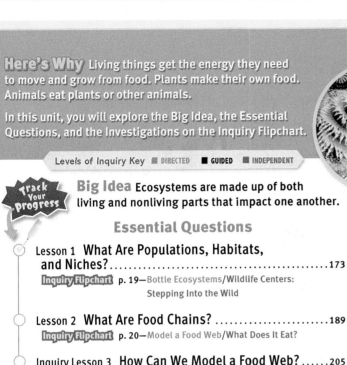

Here's Why Living things get the energy they need to move and grow from food. Plants make their own food. Animals eat plants or other animals.

In this unit, you will explore the Big Idea, the Essential Questions, and the Investigations on the Inquiry Flipchart.

Levels of Inquiry Key ■ DIRECTED ■ GUIDED ■ INDEPENDENT

Track Your Progress

Big Idea Ecosystems are made up of both living and nonliving parts that impact one another.

Essential Questions

Now I Get the Big Idea!

Science Notebook
Before you begin each lesson, be sure to write your thoughts about the Essential Question.

172 Unit 4

💻 **Go Digital**

For a complete digital curriculum and resources that provide full coverage of the objectives for this unit, see the Online Resources for this program.

Big Idea and Essential Questions

Big Idea Ecosystems are made up of both living and nonliving parts that impact one another.

Post the Unit Big Idea on the board. Have students read the Essential Questions, which are also the titles of the lessons in this unit.

- Discuss how the Essential Questions can help them focus on the Big Idea.

- Have students read the Big Idea statement. The statement describes the main science concept they will be learning.

- Have students predict other ideas that will be taught in the lessons based on the titles, or have them give examples of pictures they expect to see.

Once they have completed all the lessons, they should have a better understanding of the Big Idea.

Essential Questions You may use the following Science Notebook strategy for working with the Essential Questions before students begin the unit or lessons in the unit.

- Strategies for revisiting the Big Idea and Essential Questions are provided in Enduring Understandings on page 239A.

Notebook ▸ **Science Notebook**

- Have students copy the Essential Questions into their Science Notebooks. Suggest they leave writing lines between questions.

- Ask students to write responses to the Essential Questions. Urge students not to worry about whether their responses are correct. They should expect their ideas to change as they work in the unit. Comment that students will be able to review and revise their answers to the Essential Questions at the end of the unit.

- Tips and strategies for using Science Notebooks are provided throughout this unit, in the Planning Guide, and in Online Resources.

Options for Inquiry

FLIPCHART P. 19

Students can conduct these optional investigations at any time before, during, or in response to the lesson in the Student Edition.

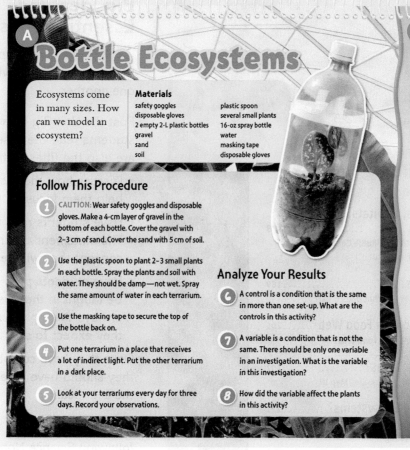

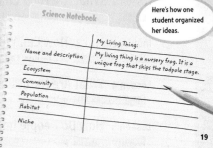

Bottle Ecosystems

Ecosystems come in many sizes. How can we model an ecosystem?

Materials
safety goggles
disposable gloves
2 empty 2-L plastic bottles
gravel
sand
soil
plastic spoon
several small plants
16-oz spray bottle
water
masking tape
disposable gloves

Follow This Procedure

1. CAUTION: Wear safety goggles and disposable gloves. Make a 4-cm layer of gravel in the bottom of each bottle. Cover the gravel with 2–3 cm of sand. Cover the sand with 5 cm of soil.

2. Use the plastic spoon to plant 2–3 small plants in each bottle. Spray the plants and soil with water. They should be damp—not wet. Spray the same amount of water in each terrarium.

3. Use the masking tape to secure the top of the bottle back on.

4. Put one terrarium in a place that receives a lot of indirect light. Put the other terrarium in a dark place.

5. Look at your terrariums every day for three days. Record your observations.

Analyze Your Results

6. A control is a condition that is the same in more than one set-up. What are the controls in this activity?

7. A variable is a condition that is not the same. There should be only one variable in an investigation. What is the variable in this investigation?

8. How did the variable affect the plants in this activity?

Wildlife Centers: Stepping Into the Wild

Some of Earth's ecosystems are found in places that most people will never visit. However, to see a variety of living things, we need only journey as far as our local wildlife center. Suppose you're a scientist who must design a new exhibit for an organism. What do you need to know about the organism before you begin? Do research to find out facts about an organism, including its ecosystem, community, population, habitat, and niche. Then make a diorama to teach others about the organism.

Here's how one student organized her ideas.

Science Notebook

My Living Thing:

Name and description	My living thing is a nursery frog. It is a unique frog that skips the tadpole stage.
Ecosystem	
Community	
Population	
Habitat	
Niche	

19

Directed Inquiry

A Bottle Ecosystems

⏱ 25 minutes
👥 small groups

Prep and Planning Tips

Allow 25 minutes for setup, and 15 minutes per day for three days for observations.

Precut the tops off the 2-L bottles. Place masking tape around the top rim to cover any sharp edges. To save time, premeasure portions of gravel, sand, and soil.

Small plants may be purchased at a local nursery and can be divided before planting. Be sure to keep roots intact. Alternatively, have students plant bean or grass seeds. Adjust activity time to allow for seeds to sprout.

Expected Results

Students will observe that plants need sunlight to grow and thrive. Guide students to understand the controls in their ecosystems are the type and layering of substrate and soil, container, type of plants, and water. The variable is the amount of light each bottle ecosystem receives.

Independent Inquiry

B Wildlife Centers: Stepping into the Wild

⏱ 30–60 minutes
👥 small groups

Prep and Planning Tips

Gather an assortment of reference materials that provide information on various ecosystems and wildlife.

Science Notebook

Suggest students use a chart similar to that shown on the Flipchart page to take and organize notes as they do their research. If possible, direct students to websites of actual wildlife centers. Have each group submit a sketch and a brief description of the diorama they wish to make, and include these details in their Science Notebooks. Have students include a sketch or a photograph of their completed displays.

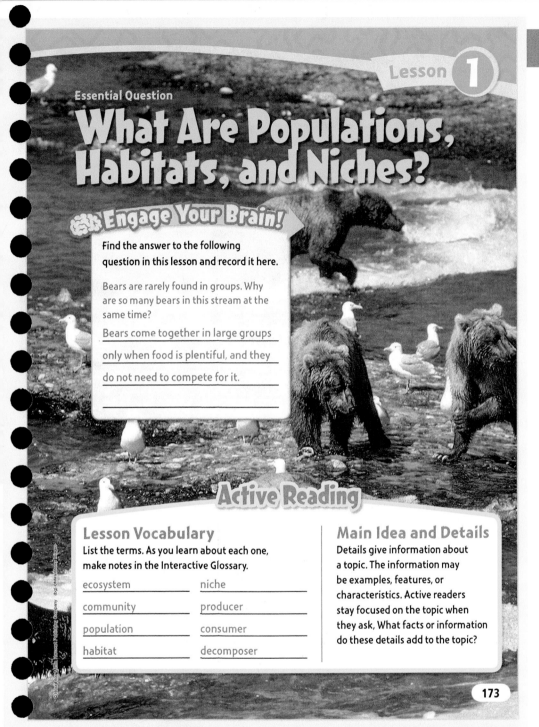

Lesson 1

Essential Question

What Are Populations, Habitats, and Niches?

Engage Your Brain!

Find the answer to the following question in this lesson and record it here.

Bears are rarely found in groups. Why are so many bears in this stream at the same time?

Bears come together in large groups

only when food is plentiful, and they

do not need to compete for it.

Active Reading

Lesson Vocabulary
List the terms. As you learn about each one, make notes in the Interactive Glossary.

ecosystem   niche

community   producer

population   consumer

habitat   decomposer

Main Idea and Details
Details give information about a topic. The information may be examples, features, or characteristics. Active readers stay focused on the topic when they ask, What facts or information do these details add to the topic?

173

Go Digital

An interactive digital lesson is available in Online Resources. It is suitable for individuals, small groups, or may be projected or used on an interactive white board.

---

1 Engage/Explore

Objectives

- Distinguish between *habitat* and *niche*.
- Distinguish between *population* and *community*.
- Explain the organization of populations, communities, and ecosystems.
- Describe an organism's niche at various stages of its life cycle.

Engage Your Brain!

Help students brainstorm answers to the question "Why are so many bears in this stream at the same time?"

Ask students to name living things found in and around the stream and to consider what bears eat. Record student responses on the board. Remind students to record their final answer to the question when they find it on the eighth page of this lesson in the discussion of how animals get the food they need to survive.

Active Reading Annotations

Inform students that active readers "make texts their own" by annotating them with notes and marks that help with comprehension. Encourage students to use pencil, not pen, to make annotations and to feel free to change their annotations as they read. The goal of annotation is to help students remember what they have read.

Vocabulary and Interactive Glossary

Remind students to find and list the yellow highlighted terms from the lesson. As they proceed through the lesson and learn about the terms, they should add notes, drawings, or sentences in the extra spaces in the Interactive Glossary

2 Explain

Generate Ideas

Have students describe the weather and the types of plants and animals that are common in their local area. After reading the title and introductory paragraph, explain to students that organisms use living things and nonliving things in their environment to meet their needs. Ask: **Would you expect to see a penguin in your neighborhood? Why or why not?** Sample answer: No. The area where we live does not have the living and nonliving things that a penguin needs to meet its needs.

Active Reading

Remind students that the main idea may be stated in the first sentence, or it may be stated elsewhere. To find a main idea, active readers ask, What is this passage mostly about?

Develop Science Concepts

Discuss how all the parts of an ecosystem are connected. For example, deserts in the southwestern United States are generally hot and dry and desert soil does not contain much moisture. Plants in this region of the United States have adaptations, such as wide root systems, for quickly absorbing rain. The plants also have adaptations, such as thick stems and leaves, for storing that water for future use. Animals use the plants as a source of water.

Where would you most likely find a polar bear—in a cold or in a warm environment? An orange tree? A walrus? Have students give reasons why these and other living things live only in certain areas.

Who Lives Where?

Rain forests have rainy weather. Deserts have dry weather. Each place meets the needs of the organisms that live in it.

Active Reading As you read this page, underline the main idea.

All of the living and nonliving things in an area make up an environment. The living things in an environment include people, plants, and animals. The nonliving things include water, air, soil, and weather. All of the living and nonliving things in an area and their interactions make up an **ecosystem** [EE•koh•sis•tuhm].

An ecosystem may be as large as a lake or as small as the area under a rock. Ecosystems are found everywhere organisms live and interact—in water or on land. Some ecosystems include coral reefs, savannas, swamps, rain forests, and the polar ecosystems.

All parts of an ecosystem are connected. For example, the soil and the temperature of a place determine the types of plants that can grow there. In turn, the types of animals in an ecosystem depend on the plants it contains.

A great variety of plants and animals thrive in rain forests, where the weather is always warm and wet.

Coral reefs are made up of the outer skeletons of coral animals. These reefs are home to many types of organisms.

174

English Language Learners

Classify Living Things and Nonliving Things Instruct students to draw pictures of living things (e.g., tree) and nonliving things (e.g., rock) on index cards. Have them work in pairs and take turns drawing cards and identifying the object represented on each one as a living thing or a nonliving thing. Provide the following sentence frames to aid students in describing each object. A _____ is a nonliving thing. A _____ is a living thing.

Polar ecosystems are very cold and dry. Organisms that live there have adaptations to survive the cold weather. Organisms that live in wetlands such as swamps, where pools of water cover the land, have adaptations, too. Cypress trees, for example, have strong trunks and thick roots that hold the tree in place.

Organisms are not evenly distributed among the different ecosystems. The greatest diversity of plants are found in tropical rain forests. By comparison, few plants live in polar ecosystems.

Within a large ecosystem, there are smaller ecosystems. Some frogs in tropical rain forests, for example, live their entire lives perched on a few trees.

Similarly, in the ocean, certain fish, sponges, seaweeds, sharks, and sea turtles make their homes in or around coral reefs. Many of these organisms could not live elsewhere in the ocean. Coral reefs make up less than one-tenth of ocean ecosystems. But about one-fourth of all kinds of sea organisms live in or around coral reefs.

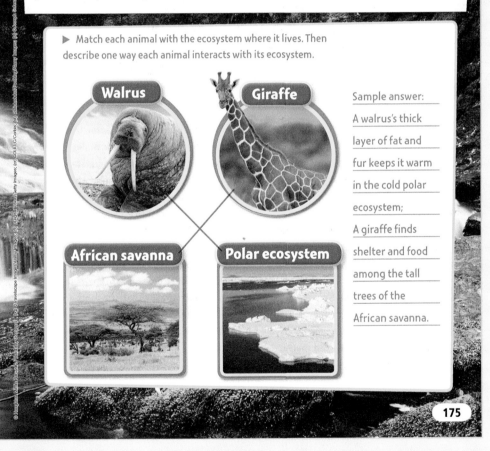

▶ Match each animal with the ecosystem where it lives. Then describe one way each animal interacts with its ecosystem.

Walrus

Giraffe

African savanna

Polar ecosystem

Sample answer: A walrus's thick layer of fat and fur keeps it warm in the cold polar ecosystem; A giraffe finds shelter and food among the tall trees of the African savanna.

175

Develop Science Vocabulary

ecosystem Write the term *ecosystem* on the board. Underline the word part *system*. Explain that a system is made up of parts that work together. Give an example of a system, such as the skeletal system, in which bones work together to support the body. Explain that an ecosystem also has parts that work together. **What are the parts of an ecosystem?** soil, weather, air, water, plants, animals, rocks

Interpret Visuals

After students complete the Interactivity, discuss ways each animal interacts with its environment. Share with students that a walrus can eat 3,000 to 6,000 clams during a single feeding. **Where might a walrus find food in its environment?** in cold waters along the shore **Which parts of the savanna does a giraffe use for food?** twigs and leaves from trees

Develop Inquiry Skills

INFER Why might many of the living things in coral reefs be unable to survive in other parts of the ocean? Sample answer: The areas of the ocean where coral reefs develop have the right temperature and light levels for the animals that live in and around them. Coral reefs provide shelter and a food source for other living things. Without the protection of a coral reef, the animals would be attacked by predators. Without food, the animals would die.

 Notebook **Summarize Ideas**

Encourage students to think about the different ecosystems described on these pages. Invite students to choose one of the ecosystems and to describe, orally or in writing, the living things and nonliving things found in that ecosystem and one way the living things and nonliving things interact.

Differentiation — Leveled Questions

Extra Support

Why doesn't a giraffe live in the Arctic? Sample answer: A giraffe doesn't have a thick layer of fat to protect it from the severe cold of the Arctic.

Challenge

Which types of animals live in wetlands with pools of water? Sample answer: I would expect to find ducks, fish, frogs, and other animals that usually live in a wet environment.

2 Explain (continued)

 ▸ **Generate Ideas**

Ask a volunteer to read aloud the introductory text. Discuss with students ways in which they have heard the term *community* used as it relates to the place in which they live. Have students describe the living things that make up their communities.

Active Reading

Remind students that the main idea may be stated in the first sentence, or it may be stated elsewhere. To find a main idea, active readers ask, What is this paragraph mostly about?

Develop Science Vocabulary

community Tell students that a community includes all of the organisms that live in the same place. Explain to students that their community includes all of the people, dogs, cats, plants and all other organisms that live in the same area.

population Write the population of several cities on the board. **What does the term *population* refer to?** (the number of people in each city) Reinforce that a population is made up of only one type of living thing. The numbers you wrote on the board represent the number of people only—not dogs and cats.

Develop Science Concepts

Remind students that the terms *community* and *population* both refer to living things. However, a population has only one type of living thing, and a community is made up of all the living things. **Which populations make up our school's community?** Sample answer: the students, teachers, and office workers make up the human population; the classroom plants and pets make up the non-human populations.

Nearby Neighbors

You and your neighbors are part of a community. Plants and animals form communities, too.

Active Reading As you read these two pages, put brackets [ ] around each paragraph's main idea.

Look at this picture. The zebras, the elephants, the grasses, and the shrubs—in fact, all the living things shown—form a community.[A **community** is made up of all the organisms that live in the same place.]

[Natural and human activities change communities over time.]On the savannas of Africa, for example, water is scarce during the dry season. As a result, many organisms die. Fires are also common. Lightning causes most of these fires; however, people start some, too.

[Fires kill some organisms, but many more survive.]Grasses have deep roots

that are not harmed by fire. Some trees have thick, fire-resistant bark. Moles, gophers, and other small animals stay away from fire by hiding underground. Larger animals, such as zebras, antelopes, lions, and hyenas, run fast to escape fire.

[Spring thunderstorms bring the rainy season to the savanna.]Grasses, shrubs, and trees grow back quickly. Animals that survived the fire give birth to their young. With so much grass to eat, the mothers are able to make enough milk to feed the calves, and the animal populations grow.

176

 Math Connection

Make a Bar Graph

In a savanna, fires can cause different populations to decrease. Have students use the following information to make a bar graph showing animal populations in a savanna ecosystem before and after a fire.

Population before fire	Population after fire
zebras 38	zebras 25
moles 212	moles 100
jackal berry trees 7	jackal berry trees 2

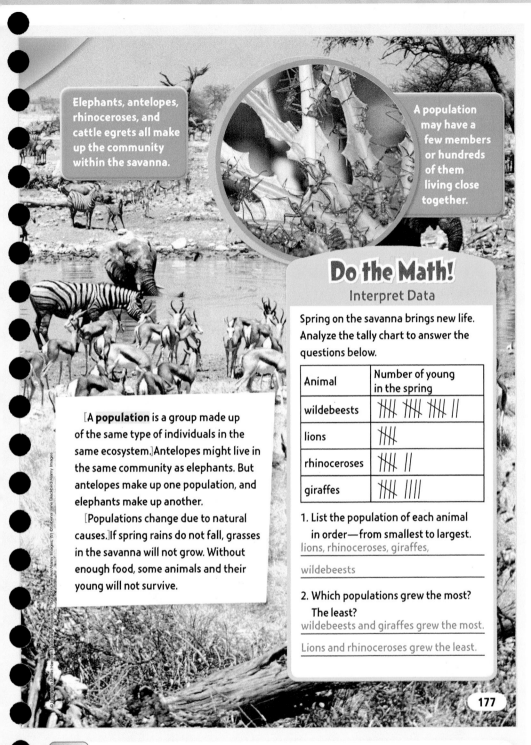

Elephants, antelopes, rhinoceroses, and cattle egrets all make up the community within the savanna.

A population may have a few members or hundreds of them living close together.

[A **population** is a group made up of the same type of individuals in the same ecosystem.]Antelopes might live in the same community as elephants. But antelopes make up one population, and elephants make up another.

[Populations change due to natural causes.]If spring rains do not fall, grasses in the savanna will not grow. Without enough food, some animals and their young will not survive.

Do the Math!
Interpret Data

Spring on the savanna brings new life. Analyze the tally chart to answer the questions below.

Animal	Number of young in the spring
wildebeests	卌 卌 卌 ||
lions	卌
rhinoceroses	卌 ||
giraffes	卌 ||||

1. List the population of each animal in order—from smallest to largest.
   lions, rhinoceroses, giraffes, wildebeests

2. Which populations grew the most? The least?
   wildebeests and giraffes grew the most.
   Lions and rhinoceroses grew the least.

177

Interpret Visuals

Direct students to the photo of the ants. **How would you classify this group of ants—as a population or as a community?** a population **What can you infer about the size of the ant population based on the number of ants on this one plant?** Sample answer: The ant population is likely very large.

Develop Inquiry Skills

INFER **How could a fire change the savanna community shown on these two pages?** Burrowing animals would dig deep in the ground to escape the fire. The elephants, antelopes, and zebra would run away. Birds would fly away. Grasses, shrubs, and trees would burn. **How could spring rains change this community again?** Spring rains would cause plants to grow again. With food available, animals could return.

Do the Math!

Interpret Data

Guide students as they complete the Do the Math activity. Ask: **What information is shown on the tally chart?** types of animals and the number of each type born in the savanna **How many populations are shown on the chart?** four **Which population had more young—wildebeests or lions?** wildebeests

Summarize Ideas

Notebook

Have students develop a summary statement that describes how living things are organized into populations and communities in the savanna. Suggest students use the main ideas they bracketed on these pages to help them. Have students share their summaries orally or in writing.

Writing Connection

Write a Brochure Have students write a travel brochure for the African savanna. Their brochures should include a description of a community of organisms found in the savanna. Encourage students to find or draw pictures of the animals and plants that make up the different populations found in the community. Tell students to add descriptive captions that describe how each population interacts with the other populations in the community.

2 Explain (continued)

 ### Generate Ideas

Ask students if they have ever gone to the refrigerator or pantry expecting to find a snack and discovered someone else had taken it. If so, they have experienced competition first hand! Two people in their household had competed for the same food, and the other person won. Have students list other examples of competition they have experienced.

Active Reading

Remind students that signal words show connections among ideas. *For example* and *for instance* signal examples of an idea. *Also* and *in fact* signal added facts. Active readers remember what they read because they are alert to signal words.

Develop Science Concepts

Explain to students that habitats include the living things and nonliving things an organism needs to live. A frog's habitat includes the insects it uses for food as well as the water in which it swims. Each population has a niche in its habitat.

What do tadpoles eat in this pond? algae **Which organism overlaps this niche?** mosquito larvae **How do their niches overlap?** The tadpoles and the mosquito larvae compete for algae in the pond.

Explain that some fish also share a niche with tadpoles because the fish also eat the algae in the pond. When tadpoles become frogs, they no longer eat algae and no longer share that niche with fish or mosquito larvae.

A Place of One's Own

All organisms have the same basic needs. Different organisms meet their needs in a number of ways. Read on to find out about where an organism finds what it needs in an ecosystem.

Active Reading As you read the next page, circle the clue words or phrases that signal a detail.

Ponds are busy ecosystems filled with different populations of organisms and habitats. In and around ponds, the habitats of many organisms overlap. As a result, different kinds of organisms often have to interact.

Tadpoles

Mosquito larvae and tadpoles often share the same habitat. They use the same resources for food and shelter

Mosquito larvae

178

English Language Learners

Understand Meaning Students may have difficulty understanding the meaning of *niche*. Use a soccer team as an analogy. Draw a soccer field on the board, and label it *habitat*.

Label the stadium *ecosystem*. Point out that each player has a different job, or role. Have students explain how each player on a soccer team is like a species in a habitat with its own niche.

Organisms find the resources they need in their habitat. A **habitat** is the physical part of the ecosystem that meets the needs of an organism. Organisms find food and shelter in their habitats.

Every organism in a habitat has a role, or **niche**. The way an organism interacts with the habitat and gets food and shelter are part of its niche. Every organism has body parts that help it fit its niche. A duck, for example, has webbed feet and oily feathers to help it swim and stay warm.

Some animals, such as frogs, change niches during their life cycle. At first, tadpoles live in water, breathe through gills, and eat algae. As adults, frogs breathe through lungs, live at the water's edge, and eat insects.

Organisms compete for resources when their habitats and niches overlap. Tadpoles and mosquito larvae, for instance, compete for algae in a pond. Crowded plants at a pond's edge may compete for a place to grow and for sunlight.

Tree swallow

Adult frog

As tadpoles grow into adult frogs, their niche changes. Adult frogs compete with tree swallows for food. They both eat insects.

▶ Identify two organisms that share food or other resources in an ecosystem. Sample answer: The adult frog and the tree swallow compete for some of the same resources. They both eat insects.

179

Differentiation — Leveled Question

Extra Support

What body parts does a frog have that help it in its niche? Sample answers: long legs for jumping, a long tongue for catching insects

Challenge

How does the niche of a mosquito larva change after it becomes an adult? Sample answer: The larvae live in water and eat algae. An adult mosquito flies through the air and eats food it finds on land.

Develop Science Vocabulary

habitat Read aloud the definition of *habitat*. Explain that the word *habitat* is from the Latin word meaning "to dwell." *Dwell* means "live." An organism's habitat is the place where it lives to get what it needs to stay alive. Be sure students understand that a habitat is not a synonym of *shelter*.

niche Reinforce that a niche is a role that one type of living thing has in its habitat. Ask students to describe their own niche. Then have them describe how that niche will likely change as they get older.

Interpret Visuals

Draw students' attention to the images on these pages. Have students compare the tadpoles and the mosquito larvae. Explain that both organisms are generally a few millimeters long. As students complete the Interactivity, ask: **Which three living things are shown?** bird, frog, and insect **Which living thing will be used for food?** the insect **What do you think would happen if the frog always got to the insect first?** the bird might not meet its need for food

Develop Inquiry Skills

DRAW CONCLUSIONS **Would a duck living in the pond ecosystem likely compete with a tadpole? With an adult frog? Explain.** Ducks may actually compete with *both* tadpoles and frogs, as they eat a wide range of foods. In fact, some ducks actually eat small frogs!

Notebook ▶ **Summarize Ideas**

Instruct students to select two organisms described on these pages and to explain orally or in writing each organisms' niche in the habitat.

2 Explain (continued)

 Generate Ideas

Direct students to examine the photos and read the captions on these pages. Brainstorm possible answers to the question, How do other living things get their food? Write students' ideas on the board.

Active Reading

Remind students that signal words show connections among ideas. *For example* and *for instance* signal examples of an idea. *Also* and *in fact* signal added facts. Active readers remember what they read because they are alert to signal words.

Develop Science Concepts

Help students understand the importance of producers. **Would most living things on Earth survive if there were no producers? Explain your answer.** No. Producers capture the energy from the sun that consumers need to survive. Energy passes from producers to consumers.

Stand in front of the class and take a bite of an apple or a carrot stick. **Am I a producer or a consumer? Explain.** You are a consumer, because you eat other living things.

Develop Inquiry Skills

INFER Help students connect the concepts they learned earlier in this lesson with the ideas presented on this page. Tell them to picture two animals. One lives in a rainforest ecosystem and has flat teeth. The other lives in a polar ecosystem and has sharp teeth. **Which animal would more likely be a consumer of other animals? Explain.** The animal that lives in a cold place and has sharp teeth will most likely eat other animals.

Dinner Time!

Water, air, sunlight, and presto, dinner is served! Plants are able to use water, air, and solar energy to make their own food. Read these pages to learn how other living things get their food.

Active Reading As you read these pages, circle the words that signal details.

A strawberry plant uses water, carbon dioxide, and energy from the sun to make its own food. The boy and the squirrel eat the strawberries for energy.

180

 Differentiation — Leveled Questions

Extra Support

How do plants get food? They make their own food using water, air, and sunlight.

How do animals get food? They eat plants or other animals; they cannot make their own food.

Challenge

Do animals that eat only other animals depend on plants? Yes. Because animals cannot make their own food, the hunted animals probably eat plants. All animals are directly or indirectly dependent on plants for food.

Any living thing that makes its own food is called a **producer**. Trees and algae are types of producers. Animals can't make their own food, but they need energy, too. An animal that eats plants or other animals to get energy is called a **consumer**.

A field of strawberry plants may provide energy for many organisms. For example, consumers, such as birds, opossums, mice, squirrels, and people may eat the plant's fruit. Deer, rabbits, and insects may prefer to eat the plant's leaves.

Consumers often compete for food in their habitats. When there is too much competition, some organisms die. For example, if there are too many rabbits in a habitat, they all won't have enough food to eat. Some will die, and the rabbit population will decrease. In time, when the plants they eat grow back, the rabbit population may grow larger again.

An overripe fruit, a falling leaf, or a dying strawberry plant provides energy for another group of organisms called decomposers. A **decomposer** is a living thing that breaks down wastes and the remains of plants and animals for energy. Fungi and bacteria are two types of decomposers.

Gray mold covers these strawberries. As the mold breaks down the fruit, it returns nutrients back to the soil for the plant to use.

▶ What could happen if too many consumers were competing for the same food source in a habitat?

Sample answer: As the amount of available food decreased, the consumer population(s) would also decrease.

181

English Language Learners

The Suffix -er Explain that the suffix -er means "one who," so the word *producer* means "one who produces." Point out that several other words on these pages have the suffix -er. Examples:

decompose (v)   decomposer (n)

consume (v)   consumer (n)

Encourage students to think of other word pairs in which the verb is changed to a noun with the addition of -er. (teach/teacher, speak/speaker, walk/walker)

Develop Science Vocabulary

producer Ask students to name some things that they produce, such as a book report, a painting, or a drawing. Point out that when they produce something, they make it. Plants make their own food, and thus are called producers.

consumer Explain that people who buy things are called consumers. **How are people who buy things like animals that eat things?** (They both use things.) Reinforce that the word *consume* means "to use."

decomposer Write the term *decomposer* on the board, and underline the prefix de-. Explain that de- means "to undo." *Compose* means "to put together." Ask students to combine the word parts and explain what a decomposer does.

Interpret Visuals

Before students complete the Interactivity, direct them to review the photos on these pages. **Which living things get energy from the strawberries?** squirrel, boy, mold **Where does the strawberry plant get energy?** The strawberry plant uses water, carbon dioxide, and energy from the sun to make its own food for energy. **Point out that there are many types of organisms eating the plants. In a healthy ecosystem, there are many more producers than consumers. Have students consider what might happen if the number of producers were reduced, or the number of consumers increased in an area. Then have them complete the Interactivity.**

Notebook ▶ **Summarize Ideas**

Suggest that students use details found on these pages to summarize what they have learned about producers, consumers, and decomposers. Students can summarize their ideas orally or in writing.

2 Explain (continued)

Notebook ▶ Generate Ideas

Ask students to list items that they recycle at home or school. Write their responses on the board. **What happens when an item is recycled?** It is broken down, and the materials it is made of are used to make something new. Remind students that decomposers get energy from breaking down wastes and remains of other living things. Ask: **In what way is decomposing like recycling?** Write students' responses on the board.

Interpret Visuals

Direct students to the image of the rotting log. **What is happening to the log?** The fungi growing on the log are breaking it down and helping it decay. **How is this process helpful?** The log will break down, and nutrients will be returned to the soil. **Direct** students to the image of the corn leaves on the facing page. **Is this fungus helpful or harmful? Explain.** It is harmful, because it is attacking a plant people use for food.

⚠ Misconception Alert ⚠

Some students may think that all bacteria are bad. After all, bacteria are involved in the spoilage of food and cause many diseases. Commercials for antibacterial cleaners try to convince consumers that the only good bacteria are dead bacteria. The truth is, most bacteria are completely harmless. They live all around us in the soil and on surfaces and generally cause no problems for people. Some bacteria are actually vital for good health. Bacteria help us digest our food, produce vitamins, and provide competition for "bad" bacteria that can cause disease.

Why It Matters

Doing the Dirty Work

You open a bag of bread and right away your nose detects a musty scent. You see greenish-blue dots in the bread and think, *"Yuck, mold!"*

Usually, finding mold growing in our foods in not a pleasant experience. Yet mold and other decomposers play important roles. Molds, mushrooms, and yeasts are types of fungi. Fungi and bacteria are the main types of decomposers.

Decomposers help recycle materials in ecosystems. When an organism dies, decomposers go to work. Fungi and bacteria produce chemicals that help them break down and absorb nutrients from dead organisms and wastes. As decomposers feed, they release useful materials back into the environment. Plants use these materials to grow. When these plants die, the decomposers go to work again.

These fungi grow on dead tree trunks, which helps the trunks decay.

182

123 Math Connection

Solve a Word Problem Each of the homes on a city block has a large backyard compost bin that holds 340 cubic decimeters (12 cubic ft) of material. The bins are emptied once each year. If there are 16 homes on the block, how much compost would be produced by these families in one year?

340 × 16 = 5,440

5,440 cubic decimeters

Bacteria in some foods, such as cheese and yogurt, help you absorb nutrients.

In a compost bin, moldy bread can be turned into soil nutrients.

Sometimes having decomposers in our food is exactly what we want. For example, yeast is used in baking to make bread rise, and bacteria add taste and texture to milk products, such as sour cream and cheese.

Decomposers can even help with human-made pollution. Scientists and engineers use bacteria and fungi to break down oil spills. Often, they simply add nutrients or oxygen to help decomposers already in the environment do their work.

Corn rust is a fungus that infects and kills sweet corn plants.

▶ Identify harmful and beneficial effects of decomposers.

Sample answer: Decomposers break down and return nutrients to ecosystems, help people process and digest food, and help us clean up the environment. Decomposers can also spoil our foods and may infect crops.

183

Develop Science Concepts

Review the meaning of the word *decomposer*. Ask a volunteer to define *decomposer* in his or her own words. A decomposer is a living thing that breaks down other living things.

Help students complete the Interactivity by reinforcing that decomposers can be both helpful and harmful to other living things. **Is mold on bread harmful or helpful?** harmful, because the bread can no longer be eaten

Suggest that students draw a vertical line down the center of the Interactivity box to make a two-column chart. Have them record harmful effects in one column and beneficial effects in the other column. Remind students to put the appropriate headings at the top of each column.

Develop Inquiry Skills

OBSERVE Display images of different types of fungi, such as slime molds, puffballs, dead man's fingers, and earthstars. Have students carefully observe the fungi and note details, including shape, color, size, and where each is growing. Model how to make a two-column chart with the names of the fungi in the first column and space for recording observations in the second column. After students complete their observations, discuss as a class what students observed about fungi.

 Notebook ▶ **Summarize Ideas**

Suggest that students review the photos and captions on these pages and then summarize the beneficial and harmful roles of decomposers. Students can summarize their ideas orally or in writing.

Differentiation — Leveled Questions

Extra Support

How would forests look without decomposers to break down logs? Dead trees would litter the forest floor without decomposers to break them down.

Challenge

Why would the material produced in a compost bin be good for a garden? Compost is plant matter that has been broken down by decomposers. This process releases nutrients that can be used by growing plants.

3 Extend/Evaluate

Sum It Up!

- Tell students to go back through the lesson and reread the highlighted terms. Suggest that they also review the images and captions to help them remember important information.

- You may wish to read the Summarize section together as a class. Point out that important words from this paragraph are to be defined in the word web that follows.

- Be sure students understand how to complete the word web. Have them reread the summary and look for the terms included in the web. Suggest that they use different colors to underline in the summary important information about each term they need to describe or define.

- Remind students to use the Answer Key to check their answers. Students should revise incorrect responses so they can use the Sum It Up! page to study for tests.

When you're done, use the answer key to check and revise your work.

Use the information in the summary to complete the idea web by writing a definition or a description for each term.

Summarize

All the living and nonliving things found in an area make up an ecosystem. Within an ecosystem, all the organisms that live in the same place make up a community. A group of elephants that live on a savanna is a population. A habitat is the phyiscal part of an ecosystem that meets the needs of an organism. Each living thing in a habitat has a role, or niche. Plants are producers because they make their own food. Animals are consumers because they get energy by eating other living things. Organisms that feed on the waste and remains of plants and animals are called decomposers.

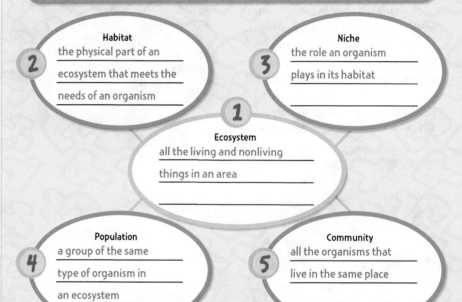

Habitat
2 the physical part of an ecosystem that meets the needs of an organism

Niche
3 the role an organism plays in its habitat

Ecosystem
1 all the living and nonliving things in an area

Population
4 a group of the same type of organism in an ecosystem

Community
5 all the organisms that live in the same place

Answer Key: 1. all the living and nonliving things in an area **2.** the physical part of an ecosystem that meets the needs of an organism **3.** the role an organism plays in its habitat **4.** a group of the same type of organism in an ecosystem **5.** all the organisms that live in the same place

© Houghton Mifflin Harcourt Publishing Company

184

 **Brain Check**

Name _____

Word Play

1 Use the examples to help unscramble the words.

1. S C R O D E P O M E   D E C O M P O S E R
   a bacteria found in yogurt

2. B A I T A T H   H A B I T A T
   where an organism finds food and shelter

3. R E C R O P U D   P R O D U C E R
   grass

4. N A T I L O P U P O   P O P U L A T I O N
   a group of elephants living on the savanna

5. N E C I H   N I C H E
   an adult frog in a pond eating dragonflies

6. M E S S Y O C T E   E C O S Y S T E M
   a rain forest

7. U S E R M O N C   C O N S U M E R
   a lion

8. M I N T M U C O Y   C O M M U N I T Y
   frogs, birds, and plants at a pond

185

Answer Strategies

Word Play

1. If students are having difficulty unscrambling the letters, provide a word bank. Suggest that students compare the number of letters in the scrambled and unscrambled words as an additional aid to solving each item.

   As a challenge, have them use each unscrambled word in a sentence that shows its meaning.

Assessment

Suggested Scoring Guide
You may wish to use this suggested scoring guide for the Brain Check.

Item	Points
1	24 (3 points per item)
2	20
3	12 (2 points per item)
4	10 (5 points per item)
5	12
6	6
7	10
8	6
Total	100

Lesson Quiz
See Assessment Guide, p. AG 38.

3 Extend/Evaluate (continued)

Answer Strategies

Apply Concepts

2. Make sure that students understand that they are to both draw a picture and then describe their drawing in terms of producers, consumers, the community they comprise, and the number of organisms in one population. Remind students that producers are plants that make their own food. Consumers eat plants or other animals for food. Encourage them to include several of each organism so that a population count can be made.

3. Have students determine if the illustration is of a plant, an animal, or a fungus. Then have them use a process of elimination, such as thinking "This organism cannot be a producer, because it eats grass." Or, "This organism must be a producer, because it makes its own food."

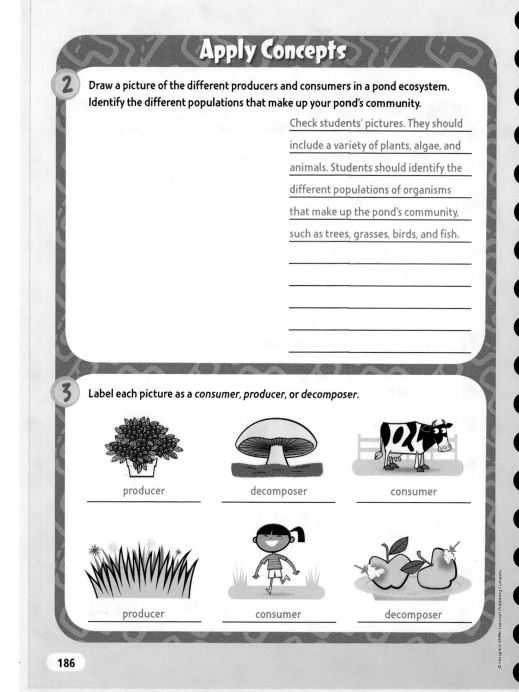

Apply Concepts

2 Draw a picture of the different producers and consumers in a pond ecosystem. Identify the different populations that make up your pond's community.

Check students' pictures. They should include a variety of plants, algae, and animals. Students should identify the different populations of organisms that make up the pond's community, such as trees, grasses, birds, and fish.

3 Label each picture as a *consumer, producer,* or *decomposer.*

producer   decomposer   consumer

producer   consumer   decomposer

186

Name _____

4 Use the picture to answer the questions below.

a. Which organisms make up this ecosystem's community?

Sample answer: The community is made up of cactuses, snakes, jackrabbits, and coyotes (or wolves).

_____

b. Which organism has the smallest population? The largest?

Coyotes have the smallest population; jackrabbits have the largest.

_____

5 Complete the Venn diagram to compare and contrast decomposers and consumers.

Decomposer

Decomposers get energy from the remains of dead plants and animals and from wastes.

Both

Neither decomposers nor consumers produce their own food.

Consumer

Consumers eat other living things for food.

© Houghton Mifflin Harcourt Publishing Company

187

Answer Strategies

Apply Concepts

4. Tell students to review portions of the lesson about ecosystems, communities, and populations. Suggest to struggling students that they circle the members of each population with different colored pencils. The different colors will aid them in determining the size of each population.

5. Make sure students understand that there are three parts of the diagram to complete. The parts of the diagram that overlap should contain information about how producers and consumers are alike. The outer circles should list the characteristics that are different between the two

3 Extend/Evaluate (continued)

Answer Strategies

Apply Concepts

6. Write *consumer*, *producer*, and *decomposer* on the board. Have volunteers give an example of each. Elicit that mold is a decomposer, and review images on the pages that describe decomposers.

7. Ask students to reread the pages on which niches are described. **What is a niche?** the way an organism interacts with its habitat **What parts of this ecosystem have a niche?** animals and plants

8. Guide students in understanding the role of the tree in the ecosystem shown. Have students describe how trees obtain energy and the functions of different tree parts.

 Take It Home!

See *ScienceSaurus*® for more information about ecology. *ScienceSaurus* is a "mini-encyclopedia" students can use to find out more about unit topics. It contains numerous resources including concise content summaries, an almanac, many tables, charts, and graphs, history of science, and a glossary.

---

6 Is mold that grows on bread a consumer, a producer, or a decomposer? How do you know?

Sample answer: Mold is a decomposer. It does not make its own food. It gets the energy it needs by breaking down the bread into simpler substances.

7 Identify the parts of the ecosystem shown.

Sample answer: The ecosystem includes the birds, insects, tree, flowers, rocks, grass, air, and bench.

8 In the picture above, what is the tree's niche?

Sample answer: The tree grows leaves full of chlorophyll that helps it make its own food. It has a bark that protects it from insects. The tree's roots anchor it to the soil. The roots also help the tree get nutrients and water from the soil.

 Take It Home! See *ScienceSaurus*® for more information about ecology.

188

Make Connections

Easy
Math Connection

Solve a Problem

A shrew is a consumer that eats about $\frac{2}{3}$ of its body weight daily. Suppose a student who weighed 30 kilograms (66 lb) could eat $\frac{2}{3}$ of his or her body weight in a single day. How many kilograms of food is that?

$30 \times \frac{2}{3} = 20$ kg (44 lb) of food every day

Average
Social Studies Connection

Ecosystems Around the World

Write on the board several types of ecosystems, such as desert, polar, rain forest, and tundra. Display a globe or world map and have students place small self-stick notes with the name of an ecosystem in areas where they think each one can be found. Allow students to use an online encyclopedia or other resources to check their guesses.

Average
Art Connection

Make a Nature Guide

Have students take a hike with a parent to a local park or around the neighborhood. Instruct them to list all of the living things they can identify. Have them use their lists to make a nature guide describing all of the populations of organisms they found in the local community. The lists can include their own pictures, or pictures from the Internet. Suggest they also include a map that shows where each organism was sighted. Challenge students to identify each organism's niche in their descriptions.

Challenging
Writing Connection

Write a News Article

Ask students to write a newspaper-style article describing an incident in which a producer was eaten by a consumer, who in turn was eaten by another consumer. Articles should include the *who, what, when, where, why,* and *how* elements. Be sure students select appropriate producers and consumers for their articles. A polar bear, for example, would not eat a giraffe, because the two animals live in different ecosystems. Students may wish to add a picture and caption to their article.

Options for Inquiry

FLIPCHART P. 20

Students can conduct these optional investigations at any time before, during, or in response to the lesson in the Student Edition.

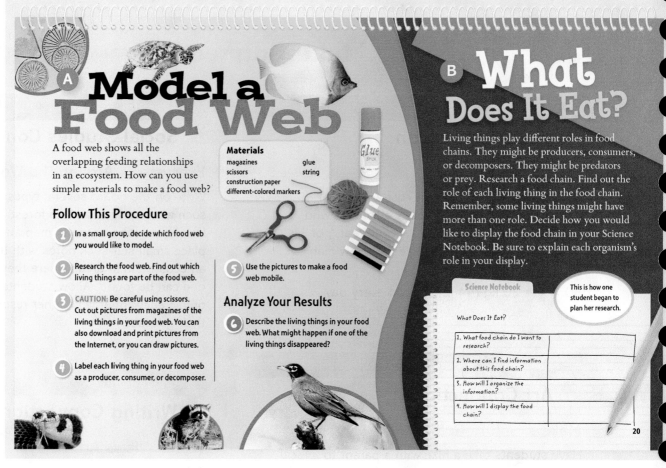

A Model a Food Web

A food web shows all the overlapping feeding relationships in an ecosystem. How can you use simple materials to make a food web?

Materials
magazines
scissors
construction paper
different-colored markers
glue
string

Follow This Procedure

1. In a small group, decide which food web you would like to model.

2. Research the food web. Find out which living things are part of the food web.

3. CAUTION: Be careful using scissors. Cut out pictures from magazines of the living things in your food web. You can also download and print pictures from the Internet, or you can draw pictures.

4. Label each living thing in your food web as a producer, consumer, or decomposer.

5. Use the pictures to make a food web mobile.

Analyze Your Results

6. Describe the living things in your food web. What might happen if one of the living things disappeared?

B What Does It Eat?

Living things play different roles in food chains. They might be producers, consumers, or decomposers. They might be predators or prey. Research a food chain. Find out the role of each living thing in the food chain. Remember, some living things might have more than one role. Decide how you would like to display the food chain in your Science Notebook. Be sure to explain each organism's role in your display.

Science Notebook

This is how one student began to plan her research.

What Does It Eat?

1. What food chain do I want to research?
2. Where can I find information about this food chain?
3. How will I organize the information?
4. How will I display the food chain?

20

Directed Inquiry

A Model a Food Web

🕐 25 minutes
👥 small groups

Prep and Planning Tips

Suggest that students bring in old magazines from home. Students can cut out photos from the magazines, or they can download or draw pictures.

Review the definitions of *producer, consumer,* and *decomposer* before students begin the activity.

Begin a class discussion about a particular food web and the food chains within the web. Allow time for students to conduct research about a particular food web they will model.

Expected Results

Student models will vary. A sample model might show a mobile of a pond food web. The living things in the food web would include algae, aquatic plants, insects, frogs, fish, snakes, turtles, and birds. Students should realize that if one living thing in the food web disappeared, all living things in the food web would be affected.

Independent Inquiry

B What Does It Eat?

🕐 35 minutes
👥 small groups

Prep and Planning Tips

See the Planning for Inquiry page for more information. Review how food chains and food webs are different and how each is useful.

Science Notebook

Students can use the Science Notebook as a model for their own investigation. Encourage them to use different formats to display their food chains. They can draw a food chain or make clay models of the organisms in a food chain. They can use computer graphics programs to make a food chain. Regardless of the format, suggest that students use arrows to show the flow of energy from one organism to the next.

Essential Question

What Are Food Chains?

Engage Your Brain!

Find the answer to the following question in this lesson and record it here.

Is this frog a predator, or is it prey?

The frog is both a predator and

prey.

Active Reading

Lesson Vocabulary

List the terms. As you learn about each one, make notes in the Interactive Glossary.

food chain

carnivore

food web

herbivore

omnivore

Main Ideas

The main idea is the most important idea of a paragraph or section. The main idea may be stated at the beginning, or it may be stated elsewhere. Active readers look for main ideas by asking themselves, What is this paragraph or section mostly about?

189

Go Digital

An interactive digital lesson is available in Online Resources. It is suitable for individuals, small groups, or may be projected or used on an interactive white board.

---

1 Engage/Explore

Objectives

- Demonstrate that a food chain shows how energy moves from producers to consumers.
- Recognize that energy for most food chains begins with energy from the sun.
- Distinguish between herbivores, carnivores, and omnivores.
- Recognize that organisms higher in the food chain are affected by changes in the number of organisms lower in the food chain.
- Explain why all animals depend on producers such as plants.

Engage Your Brain!

Ask: **What do you think this frog eats?** Students might mention plants and other animals. **Do you think any other animals eat the frog? If so, name a few.** Yes, other animals eat the frog. Students may mention common predators. Accept all reasonable answers. **Remind students to record their final answer to the question when they find it on the sixth page of this lesson.**

Active Reading Annotations

Remind students that active readers "make texts their own" by annotating them with notes and marks that help with comprehension. Encourage students to use pencil, not pen, to make annotations as they read.

Vocabulary and Interactive Glossary

Remind students to find and list the yellow highlighted terms from the lesson. As they proceed through the lesson, they should add notes, drawings, or sentences in the extra spaces in the Interactive Glossary.

2 Explain

Notebook Generate Ideas

Read the introductory paragraph aloud. Ask: **How is it possible that energy from the sun is passed along to you?** The energy is in the food that we eat.

Have students use the photos on these pages to trace the path of energy as it flows from the sun to producers to consumers.

Active Reading

Remind students that many common words have a different meaning in science. Active readers keep the possibility in mind that science text may be using familiar words in new ways and are alert to the differences in meaning.

Develop Inquiry Skills

ORDER To help students complete the interactivity, write a scrambled food chain on the board. An example might be: minnows → algae → people → bass. Have students place the food chain in the proper order. algae → minnow → bass → people

Food Chains

Did you know that you are fed by the sun? Find out how!

Active Reading As you read these two pages, circle common, everyday words that have a different meaning in science.

Lettuce is a plant that uses energy from the sun to make its own food. When you eat lettuce, some energy passes from the lettuce to you. You can show this relationship in a food chain. A **food chain** is the transfer of food energy in a sequence of living things. In a diagram of a food chain, arrows show how energy moves. Here is a food chain that shows how energy moves from lettuce to you.

lettuce ⟶ you

The food chain above has only two steps, or links. Food chains can have more than two links. Look at the pictures to see a food chain with five links.

Producers make up the first link. In this pond, tiny algae [AL•jee] are the producers. Mosquito larvae eat the algae. They make up the second link in this food chain.

190

English Language Learners

Irregular Plurals Explain that a *larva* is a young insect that has no wings yet. The plural of *larva* is *larvae*—a plural ending with which students are probably not familiar. Review the fact that most nouns take *s* or *es* to show plural (*girls, boys, boxes, foxes*). Some nouns change their spellings, such as: *woman/women; child/children*, and some nouns remain the same for both singular and plural, as *fish* and *deer*.

Make a Food Chain

Choose a food that you ate for breakfast or lunch today. Make a food chain showing how energy from the sun flowed from the food to you.

> Food chains will vary. Students should use arrows to show how energy flows from one organism to the next. The first link in the food chain should be a producer. The last link in the food chain should be the student.

Minnows are small fish. They eat the mosquito larvae. They make up the third link in this food chain.

Bass are bigger fish. They eat the minnows. They make up the fourth link in this food chain.

People eat the bass. People make up the last link in this food chain.

191

Develop Science Vocabulary

food chain Ask students to close their eyes and visualize a chain. Remind students that a chain is made of links. Ask: **What might happen if one of the links broke apart?** The chain would break.

Lead students to understand that the organisms in a food chain are dependent on one another. If one organism in the chain disappears, the other organisms are affected.

Interpret Visuals

Tell students to imagine that the pond contains bluegill fish. Bluegill eat minnows. Bluegill are eaten by bass. **Where would bluegill go in this food chain?** They would make up the fourth link. Bass would then make up the fifth link and people the sixth link.

◆ Notebook ▸ Summarize Ideas

Have students use the photos and captions on these pages to summarize what they have learned about food chains. Students can summarize their ideas orally or in writing.

👥 Differentiation — Leveled Questions

Extra Support

Make sure students understand the concept of a food chain. Point to an arrow in a food chain. Ask: **What does the arrow show?** the transfer of energy from one organism to another

Challenge

Tell students that energy can change form as it is transferred along a food chain. Have them investigate the different forms energy takes as it flows in a food chain, such as mechanical, chemical, and thermal.

2 Explain (continued)

Notebook ▸ Generate Ideas

Read aloud the introductory paragraph: "A zebra and a lion are both consumers. But they eat very different foods. How can you group consumers by what they eat?"

Challenge students to come up with a classification system to group consumers by what they eat. After students have read these pages, have them evaluate their classification systems.

Active Reading

Remind students that organisms, such as consumers, may be grouped into categories according to specific characteristics. Active readers focus on the characteristics of specific categories as a way to remember facts about consumers in general.

Develop Inquiry Skills

CLASSIFY To help students prepare for the interactivity, tell them to first make charts classifying the animals shown in the photos on these pages. rabbit = herbivore, crocodile = carnivore, raccoon = omnivore, vulture = scavenger

You Are What You Eat

A zebra and a lion are both consumers. But they eat very different foods. How can you group consumers by what they eat?

Active Reading As you read this page, underline the sentence that identifies one characteristic that is used to classify consumers.

Consumers eat other living things. <u>They can be placed into groups according to the kind of food they eat.</u>

- A consumer that eats only plants is a **herbivore**. A zebra is a herbivore. It eats grasses and other plants.

- A consumer that eats other animals is a **carnivore**. A lion is a carnivore. It eats zebras and other animals.

- A consumer that eats both plants and animals is an **omnivore**. People are omnivores. They eat plants such as tomatoes and animals such as fish.

- A consumer that eats dead plants and animals is a **scavenger**.

A crocodile is a carnivore. It eats mainly fish. But it will eat big animals, such as hippos, when it can catch them.

A rabbit is a herbivore. It eats leafy plants during spring and summer, and woody plants during fall and winter.

192

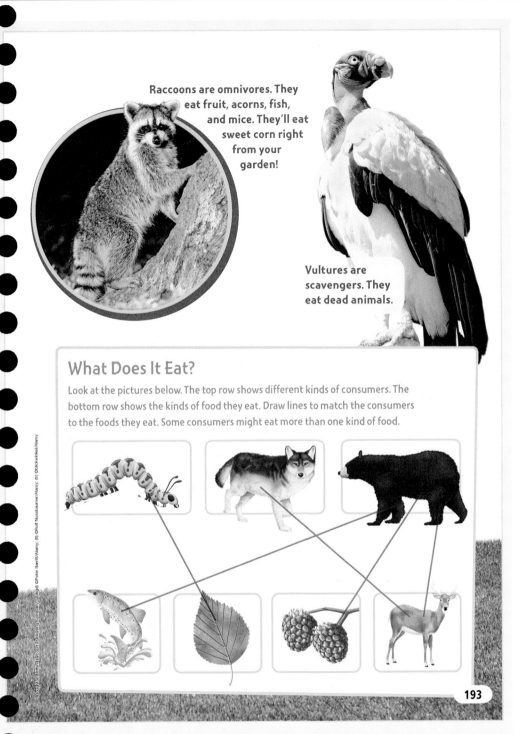

Raccoons are omnivores. They eat fruit, acorns, fish, and mice. They'll eat sweet corn right from your garden!

Vultures are scavengers. They eat dead animals.

What Does It Eat?

Look at the pictures below. The top row shows different kinds of consumers. The bottom row shows the kinds of food they eat. Draw lines to match the consumers to the foods they eat. Some consumers might eat more than one kind of food.

193

Develop Science Vocabulary

herbivore Explain that herbivore comes from the Latin words *herba*, meaning "an herb," and *vorare*, meaning "devour." Ask: **What is an herb?** a kind of plant

Suggest that students keep this meaning in mind to help them distinguish between herbivores, carnivores, and omnivores.

carnivore Explain that carnivore comes from the Latin word *carnivorus*, meaning "flesh-eating." Ask: **What do carnivores eat?** meat or flesh

Tell students that knowing the Latin origin of the word will help them distinguish between different types of consumers.

omnivore Explain that omnivore comes from the Latin word *omnivorus*, meaning "all-devouring." Ask: **What do omnivores eat?** both plants and animals

Suggest that students remember that omnivores eat "all things" to help them distinguish between different types of consumers.

 Notebook **Summarize Ideas**

Have students use their answers from the interactivity to summarize differences among herbivores, carnivores, and omnivores. Students can summarize their ideas orally or in writing.

Differentiation — Leveled Questions

Extra Support

Show students photos of different animals eating. Have students identify the animals as herbivores, carnivores, omnivores, or scavengers.

Challenge

Tell students that vegans are people who do not eat meat, fish, poultry, or animal products, such as eggs and milk. How would they classify vegans? (as herbivores)

2 Explain (continued)

Notebook **Generate Ideas**

Have students preview the title and photos on these pages. Ask: **How are the animals on these pages interacting?** Animals are either being hunted by other animals or are hunting other animals. **Tell students that these relationships represent another way to classify consumers.**

Active Reading

Remind students that active readers annotate, or mark up, text to benefit their own recollection of the information presented. It is important that students be able to explain the thinking behind their annotation.

Develop Inquiry Skills

CLASSIFY Write a list of at least 10 different consumers on the board. Direct students to first classify the animals as herbivores, carnivores, omnivores, and scavengers. Then have them reclassify the animals as predator or prey. Remind students that some animals might fit into more than one category. Ask: **What two properties did you use to classify the animals?** by what they ate and by whether they hunted or were hunters **Can you think of any other way to classify animals?** Sample answer: By species, by size, by color; accept all reasonable answers.

Hunt or Be Hunted

A lion crouches in the tall grass. Nearby, a zebra nibbles on the grass. Who is the hunter? Who will be hunted?

Active Reading As you read these two pages, draw boxes around two words that are key to understanding the main idea.

Consumers are grouped by what they eat. But you can also group consumers by whether they hunt or are hunted.

A predator is an animal that hunts other animals. Lions are predators. They often hunt in packs. This helps them catch big animals, like hippos and rhinos. They hunt smaller animals, too.

An animal that is eaten is called prey. Deer, elk, and moose are all prey for wolves in the Rocky Mountains.

Some animals can be both predator and prey. A frog might eat insects in a forest. But the frog might be eaten by a snake.

A hawk can see the movement of small animals, like this mouse, from high in the sky.

194

English Language Learners

Homophones The words *prey* and *pray* sound alike, but are spelled differently and mean different things. Write this sentence: *Predators hunt prey.* Underline the letter *e* in both words and suggest that students remember that *prey* (with an *e*) means "something hunted and eaten." The word *pray* (with an *a*) has to do with giving thanks. Call on volunteers for other homophones and ways to tell them apart.

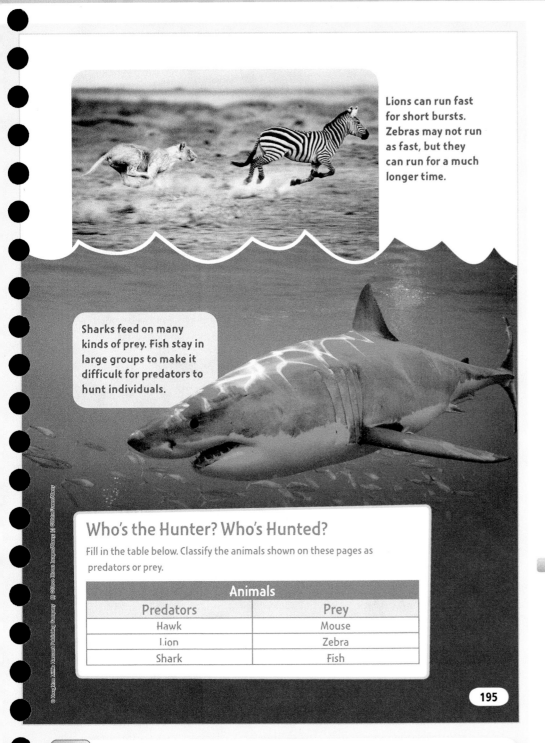

Lions can run fast for short bursts. Zebras may not run as fast, but they can run for a much longer time.

Sharks feed on many kinds of prey. Fish stay in large groups to make it difficult for predators to hunt individuals.

Who's the Hunter? Who's Hunted?

Fill in the table below. Classify the animals shown on these pages as predators or prey.

Animals	
Predators	Prey
Hawk	Mouse
Lion	Zebra
Shark	Fish

195

Writing Connection

Safari Journal Tell students to imagine that they are on a safari in Africa. They are seeing lions, zebras, hippos, and numerous other animals up close. Ask them to write a one-page journal entry describing the experience. Students can write about a predator/prey situation, or they can simply describe the animals in their natural setting.

Develop Science Skills

Have students brainstorm a list of characteristics that make an animal a good predator. Sample answer: speed, sharp teeth, sharp claws, good eyesight, good sense of smell Then ask them to repeat the activity for prey. Sample answer: ability to blend in with the surroundings, speed, good eyesight, good sense of smell

Point out that predators and prey sometimes share similar characteristics. The speed of the lion helps it to chase down prey. The speed of the zebra helps it to run away from the lion.

Interpret Visuals

To help students complete the interactivity, explain that predators have certain characteristics in common. For example, sharp teeth and razor-like claws are usually signs of a predator. Point to each photo on this page and have students decide whether the animal is a predator or prey. predator: lion, shark, hawk; prey: mouse, zebra, small fish

Notebook ▸ # Summarize Ideas

Have students use the classification charts that they completed in Develop Inquiry Skills to summarize what they have learned about predators and prey. Students can summarize their ideas orally or in writing.

2 Explain (continued)

 Generate Ideas

Ask: **What did you have for lunch today?**
Students should mention a variety of foods. **Do you always eat the same food for lunch?** no

Lead students to understand that consumers eat more than one type of food. On the next two pages, they will learn how to use a model to show different feeding relationships in an ecosystem.

Active Reading

Remind students that the main idea may be stated in the first sentence, or it may be stated elsewhere. To find a main idea, active readers ask, What is this paragraph or section mostly about?

Develop Science Concepts

Students may think that the loss of one organism in a food web might not have an impact on other organisms, given that they can eat other things. However, changes in a food web can have consequences for all the organisms in the food web.

Have students play the role of different organisms in the food web shown on these pages. Give students long pieces of yarn. Ask them to form a food web. For example, the plankton and clam should hold the ends of one piece of yarn. The lobster and clam should hold the ends of another piece of yarn, and so on. Ask: **Who would be affected if the plankton disappeared?** Tell students to tug all the ends of yarn in their hands if they are directly affected or if they feel a tug on their yarn from a feeding partner. Students should realize that all organisms would be affected if the plankton disappeared.

Food Webs

A food chain shows how energy moves from one living thing to another. But living things often eat more than one kind of food. How can you show these different feeding relationships?

Active Reading As you read these two pages, draw a line under the main idea.

Lobsters eat clams. But they also eat crabs, sea stars, and mussels. Other animals, like the shark and the octopus, eat the lobster. You can use a model to show all these feeding relationships. <u>A food web shows the relationships among different food chains.</u> Food web models use arrows to show who eats what.

These green plankton are producers. They are eaten by clams, small fish, whales, and other organisms.

Desert Food Chain

Use arrows to show how energy moves from one living thing to another in this desert food chain.

Arrows should connect cactus to insect, insect to scorpion, and scorpion to snake

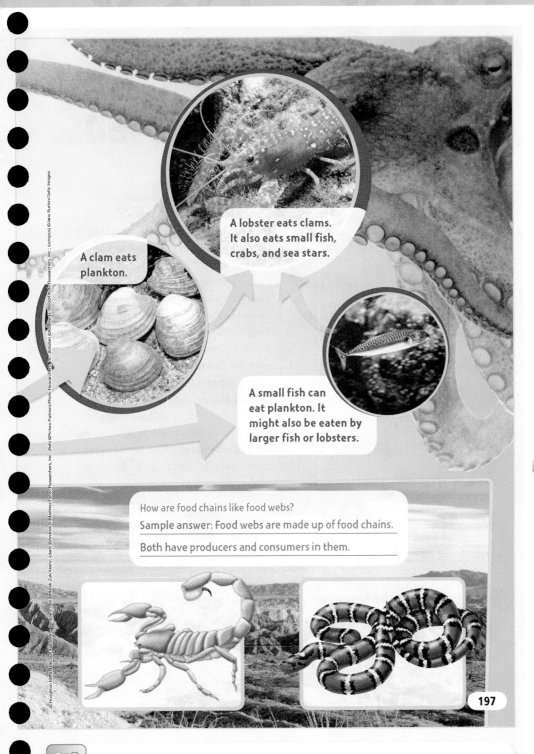

A lobster eats clams. It also eats small fish, crabs, and sea stars.

A clam eats plankton.

A small fish can eat plankton. It might also be eaten by larger fish or lobsters.

How are food chains like food webs?

Sample answer: Food webs are made up of food chains.

Both have producers and consumers in them.

197

Develop Science Vocabulary

food web Show students a photo of a spider web. Point out that the parts of the web intersect and overlap. Ask: **How is a food web like a spider web?** Sample answer: Like a spider web, a food web intersects and overlaps. It has arrows instead of thread; the arrows show feeding relationships among organisms.

Interpret Visuals

Help students complete the interactivity by discussing feeding relationships among the organisms in the photo. Ask: **What does the insect eat?** An insect eats the cactus. **How can you show this relationship?** Draw an arrow from the cactus to the insect. Repeat for the other organisms if students need additional help.

Notebook ▸ **Summarize Ideas**

Suggest that students use the photos and captions on these pages to summarize what they have learned about food webs. Students can summarize their ideas orally or in writing.

Differentiation — Leveled Questions

Extra Support

Ask students to use the photos of an ocean food web on these pages to create an ocean food chain. Suggest that they begin with the plankton. Read aloud the captions on the page to help students as they make their food chains.

Challenge

Ask students to research and draw a desert food web. Students can use the organisms shown on these pages as a starting point.

2 Explain (continued)

📓 Notebook ▸ Generate Ideas

Ask students if they have ever been to a national park, such as Yellowstone National Park in Wyoming and Montana. Show students photos of national parks. Ask: **What is a national park? Describe it in your own words.** A national park is a protected area. People cannot build houses or hunt in these parks.

Tell students that they will learn how a change in a food web in Yellowstone National Park affected other organisms, from elk to trees.

Active Reading

Remind students that signal words show connections between ideas. *For example* and *for instance* signal examples of an idea. *Also, in fact,* and *too* signal added facts. Active readers remember what they read because they are alert to signal words.

Develop Science Concepts

Have students brainstorm other factors that might affect the populations of organisms in an ecosystem. Ask: **How would disease affect the population of deer in a forest?** The population of deer would go down. **What would happen to the populations of animals that hunted the deer?** Their populations also would go down.

Why It Matters

Changes in Food Webs

Imagine that one animal disappeared. What would happen to the other living things in the food web?

Active Reading As you read these two pages, circle clue words that signal a detail such as an example or an added fact.

Changes in food webs can affect all parts of a food web. (For example,) suppose the weather was very cold in the spring. Only a few plants in a meadow might live through the cold spring. This means that the mice in the meadow would not have enough to eat. Their numbers would go down. The snakes in the meadow eat mice. Their numbers would (also) go down. The hawks in the meadow hunt snakes and mice. The hawks would be hungry, (too.)

Now suppose that the spring was warm and wet. Many plants would grow in the meadow. The mice would have plenty to eat. Their numbers would go up. The snakes and hawks would also have plenty to eat, so their numbers would go up, (too.)

198

 Math Connection

Make a Graph Have students use the data in the Do the Math Activity to make a bar graph showing the heights of the trees in Yellowstone Park. Students should plot the heights of the trees on the vertical axis. They should plot the type of tree on the horizontal axis. Suggest that students use different-colored pencils for each tree.

Food webs can be disrupted when one member of a food web goes away. This happened in Yellowstone National Park. During the early 1900s, the gray wolf was hunted in the park. Eventually, no gray wolves were left.

The gray wolf preyed mostly on elk. The number of elk in the park increased after the wolves disappeared. In 1995, scientists returned 14 gray wolves to the park. The number of wolves has since increased. As a result, the number of elk in the park has decreased.

Other changes happened, too. Elk eat trees. Before the wolves were reintroduced, the elk overgrazed the trees in the park.

This harmed the trees. Since beavers had fewer trees to build dams with, the beaver population decreased. After the wolves were reintroduced to the park, both the trees and beavers began to thrive.

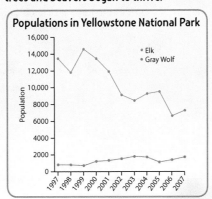

Populations in Yellowstone National Park

- Elk
- Gray Wolf

Do the Math!
Interpret Tables

The table shows the height of trees in Yellowstone National Park before and after the gray wolves returned. Study the table, and then answer the questions.

Kind of tree	Average height before 1995	Average height after 2002
Cottonwood	less than 1m	2 to 3 m
Willow	less than 1m	3 to 4 m

1. Describe the heights of the trees before the gray wolves were brought back to Yellowstone National Park.

Average height was less than 1 m.

2. Describe the heights of the trees after the gray wolves were brought back to Yellowstone National Park.

Average height ranged from 2 m to 4 m.

3. Why do you think the heights of the trees changed?

The elk were overgrazing the trees. After the wolves were returned, they preyed on the elk. The elk population decreased, and the trees began to thrive.

199

Develop Inquiry Skills

INTERPRET Use fictional data to create a line graph showing fluctuations in the population of mice over time. The graph should include peaks and valleys. Ask students to infer how a line graph of the population of snakes in the area would look over the same period of time. Students should realize that a line graph showing the population of snakes would display similar peaks and valleys, with slight variations to account for delays in responding to increases and decreases in the mouse population.

Stress that the snake data could follow a different trend if disease or other factors affected the snake population.

Do the Math!

Interpret Tables

Guide students as they complete the Do the Math activity. Suggest that they look for trends in the data. Ask: **What was the average height of the trees before 1995?** less than 1 meter **Did the average height increase or decrease after 2002?** It increased.

Suggest that students reread the text about wolves and elk in Yellowstone Park if they need additional help.

Notebook ▸ Summarize Ideas

Direct students to use the facts that are indicated by the signal words or phrases that they circled on these pages to help them identify the main idea. Suggest that they review the title and photos for additional help. They should summarize the main idea and details orally or in writing.

3 Extend/Evaluate

Sum It Up!

- Have students review the highlighted vocabulary words in the lesson.

- Tell students that each word has only one matching answer.

- It may be helpful to show students examples of photos of different consumers. Use photos in magazines or use the photos in the text.

- Point out that four of the words describe different kinds of consumers. One word describes a kind of model used to study ecosystems.

- If students are having difficulty completing the graphic organizer, have them refer to their answers in the matching activity on this page.

- Remind students to use the Answer Key to check their answers. Students should revise incorrect responses so they can use the Sum It Up! page to study for tests.

When you're done, use the answer key to check and revise your work.

Match the words in Column A to their definitions in Column B.

	Column A	Column B
1	__d__ scavenger	a. model that shows all the feeding relationships in an ecosystem
2	__c__ herbivore	b. eats other animals
3	__b__ carnivore	c. eats only plants
4	__e__ omnivore	d. eats dead animals and plants
5	__a__ food web	e. eats both plants and animals

Summarize

The idea web below summarizes the lesson. Complete the web.

Food chains show how energy moves from one living thing to another. The first link in a food chain is always a(n) 6. producer .

Herbivores are consumers that
7. eat only plants .

Omnivores are consumers that
8. eat plants and animals .

Carnivores are consumers that
9. eat other animals .

Scavengers are consumers that
10. eat dead animals and plants .

200

Answer Key: 1. d 2. c 3. b 4. e 5. a 6. producer 7. eat only plants 8. eat plants and animals 9. eat other animals 10. eat dead animals and plants

Brain Check

Name _____

Word Play

1 Use the clues to complete the crossword puzzle.

```
                                          8
                                          D
                                          E
   1                2                      C
   F O O D C H A I N                       O
         E                                 M
         R              6                  P
   4     B              P                  O
   F                    R                  S
   3
   O M N I V O R E      E                  E
   O     V              D                  R
   D     O         5                       |
         R         C A R N I V O R E
   W     E              T
   E                    O
   B              7
                  P R E Y
```

Across
1. The transfer of energy from one living thing to another
3. Consumer that eats both plants and animals
5. Consumer that eats other animals
7. Animal that is hunted

Down
2. Consumer that eats only plants
4. Shows the relationship among all the food chains in an ecosystem
6. Animal that hunts
8. Consumer that breaks down the remains of plants and animals

201

© Houghton Mifflin Harcourt Publishing Company ©Corbis

Answer Strategies

Word Play

1. Suggest that students refer back to the definitions of highlighted vocabulary words throughout the lesson. Make a word bank on the board for students who are have difficulty completing the puzzle.

Assessment

Suggested Scoring Guide
You may wish to use this suggested scoring guide for the Brain Check.

Item	Points
1	40 (5 points per item)
2	10
3	10 (2 points per item)
4	10 (5 points per item)
5	10
6	20 (10 points per item)
Total	100

Lesson Quiz
See Assessment Guide, pp. AG 39

3 Extend/Evaluate (continued)

Answer Strategies

Apply Concepts

2. Ask: **What organism always makes up the first link in a food chain?** a producer **Does a wolf eat a rabbit or does a rabbit eat a wolf?** A wolf eats a rabbit.

3. Have students scan the title, captions, and photos on the appropriate lesson pages about consumers. Students should also review the vocabulary words in the lesson.

4. Ask: **What is a predator?** an animal that hunts other animals **What is prey?** an animal that is hunted by other animals **Which picture shows a hunter?** the picture of the lion

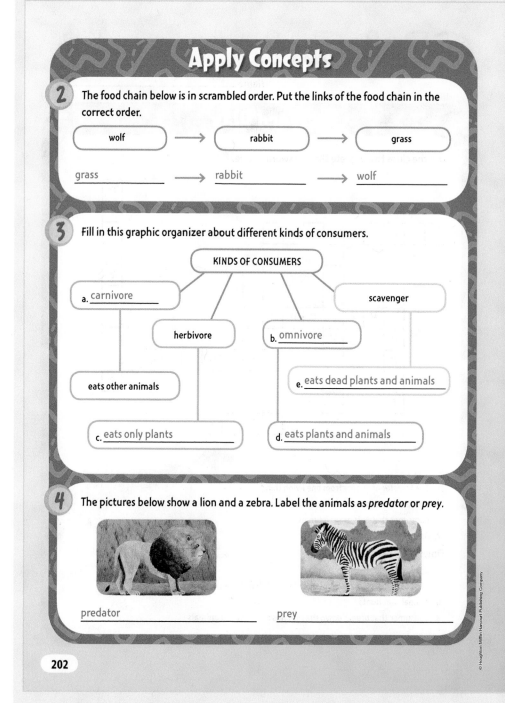

Apply Concepts

2 The food chain below is in scrambled order. Put the links of the food chain in the correct order.

wolf → rabbit → grass

grass → rabbit → wolf

3 Fill in this graphic organizer about different kinds of consumers.

KINDS OF CONSUMERS

a. carnivore

scavenger

herbivore

b. omnivore

eats other animals

e. eats dead plants and animals

c. eats only plants

d. eats plants and animals

4 The pictures below show a lion and a zebra. Label the animals as *predator* or *prey*.

predator

prey

202

© Houghton Mifflin Harcourt Publishing Company

5 The picture shows different animals in a pond food web. Use arrows to show who eats what. Remember that arrows should point from the living thing that is being eaten to the living thing that is eating.

6 In the space below, draw an ocean food chain and a forest food chain.

Question 5: Arrows should show the insects eating the small plants or other insects; the frog eating the insects; the snake eating the frogs and insects; the large fish eating the small fish; the heron eating the small fish, frogs, and large fish.

Question 6: Drawings will vary. The ocean food chain might include algae, small fish, lobsters, and sharks. The forest food chain might include shrubs, deer, and wolves. Food chains should use arrows to show the flow of energy from one organism to the next.

203

Answer Strategies

Apply Concepts

5. Suggest that students review the pond food chain in the lesson. Draw a chart on the board and list each organism in the picture. Have students say what each organism eats. Leave the chart on the board as students draw the arrows in the food web.

6. Suggest that students use only three to four links in their food chains. Remind them that all food chains start with producers.

3 Extend/Evaluate (continued)

Answer Strategies

Apply Concepts

7. Review different types of consumers. **What does an herbivore eat?** producers **What does a carnivore eat?** other animals **What does an omnivore eat?** both plants and animals **What does a scavenger eat?** dead plants and animals

8. Remind students of the wolves and elk in Yellowstone National Park. **What happened to the population of elk when the wolves were reintroduced to the park?** The population of elk went down.

 Take It Home!

As an added challenge, have students make a food chain showing the links involved in one food that they ate for dinner.

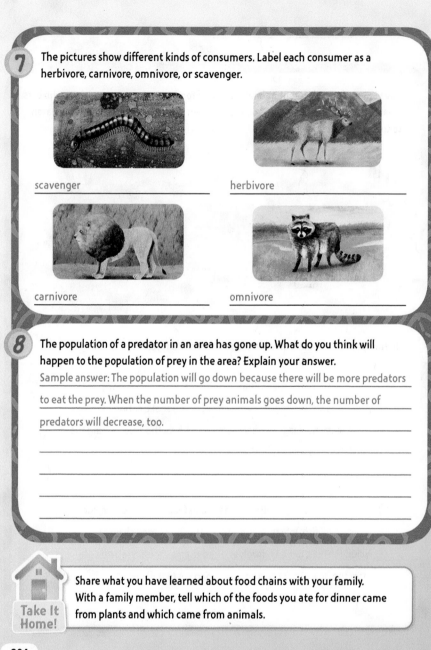

7 The pictures show different kinds of consumers. Label each consumer as a herbivore, carnivore, omnivore, or scavenger.

scavenger

herbivore

carnivore

omnivore

8 The population of a predator in an area has gone up. What do you think will happen to the population of prey in the area? Explain your answer.

Sample answer: The population will go down because there will be more predators to eat the prey. When the number of prey animals goes down, the number of predators will decrease, too.

Take It Home! Share what you have learned about food chains with your family. With a family member, tell which of the foods you ate for dinner came from plants and which came from animals.

204

Make Connections

Art Connection

Paper Food Chains

Have students cut out 4 strips of construction paper. Tell them to write one of the following words on each strip: grass, mouse, snake, and hawk. Show them how to make a chain using the strips of the paper and glue. Make sure students arrange the links of their paper food chains in the proper order.

Writing Connection

Fact Cards

Have students select a food web that they would like to learn more about. Have them make fact cards for each organism in the food web. Each fact card should contain at least two facts about the organism. Encourage students to illustrate their cards. Students can use a hole punch and string to arrange the cards into a food web.

Math Connection

Who Is Fastest?

Explain that some predators such as cheetahs run very quickly. However, prey such as gazelles can be quick, too. Have students use an online encyclopedia or nonfiction books from the school library to research the running speeds of at least five predators and five prey. Have them make a table comparing the running speeds.

Health Connection

Biomagnification

Explain that organisms can eat harmful substances. These substances can remain in the food chain and be passed on from one organism to the next. This process is called biomagnification. Have students use an online encyclopedia or nonfiction books from the school library to find out which kinds of fish might contain high levels of mercury due to biomagnification and which kinds of fish are considered safe to eat.

Guided Inquiry

FLIPCHART P. 21

⏱ 35–40 minutes

👥 pairs

Students follow the directions on the Flipchart. The accompanying Lesson Inquiry pages in the Student Edition provide scaffolding for guided inquiry.

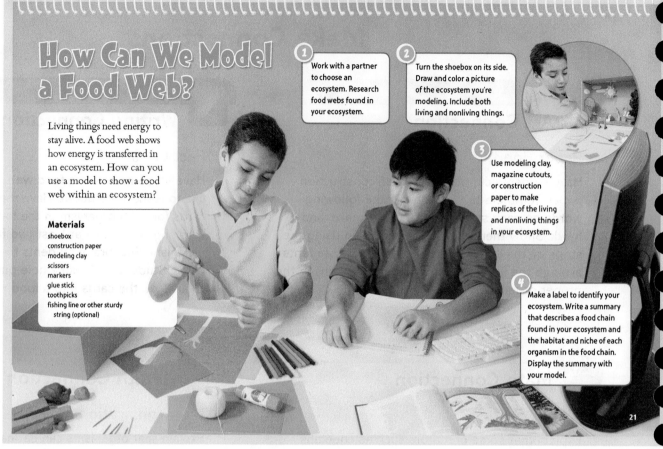

How Can We Model a Food Web?

Living things need energy to stay alive. A food web shows how energy is transferred in an ecosystem. How can you use a model to show a food web within an ecosystem?

Materials
shoebox
construction paper
modeling clay
scissors
markers
glue stick
toothpicks
fishing line or other sturdy string (optional)

① Work with a partner to choose an ecosystem. Research food webs found in your ecosystem.

② Turn the shoebox on its side. Draw and color a picture of the ecosystem you're modeling. Include both living and nonliving things.

③ Use modeling clay, magazine cutouts, or construction paper to make replicas of the living and nonliving things in your ecosystem.

④ Make a label to identify your ecosystem. Write a summary that describes a food chain found in your ecosystem and the habitat and niche of each organism in the food chain. Display the summary with your model.

21

Inquiry Skills Focus Formulate or Use Models

Objectives

- Investigate food webs.
- Model a food web.

Prep and Planning Tips

See the Planning for Inquiry page for more information.

- Review the definition of an ecosystem, a habitat, and a niche. Provide examples of each.
- Identify resources for research, including websites. You may wish to plan a trip to the library or set aside time for students to use Internet resources to research ecosystems.
- You may wish to show an image or model representation of an ecosystem and discuss the food webs within that ecosystem.

Expected Results

Student models should show both living and nonliving parts of the ecosystems. Living parts should include producers, consumers, and decomposers. Nonliving parts should include soil, water, and perhaps rocks. Students should be able to explain the role of each organism in the food web.

---

1 Engage/Explore

Attention Grabber

Invite five volunteers to stand in front of the class. Write the following terms on index cards: *prairie grass, mouse, hawk, bison,* and *fungus.* Assign each student a card. Ask each student to identify his or her role as a producer, consumer, or decomposer. Then have students take turns stating their roles in a food web. For example:

"I am prairie grass. I am a producer and food for the bison and the mouse." "I am a hawk. I am a consumer, and I use the mouse for food."

Preview Activity

Before beginning the investigation, have students review the directions on the Inquiry Flipchart and the accompanying Student Edition response pages. Then have them complete the response pages as they follow directions on the Flipchart.

Inquiry Flipchart page 21

Name _____

Essential Question

How Can We Model a Food Web?

Set a Purpose

What will you learn from this investigation?

I will learn that plants and animals in an

ecosystem are part of a food web.

Think About the Procedure

Which parts of an ecosystem will you model?

Sample answer: I will make models for

living and nonliving things found in an

ecosystem.

Why is it important to have plants, animals, and decomposers in your food web?

Plants are producers. Animals are

consumers. Some animals eat plants in

order to get energy; some eat other animals

to get energy. Decomposers get energy by

breaking down dead plants and animals

into nutrients. These nutrients are returned

to the soil, and plants use them to grow.

Record Your Data

Make a chart to classify the organisms in your ecosystem as producers, consumers, or decomposers. Describe how each organism gets its energy.

Answers will vary depending on the ecosystem chosen by the student.

205

Guide the Investigation

Develop Inquiry Skills

FORMULATE OR USE MODELS **Why do scientists use models?** Scientists use models to study objects or events that are too small or too large to observe directly. **Why are we using a model to study an ecosystem?** Many ecosystems are too large to be easily observed.

When students are choosing the ecosystem they wish to model, have them consider which nonliving things are present in the ecosystem, such as rocks, water, and air. Guide students in considering which living organisms to include. Remind them that they need producers, consumers, and decomposers.

COMMUNICATE Point out to students that models are one way scientists communicate the results of investigations to others. **How can you be sure others understand the food web shown in your ecosystem?** Sample answer: I can make a list describing all the organisms present and explain their roles in the food web.

GATHER AND RECORD DATA Tell students to carefully observe their model ecosystems and identify the organisms as producers, consumers, and decomposers. Have them use their chart to list the organisms in the proper category and describe how each one gets its energy. Remind students that organisms in a food web often get their energy by eating a variety of other living things, or they may provide energy to more than one other organism.

Go Digital

A virtual lab experience is available with the Online Resources for this program.

Complex food chains

2 Explain

Develop Inquiry Skills

DRAW CONCLUSIONS Encourage students to analyze living and nonliving parts when they are comparing ecosystems. Review with students that plants are producers and the foundations of all food chains and webs.

ANALYZE AND EXTEND Discuss students' responses to the items.

1. Remind students that predators help keep populations in check. The growth of one population can affect others, as competition for resources will increase.

2. Point out that the fungus is competing with other organisms for the energy (food) the plant provides. This competition reduces food resources for other organisms that feed on the plant.

3. With students, brainstorm events that could affect a food web (fire, flood, human activities). Point out that not all events are negative. For example, a year with plentiful rainfall and warm temperatures encourages plant growth and could result in an increase in all populations.

4. Suggest that students circle the organisms that are in both food chains. Reinforce that overlaps indicate where competition for the same food may be greatest.

3 Extend/Evaluate

5. Accept all reasonable answers. Students may ask questions about specific roles in food webs, or what would happen if some organisms were missing from the web.

Assessment

Lesson Quiz
See Assessment Guide, p. AG 40.

Draw Conclusions

How are ecosystems different from one another?

Answers will vary. Students may note that different organisms live in different ecosystems. They may also note that factors such as temperature or availability of water may differ between ecosystems.

What roles do plants have in a food web?

Plants use energy from sunlight to make their food. When animals eat plants, some of this energy is transferred to the animals.

Analyze and Extend

1. **Suppose an animal with no natural predator in an ecosystem comes to live there. How would this animal affect the food web?**

Sample answer: The population of that animal would grow. It would compete with other animals at the same level in the food web for food. Populations of other animals that eat the same food would decrease.

2. **Suppose a fungus grows on some of the plants. How might this fungus affect the food web?**

Sample answer: The plants with fungus on them might die. Then, animals that eat these plants might starve or move to a different ecosystem to find food. Animals that use these plants for shelter might need to find a new place to live.

3. **What other events might affect the food web?**

Sample answer: A flood could kill off the plants. Animals would have to find a new place to live.

---

4. **In the space below, draw two food chains that overlap in your food web. Then, write a caption that describes your picture.**

Answers will vary. Students should identify organisms in the overlapping food chains that compete for the same food.

_____
_____
_____

5. **Think about other questions you would like to ask about food webs. Write your questions below.**

Sample answer: What would happen if decomposers could not effectively do their work?

_____

© Houghton Mifflin Harcourt Publishing Company

Differentiated Inquiry

Changing Food Web Game

To help reinforce that ecosystems can change when an organism is removed or added, have students play a game in pairs or small groups.

- Ask students to write on index cards the producers, consumers, decomposers, and scavengers found in a specific ecosystem.

- Have one student shuffle the cards and lay them face up on a desk or table.

- Ask a volunteer to remove one of the cards. Have students discuss the effects on the ecosystem with the removal of that organism. Place that card in a discard pile and have a student choose another card. Repeat until all organisms have been discussed.

Aquatic Ecosystem

- Have students set up an aquatic ecosystem in order to observe its food chains and food webs. Be sure students carefully research the nonliving things that are needed for organisms to survive. Students should also make sure the living things they wish to place in the aquatic ecosystem are compatible.

- The aquatic ecosystem can be either saltwater or freshwater, although freshwater tanks are less costly to maintain.

- Living things students might consider placing in their ecosystem include *Elodea,* snails, and small community fish.

- Allow students to observe the ecosystem each day and record the interactions they see.

Build a Model Land Ecosystem

- Provide the following materials for students to build a terrarium: aquarium with screen lid, pebbles or small rocks, soil, small plants, earthworms, a water area, small pieces of wood, insects and snails, a gecko or lizard

- Layer the bottom of the container with pebbles, then charcoal, then a thicker layer of soil. Lightly moisten the soil. Add plants, then rocks and wood pieces. Carefully introduce the animals to the terrarium, and cover with a screen. Place the terrarium in a bright location, but not direct sunlight. You may want to add a thermometer to make sure the temperature remains steady. The plants should be misted regularly to maintain adequate moisture in the ecosystem.

- Allow students to observe the ecosystem each day and record the interactions they see.

Make a Computer Graphic of a Food Web

- Tell students that scientists often explain concepts by making a diagram or computer graphic that shows the interactions among living things.

- Have available software programs that allow students to utilize images, arrows, and text to model a diagram of a food web that includes labels and captions. Have students present their graphics to the class.

Options for Inquiry

FLIPCHART **P. 22**

Students can conduct these optional investigations at any time before, during, or in response to the lesson in the Student Edition.

A RECYCLE Resources YOURSELF

To recycle paper, you don't always have to toss it in a recycling bin. Here's a fun way to recycle paper yourself!

Materials
newspaper blender
large pan water
flat board screen

Follow This Procedure

1. Tear up two sheets of newspaper into small pieces.

2. Put the pieces in a blender with 4 cups of water. CAUTION: Have an adult use the blender.

3. Place the screen in the pan and cover it with water. Pour the newspaper mixture, called pulp, on the screen. Spread the pulp evenly across the screen.

4. Remove the screen with the pulp on top, letting the water drip off first. Place the screen and pulp inside a section of newspaper.

5. Use the flat board to squeeze the water out of the paper.

6. Carefully remove the screen from the layer of pulp. Let the pulp dry.

Analyze Your Results

7. How is the recycled paper like notebook paper? How is it different?

B Map It!

Find natural resources in your neighborhood. Vegetable gardens, rocks, trees, lakes, and rivers are just some examples. Make a map that shows where these natural resources are in your neighborhood.

Here is an example of one student's map.

22

Directed Inquiry

 A Recycle Resources Yourself

⏱ 20–30 minutes
👥 individuals

Prep and Planning Tips

A 13 in. × 9 in. pan and a screen of the same size or bigger size works well. A plastic dish tub or a clean cat-litter box can also be used to hold the pulp.

You may wish to have students do this activity at home instead of in the classroom, as it will take from 12 to 48 hours for the paper to dry. If they are working at home, direct them to work with an adult when using the blender.

Expected Results

Students should have a rough sheet of paper after the pulp dries. The paper can be used for greeting cards, a book cover, as stationery, and so forth. Students should conclude that the homemade paper is much different from notebook paper, because it is thicker and less smooth.

Independent Inquiry

B Map It!

⏱ 30–40 minutes
👥 individuals

Prep and Planning Tips

Have available a local map, which students can use both as an example and as a way to locate some local natural resources. Review the map key and any geographical features shown.

 **Science Notebook**

Students can organize lists of local natural resources in their Science Notebooks. Suggest they make a table in which they can list the resources they identify and the location of each resource. Alternately, students may wish to make a simple sketch of their neighborhood before they go looking for resources, and make notes on the sketch to use when they complete their final maps.

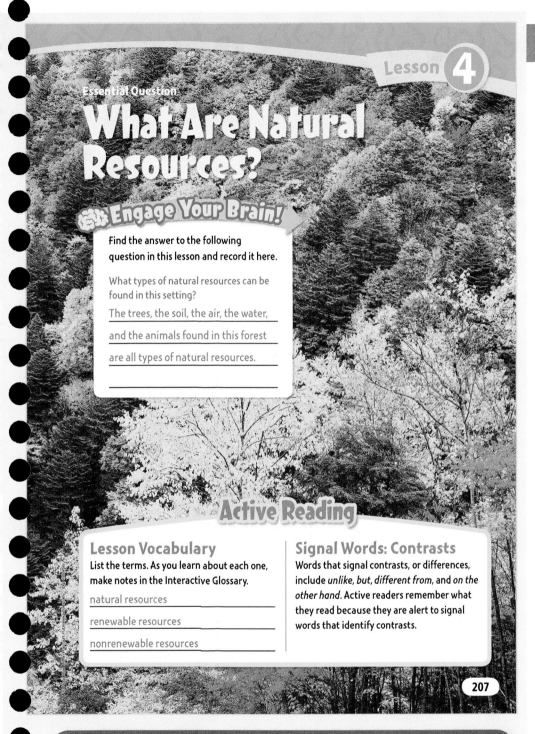

Essential Question
What Are Natural Resources?

Engage Your Brain!

Find the answer to the following question in this lesson and record it here.

What types of natural resources can be found in this setting?

The trees, the soil, the air, the water,

and the animals found in this forest

are all types of natural resources.

Active Reading

Lesson Vocabulary

List the terms. As you learn about each one, make notes in the Interactive Glossary.

natural resources

renewable resources

nonrenewable resources

Signal Words: Contrasts

Words that signal contrasts, or differences, include *unlike, but, different from,* and *on the other hand.* Active readers remember what they read because they are alert to signal words that identify contrasts.

207

Go Digital

An interactive digital lesson is available in Online Resources. It is suitable for individuals, small groups, or may be projected or used on an interactive white board.

Examples of resources

coal
wheat
aluminum
solar energy

Nonrenewable resources may take a very long time to replenish.
Click each picture to discover more.

---

1 **Engage/Explore**

Objectives

- Define and explain the term *natural resource*.
- Explain the importance of natural resources such as water, animals, and plants.
- Explain the importance of rocks, minerals, and ores.
- Explain the importance of energy sources.
- Explain the importance of forests, soil, and land.

Engage Your Brain!

Help students brainstorm answers to the Engage Your Brain question. Encourage students to think about the things trees need to stay alive. Challenge them to identify some of the natural resources that are present but not visible in the picture. Record student responses on a chart or on the board. Remind students to record their final answer to the question when they find it on the first two pages of this lesson.

Active Reading   Annotations

Inform students that active readers "make texts their own" by annotating them with notes and marks that help with comprehension. Encourage students to use pencil, not pen, to make annotations and to feel free to change their annotations as they read. The goal of annotation is to help students remember what they have read.

Vocabulary and Interactive Glossary

Remind students to find and list the yellow highlighted terms from the lesson. As they proceed through the lesson and learn about the terms, they should add notes, drawings, or sentences in the extra spaces in the Interactive Glossary.

2 Explain

📝 Notebook Generate Ideas

Tell students that all people need food, water, and shelter. Ask students to brainstorm a list of materials they use to meet their basic needs. Then have students think about other needs they have and what materials they use to meet these needs. Record their ideas.

Active Reading

Remind students that authors may use examples to illustrate a concept, such as a specific resource, to exemplify a category of renewable resources. Active readers focus on these examples as a way to deepen their understanding of the concept and remember its most important characteristics.

Interpret Visuals

Have students examine the photographs on this page. Work with students to identify the natural resources shown in the photographs. These include trees, water, wind or wind energy, and animals. Discuss with students how they use each of the resources they identified.

Why are plants and animals natural resources? Sample answer: We use plants and animals to meet our need for food. Plants also provide wood, which we use to make many products.

Develop Inquiry Skills

INFER **Why is it important for people to protect natural resources such as plants?** Accept reasonable answers. Sample answer: Plants are producers. They form the basis of all food chains. If we don't protect plants, we could damage food chains.

Resources You Can Rely On

Soap, water, clothes, wood, bricks, pencils, paper. What do all these things have in common? They are all natural resources or things made from these resources.

Active Reading As you read the next page, circle examples of renewable resources.

These pictures show natural resources. **Natural resources** are materials found in nature that are used by living things. Can you identify the natural resources in the pictures?

208

 Differentiation — Leveled Questions

Extra Support

Why are natural resources important? We use natural resources for food, water, and shelter. **Which material needs are not met by natural resources?** None; all our material needs are met by natural resources.

Challenge

Could a renewable resource such as wind or water be unusable? Explain. Sample answer: Air and water will not go away, but if they are polluted, they may not be usable for meeting needs.

▶ Look at the picture. What renewable resources are found in this setting? Sample answer: trees, air, sunlight, water, land

Some natural resources, such as water and air, are used again and again. Other resources form quickly in nature and are easy to replace. If a tree is cut to make paper, a new tree can be grown in a short time. The new tree will replace the old tree. Natural resources that can be replaced quickly are called **renewable resources**. Scientists also consider sunlight and wind renewable resources.

People need to use renewable resources wisely. The wise use of resources is called *conservation* [kahn•ser•VAY•shuhn]. Why is conservation important? People can use up renewable resources. Think about this: What would happen to fish if people ate more fish than could be replaced? Soon there would be no fish left!

209

© Houghton Mifflin Harcourt Publishing Company (t) ©Dan Forer/Beateworks/Corbis

Develop Science Vocabulary

natural resource Tell students that a natural resource is a material found in nature that living things use. Point out various items around the classroom, and have students try to identify the natural resources used to make each item. For example, a sweater might be made using cotton or dyes from plants grown in soil. A pencil might be made from wood and the mineral graphite.

renewable resource Ask students to think about when they have used the word *renew*. **What does it mean to renew a library book?** Sample answer: to check the same book out again **Based on this information, what do you think a renewable resource is?** a natural resource that can be grown or replenished in some way

Interpret Visuals

Have students examine the photograph on this page. As students complete the Interactivity, have them consider what makes the resources they are identifying renewable. Elicit that these natural resources can be replaced within a short period of time.

Could any of the natural resources you listed be permanently used up? Explain. Accept reasonable answers. Sample answer: Yes; the trees could be permanently used up if they were all cut down before they had a chance to reproduce.

Notebook ▶ **Summarize Ideas**

Instruct each student to write a list of five renewable natural resources. Encourage them to be specific. For example, instead of just writing *animals*, have students name a specific animal, such as a chicken. Have students share their lists with the class, then summarize the main idea orally or in writing.

2 Explain (continued)

Notebook   Generate Ideas

Tell students that they will now learn about a different group of natural resources called nonrenewable resources. Write the term on the board, and underline *non*. Discuss the meaning of this prefix. Then ask students to discuss what they think a nonrenewable resource is. Record their responses.

Active Reading

Remind students that when you contrast things, you point out ways they are different. Active readers remember differences because they focus on the events, objects, and ideas being contrasted.

Develop Science Vocabulary

nonrenewable resource Remind students what a renewable resource is. Then ask students how they think adding the prefix *non–* to the word *renewable* changes its meaning. Prompt with the clue that *non–* means "not."

Develop Science Concepts

What makes a natural resource nonrenewable? A natural resource is nonrenewable if it cannot be replaced quickly.

What will happen to a nonrenewable resource if it is used too quickly? The resource will be used up and will not be available any longer.

nonrenewable Resources

Not all natural resources can be replaced quickly. Some natural resources take thousands or millions of years to form.

Active Reading On these two pages, circle phrases that show how nonrenewable resources are different from renewable resources.

Natural resources that aren't replaced easily are called **nonrenewable resources**. It can take thousands or millions of years to replace a nonrenewable resource. Fossil fuels are an example of a nonrenewable resource. Coal, oil, and natural gas are all types of fossil fuels. Some are used to produce electricity. Some are used to run planes, cars, and other vehicles.

Because they form so slowly, there are limited amounts of fossil fuels and other nonrenewable resources. Once nonrenewable resources are used up, they cannot be replaced in our lifetimes. If people keep using fossil fuels at the same rate they use them today, these fuels will be gone very soon.

Oil is found deep underground. It is pumped to the surface and then refined before it can be used.

210

English Language Learners

Understand *Nonrenewable*
Write the word *nonrenewable* on the board. Underline the word *renewable* and explain its meaning (able to be replaced). Underline twice the prefix *non–* and explain its meaning (not).

Have a volunteer put the two meanings together to define the word (not able to be replaced). Have partners make a list of words that begin with *non–* and end with *–able*. Have them read aloud and define the words.

Soil takes hundreds of years to form. It is made of weathered rock and once-living plants and animals.

Limestone and aluminum are mined. Limestone is used to make cement, and aluminum is used to make cans.

Soil is a nonrenewable resource that people use to grow crops. It can be washed away if it is left uncovered or used improperly. As a result, it is important for people to conserve soil.

Minerals and rocks are other types of nonrenewable resources. A *mineral* is a nonliving solid with a crystal form. A *rock* is a solid substance made of one or more minerals. A rock that contains a valuable mineral is called an *ore*. Many minerals and rocks, such as limestone and aluminum ore, are mined. Once they have been removed from a mine, there are none left. It takes a long time for more minerals or rocks to form.

Do the Math!
Interpret a Graph

The graph shows the percentage of different natural resources used to produce electricity in the United States. How much comes from nonrenewable resources? _____ 90%

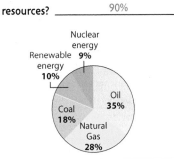

Nuclear energy 9%
Renewable energy 10%
Oil 35%
Coal 18%
Natural Gas 28%

211

© Houghton Mifflin Harcourt Publishing Company   (t) ©Jacques Jangoux/Alamy Images; (b) ©Grant Faint/Getty Images

Develop Inquiry Skills

DRAW CONCLUSIONS Soil is made of bits of weathered rock and broken-down bits of dead plants and animals. Why do you think soil is considered to be a nonrenewable resource? One component of soil—weathered rock—is a nonrenewable resource. Also, soil takes a long time to form, which is another reason it is considered a nonrenewable resource.

Do the Math!
Interpret a Graph

Which energy resources shown on the graph are nonrenewable natural resources? oil, natural gas, coal, and nuclear energy

What types of energy resources do you think are part of the *Renewable energy* category? Sample answers: solar energy, wind energy, hydroelectric energy, and geothermal energy

When you add all the percentages on the graph together, what should they equal? 100%

Notebook **Summarize Ideas**

Instruct each student to write a list of five different nonrenewable natural resources. Encourage students to be specific. For example, instead of just writing *mineral*, have students name a specific mineral, such as gold. Have students share their lists with the class. Ask students to use the information in their lists and the lists from the previous pages to summarize orally or in writing the similarities and differences in renewable and nonrenewable natural resources.

Differentiation — Leveled Questions

Extra Support

Find an item in the classroom made using a nonrenewable resource. What is it? Sample answer: The rocks used to make the walls are nonrenewable resources.

Challenge

Rock material is constantly recycled. Loose sediment, for example, can turn to rock. So why are rocks considered nonrenewable resources? Turning sediment to rock is an extremely slow process.

2 Explain (continued)

 Generate Ideas

Guide students on a walking tour of the schoolyard. Ask them to point out some natural resources they observe. **Which of these resources might not be found in other parts of the country?** Use their observations and answers to discuss natural resources that might be found locally, and how these resources might differ from those found in different parts of the country.

Active Reading

Remind students that authors may use examples to illustrate a concept, such as descriptions of different ways people use land to produce food. Active readers focus on these examples as a way to deepen their understanding of the concept and remember its most important characteristics.

Develop Science Concepts

Start a discussion with students about where local natural resources come from. For example, students may visit local farm stands or markets with their families to purchase seasonal fruits and vegetables. Then discuss how people use land to grow the foods we eat. Help students make connections between these resources and their uses.

Generate a list of items found at a grocery store. Make a graphic organizer that shows the resources used to produce and make a specific item. For example, write *oatmeal* on the board. Brainstorm with students the resources that helped make oatmeal and get it to the store. For example, *oat crops, soil, water, fossil fuels for harvesting the crop and transporting the cereal*, and so forth.

From Coast to Coast

You use natural resources every day. Some natural resources provide shelter. Others help you learn in school. On these pages, you will learn where some natural resources come from.

Active Reading As you read these pages, circle examples of land used as a natural resource in order to produce food.

Every state has natural resources. Many natural resources are found in greater quantities in some parts of the United States than in others. Trees, silver, wind, coal, and fish are just a few examples of natural resources found in the United States.

People mine land to get many natural resources. Some mining is done to get valuable minerals, such as silver, iron, and copper. Mining also takes place to get fossil fuels. Other mining gets rocks used to construct roads and buildings.

Sometimes land is used for food production. Ranchers raise cattle that graze on the land. Dairy farmers use land to raise cows that provide milk to make cream and cheese. Soil is also used to grow crops, such as corn, avocados, and oranges.

Some land is used to produce *green energy*, or energy generated using renewable resources. Wind farms, solar cells, and hydroelectric dams use wind, sunlight, and water to produce electrical energy.

Forests, or areas with large numbers of trees, provide lumber. People use lumber to make paper and furniture and to build houses.

▶ Look at the Natural Resources map, and locate the region where you live. Circle the renewable resources, and draw an *X* over the nonrenewable resources found there.

People use land to raise livestock and grow crops.

212

Differentiation — Leveled Questions

Extra Support

Show students a picture of a piece of wood furniture. **Which natural resource was used to make this piece of furniture?** trees **What are some other items made from trees?** Sample answer: homes, paper

Challenge

Minerals are natural resources used to make everyday items. **What everyday items are made from minerals?** Sample answer: metal furniture, coins, jewelry

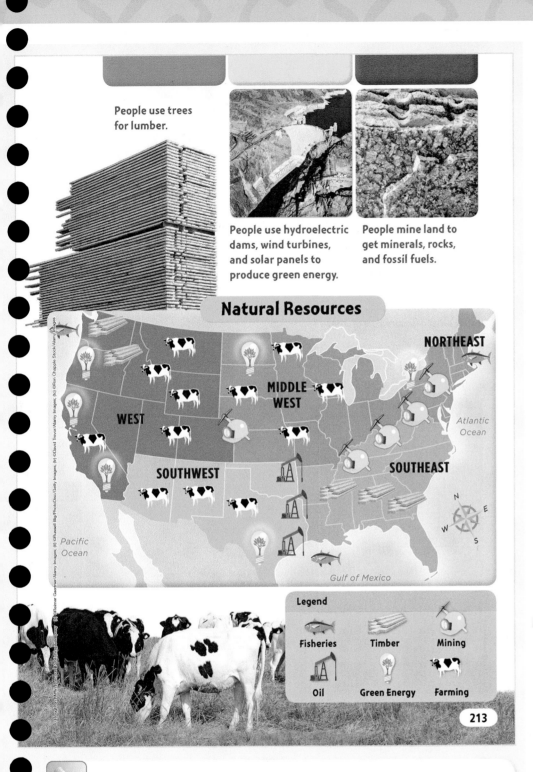

People use trees for lumber.

People use hydroelectric dams, wind turbines, and solar panels to produce green energy.

People mine land to get minerals, rocks, and fossil fuels.

Natural Resources

NORTHEAST

MIDDLE WEST

WEST

Atlantic Ocean

SOUTHWEST

SOUTHEAST

Pacific Ocean

Gulf of Mexico

Legend

Fisheries   Timber   Mining

Oil   Green Energy   Farming

213

Interpret Visuals

What is made from trees? lumber **What is lumber used for?** to build buildings and make furniture and other objects

Some natural resources are mined for materials used in homes. Are copper and granite renewable or nonrenewable resources? Explain. Copper is a mineral, and granite is a type of rock. They are both nonrenewable resources.

Why are fossil fuels important? Fossil fuels, such as coal, help provide energy for lighting homes. Other fossil fuels are used for running vehicles.

What are the renewable resources used in wind turbines, hydroelectric dams, and solar panels? wind, water, and sunlight **Why might using green energy in homes be a good alternative to fossil fuels?** Sample answer: Fossil fuels are nonrenewable resources and will run out. Using green energy helps preserve nonrenewable resources.

Guide students in completing the Interactivity. If they have difficulty identifying or categorizing natural resources, have them go back and review information provided on previous pages.

Notebook **Summarize Ideas**

Instruct students to make a three-column chart. In the first column, have them identify three natural resources from the map. In the second column, they should identify where each natural resource is found in the United States. In column three, they should classify each natural resource as renewable or nonrenewable. Then have students use the information from their charts to summarize, orally or in writing, where natural resources come from.

Writing Connection

State Natural Resources Bulletin Boards Assign or allow each student to choose a state. Direct students to research at least two natural resources found in the state, how these natural resources are used, and jobs related to these natural resources.

Help students compile the information they gathered to make a bulletin board about the variety and location of natural resources found in the United States.

2 Explain (continued)

 ### Generate Ideas

Invite students to preview the images on these pages. **What is one natural resource present in every image?** water Generate a discussion about water and all the ways it can be used. Make a list of students' answers on the board.

Active Reading

Remind students that active readers annotate, or mark up, text to benefit their own recollection of the information presented. Though students may star different sentences, they need to be able to offer a reasonable explanation for their annotations.

Interpret Visuals

Direct students to the map. Explain that the green area in the center of the map is the watershed, or the land drained by the Mississippi River and all of its tributaries, such as the Missouri River and the Ohio River. Have students label the Gulf of Mexico and use a finger or pencil to trace a line that runs from the beginning of the Mississippi River down to the Gulf of Mexico.

What is a watershed? all the land and water that drain into a river system

Which rivers are part of the Mississippi watershed? Arkansas, Illinois, Missouri, Mississippi, Ohio, Red, Tennessee

Develop Inquiry Skills

INFER **What might happen if heavy rains along the Missouri River cause flooding?** It is likely that there will be flooding along the Mississippi River as well, since the Missouri drains into the Mississippi.

Flowing Down Slope

Every second, millions of gallons of water flow from the Mississippi River into the Gulf of Mexico. Where does all this water come from?

Active Reading As you read these pages, draw a star next to each sentence that describes a use of water.

The Mississippi River watershed is an important natural resource. It is home to many living things.

214

 ## Math Connection

Calculate Mileage A barge carrying cargo has to travel 1,200 km (746 mi) down the Mississippi River. So far, it has traveled 588 km (365 mi). How many more kilometers does it need to travel to reach its destination?

1,200 − 588 = 612 km (380 mi)

If the barge has two days to complete the journey, how many kilometers should it travel each day?

$\frac{612 \text{ km}}{2 \text{ days}}$ = 306 km (190 mi) per day

From its source as a tiny stream in northern Minnesota to where it empties into the Gulf of Mexico, the Mississippi River spans 3,782 km (2350 mi). Along the way, it connects with hundreds of rivers and streams, including the Missouri and the Ohio Rivers.

Water from 31 states drains into the Mississippi River. All of this water makes the Mississippi River system one of the world's largest watersheds. A *watershed* is all of the land and water that drain into a river system.

A watershed is an important natural resource. States often share the water in a watershed. Virginia, for example, shares the water in the Chesapeake Bay watershed with five other states as well as the District of Columbia.

The rivers and streams in a watershed are used in many ways. For example, the Mississippi River supplies drinking water to more than 50 cities. People also use water from the Mississippi River to grow crops, for recreation, and for transportation.

A Day Without Water

How many ways do you use water each day? Make a list. Then describe what a day without water would be like. Sample answer: bathing, brushing teeth, cooking, drinking. A day without water would make me feel dirty and thirsty.

People use water for recreational activities such as fishing, canoeing, and swimming.

Farmers use water to grow food.

Cargo ships and barges use the Mississippi to move goods.

215

© Houghton Mifflin Harcourt Publishing Company (c) ©Corbis; (r) ©Ohio Stately David Images/Corbis; (r) ©Radius Images/Getty Images

Develop Science Concepts

Direct students to look at the images on this page. **How is water being used to grow crops?** Water is being sprayed on the crops. **Why might a farmer need an irrigation system?** Sample answer: to provide water to crops when there is little or no rain; to put water exactly where it is needed to provide what plants need

As students prepare to complete the Interactivity, have them refer back to the list the class made in the Generate Ideas section. Work with students to identify and circle any personal uses of water they had mentioned. Suggest they use these ideas as a starting point for their list in the Interactivity.

Develop Inquiry Skills

INFER Direct students to the ship transporting goods on the river. **Why do you think some goods are transported using the Mississippi River and not highways?** Sample answer: Some cargo is too wide for a road or too large to be moved on a truck.

Notebook ▸ Summarize Ideas

Have students revisit the sentences they marked that describe uses of water. Suggest they look for any uses they might have missed. Remind them that information may be in captions as well as in the text. Ask students to summarize orally or in writing the ways in which water is used.

Writing Connection

Write an Article
Have students work in small groups and research materials that are transported on the Mississippi River. Challenge students to identify the origins of the materials, and describe the route each one takes. Ask students to include the use of each material. Allow groups to present their articles to the class.

2 Explain (continued)

 Generate Ideas

Tell students that natural resources can be damaged if they become polluted. Discuss with students what pollution is. Then have students brainstorm different ways that the environment becomes polluted.

Interpret Visuals

How is the environment shown on the left different from the environment shown on the right? The environment on the left is polluted. The environment on the right is being cleaned up by the people in a community.

What do you think caused the pollution in the environment shown on the left? The pollution was probably caused by people throwing trash on the ground instead of putting it in a trash can or recycling bin.

What are the benefits of cleaning up this pollution? The environment will look better, and it will be healthier for plants and animals to live in.

Develop Science Concepts

Some pollution, such as air pollution, is hard to see. What do you think causes air pollution? Sample answer: Burning gasoline and other fossil fuels causes air pollution.

How can citizens help decrease the amount of air pollution in their community? People can burn less fuel by using public transportation; they can also use less electricity, the majority of which is produced by burning fossil fuels.

Why It Matters

Keeping It Clean

Using up natural resources too quickly is a problem. Another problem is pollution, or harmful materials in the environment. Pollution is harmful to natural resources. How can you help to conserve natural resources and prevent pollution?

Pollution can harm air, water, and soil. It can also harm plants and animals.

Many communities have cleanup projects to make the environment healthier for everyone.

216

Differentiation — Leveled Questions

Extra Support

How are natural resources affected by pollution? Natural resources are damaged by pollution. If a natural resource is polluted, it may not be healthy to use.

Challenge

How can reducing the amount of materials you use help decrease pollution? When you use fewer materials, you have less trash to throw away.

Develop Science Concepts

Do you recycle items at home? If so, which items? Students may respond that they recycle aluminum cans, paper, plastics, and glass.

Other than recycling, what is another way to conserve natural resources? You can use fewer natural resources or reuse these resources.

Interpret Visuals

Refer students to the picture of cars and trucks on a congested freeway. **Most cars and trucks are powered by gasoline. What about bicycles? Do they use gas or another type of fuel?** No; bicycles are powered by their riders.

Have students complete the Interactivity about helping to reduce air pollution. If students have trouble answering the question, remind them that cars and other automobiles release pollution into the air when they burn fuel to get energy to run.

Notebook **Summarize Ideas**

Ask students to write a brief paragraph in their Science Notebooks about how natural resources can become polluted, why it is important to conserve these resources, and some ways these resources can be conserved. Direct students to use the information in the paragraph to summarize the main idea and details orally or in writing.

Pictures will vary. Students may draw themselves riding a bicycle or walking short distances.

Reasons to Recycle

What happens to trash? It ends up in a landfill, which is wasteful. Many things we throw away can be reused. For example, some things, such as paper, glass, plastic, and metal, can be recycled and made into new products. By reducing, reusing, and recycling we help conserve natural resources.

How Can You Help?

What can you do to help cut down on air pollution caused by cars and trucks? Draw a picture of your solution in the space above.

217

123 Math Connection

Recycle Bar Graph Have students pick a recyclable item, such as aluminum cans or plastic bottles. Instruct each class member to collect that item for a week. Each class member should count how many of the item they collected at the end of the week and bring the data to class. Have students use the data to make a bar graph showing how many items each student collected and the class total.

3 Extend/Evaluate

Sum It Up!

- Before starting the Sum It Up! activity, have students review this lesson's vocabulary.

- Students will likely benefit from scanning over the images shown on the first four pages of the lesson in order to review various examples of renewable and nonrenewable resources.

- If students have trouble completing part of this exercise, suggest they review the lesson before continuing on to the Brain Check activities.

- Remind students to use the Answer Key to check their answers. Students should revise incorrect responses so they can use the Sum It Up! page to study for tests.

- Provide remediation for those students who need more instruction.

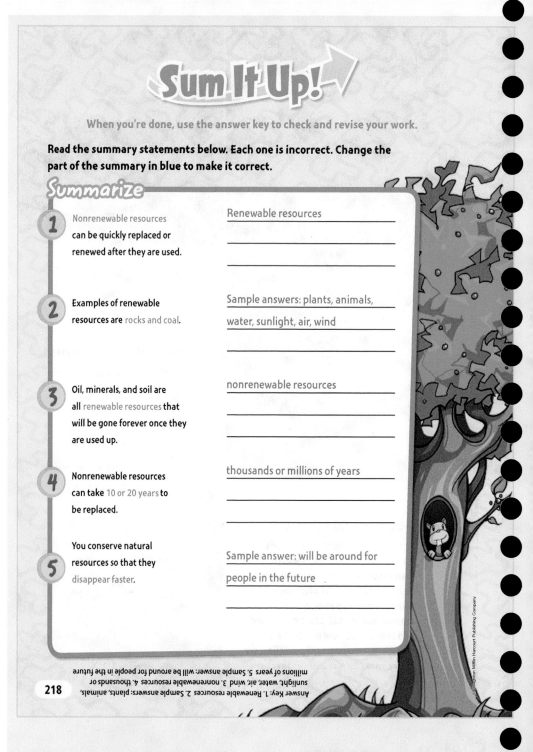

Sum It Up!

When you're done, use the answer key to check and revise your work.

Read the summary statements below. Each one is incorrect. Change the part of the summary in blue to make it correct.

Summarize

1. Nonrenewable resources can be quickly replaced or renewed after they are used.

   Renewable resources _____

2. Examples of renewable resources are rocks and coal.

   Sample answers: plants, animals, water, sunlight, air, wind

3. Oil, minerals, and soil are all renewable resources that will be gone forever once they are used up.

   nonrenewable resources _____

4. Nonrenewable resources can take 10 or 20 years to be replaced.

   thousands or millions of years _____

5. You conserve natural resources so that they disappear faster.

   Sample answer: will be around for people in the future

Answer Key: 1. Renewable resources 2. Sample answers: plants, animals, sunlight, water, air, wind 3. nonrenewable resources 4. thousands or millions of years 5. Sample answer: will be around for people in the future

218

Brain Check

Name _____

Word Play

1 Use the words in the box to complete each sentence.

watershed	fossil fuels	nonrenewable resources*	pollution
recycling	natural resources*	renewable resources*	

*Key Lesson Vocabulary

Materials found in nature and used by living things are ___natural resources___ .

All of the land and water that drain into a river system forms a ___watershed___ .

When ___fossil fuels___ are burned, they cause pollution.

Resources that are limited and cannot be replaced quickly are called ___nonrenewable resources___ .

Fish, trees, and other similar resources should be protected because if they are used too quickly, they will no longer be ___renewable resources___ .

Resources such as plastic, metal, glass, and paper can be conserved by ___recycling___ them.

Harmful materials in the environment are forms of ___pollution___ .

Apply Concepts

2 Circle the renewable resource.

219

© Houghton Mifflin Harcourt Publishing Company (c) ©JupiterImages/Getty Images

Answer Strategies

Word Play

1. If necessary, have students refer back to the pages on which each term is defined or discussed. As a challenge activity, ask students to construct their own fill-in-the-blank sentences using the same or other relevant terms.

Apply Concepts

2. Review each image with students and help them identify the natural resources displayed. Instruct students to think about how easy it would be to use up each of the natural resources shown. This thought exercise will help guide them to the correct answer.

Assessment

Suggested Scoring Guide
You may wish to use this suggested scoring guide for the Brain Check.

Item	Points
1	35 (5 points per item)
2	15
3	20 (5 points per item)
4	15 (5 points per item)
5	15
Total	100

Lesson Quiz
See Assessment Guide, p. AG 41.

3 Extend/Evaluate (continued)

Answer Strategies

Apply Concepts

3. If students have a hard time listing natural resources, suggest they scan through the photographs in the lesson for ideas.

4. Before students complete this item, ask them to think about their daily routines or recreational activities that involve water.

5. Discuss with students natural resources they may have seen in their state or region. Then brainstorm and write a list of places that may be familiar to students. Instruct students to draw their pictures in the space provided and use the lines to describe how the natural resource is used. Be sure students' descriptions match their pictures.

··

Take It Home!

To model the task for students, brainstorm a list of natural resources in your classroom. Then challenge students to name the source of each one. Encourage students to use a three-column chart to keep track of the natural resources they use in one day. They should list the item in the first column, the natural resources used in making the item in the center column, and the source of each natural resource in the third column.

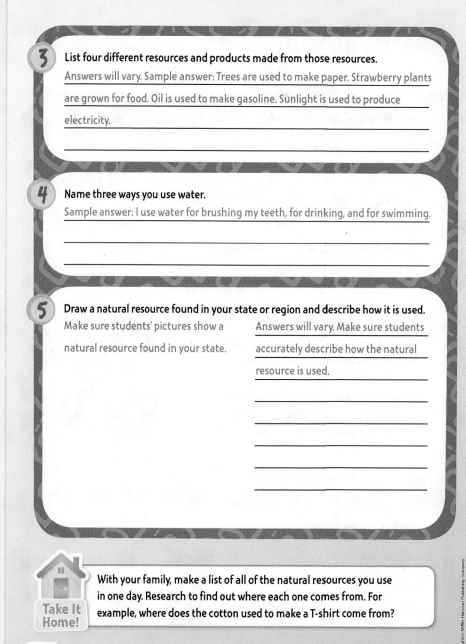

3 List four different resources and products made from those resources.

Answers will vary. Sample answer: Trees are used to make paper. Strawberry plants are grown for food. Oil is used to make gasoline. Sunlight is used to produce electricity.

4 Name three ways you use water.

Sample answer: I use water for brushing my teeth, for drinking, and for swimming.

5 Draw a natural resource found in your state or region and describe how it is used.

Make sure students' pictures show a natural resource found in your state.

Answers will vary. Make sure students accurately describe how the natural resource is used.

Take It Home! With your family, make a list of all of the natural resources you use in one day. Research to find out where each one comes from. For example, where does the cotton used to make a T-shirt come from?

220

© Houghton Mifflin Harcourt Publishing Company

Make Connections

Easy

Art Connection

Recycled Art

Have students think of different ways to turn used materials into art. Hold an art show in which each student makes a piece of art using items that might otherwise be thrown away.

Average

Writing Connection

Rhyme About Natural Resources

Instruct students to select a natural resource for which they are thankful. Then ask students to write a poem in honor of that natural resource. Tell students that their poems can be serious or funny. The poems can take the form of a ballad, haiku, limerick, sonnet, or free verse.

Challenging

Social Studies Connection

Cultural Resources

The natural resources available in a community help to shape that community's culture. For example, most cultural foods are products that can easily be raised locally. Have students select a culture that interests them and find a natural resource that has influenced an aspect (such as cooking or clothing) of that culture.

Challenging

Health Connection

Water Pollution

One of the most important natural resources for human health is fresh water. People will quickly become ill if their water supply is polluted. Have students find out where their water supply comes from and then list steps that their community can take to keep their water supply clean.

Options for Inquiry

Students can conduct these optional investigations at any time before, during, or in response to the lesson in the Student Edition.

A How Does Water Pollution Affect Plants?

Driving cars can put chemicals into the air. These chemicals are in acid rain. Acid rain is rain that is more acidic than normal rainfall. In this activity, you will simulate how plants react to acid rain.

Materials

2 potted plants — water
measuring cup — marker
ruler — vinegar
teaspoon

Follow This Procedure

1. Place two similar plants in a sunny spot. Label the plants A and B. Measure the plants. Record your measurements. Note other features of the plants, such as the number of leaves they have.

2. Give plant A about ½ cup of tap water.

3. Mix two teaspoons of vinegar, an acid, into ½ cup of water. Water plant B with the vinegar/water mixture.

4. After three days, observe the plants. Record your observations. Then water plant A with tap water. Water plant B with the vinegar/water mixture.

5. Repeat Step 4 two more times. Record your observations.

Analyze Your Results

6. What happened to the plants? Compare how they grew.

7. How does this activity model pollution in the environment?

B All About Recycling

What things can be recycled? How are these things recycled? Research the answers to these and other questions about recycling in your area. Find out if materials are picked up for recycling or if they must be dropped off at a recycling center. Find out how the materials are processed. Use your research to make a brochure about recycling. Share your brochure with the class.

Science Notebook

All About Recycling

1. What things can be recycled?

2. Where do I take things to be recycled?

3. Do the materials have to be cleaned first?

4. How are the materials recycled?

This is how one student began to plan his research.

23

Directed Inquiry

A How Does Water Pollution Affect Plants?

🕐 25 minutes
👥 small groups

Prep and Planning Tips

Allow 25 minutes to set up plants, and 10 minutes every third day for 10 days to record observations.

Make sure all variables except for the water and vinegar solution remain the same. Students should get the same type of plants; the plants should be nearly equal heights and potted in the same type of containers. Amount of sunlight and temperature should be kept the same for both plants.

Expected Results

Students should find that plant A thrived. Plant B likely stopped growing or lost leaves. Students should realize that the vinegar modeled acid rain. The activity showed how acid rain affects plants in the environment.

Independent Inquiry

B All About Recycling

🕐 35 minutes
👥 small groups

Prep and Planning Tips

See the Planning for Inquiry page for more information. You may wish to assign a different material for each group to research. Recyclable materials include plastics, different-colored glass, cardboard, newspaper, aluminum cans, steel cans, magazines, and office paper, among other items.

Science Notebook

Students can use the Science Notebook page shown on the Flipchart as a model for organizing the information they will use in their brochure. Have students sketch a design idea for their brochure in their Notebooks before they begin to assemble their information into a finished product.

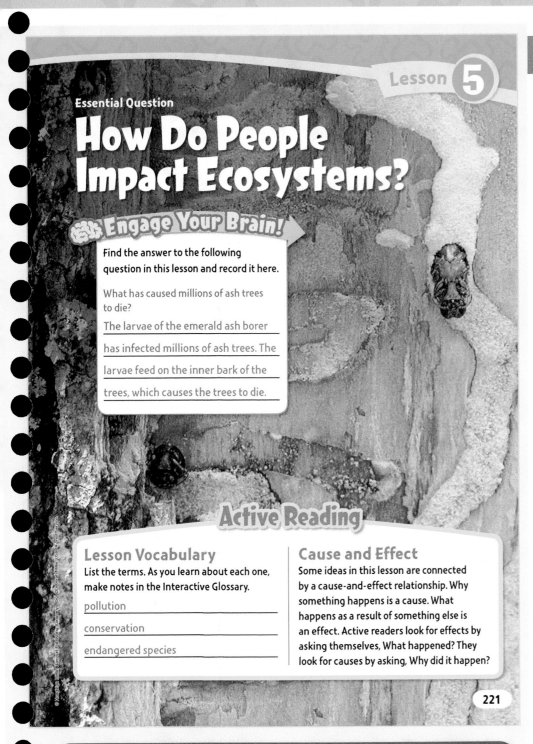

Lesson 5

Essential Question

How Do People Impact Ecosystems?

Engage Your Brain!

Find the answer to the following question in this lesson and record it here.

What has caused millions of ash trees to die?

The larvae of the emerald ash borer

has infected millions of ash trees. The

larvae feed on the inner bark of the

trees, which causes the trees to die.

Active Reading

Lesson Vocabulary
List the terms. As you learn about each one, make notes in the Interactive Glossary.

pollution

conservation

endangered species

Cause and Effect
Some ideas in this lesson are connected by a cause-and-effect relationship. Why something happens is a cause. What happens as a result of something else is an effect. Active readers look for effects by asking themselves, What happened? They look for causes by asking, Why did it happen?

221

Go Digital

An interactive digital lesson is available in Online Resources. It is suitable for individuals, small groups, or may be projected or used on an interactive white board.

1 Engage/Explore

Objectives

- Define *pollution* and *conservation*.
- Describe how human activity affects ecosystems.

Engage Your Brain!

Ask students to describe a dying or dead tree. What do the leaves look like? What does the bark look like? Point out the insects burrowing in the tree on this page. Explain that this insect is an emerald ash borer. Tell students that *to bore* means "to drill a hole." Have students speculate what role this insect might have in the death of ash trees.

Help students brainstorm answers to the question *What has caused millions of ash trees to die?* Remind students to record their final answer to the question when they find it on the sixth page of this lesson.

Active Reading   Annotations

Remind students that active readers "make texts their own" by annotating them with notes and marks that help with comprehension. Encourage students to use pencil, not pen, to make annotations and to feel free to change their annotations as they read. The goal of annotation is to help students remember what they have read.

Vocabulary and Interactive Glossary

Remind students to find and list the yellow highlighted terms from the lesson. As they proceed through the lesson and learn about the terms, they should add notes, drawings, or sentences in the extra spaces in the Interactive Glossary.

2 Explain

Notebook Generate Ideas

Ask students to describe the natural environment around their school or home. Then invite them to share descriptions of any other natural environments they have seen. **What did the nonliving parts of the environment look like? What animals and plants did you see?** Make a class list and compare the different natural environments listed with the Yellowstone National Park environment shown on these two pages.

Active Reading

Remind students that active readers annotate, or mark up, text to benefit their own recollection of the information presented. Though students may circle different words, it is important they are able to explain the thinking behind their annotation.

Develop Science Concepts

Help students understand that living things need both living and nonliving natural resources to survive. **Which natural resources might a bald eagle use to keep its young away from predators?** Bald eagles build nests in high places such as tall trees or on mountainsides to keep their young away from predators that live on the ground. **What are ways the other animals shown on these pages might use the natural resources in their environment?** Sample answer: Fish get the oxygen they need to live from the water that surrounds them, and they find food in the water as well; deer use grasses and shrubs for food; plants use sunlight, air, and water to make their own food.

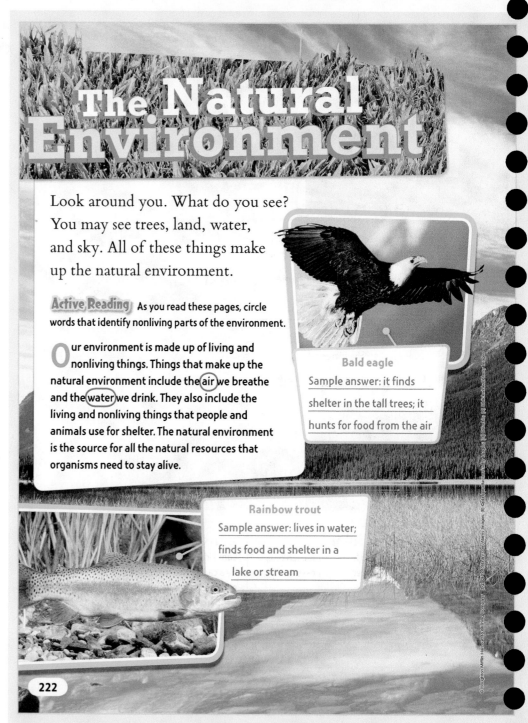

The Natural Environment

Look around you. What do you see? You may see trees, land, water, and sky. All of these things make up the natural environment.

Active Reading As you read these pages, circle words that identify nonliving parts of the environment.

Our environment is made up of living and nonliving things. Things that make up the natural environment include the air we breathe and the water we drink. They also include the living and nonliving things that people and animals use for shelter. The natural environment is the source for all the natural resources that organisms need to stay alive.

Bald eagle
Sample answer: it finds shelter in the tall trees; it hunts for food from the air

Rainbow trout
Sample answer: lives in water; finds food and shelter in a lake or stream

222

Differentiation — Leveled Questions

Extra Support
Water is a natural resource. **Where is water found on Earth?** Water is found above, on, and below Earth's surface. It is found in underground rocks, rivers, lakes, streams, oceans, glaciers, and the atmosphere.

Challenge
All of the animals shown here live in Yellowstone National Park. **Why do so many animals make this park their home?** Yellowstone is kept in its natural state and has all of the natural resources animals need to live.

Mountains valleys rivers, and oceans make up the nonliving part of the natural environment. Different parts of the environment support different types of organisms. Some trees can only grow near the top of a mountain. Others can only grow near the valley floor.

Environmental factors, such as temperature, moisture, and availability of food, may affect where an organism can live. Some organisms can only live in the water. Others can live both in the water and on land.

My Place

▶ Describe the place in the environment where each animal on these pages finds food and shelter.

Deer

Sample answer: lives on land; it may find food and shelter on the valley floor

Animals and plants make up the living part of the environment. Organisms get what they need from the environment.

223

Develop Inquiry Skills

PREDICT **What might happen to trout in a stream if a severe drought took place?** The stream might dry up, and the fish would either die or move to a new location. **How might this affect other animals living near the stream?** Animals that use trout for food would have to find another food source. **What might happen to animals in a forest that burned down from fire?** There would be no trees or plants for food or shelter for some animals; the animals might die or have to move to a new location.

Interpret Visuals

Suggest that students use the images on these pages to complete the interactivity. Ask students questions to help them identify parts of the environment. **What are some living things in the environment?** deer, eagle, trout, trees, other plants **Where does each organism live?** A deer lives on land. A fish lives in water. An eagle lives on land and flies through the air. **What needs do natural resources help these organisms fulfill in order to survive?** air, water, shelter, food, light (for the plants)

Notebook ▶ **Summarize Ideas**

Show students images of a variety of ecosystems. Ask students to identify the natural resources in each ecosystem and how living things utilize these resources. Have students summarize their answers either orally or in writing.

123 **Math Connection**

Interpret a Table Provide the table. Ask: Which population is largest? (bison) How many more grizzlies are there than wolves? (148) If 5 more wolves are born but 2 die, how many wolves are there in all?

$372 + 5 = 377 - 2 = 375$

Animals in Yellowstone

Animal	Population
bison	4,003
gray wolf	372
grizzly bear	520
moose	419

2 Explain (continued)

Notebook ▶ **Generate Ideas**

Have students scan the images on these pages. Ask students to list natural resources they see that they use at home or at school.

Active Reading

Remind students that some text segments state information essential to understanding a topic. Active readers identify and focus on these text segments as a way to deepen their understanding of the topic.

Develop Science Concepts

What are some natural resources that come from plants? Sample answer: wood and health products Discuss with students other ways plants are used. For example, cotton plants are used to weave fabric to make clothing. Plants provide many of the foods we eat, or provide food for the animals we eat.

What is paper made from? trees **Would you agree that paper is wood in its natural form? Explain.** No. Paper is made from wood that is turned to pulp, mixed with other substances, and processed to make paper.

Earth, the Global Store

People need food, water, air, and shelter. Where do these resources come from?

Active Reading As you read these two pages, underline the main idea.

Natural resources found in the environment help us meet most of our needs. These resources were used to build the road, the farm buildings, and the fence shown in this picture.

Farmers use water to help crops grow. Food such as milk, yogurt, and cheese comes from dairy farms.

224

English Language Learners

Prefixes Explain that the prefix *un-* means "not" and when added to the beginning of a word can change its meaning. The word *changed* means altered or made different. By adding the prefix *un-*, the word becomes *unchanged* and means "not different" or "the same." Have students add the prefix *un-* to the following words: *natural, clean, healthy.* Then have them guess the word meanings and check their answers using a dictionary.

Many of our natural resources come from plants. We use wood from trees to build homes, tools, and furniture. Plants are also used to make health products. Aspirin, for example, is a medicine used to relieve pain. It comes from the bark of a tree.

Land and soil are useful natural resources, too. Farmers use land to plant and grow crops, such as spinach, cotton, and pineapples. They also use land to raise animals, such as cattle and sheep, that graze on grass-covered land.

We can use a natural resource that is unchanged in its raw form or we can change it into something new. Rocks, for example, are used in their natural form to pave roads, decorate buildings, and to make floor tiles. Sand might be combined with cement to make concrete. Sand may also be heated and changed to glass that is used to make windows. We burn fossil fuels, such as oil and coal, to produce energy.

Some natural resources are required to sustain life. Plants, animals, and people would die without air and water. People drink water and use it to keep clean. On farms, we use water in irrigation systems to water fields where crops grow.

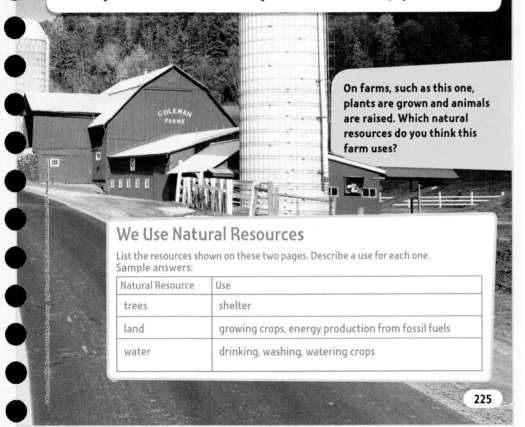

On farms, such as this one, plants are grown and animals are raised. Which natural resources do you think this farm uses?

We Use Natural Resources

List the resources shown on these two pages. Describe a use for each one.
Sample answers:

Natural Resource	Use
trees	shelter
land	growing crops, energy production from fossil fuels
water	drinking, washing, watering crops

225

Differentiation — Leveled Questions

Extra Support

What are some ways farmers use land? (to raise crops) Suggest that students read the captions and skim the text on these pages if they need help answering this question.

Challenge

In what ways are plants important to people? Sample answer: Plants provide people with many of the things they need to live, including food, shelter (lumber), medicines, and fibers for cloth.

Interpret Visuals

Tell students to examine the images on the pages. Then have them work with partners to discuss responses to the caption question, *Which natural resources do you think this farm uses?* Next, have students examine the interactivity chart. Provide guidance as they complete it.

As an extension, have students identify which of the natural resources they listed are being used in their unchanged state, and which have been changed into something new. For example, the metal used in the roofing for the silos has been changed from the raw ore. The materials that make up the asphalt have been changed to make a mixture that can be formed into a smooth, flat road.

Develop Inquiry Skills

OBSERVE Bring in samples of objects made from natural resources. These samples may include foods such as cheese or soy products or other items such as metal and wood tools, natural fabrics, bricks, glass items, or pieces of tile. Encourage students to examine the items and guess how the items were made and which natural resources were changed to make them.

Notebook Summarize Ideas

Have students try to list products from natural resources they observe or use on a typical day. Direct students to divide the list into two categories: *home* and *school*. Ask students to summarize orally or to complete their lists in writing.

2 Explain (continued)

 Generate Ideas

Have students imagine they are about to swim in a new indoor swimming pool in town. Just before they jump in, someone spills a few gallons of paint in the pool. **Do you still want to swim? Explain.**

Active Reading

Remind students that to find an effect, active readers ask, What happened? To find a cause, they ask, Why did it happen?

Interpret Visuals

Tell students to look at the images on these two pages and read the captions. Help them identify the causes and effects.

Why do people mine for fossil fuels? Fossil fuels are an important energy resource. **How is mining both helpful and harmful?** Helpful: People use coal to generate electricity; harmful: It causes damage to the land.

Why are the ash trees dying? These trees are being destroyed by the larval stage of the emerald ash borer beetles that feed on them.

How does kudzu harm other plants? It grows over other plants and smothers them.

Develop Inquiry Skills

DRAW CONCLUSIONS **What would be an effect on the land if people no longer cleared forests?** Different plant and animal populations would thrive. **What would be an effect on people if forests were no longer cleared?** There would be less lumber for building and less space to build homes and roads.

What might have happened if kudzu and the emerald ash borer beetle had never been introduced in the United States? The native plants affected by these invasive species would not have been in danger.

People Change the Environment

Sometimes people do things that can change the environment. Some of these changes can be very harmful.

Active Reading As you read these two pages, draw one line under each cause. Then draw two lines under its effect.

Rocks, ores, oil, and coal are natural resources found beneath the ground. People dig tunnels and even remove entire mountaintops to obtain these resources. In the process, they may cause pollution. **Pollution** happens when harmful substances mix with water, air, or soil.

The emerald ash borer beetle is not from North America. It came here on shipping crates from Asia. The emerald ash borer larvae feed on the inner bark of ash trees, killing them.

Mining for resources can damage the land.

226

English Language Learners

Understand Meaning Explain that *introduce* means "to lead or bring in." Students may get this confused with *introduce* as it relates to one person meeting another. When plants are introduced to an environment, they are brought in from another place.

Explain that *native* means "grown naturally in a particular place." The prefix *non-* means "not," so *nonnative* means "not grown naturally in a particular place." Plants that are nonnative to an environment would not have grown there naturally.

Farming can also harm the environment. Large herds of grazing animals can eat all the grass in a place, which loosens the soil. As a result, running water and wind can carry the soil away. Plowing fields for crops also loosens the soil. Once soil is gone, it takes a very long time to form again.

A forest also takes many years to form. People clear forests to make lumber and to make space for new roads, buildings, or homes. Plants die when a forest is cleared. The animals that live in the forest must move to find new homes. If they don't find another habitat that meets their needs, they might die.

Sometimes people introduce nonnative plants and animals to the environment. These *invasive species* have no natural enemies to control their population and can be very destructive. The kudzu plant and the emerald ash borer beetle are two nonnative organisms. They have invaded ecosystems in various regions of the United States, killing millions of trees.

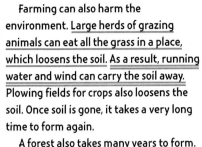
Kudzu is a fast-growing invasive vine. It grows over trees and shrubs, killing them.

Do the Math!
Solve a Problem

Kudzu grows at a rate of about 30 cm per day. Use this information to estimate its weekly and monthly growth rates.

weekly = 7 days × 30 cm = _____

210 cm per week

monthly = 30 days × 210 cm = _____

6300 cm per month

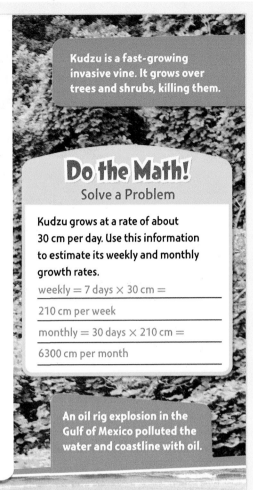
An oil rig explosion in the Gulf of Mexico polluted the water and coastline with oil.

Develop Science Vocabulary

Develop Science Vocabulary

pollution Explain that pollution can affect all parts of the environment: land, air, and water. Show students pictures that illustrate pollution, such as litter along a roadside, oil sheen in water, and smog in air. Have them classify each type of photo as land, water, or air pollution. Litter is a form of land pollution; chemicals in water is a form of water pollution; smog is a form of air pollution.

Do the Math!
Solve a Problem

Guide students in calculating both the weekly and monthly growth rates of kudzu. **How many days are in a week?** 7 **In a month?** 30

Explain that multiplying the daily growth rate by the number of days in a week will yield the weekly growth rate:

30 cm × 7 days = 210 cm per week

How can you calculate the growth rate of kudzu for the month? Multiply the daily amount by the number of days in the month (about 30):

210 cm × 30 days = 6,300 cm per month

There are 100 cm in a meter. How many meters per month does kudzu grow?
$\frac{6,300 \text{ cm}}{100 \text{ cm/m}}$ = 63 m per month

Notebook ▶ Summarize Ideas

Have students use the images and captions to summarize how people change the environment. Students can summarize their ideas orally or in writing.

Writing Connection

Write a Letter Have students use online sources or nonfiction books from the library to research ways to reduce litter in their local community. Tell students to write a list of ways to reduce litter, and then use their list to write a letter to a community leader explaining their cause and detailing suggestions for reducing litter. Students might suggest adding more public trash cans to the area, establishing a recycling center, or having volunteers pick up litter on a weekly basis.

2 Explain (continued)

Notebook ▸ Generate Ideas

Remind students that the environment encompasses everything around us. Students have just learned how our actions can harm ecosystems within the environment. Have students brainstorm ways in which people can help care for ecosystems.

Active Reading

Remind students that words signaling a cause include *because* and *if*. Words that signal an effect include *so, thus, therefore,* and *as a result*. Active readers remember what they read because they are alert to signal words.

Develop Science Vocabulary

conservation Explain that the root word *conserve* is a verb that means "to avoid wasteful or destructive use of." When the suffix *-tion* is added to verbs, it makes verbs into nouns that mean "the act of." In this case, *conservation* means "to use carefully." Explain that the term usually refers to the act of using less of a natural resource.

endangered species Explain that endangered species are those whose numbers are so low that they are in danger of the entire species dying out. A surprising number of organisms are endangered or threatened. Have students make a classroom gallery that contains pictures of endangered species. Assign each student to be responsible for adding one organism to the gallery. Students should write a one- or two-sentence caption explaining the plight of the organisms they chose before they add their picture to the gallery.

Caring for Our Ecosystems

Of all living things, people can affect ecosystems the most. What are some things we can do to care for ecosystems?

Active Reading As you read these pages, circle cause-and-effect signal words or phrases.

People share natural resources with other living things in the environment. We also have the ability to change the environment the most. Therefore, we are responsible for taking care of it.

We can practice conservation to care for the environment. **Conservation** is the use of less of something to make its supply last longer. Conservation also means preserving the natural condition of the environment.

People, communities, businesses, and governments all help care for the environment. People, for example, volunteer to locate and remove invasive species from ecosystems. Communities operate water treatment facilities, where polluted water is cleaned up before it is released to the environment.

Many businesses have adopted more efficient technology. As a result, they have found ways to make products using less energy. They have also designed *biodegradable* materials that break down quickly in the environment.

Governments have passed laws to protect the environment. As a result, many rivers and streams are cleaner than they used to be. Governments have also set aside millions of acres of land to use as national parks and animal refuges. As a result, some **endangered species**, organisms whose whole population was at risk of dying out, have thrived.

> Millions of American bison lived in the United States before people reduced their population to less than 1,000 animals. Today, because of government laws, there are about 450,000 American bison in the United States.

228

Differentiation — Leveled Questions

Extra Support

Which natural resources do we share with other living things? Sample answer: We share all resources with other living things, including air, water, and land.

Challenge

List at least two ways that using less energy helps conserve natural resources. It saves land, because it reduces the amount of resources that have to be mined. It reduces air pollution, because fewer resources are burned.

Water treatment facilities capture and remove pollutants in wastewater before the water is released into the environment.

A federal law passed in 1977 requires that land be reclaimed or restored once mining activities end.

What Can You Do?

List two ways you can practice conservation.

Sample answer: I can turn off the faucet when I brush

my teeth; I can take a shower instead of a bath.

229

Writing Connection

Write an Essay Ask students to write an essay about the effects of conservation on the environment. Suggest that students choose an area that has either improved or declined in condition and tell how those changes have affected the ecosys- tem. For example, a site that was once polluted by factories may have been cleaned up and turned into a recreational area. Students should state whether the change was positive or negative and pro- vide reasons that are supported by facts and details.

Develop Science Concepts

How is using more efficient technology helping the environment? Products are made using less energy, so energy is conserved. Con- serving energy leads to less pollution and the use of less natural resources.

Discuss how laws have helped preserve the natural environment. Help students understand that national parks and refuges are land areas that are left alone so that natural ecosystems can thrive. If these lands were not protected by laws, people would be allowed to perform actions that could cause harm to the environment. **Which population of animals has increased due to government laws?** bison

Develop Inquiry Skills

PREDICT Present a scenario in which a water-treatment facility is out of operation and water is released into the environment without being treated. **What might happen to the environment?** Polluted water might enter soil or water sources and harm or kill plants and animals that use those resources.

COMPARE Review the image of the open-pit mine shown on the previous two pages. Have students compare that photo with the reclaimed land shown here. Discuss with students how restoring the land after mining helps the environment.

Notebook ▶ Summarize Ideas

Direct students to the photo of the water-treatment facility at the top of this page. Reinforce that these facilities treat used water before it is released back into the environment. Discuss how reducing water use would reduce the amount of water that needs to be treated. Then have students complete the interactivity to summarize ways that they could help local ecosystems and the environment by conserving water.

3 Extend/Evaluate

Sum It Up!

- Suggest that students go back through the lesson and review the strategies for main ideas and details. Then have students review the headings, images, and captions on the appropriate lesson pages.

- Tell students to review the definitions of *pollution* and *conservation*.

- After students have reviewed the lesson and read the summary, have them complete the graphic organizer. First they should identify the main idea of the Summarize paragraph. Remind them that the main idea is often the first sentence of a paragraph.

- Make sure students understand that they are to write sentences that support the main idea in response to each question in the organizer.

- Remind students to use the Answer Key to check their answers. Students should revise incorrect responses so they can use the Sum It Up! page to study for tests.

When you're done, use the answer key to check and revise your work.

Use the information from the lesson and the summary below to complete the graphic organizer.

Summarize

People can change the environment in both positive and negative ways. We change the environment to meet our needs. People need shelter, food, air, and water to live. Some of the changes people make can be harmful to the environment. For example, plants and animals lose their homes when people clear forests. People can also cause pollution. However, people can have a positive impact on the environment. We all can practice conservation. We can use natural resources wisely and use less of some things to make their supplies last longer.

[1] Main Idea: People can change the environment in both positive and negative ways.

[2] Detail: Why do people change the environment?
People change the environment to meet their needs.

[3] Example: What do living things need to live?
shelter, food, air, and water

[4] Detail: How can people harm the environment?
People's activities may cause plants and animals to lose their homes.

[5] Example: What is pollution?
when harmful substances mix with air, water, or soil

[6] Detail: Who is responsible for caring for the environment?
people, businesses, and governments

[7] Example: How can we care for the environment?
We can practice conservation.

Answer Key: 1. People can change the environment in both positive and negative ways. 2. People change the environment to meet their needs. 3. shelter, food, air, and water 4. People's activities may cause plants and animals to lose their homes. 5. when harmful substances mix with air, water, or soil 6. people, businesses, and governments 7. We can practice conservation.

© Houghton Mifflin Harcourt Publishing Company   HMH Credits

230

Brain Check

Name _____

Word Play

1 Use the words in the box to complete the puzzle.

Across

5. When harmful substances mix with air, water, or soil
6. Interaction between organisms and their surroundings
7. To save natural resources
8. _____ species are organisms whose whole population are at risk of dying out.

Down

1. Oil or coal used to produce energy
2. An organism with no natural enemy in an area
3. A material that breaks down over time
4. The living and nonliving things in an area

biodegradable   fossil fuel

conservation*   nonnative

ecosystem   pollution*

environment   endangered species*

Key Lesson Vocabulary

Crossword answers:
- 5 Across: pollution
- 6 Across: ecosystem
- 7 Across: conservation
- 8 Across: endangered
- 1 Down: fossilfuel
- 2 Down: nonnative
- 3 Down: biodegradable
- 4 Down: environment

© Houghton Mifflin Harcourt Publishing Company • Image Credits

231

Answer Strategies

Word Play

1. Suggest that students review the lesson's highlighted vocabulary terms. You may want to give additional clues for students who are having difficulty completing the puzzle. For example, an additional clue for *pollution* might be *litter*.

As an extra challenge, have students provide an example for each clue. For example, an example of saving natural resources (conservation) is turning off lights when leaving a room.

Assessment

Suggested Scoring Guide

You may wish to use this suggested scoring guide for the Brain Check.

Item	Points
1	40 (5 points per item)
2	15 (5 points per item)
3	15 (5 points per item)
4	30
Total	100

Lesson Quiz

See Assessment Guide, p. AG 42.

3 Extend/Evaluate (continued)

Answer Strategies

Apply Concepts

2. Work with students to identify the items shown. Point out that all of the natural resources are in the top row, and that students are to match each natural resource with a product in the second row.

3. Suggest that students think of ways to reverse the beneficial or harmful effects of each action. Guide them by asking questions. **Which action is the opposite of cutting down trees?** planting trees **What effect does riding a bike have on the environment? What type of transportation would have a different effect?** Riding a bike reduces pollution by reducing the amount of fuel burned. Using any kind of fuel-powered vehicle is less beneficial to the environment. **What is the effect of releasing untreated sewage into a river?** The water becomes unsafe for living organisms.

4. Help students get started by having them identify the product they wish to redesign and then making a list of all the characteristics of that product. For example, a disposable juice box has the outer box and an inner leak-proof liner, as well as the straw. **What could you do to redesign your product to use fewer resources?**

 Take It Home!

Encourage students to identify whether the changes they saw harmed or helped the environment. Remind them that a change can have both positive and negative effects.

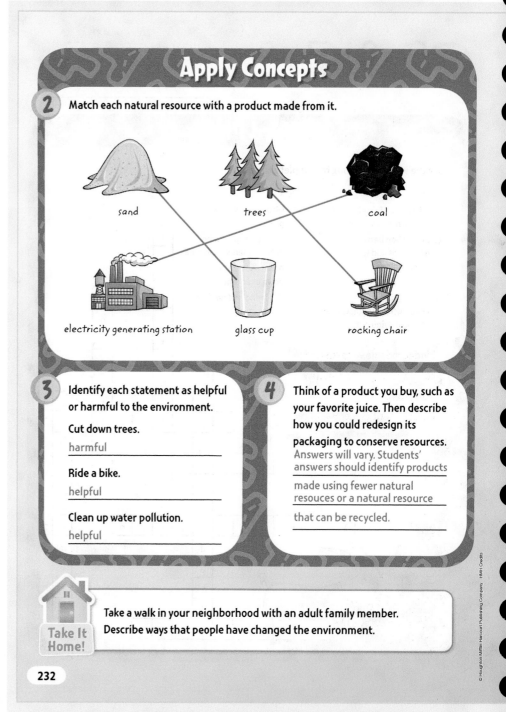

Apply Concepts

2 Match each natural resource with a product made from it.

sand   trees   coal

electricity generating station   glass cup   rocking chair

3 Identify each statement as helpful or harmful to the environment.

Cut down trees.
harmful

Ride a bike.
helpful

Clean up water pollution.
helpful

4 Think of a product you buy, such as your favorite juice. Then describe how you could redesign its packaging to conserve resources. Answers will vary. Students' answers should identify products made using fewer natural resouces or a natural resource that can be recycled.

Take It Home! Take a walk in your neighborhood with an adult family member. Describe ways that people have changed the environment.

232

Make Connections

Easy

Health Connection

Air Quality Index

Tell students that the Air Quality Index is a scale that ranks the quality of the air in a place such as a city. It lets people know how clean or polluted the air is and what health effects or potential harm pollution may cause. Have students look in the newspaper or online for the Air Quality Index for their area. Ask them to describe the quality of air that day.

Average

Art Connection

Natural Plant Dyes

Explain that before chemical dyes were invented, people often used plants to dye clothes and other objects. Slice up a red cabbage and boil it in a pot of water. Strain the liquid and let it cool. Allow students to dye small squares of white cloth in the dye. Students should wear gloves and lab aprons to keep from staining their hands and clothes. Let the pieces dry. Afterwards, students can stitch the pieces into a quilt to display in the classroom.

Average

Writing Connection

Controlled Burning

Explain that forest fires occur as a result of careless actions of humans as well as from natural causes. However, some forest fires are set deliberately by foresters themselves. Direct students to an online encyclopedia or library resources to research and write about how controlled burning is used in forests or other land areas. Students should explain why it is used and how these fires are controlled.

Challenging

Math Connection

Conservation Plan

Have students make a plan for conserving water at home. Students should first use online resources to find out how many liters of water are used for daily activities such as washing dishes, showering, brushing teeth, and flushing the toilet. Students should then determine how they could reduce the amount of water used for these activities. Have students calculate how many liters of water each day could be saved by using their plans.

Guided Inquiry

FLIPCHART P. 24

🕐 15–20 minutes to set up; 5–10 minutes every week for 3 weeks

👥 small groups

Students follow the directions on the Flipchart. The accompanying Lesson Inquiry pages in the Student Edition provide scaffolding for guided inquiry.

How Do People Affect Their Environment?

Some materials that people put in landfills are biodegradable. That means that they will break down. Other materials are not biodegradable. How can you tell which materials will break down?

Materials

apple core
banana peel
plastic spoon
plastic cup
soil

clean, empty soda can
large plastic bin
plastic disposable gloves

1 CAUTION: Wear plastic gloves. Fill the plastic bin with soil.

2 Make a data table in which you write the name and a brief description of each item you will bury. Record the date as well.

3 Bury each item in the soil. Make sure the items are covered by the soil. Put the plastic bin in a place where it will not be disturbed.

4 In three days, check the items. Note which items are breaking down and which are not.

5 Record your observations. Be sure to record the date.

24

Inquiry Skills Focus Observe, Predict, Infer

Objectives

- Observe and compare the rate of decay of different materials.
- Record numerical data in a data table and descriptive data in sketches.
- Understand that some environmental changes are beneficial and some are harmful.
- Understand the impact that trash can have on the environment.

Prep and Planning Tips

See the Planning for Inquiry page for more information.

- Find a location where the bins can be left for the duration of the activity without being disturbed.
- Pre-measure the amount of soil need for the size container you will be using.

Expected Results

Students will find that even biodegradable items take a long time to decompose. Some items are not biodegradable and will never decompose.

1 Engage/Explore

Attention Grabber

Show students a plastic fork or spoon. Ask them to estimate its length. (about 14 cm) Tell them that each year, people in the United States throw away enough paper cups, plastic cups, and plastic silverware to circle Earth 300 times!

Preview Activity

Before beginning the investigation, have students review the directions on the Inquiry Flipchart and the accompanying Student Edition response pages. Then, have them complete the response pages as they follow the directions on the Flipchart.

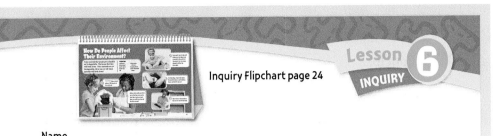

Inquiry Flipchart page 24

Name _____

Essential Question

How Do People Affect Their Environment?

Set a Purpose
How does this activity show how people affect the environment?

Sample answer: It shows that the trash
people throw away can stay in the
environment for a long time.

Think About the Procedure
Why did you need to observe the trash for three weeks?

Sample answer: Decomposition takes
time. I would not have been able to
observe results in a day or two.

Why did you wear gloves?

Sample answer: The gloves are a safety
measure. They help keep people from
catching germs and from spreading
germs.

© Houghton Mifflin Harcourt Publishing Company

Record Your Data
In the space below, write or draw your results.

Check students answers.

233

1 Engage/Explore (continued)

Guide the Investigation

Develop Inquiry Skills

OBSERVE **What are the five senses?** sight, hearing, taste, touch, and smell **Tell** students that making observations involves using their senses. **Which senses will you use to observe the trash?** sight and smell

Why do scientists use models? Some objects or events are too small or too large to observe directly. Scientists use models to study these objects or events. In this investigation, the bins are models of landfills.

PREDICT Explain that a prediction involves saying what you think will happen. Predictions are often based on prior knowledge and observations. Ask: **What happens to a piece of fruit that is overly ripe?** It begins to decompose.

Ask students to predict if food will decompose when it is buried in a landfill. Students will likely say that the food will decompose. However, they might not realize that items are not exposed to air or sunlight when they are buried in a landfill. Thus, rates of decomposition are slow.

GATHER AND RECORD DATA Remind students that, at a minimum, their data tables should have spaces in which to record the name of each buried item, initial and subsequent descriptions of the items, and the date on which each description was entered.

Go Digital

A virtual lab experience is available with the Online Resources for this program.

2 Explain

Develop Inquiry Skills

DRAW CONCLUSIONS Ask students if their predictions were supported. Remind students to consider the results of the investigation objectively and honestly.

ANALYZE AND EXTEND Discuss students' responses to the items.

1. Tell students that different factors affect rates of decomposition. Give them an everyday example to help them understand the concept. Ask: **What happens to milk that is left outside on a sunny day?** It can spoil. **Would the milk spoil if it were promptly refrigerated?** no Help students relate their answers to factors that can speed up or slow down rates of decomposition.

2. Suggest that students closely examine their data before answering the question. They should realize that items remain in landfills for a long time.

3. As a class, discuss which type of display would best suit the data. Remind students that bar graphs are used to compare data across groups or categories, such as the decomposition times for the different materials contained in the table. A time line would also be an effective data display.

3 Extend/Evaluate

4. Accept all reasonable answers. Students may want to know more about keeping trash out of landfills by recycling, reusing, and reducing.

Assessment

Lesson Quiz
See Assessment Guide, p. AG 43.

Draw Conclusions

What did the plastic container and soil represent?

a landfill

_____

_____

What did you observe about the different materials after observing them for three weeks?

Sample answer: Materials made from

once-living things started to decompose.

Materials made from non-living things did

not decompose.

Analyze and Extend

1. Compare your results with those of other groups. Did everyone have the same results? If not, what might have made the results differ?

Sample answer: Some groups might have

different results because they placed their

containers in warm places. This could

speed up rates of decomposition.

2. What did you learn about materials that go into landfills?

Sample answer: The materials can stay in

the landfills for a long time.

_____

_____

---

3. Look at the table. How could you display this data in another way? Show your work below.

Object	Time it takes to decompose
Diaper	75 yr
Paper	2–3 months
Milk carton	5 yr
Aluminum can	200–500 yr
Plastic bag	10–20 yr

Answers may vary. Students may make a bar graph or a time line to show how long it takes each object to decompose.

4. Think of other questions you would like to ask about trash disposal.

Sample answer: I would like to know more

about keeping things out of landfills by

recycling, reusing, and reducing.

Differentiated Inquiry

Easy

Make Recycled Art

- Gather materials that might normally be thrown away, such as scrap yarn, plastic lids, pieces of construction paper, and other colorful items.

- Ask students to make a piece of art from the materials. Suggest that students give their art a theme, such as "Recycling is Good for the Environment."

Average

Revisit Rates of Decomposition

- Suggest that students replicate their investigation about rates of decomposition. This time, students should explore factors that speed up rates of decomposition. Factors include heating, stirring, and adding decomposers to the mix.

- Have each group investigate a different factor. Students should share their results with the class.

Average

Make a Compost Pile

- Encourage students to set up a compost pile at school. Discuss how composting reduces the amount of waste that is discarded in landfills.

- Students can use an online encyclopedia or nonfiction books from the school library to find information about building and maintaining inexpensive compost piles.

- Suggest that students work with the cafeteria to gather appropriate food scraps.

- Interested students may want to start a school garden and fertilize it with the compost they make.

Challenging

Compare Waste Disposal Methods

- Ask students to use an online encyclopedia or nonfiction books from the school library to research other methods of waste disposal, such as incineration and recycling.

- Students should make charts that list the advantages and disadvantages of each method.

- Ask students to write a report that includes recommendations on the most environmentally friendly method of waste disposal. Students should support their recommendations with facts.

People in Science

Objectives

- Describe the scientific contributions made by Wangari Maathai and Willie Smits.

- Identify how human actions can benefit the environment.

Notebook ▸ Generate Ideas

Ask students to recall what they have learned about helpful human impacts on the environment. List their answers on the board. Tell them that they will learn about two people who made a big difference in the environment by planting trees.

Background

- Cutting down trees in certain areas of Africa and other places has led to desertification. Desertification is the spread of desert-like conditions due to human actions, such as cutting down trees. The work of the Green Belt Movement has helped reverse the trend of desertification. Wangari Maathai won the 2004 Nobel Peace Prize for her efforts as an environmentalist and human rights activist.

- In addition to his work in restoring a rain forest, Willie Smits founded a university in Indonesia. He continues to train Ph.D. candidates in sustainable forestry methods.

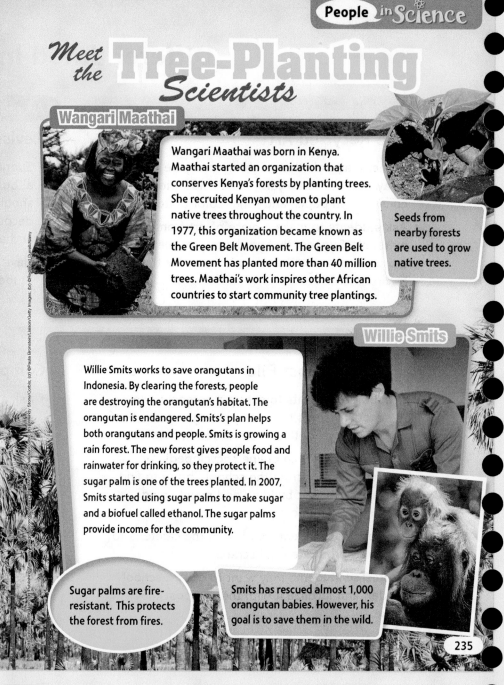

People in Science

Meet the Tree-Planting Scientists

Wangari Maathai

Wangari Maathai was born in Kenya. Maathai started an organization that conserves Kenya's forests by planting trees. She recruited Kenyan women to plant native trees throughout the country. In 1977, this organization became known as the Green Belt Movement. The Green Belt Movement has planted more than 40 million trees. Maathai's work inspires other African countries to start community tree plantings.

Seeds from nearby forests are used to grow native trees.

Willie Smits

Willie Smits works to save orangutans in Indonesia. By clearing the forests, people are destroying the orangutan's habitat. The orangutan is endangered. Smits's plan helps both orangutans and people. Smits is growing a rain forest. The new forest gives people food and rainwater for drinking, so they protect it. The sugar palm is one of the trees planted. In 2007, Smits started using sugar palms to make sugar and a biofuel called ethanol. The sugar palms provide income for the community.

Sugar palms are fire-resistant. This protects the forest from fires.

Smits has rescued almost 1,000 orangutan babies. However, his goal is to save them in the wild.

235

Writing Connection

Reflective Writing Ask students to write a one-page journal entry about how the efforts of one individual can make a difference to the environment. Students can use the examples on these pages or research an individual of their choice.

People in Science continued

Scientist saves the Day!

Read the story about the Florida scrub jay. Draw the missing pictures to complete the story.

The Problem: Florida scrub jays are endangered. They are found only in parts of Florida with shrubs and other short plants.

Fires kill tall trees that grow in the scrub jay's habitat. But people put out the fires, so the trees survive.

Drawings should show people putting out fires in tall trees.

Trees are now growing, so there are fewer shrubs. The scrub jays can't live there.

The Solution: Scientists and firefighters start fires that can be kept under control. These fires kill the tall trees.

44

Drawings should show scrub jays living in shrubs with no tall trees.

Shrubs grow and the scrub jays return.

236

Develop Science Concepts

Ask students to recall what they have learned about food webs. **Why is it important to make sure that the Florida scrub jays have safe habitats?** If the scrub jays leave the area, other organisms in the food web will be affected.

Develop Inquiry Skills

INTERPRET Help students complete the drawings by reminding them that a caption describes an illustration. They should use the captions to decide what to include in their drawings. Read the following caption aloud: "Fires kill tall trees that grow in the scrub jay's habitat. But people put out the fires, so the trees survive."

Ask: **What should your drawing show?** people putting out fires

Repeat the activity for the remaining caption for students who need additional help.

Notebook ▸ Summarize Ideas

Ask students to use their drawings to think about helpful effects of people on the environment. Students can summarize their ideas orally or in writing.

Science, Technology, and Society

Many countries rely heavily on fossil fuels, a nonrenewable resource, for power. However, fossil fuels are being used up faster than they can be replaced by natural processes. Scientists are developing alternative fuels made from renewable resources that will not run out and that do not pollute the environment. Have students use an online encyclopedia or nonfiction books from the school library to research and report on other alternative energy sources in development.

S.T.E.M.

Engineering and Technology

Objectives

- Identify some of the challenges involved in marine exploration.
- Compare and contrast past and present technology used to explore marine ecosystems.
- Explain how scuba apparatus works.
- Identify control and feedback systems found in scuba units.

Notebook **Generate Ideas**

Ask students to discuss what they know about underwater exploration. Have them share what they might like to explore in an underwater environment if given the opportunity.

Background

- Interest in underwater exploration dates back centuries. In the 1500s, scientists began experimenting with underwater breathing systems. However, the diving bell was very limiting because people who wore it could not stay underwater for long periods of time.

- There were several improvements to diving equipment through the 1800s, but the most useful improvements did not occur until the 1940s when the Aqua-Lung was invented. The Aqua-Lung allowed people to dive without being attached to cables or hoses.

- Today, people as young as 10 years of age can become certified scuba divers but must dive under adult supervision.

Develop Inquiry Skills

COMPARE As students answer the Critical Thinking Interactivity, have them review the information given about the diving bell and the diving dress to determine what the two types of equipment have in common.

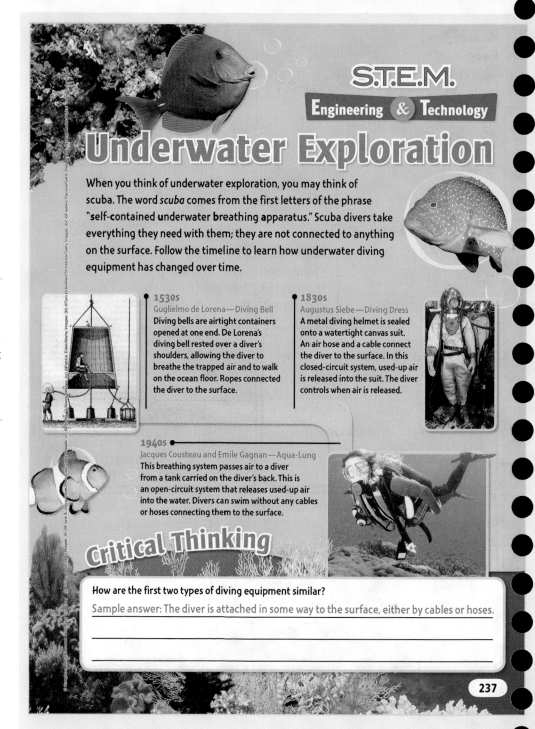

S.T.E.M.
Engineering & Technology
Underwater Exploration

When you think of underwater exploration, you may think of scuba. The word *scuba* comes from the first letters of the phrase "self-contained underwater breathing apparatus." Scuba divers take everything they need with them; they are not connected to anything on the surface. Follow the timeline to learn how underwater diving equipment has changed over time.

1530s
Guglielmo de Lorena—Diving Bell
Diving bells are airtight containers opened at one end. De Lorena's diving bell rested over a diver's shoulders, allowing the diver to breathe the trapped air and to walk on the ocean floor. Ropes connected the diver to the surface.

1830s
Augustus Siebe—Diving Dress
A metal diving helmet is sealed onto a watertight canvas suit. An air hose and a cable connect the diver to the surface. In this closed-circuit system, used-up air is released into the suit. The diver controls when air is released.

1940s
Jacques Cousteau and Emile Gagnan—Aqua-Lung
This breathing system passes air to a diver from a tank carried on the diver's back. This is an open-circuit system that releases used-up air into the water. Divers can swim without any cables or hoses connecting them to the surface.

Critical Thinking

How are the first two types of diving equipment similar?

Sample answer: The diver is attached in some way to the surface, either by cables or hoses.

237

Make Some History

Research another type of diving equipment. Describe how it works and where it should be placed on the timeline.

Answers will vary. Students may choose to research submersibles or submarines.

1960s
Rebreather

Rebreathers are closed-circuit systems. A diver breathes through a mouthpiece and used-up air is not released into the water. Instead, it is filtered to remove carbon dioxide and used again. This design feature extends the amount of time a diver can spend underwater.

1980s
ADS

Atmospheric Diving Suits (ADS) were developed for deep diving activities. They use rebreather technology and a hard suit that enable divers to safely dive to great depths. Modern ADS can work in water up to 610 m deep!

Design Your Future

What features do you think the next diving suit should have? What needs would those features meet?

Answers will vary: Students may indicate that the next diving suit should be strong, yet flexible enough to allow divers maximum range of motion.

Build On It!

 Rise to the engineering design challenge—complete **Solve It: Getting Around a Dam** on the Inquiry Flipchart.

238

Build On It!

In **Solve It: Getting Around a Dam**, the design challenge associated with this lesson, students use the steps of the engineering design process to build their own dam. See the pages that follow. Other opportunities to apply the design process appear throughout the Inquiry Flipchart.

Develop S.T.E.M. Concepts

DESIGN CRITERIA Remind students that humans use their lungs to breathe oxygen. While oxygen is present in water, humans cannot breathe this oxygen with lungs. Fish have gills instead of lungs, so their bodies naturally filter and use the oxygen from water. Explain that the purpose of an underwater breathing device for humans is to allow them to breathe oxygen from a gas mixture instead of water. **What are some design criteria for the ADS suit?** sturdy, must provide heating or cooling, articulated joints, light source

RESEARCH The Design Your Future Interactivity challenges students to think of ways in which the most current diving apparatus could be improved.

- Tell students that some features of diving gear that they may consider improving or changing are the swim fins, booties, mask, tanks, regulator, gauge and alarm that alert the diver of of air supply levels, and the diving suit itself. Point out to students that they should consider both the structure of each part and the material from which it is made. Are there other materials that might work better?

- If possible, find and hand out a diagram that shows the various parts of a dive suit and the gear that goes with it. You may also wish to allow students to search the Internet for information.

Notebook ▸ Summarize Ideas

Direct students to briefly summarize, orally or in writing, what engineers must consider when designing tools that allow people to breathe underwater.

S.T.E.M.
Engineering and Technology

FLIPCHART p. 25

- 25–30 minutes
- individuals

S.T.E.M.
Engineering & Technology

Solve It: Getting Around a Dam

A dam is a barrier usually built to control the flow of a river and prevent floods. However, some dams are built to generate electricity.

As you might imagine, building a dam affects local ecosystems. Dry land behind a dam is often flooded as water slowly rises, forming a lake. Dams decrease the amount of water and nutrients carried by the river downstream.

Dams make it hard for aquatic organisms to move freely along the river. Salmon, for instance, need to migrate upstream to lay eggs. How could you design a system to allow salmon to get around a dam?

What to Do

1. Do research to learn about dams and how they affect ecosystems.

2. Find out more about salmon behavior.

3. Think of ways to help salmon get around dams.

4. Brainstorm several designs. Make a diagram of each design in your Science Notebook.

5. List the advantages and disadvantages of each design.

6. Compare and contrast these advantages and disadvantages to select the best design to help the salmon get around the dam. Explain your selection.

Keep a record of your work in your Science Notebook.

25

Objectives

- Use the five steps of the design process to devise a way to help salmon swim around dams.
- Understand the impact of dams on ecosystems.

Prep and Planning Tips

- It may be easier for students to draw their designs on graph paper.
- Identify resources students can use to find out more about salmon behavior.

Expected Results

Students should be able to plan and draw a diagram for several different kinds of structures that would allow salmon to migrate up or down a dammed river. They should also be able to list the advantages and disadvantages of each design, select the best one, and explain their design to a group.

1 Engage/Explore

Attention Grabber

Display pictures of large U.S. dams, such as the Hoover Dam and Glen Canyon Dam. Explain that dams help control a river's flow while sometimes helping whole towns or cities generate electricity. Also show students a picture of beaver dams, and have them compare the natural dams to human-made ones.

Preview Activity

Before beginning the activity, have students review the directions on the Engineering and Technology Flipchart page. You may wish to have students review the lesson on the engineering design process earlier in this program.

Guide the Activity

Develop Inquiry Skills

INFER Ask questions about the importance of dams and how technology changes over time. **How are dams a useful technology?** Dams make it possible to prevent flooding and generate electricity. **Why do living things such as salmon need to navigate up a river?** These fish swim up river to lay their eggs. **What might happen if salmon fail to reach the area in which they lay their eggs?** The salmon may not be able to reproduce. **How can dam technology change to help salmon swim upstream?** Sample answer: Devices that allow the fish to go around the dam can be incorporated into the dam's design.

USE MODELS Lead students in brainstorming ideas for their models. **What key design criteria should the system meet?** Good designs should safely allow passage of fish upstream, minimally disrupt dam operations, and endure diverse environmental conditions.

Strategies for Success

Set up a learning center as described in the "Tips & Tricks" section on this page. As students draw their designs, encourage them to think of different features that will be unique in their design. Remind students that the features of each dam should be considered as they list advantages and disadvantages of the designs.

During the Activity In their notebooks, ask students to write a description of their dam technology and then answer the question, "How will your technology help organisms get around the dam?"

As students draw, encourage them to label parts of their dams and list any materials that could be used when building their design.

2 Explain

Develop the Engineering Design Process

2. PLAN AND BUILD Encourage students to use their research to help them come up with their own plans. Be sure they take note of any materials and think about how those materials might stand up to erosion and weather.

3. TEST AND IMPROVE Because students will not be testing their designs, they should be able to compare them with other students to decide what should be improved about their particular designs. Have students present their designs and discuss how the design meets or does not meet specific criteria. For example, the design of a fish ladder would be limited by the height salmon are able to leap.

4. REDESIGN As part of their redesign process, have students focus on just one thing they would like to change about their design.

3 Extend/Evaluate

Quick Check

Discuss with students what they learned as they went through the design process. Ask students to discuss any difficulties they encountered or solutions they devised as they considered the various designs. Have students explain what advantages led them to their final selection.

After the Activity Students should get full credit for researching dams and their impact on ecosystems, making several written plans and diagrams, and choosing the best design. They should get partial credit for performing one or two of these tasks and no credit for not completing any of them.

Michael DiSpezio's
Tips & Tricks

Learning Centers Establish a classroom learning center that includes pictures and diagrams of dams. Also have available images of salmon jumping upstream in their natural habitat. Do not show pictures of fish ladders or other structures built to assist salmon migration.

Make a Model When sketches are finished, and if time allows, you might have students construct scale models of their designs using craft sticks, tape, modeling clay, and other art materials.

Enduring Understandings
Revisit the Big Idea and Essential Questions

Big Idea Ecosystems are made up of both living and nonliving parts that impact one another.

To explore the Big Idea, post unit vocabulary terms on the board and have student pairs make and explain a word web that depicts the relationships among and between terms. Sample web:

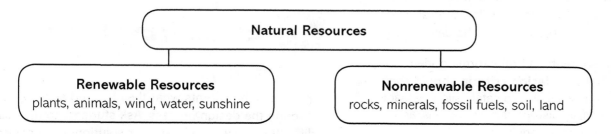

Natural Resources

Renewable Resources
plants, animals, wind, water, sunshine

Nonrenewable Resources
rocks, minerals, fossil fuels, soil, land

Essential Questions

Post the Essential Questions and use the following prompts to guide a discussion.

Lesson/Essential Question	Prompts
L1 What Are Populations, Habitats, and Niches?	• Explain how populations and communities are related.
L2 What Are Food Chains?	• Give an example of a food chain in our local area.
L3 How Can We Model a Food Web?	• Explain connections among organisms in a food web.
L4 What Are Natural Resources?	• Name a natural resource and tell why it is important.
L5 How Do People Impact Ecosystems?	• Describe how one human activity affects an ecosystem.
L6 How Do People Affect Their Environment?	• Describe the impact of trash on the environment.

Notebook ▶ Science Notebook

You may use the following strategies after students complete the unit or after each lesson.

• Have students review and edit the answers to Essential Questions they drafted at the beginning of the unit. Suggest they cross out sentences or ideas that are unnecessary or inappropriate.

• Have students list examples of producers, consumers, and decomposers on index cards. Have pairs take turns flipping a card, identifying the type of organism, and listing it in a three-column chart in their Science Notebooks.

Science Notebook

Essential Questions	Answers
What Are Populations, Habitats, and Niches?	
What Are Food Chains?	
How Can We Model a Food Web?	
What Are Natural Resources?	
How Do People Impact Ecosystems?	
How Do People Affect Their Environment?	

Unit 4 Review

Name _____

Vocabulary Review

Use the terms in the box to complete the sentences.

conservation
consumer
ecosystem
endangered
  species
habitat
niche
population
producer

1. All of the leopard frogs that live in a pond make up

   a(n) _____population_____.

2. A community of organisms and the physical environment in

   which they live is called a(n) _____ecosystem_____.

3. The use of less of something to make its supply last longer is

   called _____conservation_____.

4. A place in the environment that meets the need of an organism

   is called a(n) _____habitat_____.

5. An organism that makes its own food is called

   a(n) _____producer_____.

6. Organisms whose whole kind is at risk of dying out are

   called _____endangered species_____.

7. An organism's role in its habitat is known as

   its _____niche_____.

8. An animal that eats plants or other animals to get energy is

   called a(n) _____consumer_____.

© Houghton Mifflin Harcourt Publishing Company (border) © NElac/Age Fotostock

Item Analysis

Items	Depth of Knowledge	Cognitive Complexity
1–8	1	Low

Unit Review

Answer Key

Vocabulary Review (3 points each)

1. **population**
   Refer students to Lesson 1, where they can review the differences between populations and communities.

2. **ecosystem**
   Review with students the differences between populations, communities, and ecosystems in Lesson 1.

3. **conservation**
   Have volunteers describe ways that they help conserve resources, either at home or at school.

4. **habitat**
   Compare and contrast habitats and niches. Refer students to Lesson 1 for more help.

5. **producer**
   Remind students that producers are at the base of all food chains.

6. **endangered species**
   Emphasize that organisms are adapted to their environments. Changes in environments can threaten the existence of living things.

7. **niche**
   Remind students that a niche describes how a living thing interacts with its habitat, including how the living thing gets food and shelter.

8. **consumer**
   Emphasize that consumers cannot make their own food. Contrast this with producers, which do make their own food, most often using energy from the sun.

Assessment

Unit 4 Test and Performance Assessment

See Assessment Guide, pp. AG 44–AG 50, for Unit Test and Performance Task with Long Option rubric.

Unit Review *continued*

Answer Key

Science Concepts (5 points each)

9. B

For extra reinforcement, have students use a Venn diagram or a two-column chart to compare and contrast renewable and nonrenewable resources.

10. D

Refer students to the map of the Mississippi watershed in Lesson 4. Have them trace this watershed from its initial source to its end in the Gulf of Mexico.

11. D

Reinforce that energy for most food chains begins with energy from the sun.

12. C

If necessary, have students review feeding levels and food chains in Lesson 2.

13. B

Direct students to Lesson 4 to review the types of natural resources and their uses.

14. B

Students can review in Lessons 5 and 6 how human activities such as pollution affect the environment.

15. D

Direct students to Lesson 4 to review the types of natural resources. Point out that since limestone cannot be replaced once it is used, it is a nonrenewable resource.

UNIT 4

Science Concepts

Fill in the letter of the choice that best answers the question.

9. Many household items are made from renewable resources. Which of these objects is made from a renewable resource?

Ⓐ
plastic bag

Ⓒ
computer keyboard

Ⓑ
wooden spoon

Ⓓ
motor oil

10. Tony is studying the natural resources that supply water to his home. He traces the water from a mountain, through several small rivers, and to the large river that supplies his town with water. What is Tony studying?

Ⓐ an ecosystem

Ⓑ a habitat

Ⓒ a niche

Ⓓ a watershed

11. Carla wants to show how living things get energy. Which sequence is correct?

Ⓐ Decomposer → Consumer → Sunlight → Producer

Ⓑ Consumer → Sunlight → Producer → Decomposer

Ⓒ Producer → Decomposer → Producer → Consumer

Ⓓ Sunlight → Producer → Consumer → Decomposer

12. The picture below shows some animals you can find in grassland food chains.

Which animal is the carnivore?

Ⓐ animal 1

Ⓑ animal 2

Ⓒ animal 3

Ⓓ animal 4

13. Mica is identifying natural resources used to produce many of the items he uses every day. He has identified the source of paper and wood furniture. Which natural resource has he identified?

Ⓐ water

Ⓑ forest

Ⓒ animals

Ⓓ energy resources

240   Unit 4

Item Analysis *(continued)*

Items	Depth of Knowledge	Cognitive Complexity
9–10	2	Moderate
11–14	3	High
15	2	Moderate

Name _____

14. The table below shows how long it takes for some biodegradable items to decompose in salt water.

Item	Decomposition time
Cardboard box	2 months
Newspaper	6 weeks
Paper towel	2–4 weeks
Waxed milk carton	3 months

Which item will decompose the fastest?

(A) newspaper

(B) paper towel

(C) cardboard box

(D) waxed milk carton

15. It takes a long time for rocks to form. Limestone is a type of rock used in buildings and in road construction. Which type of resource is limestone?

(A) green

(B) energy

(C) renewable

(D) nonrenewable

16. A new highway is planned to replace a pond habitat where a frog population lives. How will this change **most likely** affect the frog population?

(A) The frog population will double.

(B) The frog population will increase.

(C) The frog population will decrease.

(D) The frog population will not change.

17. Emily is studying animals that live in marshes. She makes the following graphs to show how the number of fish and marsh birds changed in a certain area over time.

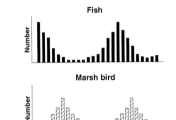

What **most likely** happened when the number of fish was highest?

(A) The bird population began to decrease.

(B) The birds moved away for lack of food.

(C) The fish population continued to increase.

(D) The bird population increased because there was more food.

18. People use land resources to help them meet their needs. Coal is a fossil fuel that people mine from the land. They burn coal to make electricity. Which type of resource is coal?

(A) a green living resource

(B) a green energy resource

(C) a renewable energy resource

(D) a nonrenewable energy resource

Unit 4   241

Item Analysis (continued)

Items	Depth of Knowledge	Cognitive Complexity
16–17	3	High
18	2	Moderate

Unit Review continued

Answer Key

Science Concepts (5 points each)

16. C

Have a volunteer identify the human act in the question. Discuss with students how this act might affect a pond ecosystem.

17. D

Students can read about the effects that populations of different organisms have on one another in Lesson 2.

18. D

Help students compare and contrast the types of resources discussed in Lesson 4.

Short Option Performance Assessment

Task

Diagram a Food Web
Have student pairs choose an animal that they know well. Instruct them to draw a food web that includes the animal. The web should include at least two food chains. Each chain should include at least three organisms. Students should label each living thing in the web as a producer, consumer, or decomposer, and, as appropriate, predator or prey.

Rubric

Preparation Provide each pair with a large sheet of paper and markers or crayons. Encourage partners to work together to choose an animal that is familiar to both of them. They might make notes about the animal before they begin drawing.

Scoring Rubric—Performance Indicators

___ Identifies two or more food chains that include the chosen animal.

___ Shows at least three living things in each food chain.

___ Labels each living thing correctly.

___ Indicates how the food chains overlap to form a food web.

Observations and Rubric Scores

3   2   1   0

Unit Review *continued*

Answer Key

Apply Inquiry and Review the Big Idea

(16 points)

19. See student page for sample answers.

If necessary, direct students to Lessons 2 and 3 to review the roles of organisms in ecosystems. Students can make a two-column chart with the types of consumers listed in one column and the foods they eat listed in the other column.

(10 points)

20. See student page for sample answer.

Write the word *decomposer* on the board, and underline *decompose*. Remind students that *decompose* means "to break down." After students review the role of decomposers in ecosystems in Lesson 2, have them summarize what decomposers do.

UNIT 4

Apply Inquiry and Review the Big Idea

Write the answers to these questions.

19. This illustration shows a food web.

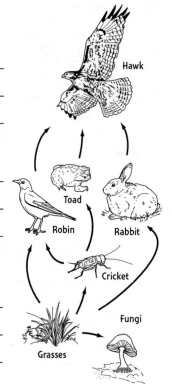

a. Identify the organisms shown in the food web as producers, consumers, or decomposers.

Producers: _____ grasses _____

Consumers: _____ cricket, robin, hawk, rabbit, toad _____

Decomposers: _____ fungi _____

b. Classify the consumers as herbivores, omnivores, or carnivores.

Herbivores: _____ cricket, rabbit _____

Omnivores: _____ robin _____

Carnivores: _____ toad, hawk _____

c. Explain why all animals depend on producers such as plants. Use an example from the food web in your explanation.

Sample answer: In this food web, the cricket eats plants, and the toad eats crickets. If there were no plants, there would be no food for crickets. As a result, there would be no food for the toads. So, the toads depend on plants to start the energy moving through the food chain.

20. Juan studied this food web and said that hawks were the last link in every food chain shown. Vicky pointed to a different organism and said that it was the last link. Which organism did Vicky identify? What was her reasoning?

Sample answer: Vicky identified the fungi as the last link in all food chains shown on this food web. Decomposers, such as fungi and bacteria, break down the wastes and dead bodies of plants and animals. Because all organisms eventually are broken down in this way, it is reasonable to say that decomposers are the last link in all the food chains.

242 Unit 4

© Houghton Mifflin Harcourt Publishing Company (border) © NClico/Age Fotostock

Item Analysis

Items	Depth of Knowledge	Cognitive Complexity
19a–19b	2	Moderate
19c	3	High
20	4	High

UNIT 5 Weather

Big Idea and Essential Questions

This Unit was designed to focus on this Big Idea and Essential Questions.

Take It Home! A School-Home Connection letter is provided in Online Resources.

Big Idea

Water moves in a regular cycle that influences the weather.

Essential Questions

L1 **What Is the Water Cycle?**

L2 **What Are Types of Weather?**

L3 **How Is Weather Predicted?**

L4 **How Can We Observe Weather Patterns?**

Professional Development

Houghton Mifflin Harcourt and **NSTA,** the **National Science Teachers Association,** have partnered to provide customized professional development resources for teachers using *ScienceFusion.*

The Professional Development Resources include:

- Do-it-yourself resources, where you can study at your own pace
- Live and archived online seminars
- Journal articles, many of which include lesson plans
- Fee-based eBooks, eBook chapters, online short courses, symposia, and conferences

> **Access to The NSTA Learning Center is provided in the *ScienceFusion* Online Resources.**

NSTA | National Science Teachers Association

The NSTA Learning Center

Unit Planning

Options for Instruction

Two parallel paths meet the unit objectives, with a strong Inquiry strand woven into each. Follow the Print Path, the Digital Path, or your customized combination of print, digital, and inquiry.

	LESSON 1	LESSON 2	LESSON 3
Essential Questions	**What Is the Water Cycle?**	**What Are Types of Weather?**	**How Is Weather Predicted?**
Print Path	☐ **Student Edition** pp. 245–258 • Water on the Move • What Goes Up Comes Down • Where Does Water Go? • A Precious Resource	☐ **Student Edition** pp. 259–272 • Up in the Air • Under Pressure • When the Wind Blows • How Clouds Form • Some Rain Anyone?	☐ **Student Edition** pp. 273–284 • Tracking the Weather • Air Masses and Fronts • Mapping the Weather • Forewarned!
Hands-On Inquiry	**Inquiry Flipchart** p. 26 **Watching the Water Cycle** ☐ Directed Inquiry **An Icy Observation** ☐ Independent Inquiry	**Inquiry Flipchart** p. 27 **Dry Under Pressure** ☐ Directed Inquiry **Warm Coast, Cool Plain** ☐ Independent Inquiry	**Inquiry Flipchart** p. 28 **Model an Air Mass** ☐ Directed Inquiry **Weather Sayings** ☐ Independent Inquiry
Digital Path	☐ **Digital Lesson** Online Resources Interactive presentation of lesson content	☐ **Digital Lesson** Online Resources Interactive presentation of lesson content	☐ **Digital Lesson** Online Resources Interactive presentation of lesson content

LESSON 4

Guided Inquiry

How Can We Observe Weather Patterns?

☐ Student Edition
pp. 287–288
- Scaffolding for Inquiry

Inquiry Flipchart
p. 30

How Can We Observe Weather Patterns?

☐ Guided Inquiry

☐ Virtual Lab
Online Resources
Interactive scaffolded inquiry

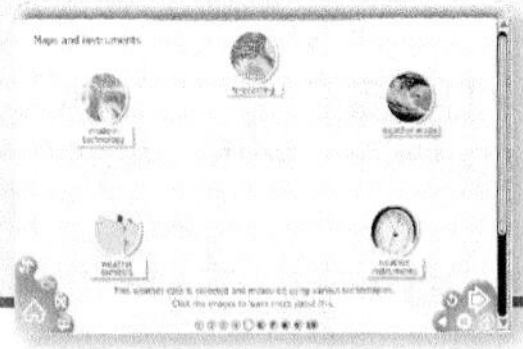

OTHER UNIT FEATURES

People in Science, p. 289

S.T.E.M. Engineering and Technology, pp. 285–286B

Online Resources

Unit Assessment

Formative Assessment
Sum It Up! and Brain Check
Student Edition, end of each lesson

Summative Assessment
Lesson Quizzes
Assessment Guide, pp. AG 51–AG 54

Unit 5 Review
Student Edition, pp. 291–294

Unit 5 Test
Assessment Guide, pp. AG 55–AG 59

Performance Assessment
SHORT OPTION: Teacher Edition, p. 293
LONG OPTION: Assessment Guide, pp. AG 60–AG 61

RTI Response to Intervention

RTI Strategies p. 243I

Online Assessment
Test-taking and automatic scoring
Banks of items from which to build tests

Teacher Notes

Planning for Inquiry

Use the following preview of Inquiry Activities and Lessons to gather and manage the materials needed for each lesson.

Activity	Inquiry and Design Process Skills Focus	Materials	Prep Tips, Troubleshooting, and Expected Results
Lesson 1 DIRECTED INQUIRY Flipchart p.26 **A** **Watching the Water Cycle** OBJECTIVE • Identify a control group and explain its importance. • Create a model to explain the parts of the water cycle. ⏱ 30–40 minutes 👥 small groups	• Measure • Observe • Compare • Model • Draw Conclusions	• beaker • water • 2 shallow pans • marker • paper labels • fan	**Prep Tips** Identify a space large enough for groups to work. Students can work in small groups. However, if space is limited, set up the two pans and fan with the help of volunteers and let the class observe the results. Make sure the fan is not drawing air or blowing toward Pan A. **Caution!** Have students notify you immediately of any spills. Water can make surfaces slippery and cause falls. Be aware of safety when using an electrical appliance near water. **Troubleshooting** Students might find it difficult to get the water from the pans back into the beaker for the final measurement. Using a funnel will help avoid spilling. **Expected Results** Students should observe that the fan increased the rate of evaporation in Pan B. In some experimental trials, Pan A resulted in 240 mL and Pan B in 230 mL. Students should recognize that the fan represented wind, and understand that rates of evaporation from a lake would be higher on clear, windy days than on cloudy, calm days.
INDEPENDENT INQUIRY Flipchart p. 26 **B** **An Icy Observation** OBJECTIVE Plan and conduct an investigation to find factors that affect rates of condensation. ⏱ 15 minutes 👥 small groups	• Plan and Conduct a Simple Investigation • Observe • Measure	• pitcher • ice • water	**Prep Tips** If glass containers are used, this activity should be done as a teacher demonstration. Review the process of condensation. Make sure students understand that during condensation, a gas changes into a liquid. Energy is released in this process. Water vapor in the air can condense on cooled surfaces. Temperature and the amount of water vapor in the air are two factors that affect the rate of condensation. Review how to set up an experiment, as described in Unit 1. Students need to be able to identify and test a condition or factor that would affect the rate of condensation. **Caution!** Have students notify you of any spills. Water can make surfaces slippery and cause falls. **Expected Results** Students will plan an investigation to find factors that affect condensation rates. They will find that temperature and humidity, among other factors, greatly influence the rate at which air condenses.

Additional teaching support for all inquiry activities is available in **Online Resources**.

 Science Notebook Strategies
- Lists of Kit-Supplied Materials
- Meeting Individual Needs
- Investigate More—Extensions and Variations and More!

Activity	Inquiry and Design Process Skills Focus	Materials	Prep Tips, Troubleshooting, and Expected Results
Lesson 2 DIRECTED INQUIRY **Flipchart** p. 27 **A** **Dry Under Pressure** **OBJECTIVE** Follow directions for an investigation to demonstrate the effects of air pressure. 🕐 10 minutes 👥 individuals	• Observe • Draw Conclusions	• 12-oz. plastic cup • water • 4 in. × 6 in. index card • 13 in. × 9 in. × 2 in. aluminum foil pan	**Prep Tips** Cover surfaces with paper towels or newspaper. Have students perform the investigation on an empty tabletop in an out-of-the-way corner of the classroom. **Caution!** Have students notify you of any spills. Water can make surfaces slippery and cause falls. **Troubleshooting** Be sure to use a plastic cup no larger than that specified in the materials list. A larger cup containing a greater amount of water will result in a greater amount of weight pressing down on the index card, which could cause a different result than expected. The cup must be completely filled and the entire rim wet for this procedure to work. If time and resources are limited, this activity can work well as a demonstration. **Expected Results** Students will probably expect the card to fall away from the cup, spilling the water. However, the card should stay in place when the cup is inverted. The card remains in place because of the force of air pressure pressing upward against it. With this small cup, the upward force exerted by air pressure is stronger than the downward force exerted by gravity acting on the water inside.
INDEPENDENT INQUIRY **Flipchart** p. 27 **B** **Warm Coast, Cool Plain** **OBJECTIVE** Plan and conduct an investigation to model heating and cooling of land and water surfaces. 🕐 15 minutes planning plus time to carry out the investigation 👥 pairs	• Plan and Conduct a Simple Investigation • Measure • Use Numbers • Infer • Draw Conclusions	• plastic boxes • water • sand • thermometers	**Prep Tips** Students can decide how to use the materials in their investigations. You may suggest students place their setups in direct sunlight. Alternatively, you may provide students with heating lamps. **Caution!** Have students notify you of any spills. Water can make surfaces slippery and cause falls. Students should wear disposable gloves when working with sand or soil. **Troubleshooting** Instruct students to avoid having direct light shine on their thermometers while measuring the temperature of each surface. **Expected Results** Water should heat up more slowly than sand or soil. Students should conclude that different materials heat up at different rates. Students should infer that the temperature of a surface affects the air temperature above it.

Planning for Inquiry (continued)

Activity	Inquiry and Design Process Skills Focus	Materials	Prep Tips, Troubleshooting, and Expected Results
Lesson 3 DIRECTED INQUIRY Flipchart p. 28 **A Model an Air Mass** **OBJECTIVE** Follow directions for an investigation to determine how an air mass forms. 🕐 20 minutes 👥 pairs	• Observe • Measure • Model • Draw Conclusions	• 16 oz. clear plastic cup • ice cubes • chilled water • pitcher • electronic stopwatch	**Prep Tips** Cover surfaces with paper towels or newspaper. Make a pitcher of chilled water and a bowl of ice cubes available for student use. To save time, you might set up the cups containing ice cubes just before starting the activity. **Caution!** Have students notify you of any spills. Water can make surfaces slippery and cause falls. **Troubleshooting** Step 1: For best results, students should wait the full five minutes before pouring cold water into the cup. Water in the pitcher must be chilled for the best results. Step 2: If students are working in pairs, have one student pour water into the cup while the other holds his her hand about 2 in. above the cup. Then have students switch roles. **Expected Results** Students should feel moisture and cool air as the water is poured over the ice. If the air in the cup were an air mass, it would be a cool, moist one. If students' hands were fronts, they would be cold fronts because at a cold front, cold air moves toward warmer air and pushes it upward.
INDEPENDENT INQUIRY Flipchart p. 28 **B Weather Sayings** **OBJECTIVE** Plan and conduct research to explore the meaning of two or more weather sayings. 🕐 45 minutes 👥 individuals	• Plan and Conduct a Simple Investigation • Draw Conclusions	• reference books • media resources	**Prep Tips** If students are to use the school's media center for research, prior to your visit inform media personnel that students will be seeking information about weather sayings and weather descriptions so that appropriate materials are on hand. The Internet is a good source for additional weather sayings that students can interpret. Suggest students type "weather sayings" or "weather proverbs" into a search engine to find websites with lists of sayings. **Troubleshooting** Share the meaning of the saying in the intro with students. *Red sky at night* refers to a brilliant red sunset. The sun sets a brilliant red when the atmosphere is not full of clouds. The sun sets in the west, and weather systems move from west to east in much of the Northern Hemisphere. So, if there are clear skies in the west, there is a good chance the weather that will arrive the next day will be clear—to the delight of sailors. **Expected Results** If students research the sayings shown on the model Science Notebook page, they will find that when clouds thicken and darken, rain is probably on the way. So, the advice is to put on your coat. When you see cirrus clouds, stormy weather might soon arrive.

Activity	Inquiry and Design Process Skills Focus	Materials	Prep Tips, Troubleshooting, and Expected Results
S.T.E.M. **Engineering and Technology** Flipchart p. 29 **Design It: Build a Wind Vane** OBJECTIVES • Use the steps of the design process to build a wind vane. • Understand the importance of wind vanes in understanding the weather. ⏱ 25–30 minutes 👥 small groups	DESIGN PROCESS STEPS 1 Find a Problem 2 Plan and Build 3 Test and Improve 4 Redesign 5 Communicate	• pencils • straight pins • straws • index cards • manila folders • modeling clay • scissors • glue	**Prep Tips** Gather materials students may use to build their wind vanes. Place the materials in workstations around the room. Review cardinal directions with students. **Expected Results** Students should research, plan, design, and build a wind vane. They should identify the design criteria their wind vane will meet. Students should test and use their wind vane and discuss how it helps them learn about weather.
Lesson **4** INQUIRY **GUIDED INQUIRY** Flipchart p. 30 Student Edition pp. 287–288 **How Can We Observe Weather Patterns?** OBJECTIVES • Measure and record weather conditions using weather tools. • Use evidence from weather observations to make predictions. • Analyze weather data. • Verify observations made by others. ⏱ 30–45 minutes	• Measure • Use Numbers • Observe • Predict • Compare • Draw Conclusions	• thermometer • barometer • rain gauge • wind vane • cloud chart • hygrometer • anemometer	**Prep Tips** Suggest that students select a location for the weather station that is sheltered from the sun. The thermometer should also be sheltered from the wind. However, the rain gauge must be placed in a spot that is open for the collection of precipitation. Before starting the collection of data, review the tools, what they do, how they are used, and the units in which each measures. **Expected Results** Students will use tools to accurately measure weather conditions. They will collect, record, and analyze weather data. They will look for patterns in weather data over time and make weather predictions.

Go Digital! Virtual Lab

How Can We Observe Weather Patterns?
Key Inquiry Skills: Measure, Observe, Record Data, Use Models, Plan and Conduct Simple Investigations
Students take measurements of weather data and try to use the information they have collected to predict the weather in the model.

Differentiated Instruction

Customize and Extend

You can extend and customize science instruction for your students using the following resources.

Leveled Readers

The **Science & Engineering Leveled Readers** can be used to provide additional nonfiction reading practice in the subject area of Unit 5.

ON-LEVEL This Reader reinforces unit concepts. It includes student response activities for your students.

TEACHER GUIDE
The accompanying **Teacher Guide** provides teaching strategies and support for using all the Readers, as well as English and Spanish worksheets that focus on vocabulary development. A correlation to the Disciplinary Core Ideas of the Next Generation Science Standards is included.

EXTRA SUPPORT This Reader shares title, illustrations, vocabulary, and concepts with the On-Level Reader. However, the text is linguistically accommodated to provide simplified sentence structures and comprehension aids. It also includes response activities.

 DIGITAL VERSIONS

All of these Leveled Readers are available online. They are also available in an innovative and engaging format for touchscreen mobile devices. Contact your HMH Sales Representative for more information.

ENRICHMENT This high-interest nonfiction Reader enriches and extends unit concepts. It reinforces some of the unit vocabulary, includes *stretch vocabulary*, and includes response activities.

RTI Response to Intervention

Response to Intervention is a process for identifying and supporting students who are not making expected progress toward essential learning goals.

The following *ScienceFusion* components have the flexibility to be used to provide Core Classroom Instruction (Tier 1), strategic intervention (Tier 2), and intensive intervention (Tier 3).		
Component	**Location**	**Strategies and Benefits**
Student Edition, Active Reading prompts Sum It Up!, Brain Check	Active Reading throughout each lesson, Sum It Up! and Brain Check at the end of each lesson	Student responses can be used as screening tools to assess whether intervention is needed.
Assessment Guide, Lesson Quizzes	pp. AG 51–AG 54	Student responses can be used as screening tools to assess whether intervention is needed.
Inquiry Flipcharts	Inquiry Flipchart pp. 26, 27, 28	Directed Inquiry for students who learn best through directed or teacher-led hands-on activities.
Teacher Edition, Unit Review Answer Strategies	TE pp. 291–294	Suggestions for intervention, guidance, and remediation for each review question.
Leveled Readers	TE p. 243H	Content support for students not meeting the learning needs during core classroom instruction.
Leveled Readers, Teacher Guides and Vocabulary Worksheets	TE p. 243H	Direct instruction with small groups of students needing additional content at various readability levels.
Extra Support for Vocabulary and Concepts (online worksheets)	Online Resources	Support for individualized instruction with practice in essential content.
Online Student Edition with Audio	Online Resources	Provides learners with multiple-modality access to science concepts and information.
Interactive Digital Lessons and Virtual Labs	Online Resources	Provides individualized learning experiences. Lessons make content accessible through simulations, animations, videos, audio, and integrated assessment.

Differentiated Instruction

English Language Learners

Choose from these instructional strategies to meet the needs of English language learners. Suggestions are provided for adapting the activity for three proficiency levels. Point-of-use strategies also appear within unit lessons.

☑ Unit Vocabulary

Lesson 1	Lesson 2	Lesson 3
water cycle	weather	air mass
atmosphere	humidity	front
evaporation	air pressure	
condensation		
precipitation		
runoff		
groundwater		

Vocabulary Cards are provided in Online Resources.

Vocabulary Activity

Words That Relate to One Another

Have students demonstrate an understanding of the relationship between pairs of words, such as *evaporation* and *condensation* and *weather* and *precipitation*.

• Provide cloze sentences in which students can insert the correct vocabulary terms. Example: When water [evaporates], it goes back into the [atmosphere].

Beginning	Intermediate	Advanced
Students create picture dictionaries for words, such as drawings of *rain* and *snow* for *precipitation*. Write the word *weather* on the board and have students create a picture cluster of related words (*humidity*, *air pressure*). Explain the difference between *air mass* and *front*.	Provide a graphic organizer entitled "Words That Go Together." Write a word on every line and encourage students to add other words to the organizer that are related. For example: add other words to these: *weather, water cycle, climate, precipitation*. Together, draw a graphic organizer that illustrates the water cycle. Call on volunteers to use vocabulary terms to label each part.	Challenge students to develop graphic organizers to help them understand and remember the terms. Students might work in pairs. When they are finished, have pairs exchange blank graphic organizers to see how well they help others recall the correct terms. Repeat this exercise several times to allow pairs to complete a number of different graphic organizers. Then have the group vote on the best one.

☑ Model Concepts

The Water Cycle

Pair students, and provide each pair with a diagram of the water cycle. Alternatively, have students draw a diagram of the water cycle themselves or use the diagram in their texts. Students will describe how water moves through the water cycle.

Beginning	Intermediate	Advanced
Have students identify each part of the water cycle. Model the pronunciation of each word. Have students repeat. Listen for correct syllable stress. Assist students in writing labels for the diagram. Give simple descriptions of what happens to water and have students identify the correct part of the water cycle. For example, *Water makes clouds.* (condensation)	Have students identify each part of the water cycle. Model the pronunciation of each word. Have students repeat. Listen for correct syllable stress. Students should label the diagram. Then have them discuss what happens to water as it goes through the cycle. Assist students in writing phrases or simple sentences to describe what happens. For example, *Water forms clouds. Water runs downhill.*	Have students identify each part of the water cycle. Model each word and have students repeat. Listen for correct syllable stress. Students should label the diagram and then discuss what happens to water as it goes through the cycle. Have students write a short paragraph describing the water cycle.

☑ Model Inquiry Skills

Observe

Pair students. Explain to students that they will observe the weather at the same time each day for one week. Provide a chart on which they can record the weather. Label each row with the days of the week. Label three columns with the heads *Temperature, Precipitation,* and *Clouds.* Supply simple weather tools, such as a thermometer, rain gauge, and cloud chart, to help students record their observations.

Beginning	Intermediate	Advanced
Each day, have pairs work together to record in the chart the temperature, precipitation, and type of clouds. Allow students to draw pictures. Assist them in writing weather words in the chart. Have students display their chart at the end of the week.	Each day, have pairs work together to record in the chart the temperature, precipitation, and type of clouds. Ask students to write two or three sentences to describe the weather. Provide sentence frames for support. For example: *It is _____ today. The temperature is _____ degrees. There were _____ centimeters of precipitation.* Have students present their findings at the end of the week.	Each day, have pairs record in the chart the temperature, precipitation, and type of clouds. Have pairs work together to write a short weather report for the day, and have them share the report with the class. Suggest that pairs take turns being "the weather reporter." At the end of the week, have pairs present a description about how the weather changed during the week.

Weather

I Wonder Why

Use the images and the question to stimulate interest in the unit topic. Ask students to describe their experiences with weather, such as changes in the sky they have seen as the weather changes from clear to stormy and back again. Discuss when they listen to weather forecasts and how they use these forecasts to plan their activities.

Here's Why

Have students turn the page and read the response to the question. You may wish to share the following background with students.

More About...

Evening Red and Morning Gray...

...two sure signs of one fine day. The large image shows St. Louis, Missouri, with a red sky at sunset. Sayings such as the one here are part of weather lore that, before the advent of modern technology, served to remind people of likely weather when certain atmospheric conditions occurred. A red sky at night as a sign of fair weather is derived from the fact that in the middle latitudes of the Northern Hemisphere, weather systems usually move from west to east. The evening red sky is caused by sunlight shining through dry dust particles to the west. By morning, that dry air is likely to be overhead.

UNIT 5

Weather

Big Idea

Water moves in a regular cycle that influences the weather.

I Wonder Why

As the sun rises, the clouds glow red. Late morning brings sunny skies. Then puffy white clouds appear. A thunderstorm rages by late afternoon! Why? *Turn the page to find out.*

243

Professional Development **Science Background**

Use the keywords to access

- Professional Development from **The NSTA Learning Center**
- **SciLinks** for additional online content appropriate for students and teachers
- Teacher Science Background in the back of this Teacher Edition and in the Planning Guide

Keywords

climate

water cycle

meteorology

SCI**LINKS**.
THE WORLD'S A CLICK AWAY

Here's Why The color of the early morning or evening sky is a clue people can use to predict changes in weather. In places where weather systems move from west to east, red skies in the morning signal an approaching storm.

In this unit, you will explore the Big Idea, the Essential Questions, and the Investigations on the Inquiry Flipchart.

Levels of Inquiry Key ■ DIRECTED ■ GUIDED ■ INDEPENDENT

Track Your Progress

Big Idea Water moves in a regular cycle that influences the weather.

Essential Questions

Now I Get the Big Idea!

Science Notebook
Before you begin each lesson, be sure to write your thoughts about the Essential Question.

244 Unit 5

Go Digital

For a complete digital curriculum and resources that provide full coverage of the objectives for this unit, see the Online Resources for this program.

Big Idea and Essential Questions

Big Idea Water moves in a regular cycle that influences the weather.

Post the Unit Big Idea on the board. Have students read the Essential Questions, which are also the titles of the lessons in this unit.

- Discuss how the Essential Questions can help them focus on the Big Idea.

- Have students read the Big Idea statement. The statement describes the main science concept they will be learning.

- Have students predict other ideas that will be taught in the lessons based on the titles, or have them give examples of pictures they expect to see.

Once they have completed all the lessons, they should have a better understanding of the Big Idea.

Essential Questions You may use the following Science Notebook strategy for working with the Essential Questions before students begin the unit or lessons in the unit.

- Strategies for revisiting the Big Idea and Essential Questions are provided in Enduring Understandings on page 291A.

Notebook ▸ **Science Notebook**

- Have students copy the Essential Questions into their Science Notebooks. Suggest they leave writing lines between questions.

- Ask students to write responses to the Essential Questions. Urge students not to worry about whether their responses are correct. They should expect their ideas to change as they work in the unit. Comment that students will be able to review and revise their answers to the Essential Questions at the end of the unit.

- Tips and strategies for using Science Notebooks are provided throughout this unit, in the Planning Guide, and in Online Resources.

Options for Inquiry

FLIPCHART P. 26

Students can conduct these optional investigations at any time before, during, or in response to the lesson in the Student Edition.

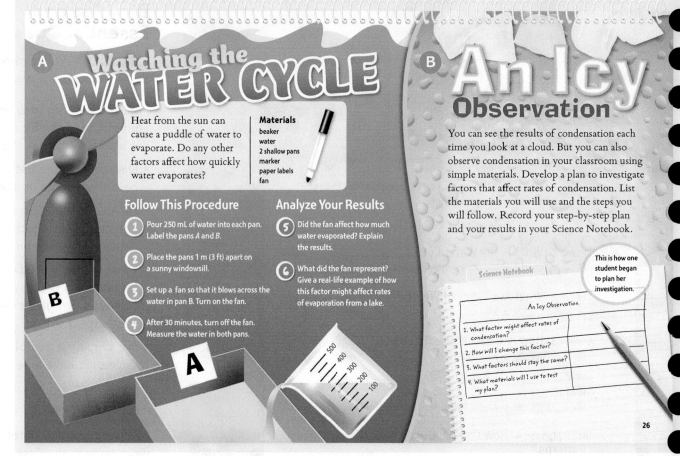

A Watching the WATER CYCLE

Heat from the sun can cause a puddle of water to evaporate. Do any other factors affect how quickly water evaporates?

Materials
beaker
water
2 shallow pans
marker
paper labels
fan

Follow This Procedure

1. Pour 250 mL of water into each pan. Label the pans *A* and *B*.

2. Place the pans 1 m (3 ft) apart on a sunny windowsill.

3. Set up a fan so that it blows across the water in pan B. Turn on the fan.

4. After 30 minutes, turn off the fan. Measure the water in both pans.

Analyze Your Results

5. Did the fan affect how much water evaporated? Explain the results.

6. What did the fan represent? Give a real-life example of how this factor might affect rates of evaporation from a lake.

B An Icy Observation

You can see the results of condensation each time you look at a cloud. But you can also observe condensation in your classroom using simple materials. Develop a plan to investigate factors that affect rates of condensation. List the materials you will use and the steps you will follow. Record your step-by-step plan and your results in your Science Notebook.

This is how one student began to plan her investigation.

Science Notebook

An Icy Observation

1. What factor might affect rates of condensation?

2. How will I change this factor?

3. What factors should stay the same?

4. What materials will I use to test my plan?

26

Directed Inquiry

A Watching the Water Cycle

⏱ 30–40 minutes
👥 small groups

Prep and Planning Tips

Students can work in small groups. However, if space is limited, set up the two pans and fan with the help of volunteers and let the class observe the results. Make sure the fan is not drawing air or blowing toward Pan A.

Caution! Ask students to notify you immediately of any spills.

Expected Results

After the fan has blown on Pan B for 30 minutes, Pan B should contain less water than Pan A. Students should observe that the fan increased the rate of evaporation in Pan B. They should recognize that the fan represented wind, and understand that rates of evaporation from a lake are likely to be higher on clear, windy days than on cloudy, calm days.

Independent Inquiry

B An Icy Observation

⏱ 15 minutes
👥 small groups

Prep and Planning Tips

See the Planning for Inquiry page for more information. Review the process of condensation. Make sure students understand that during condensation, a gas changes into a liquid. Review how to set up an experiment. Students need to be able to identify and test a condition or factor that would affect the rate of condensation.

Science Notebook

Students can use the sample Science Notebook page as a model for their own investigation. Suggest that students answer each question before developing their procedure. Have them write down each step of the procedure, and the observations they make and data they collect as they carry out their experiment.

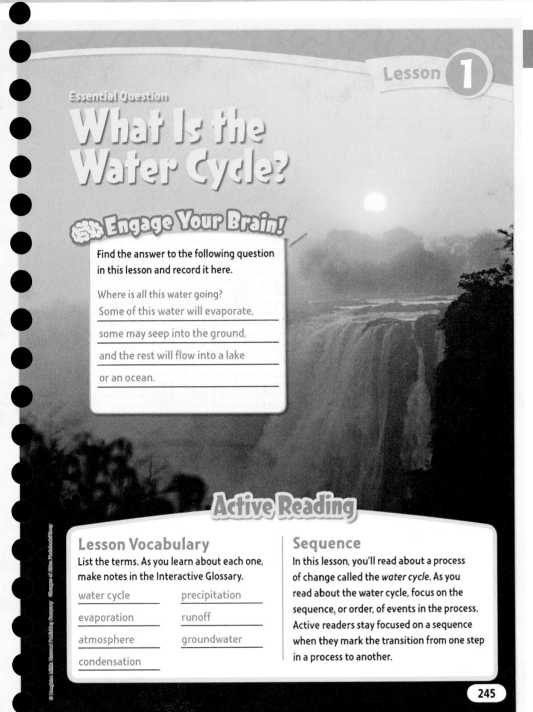

Lesson 1

Essential Question

What Is the Water Cycle?

Engage Your Brain!

Find the answer to the following question in this lesson and record it here.

Where is all this water going?
Some of this water will evaporate,

some may seep into the ground,

and the rest will flow into a lake

or an ocean.

Active Reading

Lesson Vocabulary

List the terms. As you learn about each one, make notes in the Interactive Glossary.

water cycle	precipitation
evaporation	runoff
atmosphere	groundwater
condensation	

Sequence

In this lesson, you'll read about a process of change called the *water cycle*. As you read about the water cycle, focus on the sequence, or order, of events in the process. Active readers stay focused on a sequence when they mark the transition from one step in a process to another.

245

Go Digital

An interactive digital lesson is available in Online Resources. It is suitable for individuals, small groups, or may be projected or used on an interactive white board.

Background

evaporation   condensation

runoff   precipitation

runoff and groundwater

Some water soaks into the ground.
Water flows into rivers, lakes, and oceans.

Objectives

- Describe the water cycle and the role that evaporation, condensation, and precipitation play in it.
- Explain how the sun provides the energy for the water cycle.
- Explain how the oceans and other bodies of water interact through the water cycle.
- Describe the path of precipitation from cloud to ground to runoff and groundwater.

Engage Your Brain!

Give students clues to help them answer the question, *Where is all this water going?* Tell them that water on Earth's surface is constantly on the move. It travels between the atmosphere, the oceans, and the land. Ask: **Where do you think this water comes from?** It probably came from rain and snow from a large area upstream. Remind students to record their final answer to the question when they find it on the fifth and sixth pages of this lesson.

Active Reading Annotations

Remind students that active readers "make texts their own" by annotating them with notes and marks that help with comprehension. Encourage students to use pencil, not pen, to make annotations as they read. The goal of annotation is to help students remember what they read.

Vocabulary and Interactive Glossary

Remind students to find and list the yellow highlighted terms from the lesson. As they proceed through the lesson and learn about the terms, they should add notes, drawings, or sentences in the Interactive Glossary.

2 Explain

 Generate Ideas

Ask students to imagine water in a pond. Ask: **What happens to the water in the pond during the long, dry, and hot summer months?** The pond's water level decreases, and it might even dry out. **Lead students to understand that the sun provides the energy for water to move from Earth's surface to the atmosphere and back again.**

Active Reading

Remind students that detail sentences give examples, features, characteristics, or facts about a topic. Active readers stay focused on the topic when they ask, What fact or information does this sentence add to the topic?

Develop Science Concepts

Review the states of matter. Ask: **What are the three states of matter commonly found on Earth?** solids, liquids, and gases

Ask students to give an example of water as a solid, liquid, and gas. Ice is solid water. The water in a flowing river is liquid water. Water vapor is water as a gas.

Remind students that matter can change state. Ask: **What does it take for water on Earth's surface to change state from a liquid to a gas?** energy from the sun

Explain that water vapor changes into liquid water and ice in the atmosphere. Ask: **What can you conclude about air temperature in the atmosphere?** It must be cold enough for water to condense and freeze.

Water on the Move

The water that you drink may have once been under ground or high in the sky. How does water get from Earth's surface to the air and back again?

► On the diagram, draw an X on three places where evaporation may take place.

Active Reading
As you read the next page, underline the main idea and circle details that provide information about it.

Sample detail answer shown.

Earth's water is always being recycled. It evaporates from bodies of water, the soil, and even from your skin. Water exits plants' leaves through a process called transpiration. In the air, winds and clouds can help move water from one place to another.

Condensation   Transpiration

Evaporation

After it rains, this birdbath is filled with water. When the sun comes out, its energy heats the water. The birdbath becomes empty as water changes to water vapor and returns to the atmosphere.

246

English Language Learners

Understand Words as Nouns and as Verbs Write the following sentences on the board: *We hung the picture on the wall. I can still picture her standing there.*

In the first sentence, *picture* is a noun that means "a painting or drawing." In the second sentence, *picture* is a verb that means "to imagine something in your mind." Read aloud the following sentence: "*Picture* a calm, blue ocean." Have students identify which part of speech it is (verb).

About three-fourths of Earth's surface is covered by water. Most of the water is stored in oceans. Water moves between Earth's surface and the atmosphere through a process called the **water cycle**.

The sun provides the energy for water to move through the water cycle. Sunlight heats up water particles near the ocean's surface. It causes water to evaporate.

Evaporation is the change from a liquid to a gas. When water evaporates, it forms an invisible gas called *water vapor*.

Water vapor rises into the atmosphere. The **atmosphere** is the mixture of gases that surrounds Earth. In the atmosphere, water vapor cools to form clouds. At any time, about three-fifths of Earth's surface is covered by clouds.

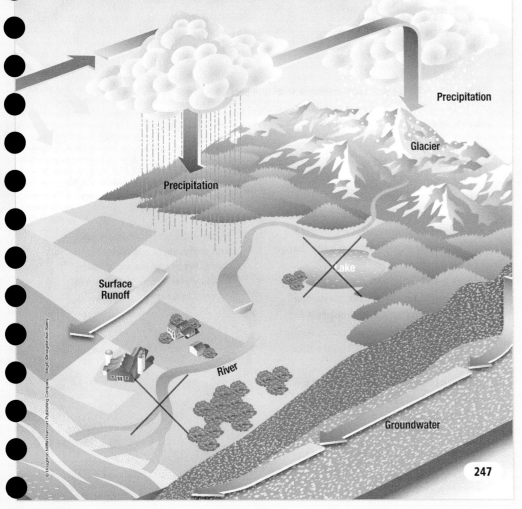

Precipitation

Glacier

Precipitation

Lake

Surface Runoff

River

Groundwater

247

Differentiation — Leveled Questions

Extra Support
Have students draw the evaporation of a puddle. They should draw one picture that shows the sun shining on the puddle and a second picture should show that the water in the puddle has evaporated.

Challenge
Would water evaporate more quickly on a sunny day or on a cloudy day? Explain. Students may suggest that water would evaporate more quickly on a sunny day because sunlight causes water to evaporate.

Develop Science Vocabulary

water cycle Make sure students understand the concept of a cycle. Draw a cycle concept map on the board. Use arrows to connect the ovals. Write the processes of the water cycle in the ovals. Point out that the water cycle has no beginning and no end.

evaporation On the board, write Liquid → Gas. Point to each part of the word equation as you reread the definition of evaporation aloud.

atmosphere Tell students that *atmosphere* comes from the Greek words *atmos*, meaning "vapor" and *spharia,* meaning "sphere." Ask: **How do these Greek words relate to the definition of *atmosphere*?** Students may note that Earth is a sphere and the atmosphere is made of gases, or vapors, that surround it.

Interpret Visuals

Use the birdbath photos and caption to begin a discussion about the process of evaporation. Ask: **What happens to water that is exposed to the sun's energy?** It evaporates and rises into the atmosphere. Encourage students to preview the next three pages, so they can better trace how water moves through the water cycle. Monitor their progress as they complete the interactivity and identify places on the diagram where water is evaporating.

Notebook ▸ Summarize Ideas

Have students use the diagram and the highlighted vocabulary terms to summarize what they have learned about the water cycle. Students can summarize their ideas orally or in writing.

2 Explain (continued)

 Generate Ideas

Read the introductory paragraph aloud: "What happens to water vapor after it rises into the air? How does it become puffy white clouds or raindrops that fall on your head?"

Have students preview the images and captions on these two pages. Ask: **How do these elements help you to answer the questions?** Students should note that the images and captions explain the processes that change water vapor into water droplets. These droplets form clouds. They join together, become larger, and fall as precipitation.

Active Reading

Remind students that sequence, or order, is important in text that describes the development of an idea or the steps in a process. Active readers stay focused on sequence when they mark the transition from one stage of an idea or step in a process to another.

Develop Science Concepts

Make sure students understand that water on Earth continually moves through the water cycle. Ask students to imagine a raindrop falling to Earth's surface. Have them describe one path the raindrop could take through the water cycle. Students should note that the raindrop could fall into a body of water, such as an ocean. There, energy from the sun could cause the raindrop to evaporate and return to the atmosphere as water vapor. In the atmosphere, the water vapor could cool and condense into a water droplet. Eventually, the water droplet would come together with other droplets to form a raindrop that falls back to Earth's surface.

What Goes Up Comes Down

What happens to water vapor after it rises into the air? How does it become puffy white clouds or raindrops that fall on your head?

Active Reading As you read these pages, write numbers next to the sentences and phrases that show the order of events from evaporation to precipitation.

Condensation

Think again of the ocean. Water from the[1] ocean's surface evaporates.[2] As water vapor rises into the atmosphere, it cools.[3] When water vapor loses enough energy, it condenses to form liquid water. **Condensation** is the change of a gas into a liquid.

There are tiny solid particles in the atmosphere. Water vapor condenses around these particles to form water droplets. A few water droplets are almost too small to see. However, when billions of droplets are close together, they form clouds.

Clouds can be made of water droplets, ice crystals, or both. They can form high in the sky or just above the ground. *Fog* is a cloud that forms near the ground.

Water vapor condenses around salt and dust particles in the air to form these water droplets.

Water vapor may condense on cool surfaces, too. It's why the cool glass below seems to "sweat." *Dew* is water droplets that form on objects near the ground.

248

 Writing Connection

Haiku Invite students to write a haiku about the water cycle. Tell them that a haiku usually has three lines. The first line has five syllables, the second line has seven syllables, and the last line has five syllables. Suggest that students devote one line in the haiku to each process in the water cycle. Read some examples of haikus to help students understand how the poems paint a visual image in the reader's mind. Have students revise and illustrate their haikus. Display their work around the classroom.

Water droplets in a cloud collide and join together. It takes many droplets to form a single raindrop.

Precipitation

Air currents keep water droplets in the air. But as droplets and snow crystals grow inside clouds, they become too heavy and fall to Earth as precipitation. **Precipitation** is water that falls from clouds to Earth's surface. Rain, snow, and hail are all forms of precipitation.

Precipitation that falls into the oceans may quickly evaporate back into the atmosphere. Precipitation that falls on land may be stored, it may flow across the land, or it may be used by living things. Depending on where it falls, water from precipitation may move quickly or slowly through the water cycle.

Do the Math!
Order Fractions

A raindrop is many times bigger than a water droplet and a dust particle. The table shows the size of droplets and dust particles in relation to the size of raindrops. Order the fractions from least to greatest.

Fractions	Ordered fractions
$\frac{1}{100}$	$\frac{1}{5000}$
$\frac{1}{1}$	$\frac{1}{100}$
$\frac{1}{5000}$	$\frac{1}{20}$
$\frac{1}{20}$	$\frac{1}{1}$

Use the ordered fractions to correctly label the items on the diagram.

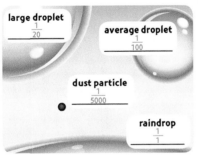

large droplet $\frac{1}{20}$

average droplet $\frac{1}{100}$

dust particle $\frac{1}{5000}$

raindrop $\frac{1}{1}$

249

Differentiation — Leveled Questions

Extra Support

Place waxed paper on a baking sheet. Tilt the baking sheet and sprinkle it with water. The water drops join together as they flow down the sheet. Have students relate the activity to cloud formation and precipitation.

Challenge

Challenge students to create a model of the water cycle. Have them list the materials they will need and the steps they will follow. They should demonstrate their models for the class.

Develop Science Vocabulary

condensation Write "*Gas → Liquid*" on the board as you read the definition of *condensation* aloud. If time permits, pour some water into a glass with ice. Students should see water condense on the outside of the glass. Explain that the air surrounding the glass contains water vapor. The water vapor that came in contact with the cold surface of the glass condensed into water droplets.

precipitation Tell students that *precipitation* comes from the Latin word *præcipitationem*, meaning "the act or fact of falling headlong." Have students discuss how this meaning pertains to forms of water that fall from clouds to Earth's surface.

Do the Math!

Order Fractions

Remind students that a fraction describes a part of a whole when the whole is cut into equal parts. A fraction has two parts. The *denominator* is the bottom number. It gives the number of parts in the whole. The *numerator* is the top number. It tells how many parts of the whole are being described by the fraction. As students examine the fractions shown here, point out that the larger the denominator, the more parts the whole has been divided into, and the smaller each single part is. So, the smallest fraction would have the largest denominator.

Notebook ▸ Summarize Ideas

Have students use the images and heads on these pages to sequence the processes of the water cycle. Encourage students to review the process of evaporation on the previous two pages. Students can summarize what they've learned orally or in writing.

2 Explain (continued)

Notebook ▶ Generate Ideas

Ask students what they know about groundwater and runoff. Make a list of their ideas on the board. After students have read these pages, ask them to revise the list. Students should add new concepts and delete inaccuracies. Help them identify and resolve any misconceptions.

Active Reading

Remind students that a lesson vocabulary term is defined once and then used as needed throughout a lesson. Active readers pause to be sure they recall the meaning of a new term as they encounter it in the text.

Develop Science Concepts

Have students consider what happens to water when it falls on land. Tell them to picture precipitation falling on a grassy meadow and on an ice-covered mountain peak. Ask: **How would water behave at each location?** Water falling on a grassy meadow would likely seep into the ground. Water falling on the mountain peak would likely be in the form of snow; the water would likely be stored as part of a glacier.

Explain that voids, or spaces, in between soil and rock particles allow water to seep into the ground. Ask: **What would happen if these spaces were to completely fill up during a rain event?** The excess water would accumulate above the ground or flow across the surface toward low-lying areas.

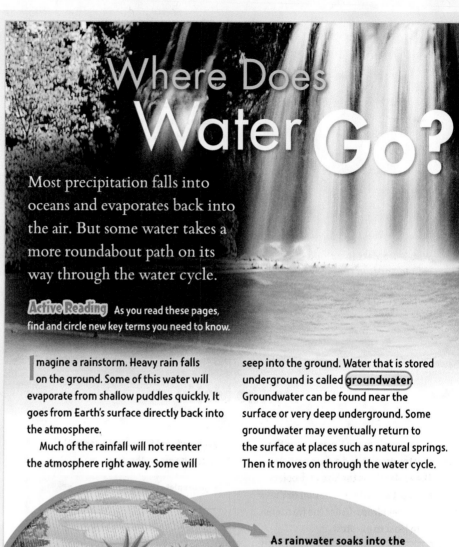

Where Does Water Go?

Most precipitation falls into oceans and evaporates back into the air. But some water takes a more roundabout path on its way through the water cycle.

Active Reading As you read these pages, find and circle new key terms you need to know.

Imagine a rainstorm. Heavy rain falls on the ground. Some of this water will evaporate from shallow puddles quickly. It goes from Earth's surface directly back into the atmosphere.

Much of the rainfall will not reenter the atmosphere right away. Some will seep into the ground. Water that is stored underground is called groundwater. Groundwater can be found near the surface or very deep underground. Some groundwater may eventually return to the surface at places such as natural springs. Then it moves on through the water cycle.

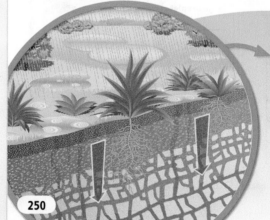

250

As rainwater soaks into the ground, it fills up spaces between soil particles and cracks in rocks. Water that seeps deep underground becomes groundwater. Groundwater moves very slowly—if at all!

123   Math Connection

Make a Graph Have students consider all the water on Earth. If that water were divided into 100 parts, 97 of the parts would be salty ocean water. Only 3 of the parts would be fresh water located in ice caps, glaciers, rivers, lakes, and underground. Have students write fractions representing each of these numbers. $\frac{97}{100}$; $\frac{3}{100}$

When glaciers melt, they quickly release stored water. Some of it may evaporate, some may seep into the ground, and some may move across the land as runoff.

Not all of the water that falls on land evaporates right away or seeps into the ground. Runoff is water that cannot soak into the ground and instead flows across Earth's surface. Too much precipitation may cause runoff. Runoff often flows into streams, rivers, and lakes. It may also flood low-lying areas.

Precipitation that falls in cold places may become part of a glacier. A glacier [GLAY•sher] is a large, slow-moving mass of ice. Water can be stored in glaciers for a very long time. Eventually, though, glaciers melt. Meltwater from glaciers can form lakes, flow into oceans, or become groundwater. Melting glaciers can increase the amount of runoff in a place.

Runaway Water

The picture shows runoff on a city street. In the space below, describe what might happen to this runoff.

Sample answer: The water cannot easily seep into the ground. It might eventually evaporate. Some might move through the city's drainage system until it reaches a river, an ocean, or a lake, or becomes groundwater.

251

Develop Science Vocabulary

groundwater Ask students to reiterate the relationship between groundwater and surface water. Remind them that all water on Earth is part of the water cycle. Eventually groundwater will return to the surface where it can again evaporate.

runoff Read the definition of runoff aloud. Point out that *runoff* is a compound word that can be broken down to better understand its meaning. For example, water that cannot soak into the ground *runs off* into low-lying areas, rivers, or streams. This water is called runoff. Ask students to repeat the definition of runoff in their own words.

Develop Inquiry Skills

PREDICT Tell students that scientific evidence indicates that Earth's average surface temperatures are warming. Ask: **How might this affect the amount of water stored in glaciers?** The amount of water stored in glaciers would likely decrease as glaciers melt.

Interpret Visuals

Ask students to describe a typical city street. **What covers most of the ground?** concrete, asphalt, buildings. Point out that precipitation cannot easily soak into these surfaces. Ask them to consider what happens to city runoff. Students should write down their ideas on the lines in the Interactivity.

Notebook ▸ Summarize Ideas

Have students use the list they developed in the Generate Ideas section on the previous page to summarize what they have learned about groundwater and runoff. Students can summarize their ideas orally or in writing.

English Language Learners

Distinguish Between Easily Confused Words: *raise, rise* The word *rise*, pronounced rīz, means "to go up", as in "water vapor rises". It can also mean "to move to a higher position." It never takes an object. The word *raise*, on the other hand, means "to move someone or something to a higher position." It always takes an object. (They raised the curtain [direct object] and the play began; Please raise your hand [direct object] if you want to speak.)

2 Explain (continued)

 Notebook **Generate Ideas**

Ask students if they know where their drinking water comes from. Explain that many people in the United States depend on groundwater to meet their water needs. Have them study the map on this page. Point out that the states shown on the map get much of their drinking water from the Floridan Aquifer, a large body of rock that stores groundwater.

Active Reading

Remind students that informational text contains many facts. Active readers process informational text with deliberate speed, which enables them to focus on and retain the facts presented. Underlining facts helps active readers focus more readily.

Develop Science Concepts

Stress that clean, fresh water is a valuable natural resource, and it can be overused. Ask students to think about how they can help conserve water at home and at school. Have students work in pairs to make lists of water conservation tips. As a class, discuss the lists. Ask: **Which tips are easy to implement?** Answers will vary. In general, those suggestions that involve individuals or small groups would be easier to implement. **Which tips would have the greatest impact on saving water?** Answers will vary. In general, those suggestions that involve commitments from governments, businesses, and communities are likely to have the greatest impact.

Suggest that students try some of the water conservation tips and report back to the class.

Why It Matters

A Precious Resource

Can you name all the ways that you use water? Water is an important resource used by all living things. People often need to share and conserve their sources of fresh, clean water.

Active Reading As you read these two pages, find and underline at least three facts about aquifers.

When you turn on a faucet, water flows out. Where does it come from? People can get fresh water from rivers or lakes. They can also get fresh water from aquifers. An *aquifer* [AH•kwuh•fuhr] is a body of rock that stores groundwater. People can drill into an aquifer and pump the water to the surface.

The water in aquifers can run low if people use more than can be replaced by precipitation. Human activities can also pollute aquifers. States that share aquifers work together to find solutions to these problems. They want to make sure there is enough fresh, clean water for everyone.

252

The Floridan Aquifer covers about 60,000 square kilometers. Billions of liters of water are pumped out of the Floridan Aquifer each day. Large cities, such as Savannah and Orlando, get water from this aquifer.

Where Does Your Water Come From?

Find out the source of your water at school or at home.

Answers will vary depending on students' locations.

Differentiation — Leveled Questions

Extra Support

Draw an aquifer on the board. Ask students to identify different parts of the aquifer as you point to the diagram on the next page. Include features such as a spring, a well, and a pump, as well as the aquifer itself.

Challenge

Ask students to infer what might happen to an aquifer during a drought, or period of below-normal rainfall. Students should realize that the level of the water in the aquifer would probably decrease.

People cannot live without water. We use water for many different purposes, including recreation.

Aquifers are huge underground water reservoirs [REZ•er•vwarz]. Precipitation adds water to aquifers in places called *recharge areas*. The water in some aquifers slowly makes its way to rivers, springs, lakes, and oceans. It may take groundwater in an aquifer up to a year to travel only 25 cm.

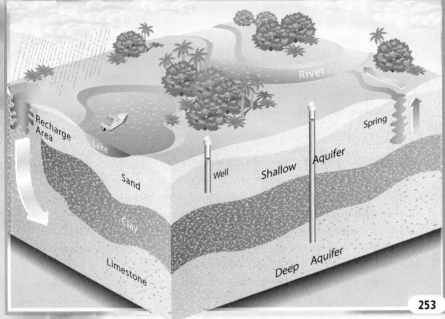

River

Recharge Area

Lake

Sand

Well   Shallow   Aquifer   Spring

Clay

Limestone   Deep   Aquifer

253

Develop Inquiry Skills

COMMUNICATE Direct students to write down a list of questions to ask a local official about sources of drinking water in the area. Then invite a local official to class. Have students interview the official. Students can use the official's responses to help them complete the Interactivity.

If a visit is not feasible, students can compose a letter or e-mail as a class and send it to the local water department.

Interpret Visuals

Point out that the aquifer lies under the shaded region shown in the map on the opposite page. Ask: **How much area does the aquifer cover?** about 60,000 square kilometers **Which states are included in this area?** Mississippi, Alabama, Georgia, South Carolina, and Florida **Why do you think it is called the Floridan Aquifer?** Accept all reasonable answers. The aquifer was first mapped and studied in Florida. Encourage students to use maps and other reference materials to identify the location of major cities which draw water from the Floridan aquifer. Have them mark the location of these cities on the map on the previous page.

 Notebook **Summarize Ideas**

Have students use the underlined facts on these pages to summarize what they have learned about aquifers. Students can summarize their ideas orally or in writing.

123 Math Connection

Number Sentences Remind students that area is the number of square units needed to cover a surface. To find the area (A) of a rectangle, you multiply its length (L) times its width (W): $A = L \times W$. Have students write three number sentences whose product is equal to the area of the Floridan aquifer (60,000 square kilometers).

3 km x 20,000 km

60 km x 1,000 km

150 km x 400 km

3 Extend/Evaluate

Sum It Up!

- If students have difficulty identifying the visuals in the questions, refer them back to photos and art on the relevant pages in the lesson. Reread the captions on the visuals with students.

- Point out key words and phrases in the captions on this page, such as "large, slow-moving mass of ice." Explain that these words and phrases are clues to the answers.

- Suggest that students make a list of the lesson vocabulary terms before they complete the lesson review. Students can refer to their lists as they answer questions.

- If students are having difficulty completing the cloze passage, make a word bank on the board. Tell students to use the words in the bank to fill in the blanks in the passage.

- Point out the Answer Key where students can check and revise their answers. Have students revise any incorrect answers so they can use the Sum It Up! page to study for tests.

When you're done, use the answer key to check and revise your work.

Write the term that matches each photo and caption.

1 Water can be stored for a long time in a large, slow-moving mass of ice.
_____glacier_____

2 Water can also be stored underground between the spaces in soil particles or cracks in rocks.
_____groundwater_____

3 During heavy rains, some water might not soak into the ground. Instead, it flows down slopes and across Earth's surface.
_____runoff_____

Summarize

Fill in the missing words to describe the water cycle.

The water cycle shows how water moves from Earth's surface to the 4. __atmosphere__ and back again. The 5. ___sun___ provides the energy for the water cycle. Water on the surface of the ocean heats up. During 6. __evaporation__, it changes from a liquid to a gas. As 7. __water vapor__ rises into the atmosphere, it cools. During 8. __condensation__, it changes from a gas to a liquid. Billions of water droplets form a 9. ___cloud___. When the droplets get too large for air currents to keep them up, they fall to Earth's surface as 10. __precipitation__.

254

Lesson 1

Name _____

Word Play

1 Use the clues to fill in the missing letters of the words.

1. g r o u n d w a t (e) r Water stored underground
   10

2. c o n d e n s a t i o n The changing of water from a gas to a liquid

3. w a t e r c (y) c l e The movement of water from Earth's surface to the
   7   atmosphere and back again

4. a t m o s p h e r (e) Mixture of gases that surrounds Earth
   4

5. p r e (c) i p i t a t i o n Water that falls from clouds to Earth's surface
   8

6. (r) u n o f f Water that flows across Earth's surface
   5

7. g (l) a (c) i e r A huge mass of frozen water that moves slowly
   9   6

8. t r a n s p i r a (t) i o n The process in which plants return water vapor
   3   to the atmosphere

9. (w) a t e r v a p o r Water as a gas
   1

10. e v a p o r (a) t i o n The changing of water from a liquid to a gas
    2

Bonus: Solve the Riddle!

Use the circled letters in the clues above to solve the riddle.

What is water's favorite way to travel?

On a w a t e r   c y c l e
      1 2 3 4 5   6 7 8 9 10

255

Answer Strategies

Word Play

1. Suggest that students refer back to the definitions of highlighted vocabulary terms throughout the lesson. Provide additional clues for students who are having difficulty with the Word Play.

Assessment

Suggested Scoring Guide
You may wish to use this suggested scoring guide for the Brain Check.

Item	Points
1	20 (2 points each)
2	10
3	10
4	10
5	15
6	15
7	10
8	10
Total	100

Lesson Quiz
See Assessment Guide, p. AG 51.

3 Extend/Evaluate (continued)

Answer Strategies

Apply Concepts

2. Suggest that students review the lesson pages that describe the formation of a cloud. Ask: **What is a cloud made of?** A cloud is made of water droplets. **Where do the water droplets come from?** They come from water vapor that cooled and condensed around tiny particles in the air. **How does water vapor get into the air?** Water is heated by the sun and evaporates.

3. Remind students that groundwater travels very slowly underground. Ask: **Where does groundwater go?** It goes into springs, rivers, lakes, or oceans. **What happens after it joins these bodies of water?** It eventually evaporates.

4. Review the definition of *condensation*. Remind students that clouds form when water condenses into water droplets in the atmosphere. Precipitation follows the formation of these water droplets.

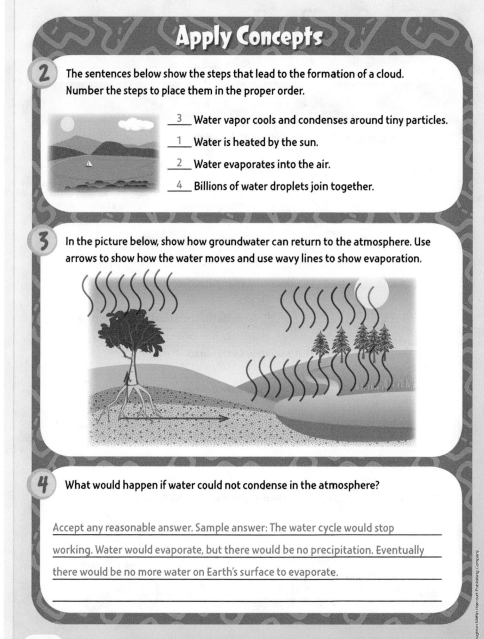

Apply Concepts

2 The sentences below show the steps that lead to the formation of a cloud. Number the steps to place them in the proper order.

___3___ Water vapor cools and condenses around tiny particles.

___1___ Water is heated by the sun.

___2___ Water evaporates into the air.

___4___ Billions of water droplets join together.

3 In the picture below, show how groundwater can return to the atmosphere. Use arrows to show how the water moves and use wavy lines to show evaporation.

4 What would happen if water could not condense in the atmosphere?

Accept any reasonable answer. Sample answer: The water cycle would stop working. Water would evaporate, but there would be no precipitation. Eventually there would be no more water on Earth's surface to evaporate.

256

5 In the spaces below, draw and label examples of water in the atmosphere as a solid, a liquid, and a gas. Hint: Wavy lines may be used to represent water vapor.

Snowflakes or hail should be labeled as *solid*.	Raindrops should be labeled as *liquid*.	Wavy lines may be labeled as *water vapor*.

6 Label each of the following scenes as an example of evaporation, precipitation, or condensation. Then briefly describe what happens during each process.

Evaporation: Water changes from liquid to gas.	Precipitation: Water falls from clouds to Earth's surface.	Condensation: Water changes from gas to liquid.

257

Answer Strategies

Apply Concepts

5. Review the states of matter. Write examples of water in each state on the board. Remind students that water vapor is invisible. **How will they represent water as a gas?** Students might suggest a blank box to represent water vapor, or they might use wavy lines.

6. Review the definitions of *evaporation*, *precipitation*, and *condensation*. Have students refer back to the pages in the lesson that describe these processes, if necessary. Suggest that they closely examine the photos and art on the lesson pages. **Which visuals are similar to the visuals shown in the question?**

3 Extend/Evaluate (continued)

Answer Strategies

Apply Concepts

7. Suggest that students review the diagram of an aquifer on the appropriate lesson page. Remind them that an aquifer is a body of rock that stores groundwater.

8. Remind students that in the past, glaciers covered large parts of Earth's surface. Ask: **Where does the water in glaciers come from?** It comes from snow that accumulates over many years. Explain that the water in the glaciers is "locked-in" and that it might take a long time before it melts and returns to the oceans. Ask: **What is the main source of water for cloud formation and precipitation?** The oceans.

Take It Home!

See *ScienceSaurus*® for more information about water on Earth. *ScienceSaurus* is a "mini-encyclopedia" students can use to find out more about unit topics. It contains numerous resources including concise content summaries, an almanac, many tables, charts, and graphs, history of science, and a glossary.

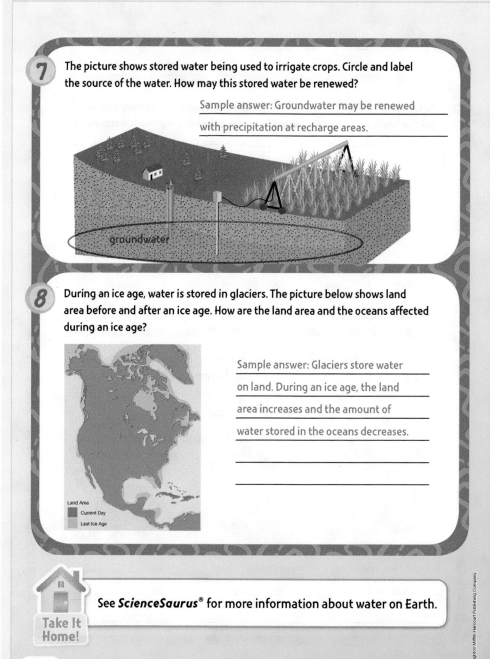

7 The picture shows stored water being used to irrigate crops. Circle and label the source of the water. How may this stored water be renewed?

Sample answer: Groundwater may be renewed with precipitation at recharge areas.

groundwater

8 During an ice age, water is stored in glaciers. The picture below shows land area before and after an ice age. How are the land area and the oceans affected during an ice age?

Sample answer: Glaciers store water on land. During an ice age, the land area increases and the amount of water stored in the oceans decreases.

Land Area
Current Day
Last Ice Age

Take It Home!

See *ScienceSaurus*® for more information about water on Earth.

258

Make Connections

Easy

Math Connection

Find Groundwater Travel Time

Suppose that groundwater in your area travels 25 centimeters in one year. How many centimeters has that groundwater traveled since you were born?

Sample answer: 25 cm/yr x 10 yr = 250 cm

Average

Art Connection

Raindrop Drawings

Have students use their answers from the Do the Math! activity in this lesson to make scale drawings of dust particles, cloud droplets, and raindrops. Students' scales should be large enough to make the smallest object in the list easily visible. They should also add labels and captions that explain the formation of clouds and precipitation.

Average

Social Studies Connection

Demand for Water

Have students use an online encyclopedia or nonfiction books from the school library to find out more about how people use water. Then have students role-play a meeting in which participants must decide how to share water from an aquifer. The meeting should include ranchers, farmers, power-plant managers, city residents, and other relevant constituents.

Challenging

Health and Physical Education

Importance of Clean Water

Ask students to write a report on the importance of clean water to living things. Students can use an online encyclopedia or nonfiction books from the school library to research different topics, such as how the human body uses water for life functions or how water pollution affects human health. Ask students to share their reports with the class.

Options for Inquiry

FLIPCHART P. 27

Students can conduct these optional investigations at any time before, during, or in response to the lesson in the Student Edition.

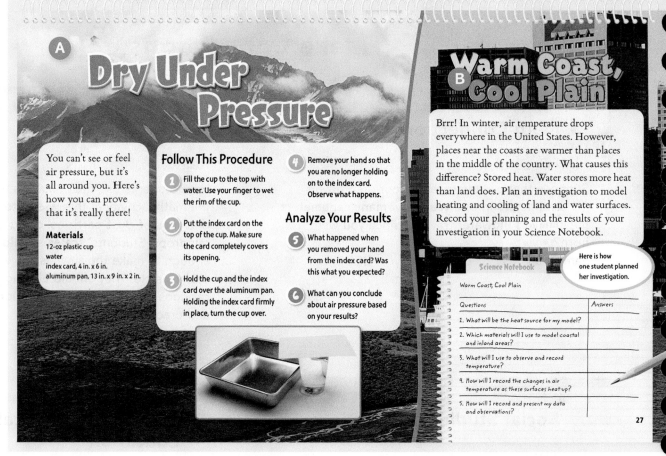

A Dry Under Pressure

You can't see or feel air pressure, but it's all around you. Here's how you can prove that it's really there!

Materials
12-oz plastic cup
water
index card, 4 in. x 6 in.
aluminum pan, 13 in. x 9 in. x 2 in.

Follow This Procedure

1. Fill the cup to the top with water. Use your finger to wet the rim of the cup.

2. Put the index card on the top of the cup. Make sure the card completely covers its opening.

3. Hold the cup and the index card over the aluminum pan. Holding the index card firmly in place, turn the cup over.

4. Remove your hand so that you are no longer holding on to the index card. Observe what happens.

Analyze Your Results

5. What happened when you removed your hand from the index card? Was this what you expected?

6. What can you conclude about air pressure based on your results?

B Warm Coast, Cool Plain

Brrr! In winter, air temperature drops everywhere in the United States. However, places near the coasts are warmer than places in the middle of the country. What causes this difference? Stored heat. Water stores more heat than land does. Plan an investigation to model heating and cooling of land and water surfaces. Record your planning and the results of your investigation in your Science Notebook.

Here is how one student planned her investigation.

Science Notebook

Warm Coast, Cool Plain

Questions	Answers
1. What will be the heat source for my model?	
2. Which materials will I use to model coastal and inland areas?	
3. What will I use to observe and record temperature?	
4. How will I record the changes in air temperature as these surfaces heat up?	
5. How will I record and present my data and observations?	

27

Directed Inquiry

A Dry Under Pressure

 10 minutes

individuals

Prep and Planning Tips

If time and resources are limited, present this activity as a demonstration.

Cover surfaces with paper towels or newspaper. Have students perform the investigation on an empty tabletop in an out-of-the-way corner of the classroom.

The cup must be completely filled and the entire rim wet for this procedure to work.

Caution! Have students notify you of any spills.

Expected Results

Students will probably expect the card to fall away from the cup, spilling the water. However, the card should stay in place when the cup is flipped over. The card stays put because of the force of air pressure pressing upward against it. With this small cup, the upward force exerted by air pressure is stronger than the downward force exerted by gravity acting on the water inside.

Independent Inquiry

B Warm Coast, Cool Plain

15 minutes planning plus time to carry out the activity

pairs

Prep and Planning Tips

Make the following materials available for students: plastic boxes, water, sand, thermometers. Students can then decide how to use these materials in their investigation.

Caution! Have students notify you of any spills. Students should wear disposable gloves when working with sand or soil.

Science Notebook

Students can use the sample Science Notebook page as a model for planning their investigations. Suggest that students make a chart in which they can record water temperatures over different surfaces. Students should find that surface temperature varies with the material and should infer that air temperature above a surface also varies with surface temperature.

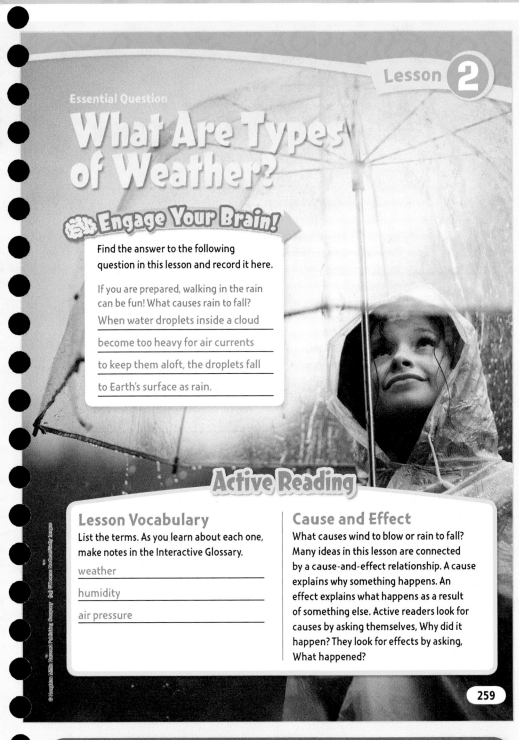

Essential Question

What Are Types of Weather?

Engage Your Brain!

Find the answer to the following question in this lesson and record it here.

If you are prepared, walking in the rain can be fun! What causes rain to fall? When water droplets inside a cloud become too heavy for air currents to keep them aloft, the droplets fall to Earth's surface as rain.

Active Reading

Lesson Vocabulary

List the terms. As you learn about each one, make notes in the Interactive Glossary.

weather

humidity

air pressure

Cause and Effect

What causes wind to blow or rain to fall? Many ideas in this lesson are connected by a cause-and-effect relationship. A cause explains why something happens. An effect explains what happens as a result of something else. Active readers look for causes by asking themselves, Why did it happen? They look for effects by asking, What happened?

259

Go Digital

An interactive digital lesson is available in Online Resources. It is suitable for individuals, small groups, or may be projected or used on an interactive white board.

---

1 Engage/Explore

Objectives

- Describe the composition of the atmosphere.
- Identify factors that make up weather.
- Explain how weather conditions are measured.
- Explain how different types of precipitation form.
- Describe some forms of severe weather.

Engage Your Brain!

Have students brainstorm answers to the question, *What causes rain to fall?* as you record their responses on the board. You may wish to direct students back to the water cycle diagram in the What Is the Water Cycle? lesson. Students should recall that precipitation is part of the water cycle. Remind students to record their final answer to the question when they find it on the last spread of this lesson.

Active Reading

Remind students that active readers "make texts their own" by annotating them with notes and marks that help with comprehension. Encourage students to use pencil, not pen, to make annotations and to feel free to change their annotations as they read. The goal of annotation is to help students remember what they read.

Vocabulary and Interactive Glossary

Remind students to find and list the yellow highlighted terms from the lesson. As they proceed through the lesson and learn about the terms, they should add notes, drawings, or sentences in the extra spaces provided in the Interactive Glossary.

2 Explain

Notebook **Generate Ideas**

Read the introductory paragraph aloud. Ask students to respond to the questions. Make a list of their answers on the board. Have students revisit this list as you develop a working definition of the term *weather*.

Active Reading

Remind students that informational text contains many facts. Active readers process informational text with deliberate speed that enables them to focus on and retain the facts presented. Underlining facts, such as the factors that describe weather, helps active readers focus more readily.

Do the Math!

Graph Data

Review the construction of a bar graph with students. Remind them that as they draw the bars, the bar heights must correspond to the temperatures shown. You may wish to reproduce the graph grid and have volunteers draw the three bars on the board. Discuss how visually representing the data makes the pattern of rising then falling temperature through the day more apparent.

Up in the Air

Quick! Describe today's weather. Is it cold and windy? Warm and dry? Many things you do depend on the weather. What *is* weather?

Active Reading As your read these pages, circle factors that help us describe weather. Then, underline a detail about each factor.

Earth's atmosphere protects living things from the sun's harmful ultraviolet rays and shields Earth from space debris. It is about 600 km (372 mi) thick, which seems very thick. However, in comparison with the rest of Earth, the atmosphere is actually quite thin.

The atmosphere is a mixture of gases. It is mostly made up of nitrogen and oxygen. The condition of the atmosphere at a given place and time is called **weather**. Weather takes place in the layer of the atmosphere closest to Earth's surface. Without the movement of gases in the atmosphere, there would be no weather.

Many factors, including air temperature, humidity, and air pressure, help us describe the weather of a place. *Air temperature* is how warm or cool the air is around us. Air temperature affects how much moisture is in the air. The air temperature also affects how we dress and what we do outside.

Do the Math!
Graph Data

A student recorded the temperature of the air at three times during the day: 50 °F at 8:00 a.m., 62 °F at 12:00 p.m., and 56 °F at 4:00 p.m. Graph the data.

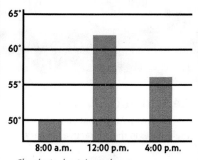

Check students' graphs.

What can you conclude?

Sample answer: Temperature increases toward midday and decreases toward the evening.

260

English Language Learners

Factors That Describe Weather List these weather-determining factors on the board: humidity, temperature, precipitation, and wind. As you define each word in simple terms, have a student act out characteristics of that weather factor. For example, for air temperature, a student might act out shivering or sweating. Have students then write short definitions for the words in their notebooks. Suggest that students draw pictures that illustrate the terms next to the words.

Humidity is the amount of water vapor in the air. When the air feels dry, we have low humidity. When the air feels damp, we have high humidity. High humidity can also affect another weather factor—precipitation. *Precipitation* is water that falls back to Earth. Depending on air temperature, precipitation falls as rain, snow, sleet, or hail.

Air pressure is the weight of the atmosphere pressing down on Earth's surface. Air temperature and humidity both affect air pressure. Changes in air pressure usually bring changes in weather.

Weather determines whether we can go for a cool dip in a pool, whether we should be careful of strong winds, or whether we can skate on a frozen lake.

What's the Weather?

Which of these pictures shows weather that is most like the day's weather where you live? Describe your current weather conditions.

Answers will vary. Sample answer: The middle picture. It is cloudy, cool, and windy outside.

261

Develop Science Vocabulary

weather Refer to the descriptions students gave of the weather as the lesson started. Point out that when speaking of weather, they usually mention factors such as temperature, precipitation, cloud cover, and wind.

humidity Tell students that there is usually water vapor in the air. Demonstrate this by placing a very cold glass on a counter and allowing water from the air to condense onto it in drops. Ask: **Where did the water come from?** It was in the air. Note that even when the air feels dry, there is usually water vapor in it.

air pressure Point out that even though air is matter and has weight, you can't "feel" air pressure except in special circumstances. Ask students if they have ever flown and felt their ears pop or close up on takeoff and landing. Explain that this takes place as the plane moves quickly between altitudes with different air pressures.

Interpret Visuals

Answers for the Interactivity will vary based on current conditions. Encourage students to include as much information as they can about air temperature and humidity.

Notebook ▸ Summarize Ideas

Have students briefly summarize the material on these pages by describing the major factors that determine weather. The weather, which is the condition of the atmosphere at a given place and time, is determined by factors such as air temperature, humidity, precipitation, and air pressure.

Differentiation — Leveled Questions

Extra Support

What is weather? Weather is the condition of the atmosphere at a given place and time. **What are four major factors that determine weather?** They are air temperature, humidity, air pressure, and precipitation.

Challenge

How is precipitation related to humidity? High humidity can lead to precipitation. How is precipitation related to air temperature? The air temperature helps determine the type of precipitation that falls.

2 Explain (continued)

 Generate Ideas

Draw students' attention to the title on this page, "Under Pressure." Remind them of what they learned about air pressure on the previous spread. Then ask: **What is "under pressure"?** Earth's surface

Help students set a purpose for reading. Ask: **What would you like to learn about air pressure?** Sample answer: Why does air pressure change from high to low and back again? How does air pressure affect weather? Encourage students to look for the answers to their questions as they read.

Active Reading

Remind students that to find an effect, active readers ask themselves, "What happened?" To find a cause, active readers ask, "Why did it happen?"

Develop Science Concepts

Explain to students why temperature and humidity affect air pressure. Air particles are closer together in cold air than in warmer air. Ask: **Why would this make the air pressure higher?** There are more particles per unit of volume, so a parcel of cold air is heavier than a warmer one of the same size. Explain that particles of water vapor are lighter than particles of nitrogen and oxygen. **Why would this make humid air lighter than dry air?** Students should conclude that dry air would have a greater number of heavier nitrogen and oxygen particles and that humid air would have a greater number of lighter water vapor particles.

Under Pressure

Have you heard a meteorologist talk about high and low pressure? High and low pressure describe the air around you.

Active Reading As you read these pages, circle the cause of the change in air pressure as elevation changes.

You can't feel the atmosphere pressing down on you, but it is! Air pressure is the measure of the weight of the atmosphere on Earth's surface. Changes in air pressure bring changes in weather. A *barometer* is a weather instrument used to measure changes in air pressure.

Temperature, humidity, and distance above sea level all affect air pressure. Cold air is denser than warm air, which means air pressure is higher in cold areas than in warm areas. A volume of humid air is less dense than an equal volume of dry air. As a result, humid air has lower air pressure than dry air. Most air particles are found closer to Earth's surface. Air pressure decreases as elevation, or distance above sea level, increases.

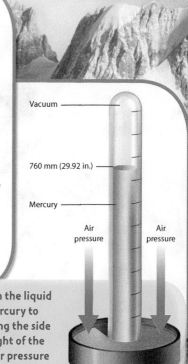

Vacuum

760 mm (29.92 in.)

Mercury

Air pressure   Air pressure

In a classic barometer air presses on the liquid mercury in the pan, causing the mercury to push up inside the tube. A scale along the side of the barometer measures the height of the mercury in the tube. The average air pressure at sea level is 760 mm (29.92 in) of mercury.

262

 Differentiation — Leveled Questions

Extra Support

Which instrument measures air pressure? a barometer Would a barometer register higher air pressure at the top of a mountain or in a valley? in a valley

Challenge

Is air pressure higher at the base of a mountain or at its peak? Explain. Because of gravity, air particles are closer together at lower altitudes. Where there are more particles per unit of volume, pressure is higher.

Interpret Visuals

What is different about the way a classic barometer and a modern barometer work? In a classic barometer, air pressure causes mercury to rise and fill a tube. The barometer reading is the height of mercury in the tube. In a modern barometer, air pressure moves a vacuum chamber attached to a pointer up and down.

For the Interactivity, accept any answer that states that air pressure is higher in the valley than at the mountaintop, as indicated by students drawing a higher mercury column for the valley.

Develop Science Concepts

Tell students that meteorologists watch the changes in barometer readings to determine air pressure. **If a barometer is showing that air pressure is rising, what could be happening to humidity?** It is possible that humidity is decreasing and that the air is getting drier. **What else could be affecting the pressure, provided that the elevation of the barometer doesn't change?** The air temperature could be falling.

Develop Inquiry Skills

DRAW CONCLUSIONS **Do you think changes in air pressure occur frequently or rarely?** Based on the factors that affect air pressure—such as temperature and humidity—students should conclude that air pressure changes frequently. Temperature and humidity change many times each day. As a result, air pressure does as well.

Notebook ▸ **Summarize Ideas**

Have students briefly summarize either orally or in writing the causes of changes in air pressure. Students should understand that air pressure changes as air temperature, humidity, and elevation change.

Dial and Pointer

In a modern barometer, air presses down on a vacuum chamber, a sort of airless can. As the air pressure changes, the vacuum chamber moves up or down. A lever attached to the chamber moves a pointer along a dial to measure the air pressure.

Lever system

Vacuum chamber

Air pressure is higher at the base of a mountain than at its top. The force of gravity holds most air particles close to Earth's surface. So, when you climb a mountain, the higher you go, the atmosphere thins and air pressure decreases.

What's the Pressure?

In the picture above, fill in the height of mercury inside each tube to show the air pressure at each location. In the space below, explain the air pressure you would find at each location.

Answers will vary. Accept any answer that explains that air pressure is higher at the base of the mountain than at its top; the mercury column of the barometer at the base of the mountain will be higher than the barometer at the top of the mountain.

263

 123 Math Connection

Solve a Problem Share this information: Average air pressure at sea level is 759.97 mm (29.92 in.) of mercury. When Hurricane Katrina hit the Gulf Coast in August 2005, a barometric pressure of about 678.43 mm (26.71 in.) of mercury was recorded.

Based on this information, is a hurricane a low-pressure or a high-pressure system? low How much did air pressure readings for Katrina differ from average readings? Katrina had air pressure readings of 81.54 mm (3.21 in.) below average at sea level.

2 Explain (continued)

 Generate Ideas

In a closed classroom, hold a pinwheel 6 in. or so above a lit incandescent bulb so that students can observe the pinwheel spin. Hold the pinwheel still. **What is making the pinwheel spin?** Allow students to respond. Record their answers on the board and correct any inaccuracies after they have read these two pages.

Active Reading

Signal words show connections between ideas. *For example* and *for instance* signal examples of an idea. *Also*, *in fact*, and *such as* signal added facts. Active readers remember what they read because they are alert to signal words that identify examples and facts about a topic.

Develop Science Concepts

Why does unequal heating of Earth's surface cause wind? It causes some areas to be warmer than others. Wind blows when air flows from areas of higher pressure (cooler areas) to areas of lower pressure (warmer areas).

On a global scale, where are the areas of high pressure located? low pressure? High pressure areas are located near the poles, low pressure areas are located near the tropics.

How would wind be different if the sun heated Earth's surface evenly? There would be little or no wind.

If a breeze blows at night down a mountain toward a valley floor, how will the wind blow during the day? Explain. From the valley up the mountain; During the day, air on the slope heats more quickly than air in the valley, causing higher pressure in the valley. Air flows up the slope. At night, air on the mountain cools quickly, producing higher pressure. This pressure causes air to slip down the mountain slope into the valley.

When the Wind Blows

A gentle wind can be pleasant, cooling you off when it is hot outside. However, a windstorm can cause damage. What causes wind to blow?

Active Reading As you read these pages, circle two clue words or phrases that signal a detail such as an example or an added fact.

The sun warms Earth's surface unevenly. This uneven heating causes differences in air pressure. Air moves away from areas of higher pressure to areas of lower pressure similar to how water flows downhill. This movement of air is called *wind*.

Areas near Earth's poles receive less sunlight than areas near the tropics. At the poles, the air is cold and has higher pressure. As a result, air moves along Earth's surface from the poles toward the tropics. At the tropics, air warms, rises, and moves toward the poles. These winds, called *global winds*, blow over large areas of Earth. They move large weather systems, such as hurricanes.

Local differences in temperature can also cause winds. Earth's surface heats up at different rates. For example, the side of a mountain heats up more quickly than the valley below. As a result, a valley wind forms as air moves from the valley up the side of the mountain. This is an example of a *local wind*.

264

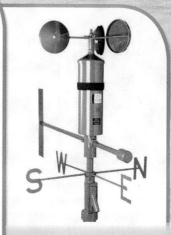

An *anemometer* measures wind speed. Wind pushes against the cups on the anemometer, causing it to spin. The rate at which the cups spin is measured and used to determine wind speed. A *wind vane* points in the direction from which the wind blows.

 Differentiation — Leveled Questions

Extra Support

Which tool measures wind speed? an anemometer Which tool indicates wind direction? a wind vane

Challenge

Would an anemometer or a wind vane be more useful for recording the movements of a sea breeze and a land breeze? Explain. A wind vane; it could record the change in wind direction between these local winds.

Local winds move short distances and can change direction. Daily changes in temperatures can cause local winds to change direction. For example, at night, the mountainside cools quicker than the valley below. The wind at night blows from the mountainside to the valley floor. In coastal areas, daily temperature changes result in local winds known as land breezes and sea breezes.

Sea Breeze
During the day, land heats up more quickly than water. Air over the land also warms, causing the air pressure to drop. Cooler, higher-pressure air flows from over the water to the land, forming a sea breeze.

Land Breeze
At night, land loses heat more quickly than water. As the air over land cools, the air pressure rises. Cooler, higher-pressure air flows from the land toward the sea, forming a land breeze.

▶ Draw an *L* over the low pressure and a *H* over the high pressure. Then describe the direction wind is blowing and why.

Sample answer: There is low pressure over the land and high pressure over the water, so air is blowing from over the water to the land, forming a sea breeze.

265

Develop Inquiry Skills

COMPARE **How are local winds similar to and different from global winds?** Sample answer: Both types of wind are caused by air moving from areas of high pressure to low pressure. Global winds blow over large areas of Earth. Local winds occur in a more localized area.

Interpret Visuals

Have students look at the diagram. **When does wind blow from the sea toward the land?** during the day **Explain why this happens.** Land heats faster than water, causing a low air pressure area over the land. Cooler air flows from a higher pressure area over the sea toward the land. **What happens to the direction of wind at night?** It reverses. **Explain why this happens.** Air over the land cools more rapidly than air over the water, producing a higher pressure area over the land. Air moves from the higher pressure area over land toward a lower pressure area over the water.

Direct students to the Interactivity. Point out that they can tell which direction the wind is blowing by examining the leaves on the trees. Then have them apply the information from the diagram of sea breeze/land breeze to label the drawing and write their explanation.

Notebook ▶ **Summarize Ideas**

Revisit the pinwheel demonstration with students. Ask again what caused the movement of air that spun the pinwheel. Heat from the bulb caused air to rise over the bulb. Colder heavier air around it rushed in to take its place, which made a gentle current of wind that drove the pinwheel. **Have students use what they have learned to summarize the cause of wind, either orally or in writing.**

Writing Connection

Write a Poem Have students write a poem about wind. The poem can be in any form and of any length. Encourage students to draw on their experiences with wind. They can also write about what wind does, such as making ripples on a pond or pushing fallen leaves along a street. Encourage students to be creative and use descriptive language. Have motivated students share their poems with the class.

2 Explain (continued)

 **Generate Ideas**

Read the main title aloud. **Did you see clouds on the way to school today? If so, which words would you use to describe them?** Write students' answers on the board. Answers will vary based on the type of clouds, if any, that are in the sky.

Active Reading

Remind students that matter, such as clouds, may be grouped into categories according to specific characteristics. Active readers focus on the characteristics of these categories as a way to remember facts about clouds in general.

Develop Science Concepts

Emphasize that air generally has water vapor in it, although you can't see it. If the air is relatively dry, you don't generally sense it, either. **What is happening when you can see water in the air?** When you can see water in the air, water vapor has cooled to condense into drops of water or freeze into bits of ice.

Interpret Visuals

Have students study the diagram on this page. **Why is the sun needed to form clouds?** Sample answer: It warms Earth's surface, causing humid air to rise. **Infer why cloud droplets usually form high in the air and not near the ground.** The air usually becomes cooler as you rise higher in the atmosphere.

How Clouds Form

Some clouds signal precipitation. Others signal fair weather. How can you use clouds to predict weather?

Active Reading As you read these pages, circle the three types of clouds.

Air often has some water in it. Most of the time you can't see the water because it is an invisible gas called *water vapor*. Clouds form as water vapor cools and condenses. A cloud is made up of tiny water droplets and ice crystals; these are so small that air currents can hold them up. A water droplet can be thousands of times smaller than a raindrop!

There are three main types of clouds. (Cumulus) clouds are white and puffy and are common on clear, sunny days. Under the right conditions, cumulus clouds can develop into massive thunderstorm clouds. (Cirrus) clouds look like white streaks and are high and thin. Cirrus clouds usually signal cool, fair weather. (Stratus) clouds are low and gray, making the day dark and gloomy. These clouds can produce or signal incoming rain or snow.

Producing a Cloud

(1) The sun warms Earth's surface, causing air to rise into the atmosphere.

(2) Water vapor in the air cools and condenses around tiny specks of dust, forming water droplets.

(3) These droplets join together, forming a cloud.

266

 Differentiation — Leveled Questions

Extra Support

What are the three types of clouds? cumulus, cirrus, and stratus **Which clouds are you most likely to see on a sunny day?** cumulus or cirrus **Which clouds are you most likely to see on a rainy or snowy day?** stratus

Challenge

It's a hot, sunny summer day. There are white, puffy cumulus clouds in the sky. Is rain likely? Explain. It could rain late in the day. Cumulus clouds can develop into thunderstorm clouds as the day continues.

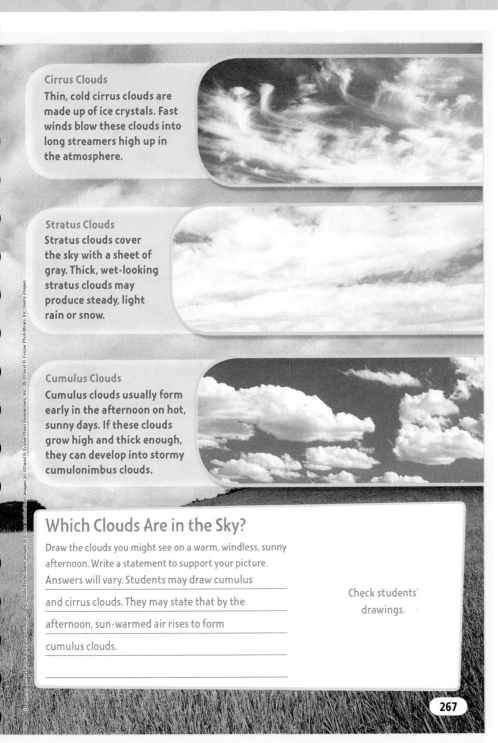

Cirrus Clouds

Thin, cold cirrus clouds are made up of ice crystals. Fast winds blow these clouds into long streamers high up in the atmosphere.

Stratus Clouds

Stratus clouds cover the sky with a sheet of gray. Thick, wet-looking stratus clouds may produce steady, light rain or snow.

Cumulus Clouds

Cumulus clouds usually form early in the afternoon on hot, sunny days. If these clouds grow high and thick enough, they can develop into stormy cumulonimbus clouds.

Which Clouds Are in the Sky?

Draw the clouds you might see on a warm, windless, sunny afternoon. Write a statement to support your picture.
Answers will vary. Students may draw cumulus and cirrus clouds. They may state that by the afternoon, sun-warmed air rises to form cumulus clouds.

Check students' drawings.

267

Interpret Visuals

Allow students time to study the photos of clouds. Guide them in discussing the identifying characteristics of each type of cloud. For example, cumulus clouds are white and puffy like cotton balls; cirrus clouds look thin and stringy. Then have students look outside the classroom window. **Do you see any of these types of clouds now?** Answers will depend on the weather at the time.

Direct students to the Interactivity. Have a volunteer identify important information in the directions—it is afternoon, and it is warm, windless, and sunny. Then suggest students review the three types of clouds with this information in mind before making their drawings and writing their answers.

▨ Misconception Alert ▨

Students might be confused about what clouds are made of, thinking they are some sort of semi-solid but wispy and gauzy substance. Explain that clouds are huge piles of water droplets. Ask students if they have ever experienced fog. Point out that fog is basically a cloud that forms near ground level. So the wet, misty material they experience walking through the fog is what it would feel like to walk through a cloud.

Notebook ▸ Summarize Ideas

Ask students to summarize the main idea of the text on these two pages, either orally or in writing. They should be able to explain that there are three main types of clouds: white, puffy cumulus clouds seen in fair weather; high, cold, stringy cirrus clouds also seen in fair weather; and low, gray stratus clouds that are associated with rain and snow. Students may also mention cumulonimbus clouds.

English Language Learners

Identify Clouds Have students make posters that show the three basic types of clouds. Provide construction paper and crayons or colored pencils. Review the three types of clouds, one by one. First, write the cloud name on the board. Pronounce it, and have students repeat. Then have students look at the photo of the cloud, draw their own version, and label the drawing. Repeat these steps for each cloud type. As an alternative, students can arrange their cloud drawings as a graphic organizer.

2 Explain (continued)

Notebook Generate Ideas

Have students read the main title: "Some Rain Anyone?" Talk about rainfall where you live. Discuss what happens in your area when there is not enough rain—or when there is too much.

Develop Science Concepts

Point out that although there are several different types of precipitation, they all start out in basically the same way. **What steps do all types of precipitation share as they form?** All precipitation starts when water vapor in the air cools and condenses or freezes to form clouds. When particles in the clouds become large enough and heavy enough to fall, they drop toward the ground as precipitation. **How are conditions in which rain forms different from conditions in which snow and sleet form?** Rain may form as ice that melts as it falls. Snow forms when water vapor freezes as it condenses. Sleet forms as rain that falls through a layer of freezing air.

⚡ Misconception Alert ⚡

Many students associate precipitation with clouds but are not sure how they are connected. Some students might believe that clouds are in the sky when precipitation occurs but are not fully aware that the clouds themselves are the source of the precipitation. Emphasize that cloud drops become precipitation as they increase in size and weight and then fall from the sky. Point out that all precipitation comes from clouds—but all clouds do not produce precipitation.

Some Rain, Anyone?

You might not think about rain—unless there is too much or too little of it. What causes precipitation?

Active Reading As you read this page, underline the cause of precipitation and circle kinds of precipitation.

Precipitation forms when water particles inside of clouds grow too large and fall to Earth's surface. Rain, snow, freezing rain, sleet, and hail are common kinds of precipitation.

Rain may start as ice crystals that melt as they fall to Earth's surface. Snow forms when water vapor changes directly into ice. Freezing rain occurs when falling, super-cooled raindrops do not freeze in the air but instead freeze when they strike objects near the ground.

Sleet is made of small lumps of ice. It forms when rain falls through a layer of freezing air. The raindrops turn to ice before hitting the ground.

Hail is made up of layers of ice. The layers form as air currents inside a thunderstorm cloud repeatedly lift and drop a hail particle. Each up-and-down trip adds ice to the particle. A ball of hail can be smaller than a pea or larger than a grapefruit!

Rain

Snow

Hail

A *rain gauge* measures rainfall. Rain fills the gauge, and the scale on the side shows how much rain fell.

268

👥 Differentiation — Leveled Questions

Extra Support

What are the four main types of precipitation? rain, snow, sleet, and hail What do meteorologists use to measure the amount of rainfall? a rain gauge

Challenge

Why is hail unlikely to fall on a day when it is raining heavily and the sky is covered with thick, low clouds? The stratus clouds described are not associated with hail. Hail forms in tall thunderstorm clouds.

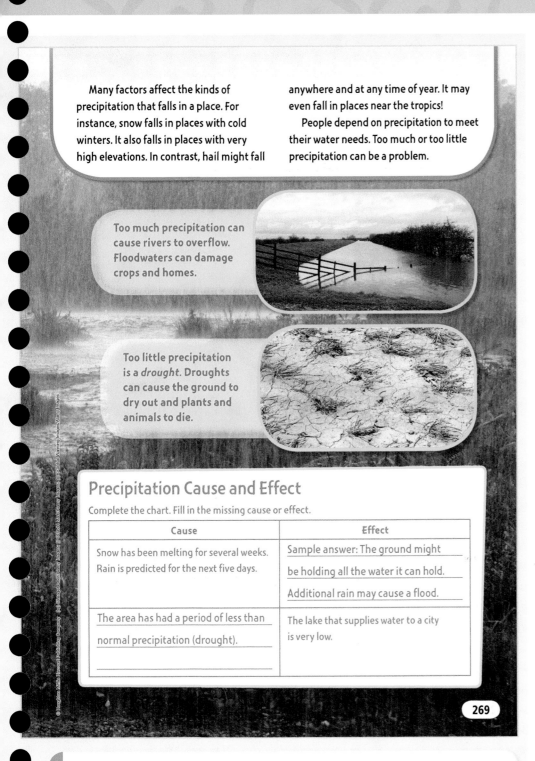

Many factors affect the kinds of precipitation that falls in a place. For instance, snow falls in places with cold winters. It also falls in places with very high elevations. In contrast, hail might fall anywhere and at any time of year. It may even fall in places near the tropics!

People depend on precipitation to meet their water needs. Too much or too little precipitation can be a problem.

Too much precipitation can cause rivers to overflow. Floodwaters can damage crops and homes.

Too little precipitation is a *drought*. Droughts can cause the ground to dry out and plants and animals to die.

Precipitation Cause and Effect

Complete the chart. Fill in the missing cause or effect.

Cause	Effect
Snow has been melting for several weeks. Rain is predicted for the next five days.	Sample answer: The ground might be holding all the water it can hold. Additional rain may cause a flood.
The area has had a period of less than normal precipitation (drought).	The lake that supplies water to a city is very low.

269

Develop Inquiry Skills

SEQUENCE **What are the steps involved in the formation of hail?** Pellets of ice form inside thunderstorm clouds. As air currents inside the clouds bounce them up and down, layer after layer of ice is added to the pellets. When they become heavy enough, the balls of hail fall from the clouds.

Develop Science Concepts

What can happen when the amount of precipitation is less than normal? greater than normal? prolonged less-than-normal precipitation is a drought, and greater than normal precipitation can cause floods. If your area has experienced either drought or flood conditions, discuss what students have observed and what the effects on the land and people in the area have been. Encourage students to find out more about the causes of drought or flood and share what they find with the class.

Interpret Visuals

As students fill in the chart, remind them that a cause can have more than one effect and that an effect can result from more than one cause.

Notebook ▶ Summarize Ideas

Have students write a brief paragraph in which they summarize the formation of the four main types of precipitation.

3 Extend/Evaluate

Sum It Up!

- Direct struggling students to look back through the lesson for photographs that match those shown here.

- After students identify each instrument and what it measures, challenge them to identify the units used to describe each factor of weather. For example, wind speed is recorded in miles or kilometers per hour.

- If students have difficulty finding the correct words to complete the Summarize paragraph, have them review the material that covers each subject area within the lesson.

- Remind students to use the Answer Key to check their answers. Students should revise incorrect responses so that they can use the Sum It Up! page to study for tests.

When you're done, use the answer key to check and revise your work.

Identify each weather instrument and what it measures.

1

anemometer/wind vane;

wind speed/wind direction

2

barometer;

air pressure

3

rain gauge;

amount of precipitation

Summarize

Fill in the missing words to tell about weather.

Weather is the condition of the 4. _____atmosphere_____ at a given place and time. Factors that affect weather include temperature and air pressure. Air moves from areas of 5. __high (or higher)__ air pressure to the areas of 6. _____low (or lower)_____ air pressure. This movement of air causes 7. _____wind_____ . Humidity also affects weather. Humidity is the amount of 8. _____water vapor_____ in the air. In the air, tiny water droplets form 9. _____clouds_____ . Water falls from the sky as 10. _____precipitation_____ .

270

Brain Check

Name _____

Word Play

1 Use the terms in the box to complete the crossword puzzle.

Across

3. The layer of gases that surrounds Earth
4. The weight of the atmosphere on the surface of Earth is _____ pressure.
6. Water that falls from clouds
7. A tool that points in the direction from which the wind blows
8. The amount of water vapor in the air

Down

1. The condition of the atmosphere at a given place and time
2. How warm or cool the air is around us
5. Air in motion

Crossword answers:
- 1 Down: WEATHER
- 2 Down: AIRTEMP...
- 3 Across: ATMOSPHERE
- 4 Across: AIR
- 5 Down: WIND
- 6 Across: PRECIPITATION
- 7 Across: WINDVANE
- 8 Across: HUMIDITY

air pressure*	air temperature
atmosphere	humidity*
precipitation	weather*
wind	wind vane

* Key Lesson Vocabulary

© Houghton Mifflin Harcourt Publishing Company

271

Answer Strategies

Word Play

1. If students need additional support with the vocabulary terms, have them consult the word bank and refer to the glossary to review definitions. As an added challenge, suggest that students make up their own puzzles to trade and solve.

Assessment

Suggested Scoring Guide

You may wish to use this suggested guide for the Brain Check.

Item	Points
1	40 (5 points each item)
2	18 (6 points each item)
3	18
4	24 (8 points each item)
Total	100

Lesson Quiz

See Assessment Guide, p. AG 52.

3 Extend/Evaluate (continued)

Answer Strategies

Apply Concepts

2. Suggest that students visualize each type of cloud as a way to recall its form and the type of weather with which it is most often associated.

3. Hint that students should think of this question in terms of differences in temperature and air pressure. Ask them to recall where temperatures would be highest during the day and what type of air pressure would result. Then have students contrast this with conditions at night. Students who need review can find a diagram showing how sea and land breezes form.

4. Have students review the three factors that affect air pressure—elevation, air temperature, and humidity—in the section titled "Under Pressure."

Take It Home!

Students should find that, just as with local winds, unequal heating and the resulting unequal pressure cause global winds. Polar areas get less solar energy than tropical areas. The colder polar air has higher pressure and moves toward the warmer tropics. Warmer tropical air moves toward the poles.

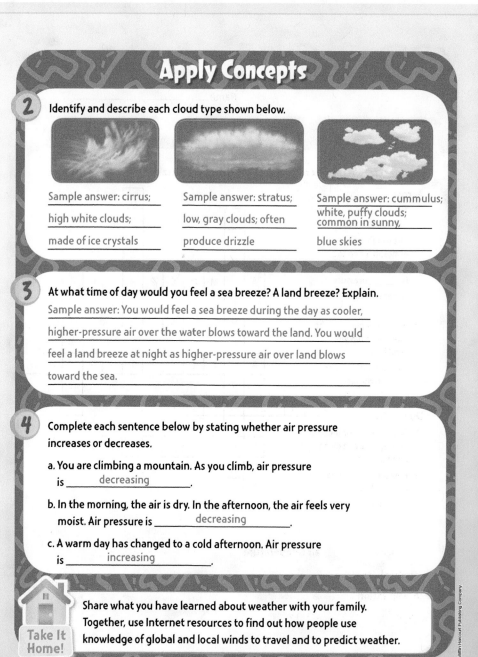

Apply Concepts

2 Identify and describe each cloud type shown below.

Sample answer: cirrus; high white clouds; made of ice crystals

Sample answer: stratus; low, gray clouds; often produce drizzle

Sample answer: cummulus; white, puffy clouds; common in sunny, blue skies

3 At what time of day would you feel a sea breeze? A land breeze? Explain.

Sample answer: You would feel a sea breeze during the day as cooler, higher-pressure air over the water blows toward the land. You would feel a land breeze at night as higher-pressure air over land blows toward the sea.

4 Complete each sentence below by stating whether air pressure increases or decreases.

a. You are climbing a mountain. As you climb, air pressure is ___decreasing___.

b. In the morning, the air is dry. In the afternoon, the air feels very moist. Air pressure is ___decreasing___.

c. A warm day has changed to a cold afternoon. Air pressure is ___increasing___.

Take It Home! Share what you have learned about weather with your family. Together, use Internet resources to find out how people use knowledge of global and local winds to travel and to predict weather.

272

Make Connections

Music Connection

Identify Lyrics Connected to Weather

Many songs have lyrics about weather. Have students choose one and write down its lyrics. Then have students identify and analyze the weather connection in the song. How does the songwriter use weather? Does it cause you to feel a certain way? How do the type of weather and the melody or rhythm of the song work together? Have students share their songs and their analyses with the class.

Writing Connection

Research a Career in Meteorology

Tell students that there are different jobs in the field of meteorology. For example, some meteorologists make weather forecasts that help students decide if they should take an umbrella to school, while others help plan space missions by studying weather on other planets. What does it take to be a meteorologist? What types of jobs are available to meteorologists? Have students do research and write a report to answer these questions and share what they find with the class.

Math Connection

Chart Cloud Patterns to Predict Weather

Have students observe clouds two or three times per day for two weeks. Each time, students should sketch the type of cloud and record the type of weather associated with it. Students can make a chart to organize this information. After two weeks, instruct students to look for patterns in the data. Do certain cloud types generally follow others? Do these clouds generally remain in the sky for a certain period? Are certain cloud types associated with certain types of weather? Have students use the patterns the chart shows to write a brief analysis of common clouds and sequences of clouds in your area and how they used the clouds to predict weather. Students can work in pairs or small groups.

Art Connection

Design an Informative Bulletin Board

Have students make a bulletin board that uses art, photos, and text to explain the types of information gathered for weather forecasts. Students should prepare a short introduction to the "exhibit" when the bulletin board is unveiled. Allow students to work in small groups to design and make the bulletin board display.

Options for Inquiry

FLIPCHART P. 28

Students can conduct these optional investigations at any time before, during, or in response to the lesson in the Student Edition.

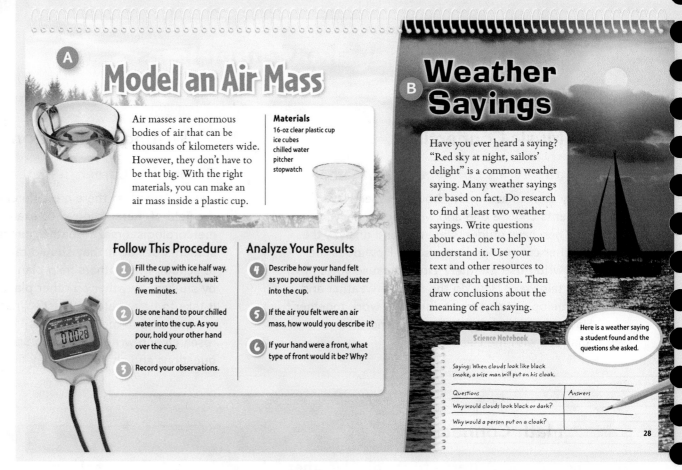

A

Model an Air Mass

Air masses are enormous bodies of air that can be thousands of kilometers wide. However, they don't have to be that big. With the right materials, you can make an air mass inside a plastic cup.

Materials
16-oz clear plastic cup
ice cubes
chilled water
pitcher
stopwatch

Follow This Procedure

1. Fill the cup with ice half way. Using the stopwatch, wait five minutes.

2. Use one hand to pour chilled water into the cup. As you pour, hold your other hand over the cup.

3. Record your observations.

Analyze Your Results

4. Describe how your hand felt as you poured the chilled water into the cup.

5. If the air you felt were an air mass, how would you describe it?

6. If your hand were a front, what type of front would it be? Why?

B

Weather Sayings

Have you ever heard a saying? "Red sky at night, sailors' delight" is a common weather saying. Many weather sayings are based on fact. Do research to find at least two weather sayings. Write questions about each one to help you understand it. Use your text and other resources to answer each question. Then draw conclusions about the meaning of each saying.

Here is a weather saying a student found and the questions she asked.

Science Notebook

Saying: When clouds look like black smoke, a wise man will put on his cloak.

Questions	Answers
Why would clouds look black or dark?	
Why would a person put on a cloak?	

28

Directed Inquiry

A **Model an Air Mass**

🕐 20 minutes
👥 pairs

Prep and Planning Tips

Make a pitcher of chilled water and a bowl full of ice cubes available for students to use.

For safety and to save time, make up the cups containing ice cubes just before starting the lab.

If students work in pairs, have one student pour water into the cup while the other holds his or her hand about 2 in. above the cup.

Caution! Have students notify you of any spills.

Expected Results

Students should feel moisture and cool air as the water is poured over the ice. If the air in the cup were an air mass, it would be a cool, moist one. If students' hands were fronts, they would be cold fronts because at a cold front, cold air moves toward warmer air and pushes it upward.

Independent Inquiry

B **Weather Sayings**

🕐 45 minutes
👤 individuals

Prep and Planning Tips

See the Planning for Inquiry page for more information. The Internet is a good source for additional weather sayings that students can interpret. Suggest that students type "weather sayings" or "weather proverbs" into a search engine to find websites with lists of sayings.

Science Notebook

Students can use the sample Science Notebook page shown on the Flipchart as a model for setting up their sayings, along with possible questions and answers. Students should conclude that the saying on the sample page means that when clouds thicken and darken, rain is probably on the way. So the advice is to put on your coat (cloak).

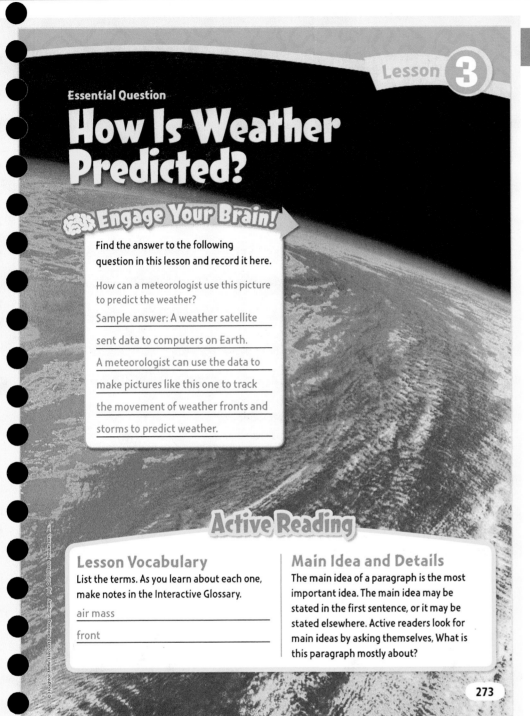

Essential Question
How Is Weather Predicted?

Lesson 3

Engage Your Brain!

Find the answer to the following question in this lesson and record it here.

How can a meteorologist use this picture to predict the weather?

Sample answer: A weather satellite sent data to computers on Earth. A meteorologist can use the data to make pictures like this one to track the movement of weather fronts and storms to predict weather.

Active Reading

Lesson Vocabulary
List the terms. As you learn about each one, make notes in the Interactive Glossary.

air mass

front

Main Idea and Details
The main idea of a paragraph is the most important idea. The main idea may be stated in the first sentence, or it may be stated elsewhere. Active readers look for main ideas by asking themselves, What is this paragraph mostly about?

273

Go Digital

An interactive digital lesson is available in Online Resources. It is suitable for individuals, small groups, or may be projected or used on an interactive white board.

Objectives

- Explain how air masses form.
- Explain how fronts affect weather.
- Explain how meteorologists obtain and analyze weather data.
- Describe types of severe weather, such as hurricanes.

Engage Your Brain!

Explain that the photo is a color-enhanced image of Earth and its atmosphere. The colors indicate different temperatures. Give students clues to help students answer the question, *How can a meteorologist use this picture to predict weather?* Places where air temperature changes bring about changes in the weather. Remind students to record their final answer to the question when they find it on the last spread of this lesson.

Active Reading Annotations

Remind students that active readers "make texts their own" by annotating them with notes and marks that help with comprehension. Encourage students to use pencil, not pen, to make annotations and to feel free to change their annotations as they read. The goal of annotation is to help students remember what they read.

Vocabulary and Interactive Glossary

Remind students to find and list the yellow highlighted terms from the lesson. As they proceed through the lesson and learn about the terms, they should add notes, drawings, or sentences in the extra spaces provided in the Interactive Glossary.

2 Explain

Notebook ▸ Generate Ideas

Ask students if they listened to a weather forecast this morning and, if so, why. Discuss how what they heard in the forecast helped them plan their day.

Active Reading

Remind students that informational text contains many facts. Active readers process informational text with deliberate speed that enables them to focus on and retain the facts presented. Circling facts, such as the five tools used to collect weather data, helps active readers focus more readily.

Develop Science Concepts

Discuss the wide range of sources used to make weather forecasts. Ask students if they can think of any other places meteorologists could collect data. **Why do you think scientists gather weather data from space?** Satellites are so high above Earth's surface that they get a much wider view of Earth and can track weather systems over a wide area.

▨ Misconception Alert ▨

It's likely that students think that a staff of meteorologists runs the network of weather-monitoring stations. That isn't the case. Professionals do operate some stations. However, many stations across the United States are operated by unpaid volunteers, who collect and record weather data daily and send periodic reports to the National Weather Service. Our weather forecasts are the result of a team effort between professional meteorolgists and citizen-scientists.

»Tracking the Weather

The weather forecasters on TV say, "Sunny and warm today, with rain tonight and tomorrow." How do they know?

Active Reading As you read this page, circle five tools used to collect weather data.

The forecasters have a lot of help! Meteorologists, or scientists who study weather, collect data from all over the world. They use automated systems at sea, on land, in the air, and in space to help track the weather.

At sea, weather buoys collect data on coastal weather conditions. These data help keep people in coastal cities safe. On land, weather-monitoring stations track weather conditions in remote locations. They can send advance notice about incoming weather. Scientists also use Doppler radar towers to observe how storm clouds are moving. Weather balloons and weather satellites collect data from high above Earth's surface. Weather satellites can track the weather over very large areas. They also help relay data from land-based tools to meteorologists around the world.

In the United States, nearly 100 buoys like this one collect data about air temperature, air pressure, wind, and waves at sea.

274

English Language Learners

Weather Gathering Tools
Instruct students to fold a sheet of construction paper in four parts and write one of the following words in each quadrant: *land, water, air, space*. Write the name of the weather instrument that gathers data in each place on the board, pronounce, and have students repeat. Then have them draw each tool (weather satellite, radiosonde, weather station, ocean buoy) in its proper quadrant. Students should label each instrument and write a brief sentence that uses the word.

Weather satellites orbit Earth. They collect weather data, such as cloud cover, and track storms, such as hurricanes. These satellites use radio signals to transmit data back to Earth.

Scientists launch weather balloons that carry tools, called *radiosondes*, into the atmosphere. A typical radiosonde measures air temperature, air pressure, and humidity.

Weather Wonder

Why do scientists use so many tools to collect weather data?

Answers will vary. Students should reason that data must be collected from a wide range of places on and above Earth's surface to get enough data for accurate weather forecasts.

Thousands of weather-monitoring stations collect data on air temperature, air pressure, wind, humidity, and precipitation. Some weather stations use radar to track storms.

275

Develop Inquiry Skills

INFER Tell students dropsondes are weather instruments similar to radiosondes. Dropsondes are dropped out of airplanes, usually over the ocean—and often from planes that fly into hurricanes. These instruments radio back data on temperature, pressure, humidity, and wind speed as they fall. **Why use a dropsonde over the ocean instead of a radiosonde?** Finding a place to stand and release a radiosonde on the ocean is difficult. Flying over and dropping the instrument is easier.

COMMUNICATE Tell students that the huge network of tools that help meteorologists gather weather data is extremely expensive to build and maintain. **Do you think it is worth all the money governments spend to buy and build the equipment to collect weather data?** Answers will vary. Ask students to defend their positions.

Interpret Visuals

Before students complete the Interactivity, direct them to examine the photos and read the captions relating to the weather data collection tools. Lead students to recognize that these tools collect data from different environments—sea, air, land, and space. They should reason that the amount of data available affects how accurate a forecast can be.

Notebook ▸ Summarize Ideas

Have students write a brief statement in which they list five tools important in collecting weather data. They should state that weather-monitoring stations and Doppler radar on land, weather buoys at sea, weather balloons in the atmosphere, and satellites orbiting Earth all collect weather data.

👥 Differentiation — Leveled Questions

Extra Support

How do meteorologists use special balloons to collect weather data from the atmosphere? What data do they collect? They release radiosondes into the air to gather data on temperature, humidity, and air pressure.

Challenge

Why do scientists collect weather data at sea where there are few people? Students should infer that many weather systems form at sea and affect land; having the data gives a more complete picture of the atmosphere.

2 Explain (continued)

 Generate Ideas

Ask students to describe the weather today, yesterday, and two days ago. Establish that weather changes from day to day. **What makes the weather change?** Record student responses on the board.

Active Reading

Remind students that detail sentences give examples, features, characteristics, or facts about a topic. Active readers stay focused on the topic when they ask, What fact or information does this sentence add to the topic?

Develop Science Vocabulary

air mass Explain that one meaning of *mass* is "a mound or pile of something." So an "air mass" is a mound or pile of air—usually with the same temperature and humidity throughout.

front The word *front* has several meanings. Examples: forward part of something; land along a lake or river (*waterfront*); an outward appearance (to put up a front). Ask students to identify the meaning of front that relates most closely to the meteorological term.

Interpret Visuals

Explain that temperatures in northern areas of the map are colder because they are closer to the pole. Temperatures in the southern areas of the map are warmer because they are closer to the tropics.

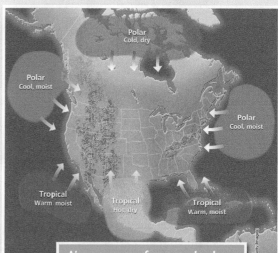

>> Air Masses and Fronts

One day, it is so cool outside. The next day, it is warm enough to wear shorts. What happened to the weather?

When cold, dry freezer air meets warm, moist room air, a mini-front is formed!

Active Reading As you read these pages, underline the definition of an air mass. Circle four characteristics that air masses may have.

Packets of air move across Earth's surface. An **air mass** is a large body of air with the same temperature and humidity throughout.

An air mass reflects the conditions of the place where it forms. Air masses that form over land are dry. Air masses that form over water are moist. Cold air masses form near the poles, and warm air masses form near the tropics.

As air masses move across an area, they can collide. The boundary between two air masses is called a **front**. Weather changes take place at fronts. For example, as a warm front passes over an area, warm air replaces cooler air and the temperature rises. The movement of air masses and fronts explains why you might be chilly one day and warm the next. At a front, stormy conditions are common.

Polar
Cold, dry

Polar
Cool, moist

Polar
Cool, moist

Tropical
Warm, moist

Tropical
Hot, dry

Tropical
Warm, moist

Air masses may form over land or water. The masses that form over land near the poles will be cold and dry. The masses that form over water near the poles will be cold and moist. Which types of air masses will form near the tropics?

276

Differentiation — Leveled Questions

Extra Support

What is an air mass? An air mass is a large body of air with the same temperature and pressure throughout **What happens when different air masses bump into each other?** A front forms.

Challenge

In which region would a cold, dry air mass form? over land in a polar (northern) region. **How might a cold, dry air mass become a warm, wet one?** by moving over an area of warm water

Cold Front

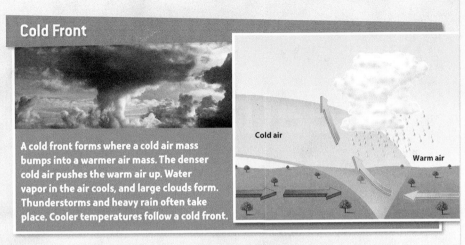

A cold front forms where a cold air mass bumps into a warmer air mass. The denser cold air pushes the warm air up. Water vapor in the air cools, and large clouds form. Thunderstorms and heavy rain often take place. Cooler temperatures follow a cold front.

Cold air

Warm air

Warm Front

A warm front forms where a warm air mass moves over a cold air mass. A warm front forms a wider area of clouds and rain than a cold front. Steady rain or snow may fall. Warmer temperatures follow a warm front.

Warm air

Cold air

Home Front

Identify a front inside of your home. Explain where the different air masses form, the characteristics of each one, and how the two air masses meet.

Sample answer: A front forms in my bathroom when

I shower. The hot, humid air from the shower mixes with

the colder, drier air in the room, and a mist forms.

277

© Houghton Mifflin Harcourt Publishing Company (bg) ©PhotoDisc/Getty Images, (t) ©Michael Spencer/Alamy Images, (b) ©Ray Ellis/Photo Researchers, Inc.

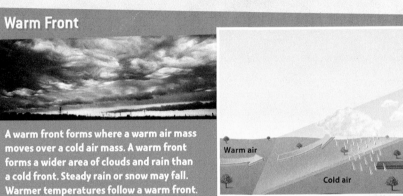

Math Connection

Read a Bar Graph Present data on the number of tornadoes in the United States by month in 2010 in a bar graph: Mar: 33; Apr: 139; May: 304; Jun: 324; Jul: 146; Aug: 55; Sept: 57; Oct: 108; Nov: 53; Dec: 30; Jan: 30; Feb: 1. Have students interpret the data by asking questions such as: **Which month has the most tornadoes?** June **In which three months are tornadoes most likely to occur?** May, June, July **In which four months are you least likely to see one?** November, December, January, February

Develop Science Concepts

Point out that as an air mass crosses an area, it changes the weather. Say: **Yesterday the weather was warm and rainy. Today it is clear and cool.** Ask: **What happened?** A warm, wet air mass was replaced by a cool, dry air mass. **What type of front formed where these two air masses met?** a cold front

Have students think about the weather at a front. **What will you always see in the sky at a front?** clouds **Why do clouds form at fronts?** They form because air rising at the front cools and condenses to form droplets.

Interpret Visuals

Describe the difference in the way air masses meet at a cold front and a warm front. The boundary between air masses at a cold front is much steeper and more abrupt than the boundary at a warm front.

Why does warm air rise over colder air at a front? because the warmer air is less dense and gets pushed upward when the cold air moves beneath it

What effect does this have? Clouds rise higher over a smaller area at a cold front.

For the Interactivity, ask students to think about what happens at a front. (Air masses of two different temperatures collide.) Then guide students to think of a place in their home where air of two different temperatures would meet. (the kitchen or the bathroom)

Notebook Summarize Ideas

Present this scenario to students: **It is late afternoon. The wind has picked up, and tall clouds are building on the horizon. The sky is darkening. Which type of weather is likely to happen soon?** a thunderstorm **Which type of front is about to move through?** a cold front

Have students summarize, either orally or in writing, how weather changes as air masses move.

2 Explain (continued)

Notebook ▶ Generate Ideas

Ask students to recall the last time they saw a TV weather forecast. Have them brainstorm a list of the elements of the forecast. They might mention that they saw weather maps, charts, or radar or satellite images. Single out the weather map when it is mentioned. Remind students that these maps were once drawn by hand but are now produced by computers. Explain that weather maps are one of the most important tools used to communicate weather events.

Active Reading

Remind students that active readers annotate, or mark up, text to benefit their own recollection of the information presented. Though students may star different sentences, it is important that they are able to offer a reasonable explanation for their annotations.

Develop Science Concepts

Remind students that weather data are collected by a huge network of instruments each day. **How do those instruments contribute to weather maps?** The data on weather maps come from these instruments. Explain that in the United States, weather systems usually move from west to east; these weather systems are driven by strong air currents called westerlies. **When looking at a weather map, what might tell you that weather will soon turn cloudy where you are?** Sample answer: The map might show an area of approaching precipitation, an approaching front, or a nearby symbol indicating cloud cover. **Why are short-term weather forecasts more accurate than long-term weather forecasts?** because a variety of factors contribute to weather conditions, so changes in any of those factors over time affect the weather outcome

Mapping the Weather

Meteorologists use maps to show the current weather and how it will change. What does it take to make a weather map?

Active Reading As you read these two pages, put a star [*] next to the main idea of each paragraph.

Most weather forecasts are accurate within five to seven days. A *weather forecast* is a prediction about the future weather conditions of a place. Weather forecasts beyond seven days are not very accurate.
Meteorologists forecast the weather based on the local weather data and observed weather patterns. They analyze the air temperature, humidity, and air pressure data of a place. They also analyze weather patterns, such as the movement of air masses and fronts, to prepare a weather forecast. In North America, air masses and fronts generally move from west to east.

278

 Differentiated — Leveled Questions

Extra Support

What can you find out from weather maps? The maps show current weather in many locations. **What do meteorologists do with weather maps?** They use them to forecast weather.

Challenge

Explain how a weather map can help predict future weather. The weather map shows current weather, frontal boundaries, and highs and lows. A person can use this information to predict future weather.

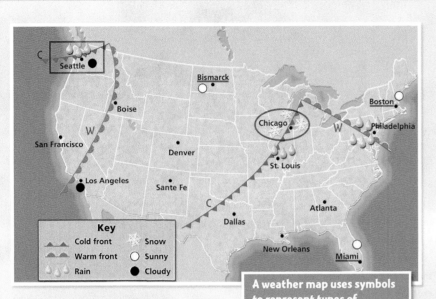

Recall the different tools used to monitor the weather from Earth's surface, the oceans, and the atmosphere. These tools collect lots of weather data. Computers help us store and analyze weather data and weather patterns to make *weather maps*. Meteorologists study weather maps and use them to make weather forecasts.

A weather map uses symbols to represent types of weather. The map legend tells you what each symbol means. The triangles or half circles on a front symbol point in the direction the front is moving.

Computer programs help interpret weather information. Computer simulations help meteorologists forecast the weather.

Read a Weather Map

Show these weather events on the map.

- Circle the name of a city where snow is falling.

- Draw a line under the names of two cities where it is sunny.

- Write a *C* on a cold front, and a *W* on a warm front.

- Draw a rectangle around the name of a city that has cloudy skies now, but will soon have rain.

279

© Houghton Mifflin Harcourt Publishing Company; (bg) ©Photodisc/Getty Images; (b) ©Ryan McGinnis/Alamy Images

Develop Inquiry Skills

INFER **Why do you think meteorologists use computers to collect and process weather data?** Sample answer: A lot of weather data come from many sources each day. Computers can easily collect the data, make calculations, and make maps and charts. This system makes it quicker and easier for meteorologists to make forecasts.

Interpret Visuals

Review the use of a map key with students. Tell them to refer to the key to understand the symbols used on the weather map. Note the raindrop and snowflake symbols for precipitation, the curved blue and red lines that represent fronts, and symbols for cloud cover. Clarify that local weather maps depict conditions in a small area, regional maps show weather conditions in a broader area, and national weather maps generalize the weather conditions in vast sections of the country. To aid students in completing the Interactivity, you may wish to read each statement as students find the appropriate area and mark it on the map.

Notebook **Summarize Ideas**

Ask students to summarize the main idea of these two pages, either orally or in writing. They should be able to summarize that weather maps contain a wide range of weather data and provide important information that meteorologists use to make weather forecasts.

English Language Learners

Learn New Terms Four terms that start with "weather" are used on these pages—and throughout the rest of the lesson. Write these terms on the board: weather data, weather forecast, weather map, weather patterns. Review their definitions with students. Then have students make flash cards with the terms on one side and definitions on the other. Have students work in pairs, flashing the term as their partner states its definition. Students can add pictures to the front of the cards next to the terms.

2 Explain (continued)

 Generate Ideas

Ask students if they made plans today—or changed their plans—based on a weather forecast. Reinforce the idea that weather forecasts can influence small things, such as whether you go to a baseball game, or big things, such as knowing in advance to take shelter from a coming storm. Tell students they will learn more about the importance of accurately forecasting the weather.

Develop Science Concepts

How has the use of technology changed weather forecasts? It has made it possible to gather data from many more places quickly and to analyze the data and make forecasts faster. **What is the advantage of making weather forecasts more quickly?** In the case of severe weather, such as hurricanes, advance warning can give people time to prepare and evacuate dangerous areas. It can help save lives.

Develop Inquiry Skills

DRAW CONCLUSIONS **Why do you think fewer areas were surprised by hurricanes after weather satellites were placed in Earth orbit?** These satellites make it possible for meteorologists to see a large part of Earth's surface at once. As a result, they can see large weather systems, such as hurricanes, as these systems form and move toward places where people live.

≫Forewarned!

Weather forecasts help us plan each day. When severe storms strike, weather forecasts can also help save lives.

In August 2004, Hurricane Charley moved across the Atlantic Ocean and along the eastern coast of the United States. Data collected by satellites and airplanes helped meteorologists make forecasts to warn people about this storm.

Technology has changed how we measure, analyze, forecast, and share weather data. Weather tools, for example, help us accurately measure the weather conditions of a place. Modern communication technology lets scientists share global weather data quickly and over long distances. These data can then be used to make computer models to predict weather events.

Meteorolgists work hard at predicting the strength and path of storms. In the past, meteorologists had to rely on weather ships and weather-monitoring stations on tropical islands to track hurricanes—the largest, most powerful storms on Earth. The data from these sources were limited. As a result, predicting the strength and path of these storms was very difficult.

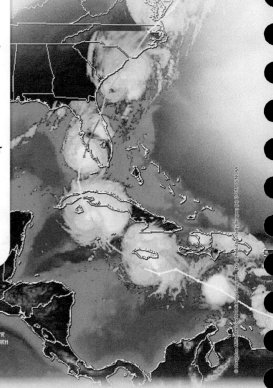

TROPICAL DEPR
TROPICAL STORM
CATEGORY 1
CATEGORY 2
CATEGORY 3
CATEGORY 4
CATEGORY 5

280

 Differentiated — Leveled Questions

Extra Support

Why is weather forecasting important? It warns people of approaching severe weather. **Why is hurricane forecasting very important?** Hurricanes are powerful, dangerous storms with very strong winds.

Challenge

Why is it important for meteorologists to share weather data? Sample answer: Sharing data on the formation of severe storms could help more people prepare for or evacuate from them.

Starting in the 1960s, the United States launched the first of many weather-satellite systems. For the first time, scientists were able to monitor and collect data from the uninhabited parts of Earth. As a result, the accuracy of weather forecasts and hurricane tracking improved. Today, satellites along with land- and sea-based weather tools provide information to warn people about the changing weather.

Tropical Depression

Tropical Storm

Hurricane

A hurricane begins as a thunderstorm near the western coast of Africa. As its winds strengthen, the storm becomes a tropical depression. When winds reach 63 km/h (39 mph), it becomes a tropical storm. A tropical storm becomes a hurricane when there are winds of 119 km/h (74 mph) or more.

Category	Wind Speed (km/h)	Damage
1	119–153	Minimal
2	154–177	Moderate
3	178–209	Major
4	210–249	Extensive
5	> 249	Catastrophic

Do the Math!
Interpret Data

Use information from the table to answer the following questions.

1. What is the wind speed and category of hurricanes that may cause extensive damage?

   Category 4 and 5 hurricanes with wind speeds of over 210 km/h may cause extensive damage.

2. How much stronger is a category 5 hurricane than a hurricane that causes only minimal damage?

   since wind speed is the measure of a hurricane's strength: 250 km/h – 119 km/h = 131 km/h

281

Do the Math!
Interpret Data

Before students complete Do the Math!, review with them how the table detailing hurricane strength is constructed. Hurricane categories range from Minimal, which is the least powerful hurricane, to Catastrophic, the most powerful. Point out that each category lists a range of wind speeds. Note that there is no upper limit for a Category 5 storm. The symbol says that winds are "greater than" 249 km/h. **Why is there no upper limit on the wind speed of a Category 5 storm?** Meteorologists don't know the highest wind speed possible for a Category 5 storm, so they left it open-ended.

⁄⁄ Misconception Alert ⁄⁄

Some students might think that today's sophisticated technology makes it possible for meteorologists to predict exactly where and when a hurricane will strike. Explain that while technology cannot make exact predictions, it has made the tracking and prediction of hurricanes much more accurate. Meteorologists can use technology to determine the possible tracks a hurricane will take several days before it makes landfall. As a hurricane develops and approaches North America, meteorologists are better able to use conditions within the hurricane and the atmosphere around it to narrow their predictions as to where the hurricane will make landfall. Still, meteorologists can only make predictions for an area of coastline, not a precise spot.

Notebook ▸ Summarize Ideas

Have students summarize, either orally or in writing, how a hurricane develops and how forecasting helps saves lives. Students may wish to use a three-column chart to illustrate the development of a storm from tropical depression to tropical storm to full-fledged hurricane.

Writing Connection

Writing Fiction Direct students to write an original story in which a weather forecast plays an important role. It can be the major role of the story, or it can be a small device that makes the plot work. Encourage students to use concrete words and sensory details to describe the event. When they finish, have a few volunteers share what they have written.

3 Extend/Evaluate

Sum It Up!

- Remind students that if they are having difficulty remembering the details from the lesson, they should look back and review the photos, captions, and bold words.

- In question 1, remind students that meteorologists use different tools to collect data on land, at sea, in the atmosphere, and from space.

- Suggest that students review the material in the lesson's second spread, "Air Masses and Fronts," before answering this question.

- Remind students that weather maps are summaries of current weather in many places. Symbols are a shorthand way of representing a lot of data. Suggest students make a list of types of information they have seen presented on weather maps and the symbols used to represent the data.

- To complete the "Summarize" activity, students must know the sequence of steps involved in preparing a weather forecast. Remind students to think logically about the order in which these tasks must be done. The data needed to predict weather must be gathered first. Then computers analyze the data. Finally, a weather map is produced, from which predictions can be made.

- Remind students to use the Answer Key to check their answers. Encourage them to revise any incorrect responses so that they can use the Sum It Up! to study for tests.

When you're done, use the answer key to check and revise your work.

Complete the details about each main idea.
Sample answers shown.

1 Meteorologists collect weather data from all over the world. Some of the tools that they use include weather buoys, weather balloons, weather-monitoring stations and weather satellites.

2 Air masses meet at boundaries called fronts. Weather that happens along fronts includes thunderstorms, cloudy skies, steady rain, and windy weather.

3 Meteorologists use weather maps to make forecasts. Symbols on weather maps indicate the weather. Symbols show precipitation, cloud cover and fronts.

Summarize

4 Meteorologists use many tools to track and forecast the weather. Explain how a meterologist might use the three tools pictured below to predict the weather.

Sample answer: Weather satellites send data to computers on Earth.

Meteorologists use computers to analyze the data and make weather maps.

Answer Key: 1. weather buoys, weather balloons, weather-monitoring stations, and weather satellites. **2.** thunderstorms, cloudy skies, steady rain, and windy weather. **3.** precipitation, cloud cover, and fronts. **4.** Sample answer: Weather satellites send data to computers on Earth. Meteorologists use computers to analyze the data and make weather maps.

282

 **Brain Check**

Name _____

Word Play

1 Use the clues to unscramble the terms.

1. C A E N R I R U H H U R R I C A N Ⓔ
   a storm with wind speeds of at least 119 km/h

2. F N O R T F R O Ⓝ T
   the boundary between two different air masses

3. L O O S T I G R O E T M E M E T E Ⓞ R O L O G I S T
   a person who studies weather and the atmosphere

4. R A I S S M A A I R M A Ⓢ S
   a large body of air with the same temperature and humidity

5. R E W E A T H C A E O F T S R
   W E A T H E R F O R E C A Ⓢ T
   a prediction of future weather conditions

6. L P O D P R E D A A R R
   Ⓓ O P P L E R R A D A R
   a tool used to see the movement of storm clouds

Solve the riddle by unscrambling the circled letters to find the missing part of the word.

What kind of radios do weather balloons carry?

RADIO S O N D E S

© Houghton Mifflin Harcourt Publishing Company

283

Answer Strategies

Word Play

1. If students need additional support with the vocabulary terms, provide them with a word bank. You may wish to provide the answer to the riddle as an additional hint. As an added challenge, have students make up their own puzzles that they can trade and solve.

Assessment

Suggested Scoring Guide
You may wish to use this suggested guide for the Brain Check.

Item	Points
1	30 (5 points each item)
2	24 (8 points each item)
3	10
4	18
5	18
Total	100

Lesson Quiz
See Assessment Guide, p. AG 53.

3 Extend/Evaluate (continued)

Answer Strategies

Apply Concepts

2. Point out the environment surrounding each instrument. Remind students that weather data are collected at sea, on land, in the atmosphere, and from space.

3. Point out that each phrase describes a different type of weather event. A swirling funnel cloud is a tornado. A short-lived, local storm is a thunderstorm. Low sheets of thick clouds are stratus clouds. A large storm that forms over the ocean is a hurricane.

4. Students should review air mass source regions and identify the one that forms an air mass that is both cool and wet. Remind them that wet air masses form over water and that cool air masses form in northern regions.

5. Students who find this difficult can look at contrasting diagrams of cold fronts and warm fronts in the lesson. The steeper gradient at the place where the air masses meet is characteristic of a cold front.

....

🏠 **Take It Home!**

As students begin, suggest they decide on a specific type of severe weather to research. Students can start by identifying common weather conditions that result from their chosen type of weather. Then they can make a hypothesis as to how they think these weather conditions both during and after the storm would affect energy generation, distribution, and use. Following these steps will help provide a direction and focus for research.

Apply Concepts

2 Identify each weather instrument and describe what it does.

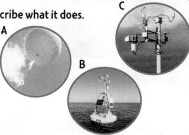

A: a radiosonde collects data at different heights in the atmosphere; *B:* a weather buoy collects weather data at sea; *C:* a weather-monitoring station collects data on Earth's surface.

3 Circle the correct answer.

Which statement best describes a hurricane?

- A swirling funnel cloud
- A short-lived, local storm
- Low sheets of thick clouds
- A large storm that forms over the ocean

4 Where does a cold, moist air mass form? What type of weather will it cause?

A cold, moist air mass develops over water near the poles. This air mass will cause weather that is cool and humid, possibly with precipitation.

5 Identify the type of front shown in the picture. Explain your answer.

This is a cold front. Cold air is forcing warm air higher into the sky.

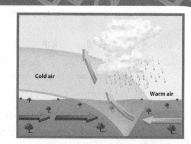

Cold air   Warm air

🏠 **Take It Home!** Work with a family member to research how severe weather affects electrical energy generation, distribution, and use. Describe what experts recommend people do to conserve energy during severe weather.

284

Make Connections

Easy

Art Connection

Make a Poster

Have students make a poster that contrasts cold fronts and warm fronts. Text should be minimal. The poster should highlight the visual difference between the two types of fronts—gradient where the two air masses meet, type of cloud formation (such as cumulonimbus or stratus), and type of precipitation (such as light rain or thunderstorm downpour). Invite students to hang their posters in the classroom.

Average

Writing Connection

Write a Weather Forecast

Give students these weather data: The present temperature at Ocean City is 50 °F. It is clear and sunny. There is a warm front approaching from the west. Cities behind the front are having unusually warm weather for this time of year, 70 °F or more. Students must use this information to write a weather forecast for Ocean City for the next couple of days. Students should work alone on this assignment.

Average

Math Connection

Determine Average Temperature and Precipitation

Have students determine the average temperature and precipitation for your area for the four seasons of the last year for which data are available. Data for your state or a nearby city should be available on the Internet. Students will need the average temperature and rainfall for each month during that year. Students will make a new data set, calculating the average temperature and precipitation for each season: winter (Dec–Feb); spring (March–May); summer (June–Aug); fall (Sep–Nov). Have students display the data in a table.

Challenging

Health Connection

Make a Family Preparedness Plan Brochure

Regardless of where students live, emergencies and natural disasters are an unfortunate but very real possibility. Families should know what to do in the event of a fire, hurricane, blizzard, or tornado. Have students do research on the Internet to make a brochure that families can use to make a preparedness plan. Good sources of information include the webpages of FEMA and the American Red Cross. Many states also have sites that give helpful information. Students can work alone or with a partner.

S.T.E.M.
Engineering and Technology

Objectives

- Explain that information about the natural world can be gained through repeated observations.
- Explain how the Beaufort scale system works.
- Explain how wind speed is measured today.

Notebook ▶ ## Generate Ideas

Ask students to think about a windy day. Have them discuss the effects wind has on objects and outside activities, such as games. Remind students that scientists have ways to measure and describe wind.

Background

- The Beaufort scale was developed in 1805 by Sir Francis Beaufort, a British admiral. It was originally designed to help sailors estimate wind speed based on sea conditions. The scale is still used today and has been adapted for use on land as well as sea.

- The earlier classifications of sailing conditions used only words to describe winds at different points on a relative scale. The Beaufort scale uses both numbers and descriptions.

Develop Inquiry Skills

RESEARCH Explain that the chart that they are to complete for the Interactivity is only a small portion of the Beaufort scale. Provide reference material or have students use the Internet to help fill in the missing information.

INFER **Why is it important for people to have one standard scale for measuring wind?** Sample answer: When one standard scale is used, it is easier for people to communicate about the wind and understand the observations that others make.

S.T.E.M.
Engineering & Technology

Stormy Weather:
Beaufort Wind Scale

If you were a sailor on a ship, being able to measure wind speed would be very important. In the past, wind speed was estimated by observating its effect on things. Today, we use tools to measure wind speed. Read on to find out about ways to measure wind speed.

In 1805, Sir Francis Beaufort developed a scale to classify wind speed. This scale assigned levels based on sailors' observations. For example, a Force 3 wind describes a gentle breeze in which ships move steadily across the water. Force 6 describes a strong breeze that produces large waves, whitecaps, and spray. And Force 11 describes a violent storm.

You can observe a flag to see how wind blows. A windsock shows the relative direction and speed of winds. The windsock droops during low wind speed. It flies straight out from the pole during high wind.

Use the text and information from reference materials to complete the Beaufort Wind Scale table.

Beaufort Wind Force	Average Wind Speed (km/h)	Description	Beaufort Wind Force	Average Wind Speed (km/h)	Description
0	0	Calm	7	56	Near Gale
1	3	Light Air	8	68	Gale
2	9	Light Breeze	9	82	Severe Gale
3	16	Gentle Breeze	10	96	Storm
4	24	Moderate Breeze	11	110	Violent Storm
5	34	Fresh Breeze	12	124	Hurricane
6	44	Strong Breeze			

285

S.T.E.M.
continued

Today, wind speed is measured using anemometers.

This anemometer uses cuplike devices to measure wind speed. The faster the wind blows, the faster the cups spin. The cups are attached to sensors that measure the actual wind speed.

This digital anemometer uses spinning fans to generate magnetic pulses. Then, the instrument translates these pulses into measurements of the wind speed.

An ultrasound anemometer has pairs of sound speakers and microphones. Electronic circuits measure the time it takes for sound to travel from each speaker to its microphone. The anemometer uses the data collected to determine wind speed as well as wind direction.

Design Your Future

Use observations to design your own scale to measure something such as temperature, cloud cover, or amount or strength of rainfall. Write the process for using the scale, and then try it out.

Students may attempt to estimate the size of raindrops by observing the

loudness of the sound the raindrops make when they strike a surface.

Build On It!

Rise to the engineering design challenge—complete **Design It: Build a Wind Vane** on the Inquiry Flipchart.

286

Build On It!

In **Design It: Build a Wind Vane**, the design challenge associated with this lesson, students use the steps of the engineering design process to build their own wind vane. See the pages that follow. Other opportunities to apply the

design process appear throughout the Inquiry Flipchart.

Develop S.T.E.M. Concepts

DESIGN CRITERIA Explain to students that measuring wind speed is an important safety issue. The criteria used to measure the wind must be accurate under many different circumstances, and they must be easy for people to understand. Ask students to discuss what could happen if the scale did not work the same way for everyone who used it in different types of weather.

FORMULATE In the Design Your Future Interactivity, students develop and test a standardized way to communicate other weather conditions, such as cloud cover, rainfall, and temperature.

- Explain to students that when measuring various kinds of weather and natural phenomena, the word *scale* does not usually refer to a physical object that is placed outside to record or measure something. Instead, it refers to a series of words or numbers that are used to show the relationship between a natural event and its effects on the environment.

- When students have finished devising a scale, have them give it to a partner to try. Depending on the weather, they may have to wait for a different day to test the scale.

Notebook **Summarize Ideas**

Direct students to briefly summarize what engineers must consider when designing a tool that measures an aspect of the weather. Students can give their summaries orally or in writing.

S.T.E.M.
Engineering and Technology

FLIPCHART p. 29

- 25–30 minutes
- small groups

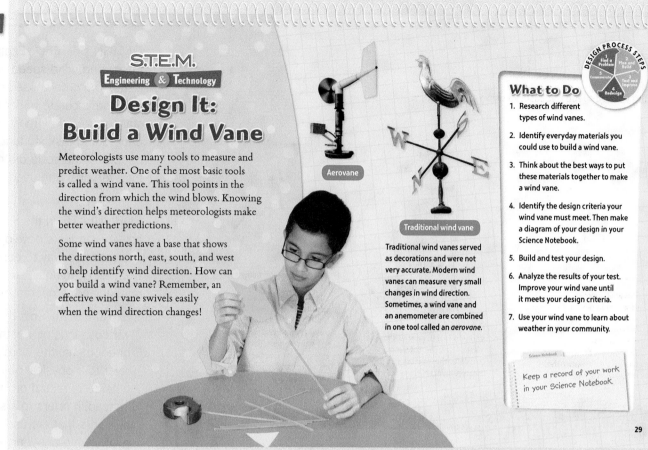

S.T.E.M.
Engineering & Technology
Design It: Build a Wind Vane

Meteorologists use many tools to measure and predict weather. One of the most basic tools is called a wind vane. This tool points in the direction from which the wind blows. Knowing the wind's direction helps meteorologists make better weather predictions.

Some wind vanes have a base that shows the directions north, east, south, and west to help identify wind direction. How can you build a wind vane? Remember, an effective wind vane swivels easily when the wind direction changes!

Aerovane

Traditional wind vane

Traditional wind vanes served as decorations and were not very accurate. Modern wind vanes can measure very small changes in wind direction. Sometimes, a wind vane and an anemometer are combined in one tool called an *aerovane*.

DESIGN PROCESS STEPS
1 Find a Problem
2 Plan and Build
3 Test and Improve
4 Redesign
5 Communicate

What to Do
1. Research different types of wind vanes.
2. Identify everyday materials you could use to build a wind vane.
3. Think about the best ways to put these materials together to make a wind vane.
4. Identify the design criteria your wind vane must meet. Then make a diagram of your design in your Science Notebook.
5. Build and test your design.
6. Analyze the results of your test. Improve your wind vane until it meets your design criteria.
7. Use your wind vane to learn about weather in your community.

Keep a record of your work in your Science Notebook.

29

Objectives

- Use the steps of the design process to build a wind vane.
- Understand the importance of wind vanes in understanding the weather.

Prep and Planning Tips

- Gather materials students may use to build their wind vanes, such as pencils, straight pins, straws, index cards, old manila folders, modeling clay, scissors, and glue. Place the materials in workstations around the room.
- Review cardinal directions with students.

Expected Results

Students should research, plan, design, and build a wind vane. They should identify the design criteria their wind vane will meet. Students should test and use their wind vane and discuss how it helps them learn about weather.

1 Engage/Explore

Attention Grabber

Display pictures of hurricanes or other very windy events. Ask students to talk about how they can tell from the pictures that a strong wind is blowing. Point out tree branches that are bent, clothing and hair that are set at odd angles, or other visual clues that show it is a windy day. Have students order the pictures from least windy to most windy weather conditions.

Preview Activity

Before beginning the activity, have students review the directions on the Engineering and Technology Flipchart page. You may wish to have students review the lesson on the engineering design process earlier in this program.

Guide the Activity

Develop Inquiry Skills

COMPARE Have students compare the traditional wind vane and the aerovane shown on the Flipchart page. Ask them to identify similarities between the two devices. Students should note that they both have some sort of flat projection to catch the wind. Explain that a similar type of projection will be an important part of their design.

Strategies for Success

A common misconception is that a wind vane shows the direction in which the wind is blowing. Reinforce that a wind vane's arrow actually points in the direction from which the wind is coming. This is achieved by making the tip of the arrow smaller and lighter than its other end.

Point out that because windy conditions are necessary, they may have to wait several days to test their designs.

 Science Notebook

During the Activity Remind students to record the problem they are trying to solve, design criteria, and materials they will use to make their wind vane. Suggest that they also record any problems they encounter and any redesigning they do as they build their first prototype.

Students should also record the results of their test and ideas for improving their design.

2 Explain

Develop the Engineering Design Process

2. PLAN AND BUILD As students plan their designs, remind them to consider how the materials they use would stand up to wind, precipitation, heat, and cold. Explain that they are not restricted to the provided materials. Some students may have additional ideas.

3. TEST AND IMPROVE Some common problems students might have with their designs are that the wind vanes may be too heavy to move easily in the wind or that they may be too flimsy to stand up to strong gusts. Start a class brainstorming session to find solutions to these problems.

4. REDESIGN Students' designs may not work the first time, or even the second. Encourage them to question other groups to find out what works and what doesn't and to apply this information to their own design.

3 Extend/Evaluate

Quick Check

Discuss with students what they learned as they went through the design process. Ask: **What part of your design do you think worked best? What did you change about your original design? Why?**

5. COMMUNICATE Once students complete their redesign, have them prepare a brief presentation in which they evaluate the effectiveness of the changes that they implemented. Encourage students to ask questions during each presentation.

 Science Notebook

After the Activity Students should get full credit if they actively participated in their group researching, designing, and building the wind vane. They should get partial credit for performing at least one of these tasks and should not receive any credit for not completing any of the tasks.

 Michael DiSpezio's  **Tips & Tricks**

Materials Other available materials could include heavy stock paper, large paper clips, tape, chopsticks, and markers.

Building a Bracket A bracket that permits unrestricted spinning of the indicator can be made from a straightened paper clip inserted into a straw segment, cylindrical piece of pasta, or large jewelry bead.

Guided Inquiry

⏱ 30–45 minutes

👥 small groups

Students should follow the directions on the Flipchart. The accompanying Lesson Inquiry pages in the Student Edition provide scaffolding for guided inquiry.

How Can We Observe Weather Patterns?

Meteorologists use weather tools to observe and measure weather. They look for patterns in the data they collect to make weather predictions. How can we use these same tools to find weather patterns?

_____

Materials

thermometer   cloud chart
barometer   hygrometer
rain gauge   anemometer
wind vane

1. With your teacher's help, practice taking measurements using weather tools. Make sure you know what each tool measures. Also, review the units of measurement for each tool.

2. As a class, select a place on the school grounds to set up a weather station. The place should be sheltered from the sun.

_____

3. Set up the weather station using the tools listed in the materials section.

_____

4. As a class, take turns and work in teams to measure weather data at the same times each day for five days. Use the cloud chart to identify cloud types. Record your weather observations.

_____

5. After the fifth day, look for patterns in your observations. Predict the weather for the following three days.

30

Inquiry Skills Focus Observe, Predict, Gather and Record Data

Objectives

- Measure and record weather conditions using weather tools.
- Use evidence from weather observations to make weather predictions.
- Analyze weather data.
- Verify observations made by others.

Prep and Planning Tips

- Suggest that students select a location for the weather station that is sheltered from the sun. The thermometer should also be sheltered from the wind. However, the rain gauge must be placed in a spot that is open for the collection of precipitation.
- Review the tools, what they do, and how they are used.

Expected Results

Students will use tools to measure weather conditions. They will collect, record, and analyze weather data. They will look for patterns in weather data over time and make weather predictions.

1 Engage/Explore

Attention Grabber

Show students photos of areas damaged by tornadoes, hurricanes, blizzards, or floods. Ask students if they can identify the type of weather that caused the damage in each photo. Stress that predicting the weather is an important task because it can help prevent property damage and save lives.

Preview Activity

Before beginning the investigation, have students review the directions on the Inquiry Flipchart and the accompanying Student Edition response pages. Then have them complete the response pages as they follow directions on the Flipchart.

Inquiry Flipchart page 30

Name _____

Essential Question

How Can We Observe Weather Patterns?

Set a Purpose

Why is it helpful to observe the weather?

Sample answer: People need to know what

the weather will be like to plan their day and

to stay safe if there is dangerous weather.

_____

Think About the Procedure

Why should the location for your weather station be sheltered from the sun?

Sample answer: The location should be

sheltered to prevent the sun from directly

heating the thermometer, so we can get

accurate readings of air temperature.

Why would it be useful to measure the weather conditions at the same time every day?

Sample answer: It would be a useful

control. Air temperature and other

weather conditions may vary throughout

the day.

© Houghton Mifflin Harcourt Publishing Company

Record Your Data

Day	Weather Observations
1	Sample entry: cloudy, 69 °F, humidity 70%, south winds at 3 km/hr, rising air pressure, no precipitation
	Weather Predictions

287

---

1 Engage/Explore (continued)

Guide the Investigation

Develop Inquiry Skills

OBSERVE/PREDICT Ask: **What is an observation?** information that can be obtained using the senses **What is a prediction?** a statement about what might happen in the future **What are predictions based on?** They are based on observations, scientific reasoning, and/or prior knowledge.

Give students scenarios so they can practice making observations and predictions. Tell them to describe what they would expect to observe during an approaching storm. Then have them imagine that tall, dark clouds have moved into their area. Ask: **Which type of weather do you predict will follow?** Sample answer: It will be stormy with gusting winds, rain, and falling temperatures. Ask: **Which strategy did you use to make your prediction?** scientific reasoning, prior knowledge

GATHER AND RECORD DATA Suggest that students double-check all measurements to reduce chances of human error. Allow students to gather data in pairs. One student can read the weather tool while a second student records the measurement. You may want to keep a class chart of the data on the board.

Go Digital

A virtual lab experience is available with the Online Resources for this program.

2 Explain

Develop Inquiry Skills

DRAW CONCLUSIONS Ask students to review their predictions. Did their data support their predictions? Remind them to consider the results of the investigation objectively and honestly.

ANALYZE AND EXTEND Discuss students' responses to the items.

1. Help students recognize patterns between air temperature and air pressure. Point out that falling air pressure often indicates an approaching storm; it usually brings a change in temperature. Student data also may indicate that wind direction affects temperature and humidity.

2. Suggest that students review their data tables to see when the weather began to change. Ask: **Which atmospheric conditions changed just before the weather changed?** Sample answer: air pressure, cloud cover

3–5. Explain that short-term weather predictions tend to be more accurate than long-term weather predictions. Ask students to consider the factors that may have affected their ability to make an accurate prediction. Explain that data from a wider area might have helped them improve their weather predictions.

3 Extend/Evaluate

6. Accept all reasonable answers. Students may want to know how scientists use radar and satellites to predict the weather.

Assessment

Lesson Quiz
See Assessment Guide, p. AG 54.

Draw Conclusions

How can we observe weather patterns?
Sample answer: Careful observations of weather conditions every day and the use of tools such as a barometer can help us gather accurate weather data.

Analyze and Extend

1. **Describe weather patterns in your data.**
Sample answer: Air pressure and humidity often changed with wind direction. Whenever air pressure decreased, it became cloudy.

2. **Which weather conditions were most likely to change before the weather changed?**
Sample answer: Air pressure and wind direction were most likely to change before the rest of the weather changed.

3. **What were your weather predictions? On which weather pattern did you base your predictions?**
Sample answer: We predicted that our rainy weather would become sunny within three days. We based this prediction on the fact that the air pressure was rising.

4. **Were your predictions accurate? Explain.**
Sample answer: No, it rained for two days more than what we had predicted.

5. **What would have made your weather predictions more accurate?**
Sample answer: Our predictions would have been more accurate if we had more experience observing weather patterns, or if we had analyzed additional data from other nearby weather stations.

6. **Think of other questions you would like to ask about weather patterns and predictions.**
Sample answer: I would like to know how scientists use radar and satellites to predict the weather.

288

Differentiated Inquiry

Easy

Cloud Poster

Give students cotton balls, glue, and construction paper. Have them use the materials and the cloud identification chart in their Student Edition to make their own cloud posters. Students should label each cloud type.

Average

Temperature and Altitude

- Obtain a helium-filled balloon and two thin, liquid-crystal temperature strips. Take the class outside on a sunny day. Place one temperature strip on the sidewalk. Attach the other to the balloon. Attach kite string to the balloon and allow it to rise into the sky.

- Ask students to predict how the temperature of the air around the balloon will compare to the temperature of the air near the ground.

- After 30 minutes, reel in the balloon and have students see if their predictions were correct.

- Students should observe that the temperature of the balloon was cooler than the temperature of the sidewalk.

Average

Temperature Graphs

- Suggest that students make line graphs showing daily temperature changes over the time period covered by the activity.

- Students should plot days of the week on the horizontal axis. They should plot temperature on the vertical axis. Students should make a graph for each week of data they collect.

- Discuss how graphs help students recognize trends in data.

Challenging

Weather Reporters

- Encourage students to continue measuring and recording weather data throughout the year.

- Suggest that students take turns making weather predictions each Friday for the upcoming weekend.

- Arrange for students to give their weather forecasts over the school intercom.

- Students should continue to monitor the accuracy of their weather predictions and strive to improve them.

People in Science

Objectives

- Recognize that the atmosphere is made up of solids, liquids, and gases.
- Describe how scientists contribute to our knowledge of the atmosphere.

Notebook ▶ Generate Ideas

Read aloud item number 4, which describes aerosols. **Why do you think aerosols are important for scientists to study?** Sample answer: Some aerosols, such as smoke and soot, can cause air, water, and land pollution. Pollution is harmful to living things.

Background

- Dr. Hsu studied "The Perfect Dust Storm" of 2001, which brought dust from Asia across the Pacific Ocean to North America. Her illustrated report on this dust storm can be viewed on the National Aeronautics and Space Administration (NASA) website.
- Students may think that NASA scientists study only space. However, Dr. Hsu uses satellites in orbit to collect her data to study Earth's atmosphere.
- Aerosols may be either solids or liquids, but not gases. Water vapor, which is the gas state of water, is not an aerosol.
- Levels of solid aerosols in the air can increase dramatically after a volcanic eruption. In April 2010, aerosols from a volcano in Iceland drifted over much of western Europe, causing flight cancellations and other problems.
- Aerosols help explain the mercury contamination of many lakes. Every year, coal-burning power plants release tons of mercury into the air. This mercury travels in aerosols and returns to the surface in precipitation.

People in Science

8 THINGS YOU SHOULD KNOW ABOUT N. Christina Hsu

1 Dr. Hsu is an atmospheric scientist. She studies how Earth's atmosphere changes, and how these changes affect Earth's surface.

2 Dr. Hsu earned a Ph.D. degree in atmospheric science from the Georgia Institute of Technology.

3 Today, Dr. Hsu works for NASA—the U.S. agency that explores space and studies Earth from space.

4 Dr. Hsu studies aerosols, which are tiny particles that hang in the air. Aerosols include solids, such as smoke and soot, and liquids, such as tiny water droplets.

5 Dr. Hsu studies aerosols because water vapor condenses on them to form water droplets. She is interested in the source, amount, and distribution of these particles in the atmosphere.

6 Dr. Hsu uses satellites to measure and track the movement of aerosols.

7 Dr. Hsu studies the effects of aerosols blocking sunlight.

8 Dr. Hsu has received numerous NASA Goddard awards for her achievements.

289

Writing Connection

Write a Narrative Have students demonstrate their knowledge of aerosols by writing a paragraph about how aerosols enter the atmosphere. If necessary, students may conduct further research on aerosols either on the Internet or in the school library before they begin writing. Students' paragraphs should include both natural events and human activities that produce aerosols. Encourage students to use sensory details in their narratives.

People in Science *continued*

Now You Be an Aerosol Detective!

Each clue describes a source of aerosol particles. Match each clue with the picture that illustrates it.

1. It may be quiet for years, then it releases smoke and ash with a *boom!*

2. Blustery winds launch sandy aerosols every day from dry places such as this one.

3. People are the source of this air pollution.

4. Tiny water droplets are aerosols, too. They often come from this source.

5. One little match can spark one of these.

Think About It!

How might human activities add aerosols to the atmosphere?

Sample answers: Human activities, such as burning fossil fuels, produce particles that add to the aerosols in the air.

290

Develop Science Concepts

Students may think that the atmosphere is made only of gases. Explain that while the atmosphere is mostly gases, it contains tiny droplets of liquids, too. Aerosols travel in these gases and liquids.

Why don't aerosols fall immediately back to Earth's surface? An aerosol particle is very small and lightweight. **How do aerosols eventually end up in Earth's land and water?** When water droplets or ice crystals become heavy enough, they fall to Earth's surface as precipitation. Soot, smoke, and other solid aerosols sometimes mix into the precipitation. Aerosols also can settle to Earth's surface on their own.

Develop Inquiry Skills

INFER Remind students that Dr. Hsu works for NASA, the government agency that studies Earth and space. **How might atmospheric scientists such as Dr. Hsu work with other NASA scientists to study Earth?** Sample answer: They could help other scientists understand changes in climate; they could help other scientists discover and understand changes in the ozone layer; they could help scientists study effects of pollution on air quality and how it affects Earth's organisms.

Notebook ▸ Summarize Ideas

Have students review the work of Dr. Hsu and the effects of aerosols in the atmosphere. Then have them summarize what they have learned either orally or in writing.

Nature of Science

Erupting volcanoes and forest fires can send a huge volume of soot, smoke, and ash into the air. How far can these particles travel? Where do they land, and what kinds of effects do they have on living things? Tell students to imagine that they are scientists investigating the flow of soot, smoke, and ash from a volcano. Have them make a list of ways to predict where the particles will land and how they might disrupt daily life on Earth's surface.

Enduring Understandings

Revisit the Big Idea and Essential Questions

Big Idea Water moves in a regular cycle that influences the weather.

To explore the Big Idea, post the unit vocabulary terms on the board. Have student pairs make and explain a word web that depicts the relationships among and between terms. Sample web:

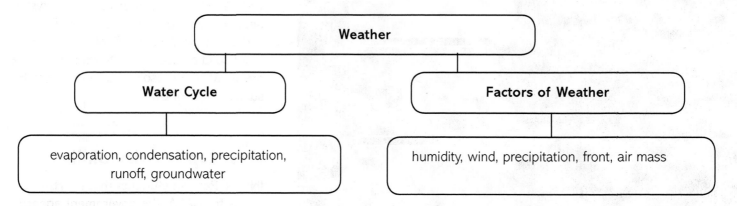

Essential Questions

Post the Essential Questions and use the following prompts to guide a discussion.

Lesson/Essential Question	Prompts
L1 What Is the Water Cycle?	• Draw the water cycle, and label the changes water goes through during its cycle.
L2 What Are Types of Weather?	• Describe three types of precipitation, and explain how each type forms.
L3 How Is Weather Predicted?	• Explain the differences between air masses and fronts.
L4 How Can We Observe Weather Patterns?	• Describe tools we use to measure weather conditions.

Notebook **Science Notebook**

You may use the following strategies after students complete the unit or after each lesson.

• Have students review and edit the answers to Essential Questions they drafted at the beginning of the unit. Suggest they cross out sentences or ideas that are unnecessary or inappropriate.

• Have students write clues in their Science Notebooks in preparation for a game. On opposite sides of index cards, instruct them to write the clues (to serve as questions) and answers in the form of questions. Allow small groups of students to use the clues to play the game.

Science Notebook

Essential Questions	Answers
What Is the Water Cycle?	
What Are Types of Weather?	
How Is Weather Predicted?	
How Can We Observe Weather Patterns?	

Unit 5 Review

Name _____

Vocabulary Review

Use the terms in the box to complete the sentences.

air mass
air pressure
atmosphere
condensation
humidity
precipitation
runoff
weather

1. The condition of the atmosphere at a certain place and time

    is _____ weather _____.

2. The amount of water vapor in the air

    is _____ humidity _____.

3. The weight of the atmosphere pressing down on Earth's surface

    is _____ air pressure _____.

4. A large body of air with the same temperature and humidity

    throughout is an _____ air mass _____.

5. The mixture of gases that surround Earth is

    the _____ atmosphere _____.

6. The process by which a gas changes into a liquid
    is _____ condensation _____.

7. Water that falls from clouds to Earth's surface

    is _____ precipitation _____.

8. Water that cannot soak into the ground and instead flows across

    Earth's surface is _____ runoff _____.

© Houghton Mifflin Harcourt Publishing Company   (border) ©NDisc/Age Fotostock

Unit 5   291

Item Analysis

Items	Depth of Knowledge	Cognitive Complexity
1–8	1	Low

Unit Review

Answer Key

Vocabulary Review (3 points each)

1. **weather** Have students describe the weather you are experiencing today.

2. **humidity** Have volunteers contrast a hot, muggy day with one in which the air feels dry. The difference is the amount of moisture in the air, or the humidity.

3. **air pressure** Remind students that air exerts pressure on everything on Earth's surface, including them. Students can reread an extended discussion of air pressure in Lesson 2.

4. **air mass** As students review the third and fourth pages of Lesson 3, have volunteers describe the different regions shown on the air-mass source map.

5. **atmosphere** Emphasize that Earth's atmosphere is a mixture of gases. Ask students to name the two most plentiful gases in Earth's atmosphere.

6. **condensation** Students can review the processes of condensation and evaporation in the Lesson 1 explanation of the water cycle.

7. **precipitation** Have volunteers list the four main types of precipitation covered in the unit. Students can find a refresher on precipitation on the last two pages of Lesson 2.

8. **runoff** Remind students that in Lesson 1, they learned about runoff as a part of the water cycle. Have volunteers identify places where they have seen runoff form.

Assessment

Unit 5 Test and Performance Assessment
See Assessment Guide,
pp. AG 55–AG 61, for Unit Test and Performance Task with Long Option rubric.

Unit Review *continued*

Answer Key

Science Concepts (4 points each)

9. A Direct students to analyze the data in the chart. They should look for the day that combines the highest humidity with the highest temperature.

10. D Refer students to a discussion of air masses and their source regions on the third and fourth pages of Lesson 3.

11. B Reinforce that constant evaporating of water from the ocean's surface is an important part of the water cycle.

12. B Suggest that students draw sketches of each choice shown. This should lead them to conclude that the only logical answer is B.

13. B Elicit from students that moving air is wind. A discussion of air pressure and wind can be found on the fifth and sixth pages of Lesson 2.

14. C Have volunteers describe what is happening in each numbered step shown in the diagram. Direct students to Lesson 1 to review all of the processes involved in this cycle.

15. A Remind students that barometers measure air pressure. Have students identify what the weather instruments that measure temperature (thermometer) and precipitation (rain gauge or snow board) are called. Note that humidity is measured with a hygrometer.

16. A Point out that a sea breeze blows from an area of higher pressure over the sea to an area of lower air pressure on land. Students can take a second look at the diagram showing the formation of sea and land breezes in Lesson 2.

17. B Have volunteers describe what is occurring in this set of diagrams. This component process of the water cycle is covered in Lesson 1.

Science Concepts

Fill in the letter of the choice that best answers the question.

9. Deanna measured the temperature and humidity every afternoon for four days. She recorded the results in this table.

Day	Temperature (°C)	Relative Humidity (%)
Monday	28 (82 °F)	90
Tuesday	27 (81 °F)	79
Wednesday	24 (75 °F)	70
Thursday	28 (82 °F)	69

Which day could Deanna conclude was hottest and **most** humid?

(A) Monday   (C) Wednesday
(B) Tuesday   (D) Thursday

10. Carl reads the weather forecast on the Internet. It says that a cool, wet air mass is moving toward the town where he lives. What type of weather should Carl expect?

(A) cool temperatures, sun, and clear skies

(B) warm temperatures, sun, and clear skies

(C) warm temperatures, sun, and decreasing cloudiness

(D) cool temperatures, increasing cloudiness, and precipitation

11. Oceans get fresh water from precipitation and rivers. However, ocean water levels do not change very much as a result. Why are these levels not greatly affected?

(A) Water is constantly seeping into the ocean floor.

(B) Water is constantly evaporating over the ocean's surface.

(C) Water is constantly flowing back into rivers from the oceans.

(D) Water is constantly deposited back on land by ocean wave action.

12. Which of the following sequences shows how water may move from an ocean to land and back to an ocean?

(A) precipitation → runoff → cloud formation → groundwater

(B) evaporation → cloud formation → precipitation → runoff

(C) groundwater → cloud formation → precipitation → runoff

(D) cloud formation → precipitation → evaporation → runoff

13. Scientists study many factors that help them predict weather. Which factor **most** directly affects the movement of air?

(A) humidity   (C) precipitation
(B) air pressure   (D) temperature

14. This diagram shows the water cycle.

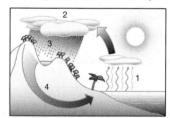

At which point in the cycle does precipitation take place?

(A) 1   (C) 3
(B) 2   (D) 4

15. Sarah looks at a barometer to record a reading. What is Sarah measuring?

(A) air pressure   (C) precipitation
(B) humidity   (D) temperature

Item Analysis *(continued)*

Items	Depth of Knowledge	Cognitive Complexity
9–11	2	Moderate
12–13	3	High
14	2	Moderate
15	2	Low
16–17	2	Moderate

Name _____

16. This diagram shows the pattern of air movement in a coastal area.

Which type of wind is illustrated in the diagram?

(A) sea breeze

(B) land breeze

(C) valley breeze

(D) coastal breeze

17. This picture shows how a puddle changes over the course of a day.

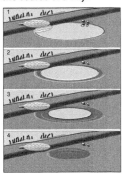

Which process is taking place?

(A) runoff

(B) evaporation

(C) precipitation

(D) condensation

18. Taro is studying the water cycle. He knows that energy is needed for matter to move and change state. What is the main source of energy for the water cycle?

(A) clouds

(B) the sun

(C) the oceans

(D) chemical reactions

19. Jerry notices that the air pressure is rising. Based on this observation, which type of weather does Jerry expect?

(A) fair weather

(B) windy weather

(C) stormy weather

(D) unstable weather

20. The following diagram shows a location where two air masses meet.

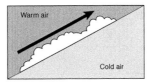

What is the weather like at this type of air boundary?

(A) clear and cold

(B) clear and warm

(C) cloudy and rainy

(D) windy and cold

© Houghton Mifflin Harcourt Publishing Company (border) ©ktkto/Age Fotostock

Item Analysis *(continued)*

Items	Depth of Knowledge	Cognitive Complexity
18	2	Moderate
19–20	3	High

Unit Review *continued*

Answer Key

Science Concepts (4 points each)

18. B Remind students that they learned that the sun is the source of energy for the water cycle in Lesson 1.

19. A Ask students to think about the type of weather that would accompany rising air pressure. Remind them that humid air is lighter, and thus has lower air pressure, than drier air. Therefore, rising pressure leads to drier or fair weather.

20. C Students should recall from Lesson 3 that the place where different air masses meet is called a front—and that clouds and precipitation are common at fronts.

Short Option Performance Assessment

Task

Diagram the Water Cycle

Have students work in pairs to draw a simple picture of the water cycle. Tell them to label the water changes and tell whether water has been warmed or cooled to make each change. Students may begin the water cycle at any point, but must show the correct order from the point at which they choose to begin.

Rubric

Preparation Provide each student pair with drawing paper and crayons or markers. Encourage students to work together to plan their diagrams before beginning to draw.

Scoring Rubric—Performance Indicators

____ Indicates that evaporation happens from bodies of water.

____ Indicates that heating must take place in order for evaporation to occur.

____ Indicates that condensation occurs in the atmosphere to form clouds.

____ Indicates that cooling must take place in order for condensation to occur.

Observations and Rubric Scores

3   2   1   0

Unit Review *continued*

Answer Key

Apply Inquiry and Review the Big Idea

(10 points)

21. See student page for sample answer.
Have students review the information on how different types of precipitation form in Lesson 2. Then have a volunteer describe what is shown in the diagram, and identify which type of precipitation forms in this manner.

(9 points)

22. See student page for sample answer.
Have students reread the last two pages of Lesson 3, which covers the danger of hurricanes and the importance of our ability to predict them.

(9 points)

23. See student page for sample answer.
Review with students the material on the first and second pages of Lesson 3 on tools used to gather weather data. Also review the material in this same lesson about types of fronts and about the role of weather maps and computer models in predicting the weather.

Apply Inquiry and Review the Big Idea

Write the answers to these questions.

21. This diagram shows the atmosphere on a day in late winter. Precipitation is falling.

    Which type of precipitation is **likely** to form in the freezing cold layer of air? Explain how you know.

    Sample answer: Sleet is likely to form.

    Sleet forms when raindrops fall

    through a layer of freezing air near

    the ground.

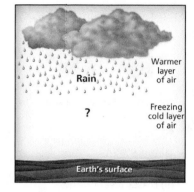

22. Hurricanes are one type of severe storm. Explain why predicting hurricanes is important.

    Sample answer: Hurricanes are powerful storms that can cause great damage and

    loss of life. The ability to predict hurricanes allows people in their paths to seek shelter

    or leave areas that could become dangerous.

23. A weather forecaster says that a front is approaching. She says that the weather will be warmer the next day, with increased cloudiness and late day rain. What type of front is headed for the area? How were the data gathered to make this prediction?

    Sample answer: A warm front is approaching. Thousands of weather instruments

    on land, at sea, in the air, and in orbit contribute data to produce weather maps and

    computer models, which forecasters use to predict the weather.

Item Analysis

Items	Depth of Knowledge	Cognitive Complexity
21–23	3	High

UNIT 6 Earth and Space

Big Idea and Essential Questions

This Unit was designed to focus on this Big Idea and Essential Questions.

Big Idea

Objects in space including Earth and its moon move in regular observable patterns.

Essential Questions

L1 **How Do the Sun, Earth, and Moon Interact?**

L2 **What Are Moon Phases?**

L3 **How Does the Moon Move Around Earth?**

L4 **What Are the Planets in Our Solar System?**

L5 **How Can We Model the Sun and Planets?**

Take It Home!
A School-Home Connection letter is provided in Online Resources.

Professional Development

Houghton Mifflin Harcourt and **NSTA,** the **National Science Teachers Association,** have partnered to provide customized professional development resources for teachers using *ScienceFusion*.

The Professional Development Resources include:

- Do it yourself resources, where you can study at your own pace
- Live and archived online seminars
- Journal articles, many of which include lesson plans
- Fee-based eBooks, eBook chapters, online short courses, symposia, and conferences

    Access to The NSTA Learning Center is provided in the *ScienceFusion* Online Resources.

Unit Planning

Options for Instruction

Two parallel paths meet the unit objectives, with a strong Inquiry strand woven into each. Follow the Print Path, the Digital Path, or your customized combination of print, digital, and inquiry.

	LESSON 1	LESSON 2	LESSON 3
			☑ **Guided Inquiry**
Essential Questions	**How Do the Sun, Earth, and Moon Interact?**	**What Are Moon Phases?**	**How Does the Moon Move Around Earth?**
Print Path	☐ **Student Edition** pp. 297–312 • Night and Day • The Sun-Earth-Moon System • Seasons • Patterns in the Sky • Our Place in Space	☐ **Student Edition** pp. 315–324 • Our Moon • Moon Phases • Lunar and Solar Calendars	☐ **Student Edition** pp. 325–326 • Scaffolding for Inquiry
Hands-On Inquiry	**Inquiry Flipchart** p. 31 **Spin and Model** ☐ Directed Inquiry **Constellation Patterns** ☐ Independent Inquiry	**Inquiry Flipchart** p. 32 **From Full to New and Back Again** ☐ Directed Inquiry **On the Moon** ☐ Independent Inquiry	**Inquiry Flipchart** p. 33 **How Does the Moon Move Around Earth?** ☐ Guided Inquiry
Digital Path	☐ **Digital Lesson** Online Resources Interactive presentation of lesson content	☐ **Digital Lesson** Online Resources Interactive presentation of lesson content	☐ **Virtual Lab** Online Resources Interactive scaffolded inquiry

	☑ **Guided Inquiry**
What Are the Planets in Our Solar System?	**How Can We Model the Sun and Planets?**

OTHER UNIT FEATURES

🌐 **People in Science, p. 313**

S.T.E.M. Engineering and Technology, pp. 341-342B

🖱 **Online Resources**

☐ **Student Edition**
pp. 327–340
- In Our Corner of Space
- Planets Near and Far
- The Inside Track
- The Outside Track
- The Right Spot

☐ **Student Edition**
pp. 343–344
- Scaffolding for Inquiry

Unit Assessment

Formative Assessment
Sum It Up! and Brain Check
Student Edition, end of each lesson

Summative Assessment
Lesson Quizzes
Assessment Guide,
pp. AG 62–AG 66

Unit 6 Review
Student Edition, pp. 345–348

Unit 6 Test
Assessment Guide,
pp. AG 67–AG 71

Performance Assessment
SHORT OPTION: Teacher
Edition, p. 347
LONG OPTION: Assessment
Guide, pp. AG 72–AG 73

RTI ▶ **Response to Intervention**

RTI Strategies p. 295K

🖱 **Online Assessment**
Test-taking and automatic scoring
Banks of items from which to
build tests

Inquiry Flipchart
p. 34

How Can We Model the Orbits of Comets and Planets?
☐ Directed Inquiry

My Space Mission
☐ Independent Inquiry

Inquiry Flipchart
p. 36

How Can We Model the Sun and Planets?
☐ Guided Inquiry

☐ **Digital Lesson**
Online Resources

Interactive presentation
of lesson content

☐ **Virtual Lab**
Online Resources

Interactive scaffolded
inquiry

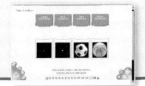

Planning for Inquiry

Use the following preview of Inquiry Activities and Lessons to gather and manage the materials needed for each lesson.

Activity	Inquiry and Design Process Skills Focus	Materials	Prep Tips, Troubleshooting, and Expected Results
Lesson 1 DIRECTED INQUIRY Flipchart p.31 **A** **Spin and Model** **OBJECTIVE** Follow directions for an investigation to demonstrate two ways that Earth moves in space. 🕐 15–20 minutes 👥 small groups	• Model • Observe • Draw Conclusions	• flashlight • basketball • marker	**Prep Tip** Before starting, mark a spot on the basketball to represent where you are on Earth. You may also want to mark an axis. **Troubleshooting** Step 1: Be sure the student holding the basketball (Earth) holds it level with the flashlight. Step 2: The room does not need to be totally darkened. **Caution!** Warn students to use care when moving around in a dimly lit room. Be sure no tripping hazards are present. **Expected Results** Rotation: Students should find that the side of the basketball facing the flashlight is always illuminated. The side facing away from the flashlight is never illuminated. As Earth spins on its axis, different areas of Earth move into and pass through the sunlit zone. Revolution: Students should note that Earth keeps rotating as it revolves around the sun. If students keep the axis tilted, they should see that the amount of time an area spends in daylight varies as Earth revolves.
INDEPENDENT INQUIRY Flipchart p.31 **B** **Constellation Patterns** **OBJECTIVE** Plan and conduct research in order to classify constellations by where they are seen from Earth and how they move. 🕐 30–40 minutes 👥 small groups	• Plan and Conduct a Simple Investigation • Classify	• globe	**Prep Tip** Show students the Northern and Southern Hemispheres on a globe. Emphasize that people in different hemispheres see different constellations because of their location on Earth. You may wish to locate several websites to show students constellations or obtain nonfiction books from the school media center that they can use for research. **Troubleshooting** You may wish to assign each group a different area of the sky to research in order to have a wider variety of results. **Expected Results** Students will research and prepare a chart with constellations classified by the place from which they can be seen and how they move.

Additional teaching support for all inquiry activities is available in **Online Resources.**

Notebook **Science Notebook Strategies**
- Lists of Kit-Supplied Materials
- Meeting Individual Needs
- Investigate More—Extensions and Variations and More!

Activity	Inquiry and Design Process Skills Focus	Materials	Prep Tips, Troubleshooting, and Expected Results
Lesson 2 DIRECTED INQUIRY Flipchart **p.32** **A** **From Full to New and Back Again** **OBJECTIVE** Follow directions for an investigation to observe the cycle of moon phases. ⏱ 10–15 minutes 👥 individuals	• Observe • Predict • Calculate • Draw Conclusions	• blank monthly calendar	**Prep Tip** Time listed is for initial discussion and distribution of the calendars. Students will carry out the bulk of this activity at home. At the end of the month, set aside time for students to share what they observed. Prepare a blank calendar grid and distribute a copy to each student. **Troubleshooting** Observations can't be made on cloudy nights. In these cases, have students use the appearance of the moon before and after the night when it was not visible to determine how it would have appeared. Step 2: If resources are available, try to observe the moon online. Step 3: Students should make their observations for a 30-day period. **Expected Results** Students will find that the moon appears to change shape during its phases, and that it takes approximately 29 days to complete one cycle of phases. There is about one week from the new moon phase to the first quarter moon and about two weeks between the full moon and new moon phases. Students should be able to predict when the next full moon will occur.
INDEPENDENT INQUIRY Flipchart **p.32** **B** **On the Moon** **OBJECTIVE** Plan and conduct research to determine how the moon's surface and Earth's surface compare, and use that information to plan and make a model of the moon's surface. ⏱ 20–25 minutes 👥 individuals or small groups	• Plan and Conduct a Simple Investigation • Model	• reference materials, such as books, newspapers, the Internet	**Prep Tip** Students will need the initial 20–25 minutes for research. Model design and construction will take additional time. Students may use a variety of research sources such as books, newspaper articles, and the Internet. They can gather a great deal of useful information on the moon and its surface from the NASA website. When students are ready to construct their models, provide them with a variety of materials such as clay, newspaper, glue, scissors, paints, and so on. Caution! If students use materials to represent the powdery surface of the moon, check for allergies. Remind students to be careful using sharp objects. **Expected Results** Students will research, plan, and then make a model of the moon's surface.

Planning for Inquiry (continued)

Activity	Inquiry and Design Process Skills Focus	Materials	Prep Tips, Troubleshooting, and Expected Results
Lesson 3 INQUIRY GUIDED INQUIRY Flipchart p.33 **Student Edition** pp.325–326 **How Does the Moon Move Around Earth?** OBJECTIVES • Observe and sketch apparent changes in the shape of the moon. • Predict when and how the shape of the moon appears to change. ⏱ 30–40 minutes 👥 small groups	• Use Models • Observe • Draw Conclusions	• plastic foam ball on a pencil • masking tape • flashlight • paper • pencil • chair	**Prep Tip** For safety and to save time, prepare the moon ahead of time using plastic foam balls about 4 inches in diameter stuck onto the end of a sharpened pencil. Students must work in groups of at least three. They can take turns using the equipment. Students can also take turns playing different roles in the activity. **Troubleshooting** The student holding the moon should move in a counterclockwise direction, stopping at three different points before returning to the starting position. The student representing Earth stays seated throughout the activity, but turns to face the moon and record observations. Step 2: Have the student holding the flashlight and moon at a level consistent with the height of the student in the chair. Step 4: It is important that the "moon" keep the marked side of the moon toward Earth at all times. **Caution!** Warn students to be careful when using sharp objects. To avoid hazards, you may wish to set up the pencils and ball beforehand. Remind students not to shine the flashlight directly into their own or others' eyes. **Expected Results** In the time that the moon takes to revolve once around Earth, it also rotates once on its axis. This results in the same side of the moon always facing Earth.

🖥 Go Digital! Virtual Lab

How Does the Moon Move Around Earth?

Key Inquiry Skills: observe, use models, record data, compare
Students observe a model of the Earth-Moon system and capture images of the moon's phases at different points in its orbit.

Activity	Inquiry and Design Process Skills Focus	Materials	Prep Tips, Troubleshooting, and Expected Results
Lesson **4** DIRECTED INQUIRY Flipchart **p.34** **A** **How Can We Model the Orbits of Comets and Planets?** OBJECTIVE Follow directions for an investigation to model the orbits of comets and planets. ⏱ 20 minutes 👥 pairs	• Observe • Measure • Compare • Draw Conclusions	• One 20 cm (8 in.) piece of cotton string • 2 pushpins • 1 sheet of corrugated cardboard (30 cm × 30 cm or 12 in. square) • ruler • 1 red pencil • 1 blue pencil	**Prep Tip** Cut a piece of corrugated cardboard for each pair prior to class. To save time, you might pre-tie loops of string. Pencils do not have to be red and blue, as long as they are different colors. **Caution!** Warn students to use care when using sharp objects such as pushpins. **Troubleshooting** Show an example of the orbit of a planet so students understand that planetary orbits are not perfectly circular. Provide background on ellipses and explain that in the model, the sun is at one of the foci. Describe the extremely large and elongated shape of the elliptical orbits of most comets. It can be hundreds of years or more between the times in their orbits that bring them closest to the sun. NASA online provides visuals of orbits. Remind students to put cardboard under the paper before they insert the pushpins. **Expected Results** Students will find that the first setup (red pencil) forms a circle, while the second one (blue pencil) forms an ellipse—the shape of a comet's orbit.
INDEPENDENT INQUIRY Flipchart **p.34** **B** **My Space Mission** OBJECTIVE Plan and conduct online research about NASA missions, and use the information to design a proposed space mission. ⏱ 20 minutes 👥 pairs	• Plan and Conduct a Simple Investigation • Gather Data	• craft materials, such as construction paper, glue, markers, tape	**Prep Tip** The NASA website has a wealth of information that students can access on past, present, and future space missions to the planets, moons, and other objects in the solar system. Encourage students to make use of this Internet resource. **Expected Results** Students will research, plan, and write a proposal for a future NASA space mission.

Planning for Inquiry (continued)

Activity	Inquiry and Design Process Skills Focus	Materials	Prep Tips, Troubleshooting, and Expected Results
S.T.E.M. **Engineering and Technology** Flipchart p.35 **Design It: Build a Sundial** **OBJECTIVES** • Use the steps of the design process to make a sundial. • Understand the purpose of sundials in telling time. ⏱ 25–30 minutes 👥 small groups	**DESIGN PROCESS STEPS** 1 Find a Problem 2 Plan and Build 3 Test and Improve 4 Redesign 5 Communicate 1 **Find a Problem** 2 Plan and Build 3 Test and Improve 4 **Redesign** 5 Communicate	• pencils • clay • craft sticks • chalk • game chips • scissors • tape • compass	**Prep Tip** Identify resources students can use to learn about sundials. Gather materials students may use to build their designs, including sharpened pencils, modeling clay, cardboard or heavy card stock, craft sticks, chalk, game chips, scissors, and tape. Supply each group of students with a compass. **Expected Results** Students should be able to research, plan, design, and build a sundial. They should be able to test the sundial for accuracy and improve its design for final use.

Activity	Inquiry and Design Process Skills Focus	Materials	Prep Tips, Troubleshooting, and Expected Results
Lesson 5 INQUIRY GUIDED INQUIRY Flipchart **p.36** Student Edition pp.343–344 **How Can We Model the Sun and Planets?** OBJECTIVES • Model an inner planet and an outer planet. • Compare and contrast the structure of an inner planet and an outer planet. ⊘ 90 minutes 👥 pairs or small groups	• Model • Measure • Use Numbers • Observe • Compare • Draw Conclusions	• safety compass • construction paper • 160 × 160 cm butcher paper (4, one for each group for modeling the Sun) • yarn or string • pencils • scissors • sheet of cardboard (for use as surface protectors when students use the compass or pushpin) • pushpin • colored pencils or markers	**Prep Tip** Plan for at least 2 class periods to complete this activity. It may work best to organize the class into four groups and assign each group to make one-quarter of the sun and two of the planets. Identify a location that provides the space for students to lay out their paper. You may need to tape lengths of butcher paper side by side in order to achieve the 160 × 160 cm (160 cm = 5.24 ft) of paper needed for students to construct the massive comparative model of the sun. If there is minimal space available in the classroom, groups can work in shifts. Cut 310-cm lengths of string needed to outline the sun prior to the activity. This will allow for the string needed to tie the loop. Finished loops should be 150 cm long. **Caution!** Remind students to use care when working with scissors. **Troubleshooting** Step 1: Reinforce that students are to divide the *Scale Diameter* by two, not the *Actual Diameter*. Step 3: Demonstrate how to place a string and draw an arc using a smaller sheet of paper. Step 4: You may wish to cut and assemble loops of yarn for both Jupiter and Saturn. If students are cutting loops, remind them to add enough length so they can tie the knot. Be sure students place cardboard under the construction paper before inserting the pushpin in the center of the paper. Step 5: Review the use of a compass with students. **Expected Results** Students will be able to visualize the relative sizes of the sun and planets as a result of completing their scale models.

Go Digital! Virtual Lab

How Can We Model the Sun and Planets?
Key Inquiry Skills: **measure, compare, order, use models**
Students measure and compare planets to place them in order from smallest to largest.

Differentiated Instruction
Customize and Extend

You can extend and customize science instruction for your students using the following resources.

Leveled Readers

The **Science & Engineering Leveled Readers** can be used to provide additional nonfiction reading practice in the subject area of Unit 6.

ON-LEVEL This Reader reinforces unit concepts. It includes student response activities for your students.

EXTRA SUPPORT This Reader shares title, illustrations, vocabulary, and concepts with the On-Level Reader. However, the text is linguistically accommodated to provide simplified sentence structures and comprehension aids. It also includes response activities.

ENRICHMENT This high-interest nonfiction Reader enriches and extends unit concepts. It reinforces some of the unit vocabulary, includes *stretch vocabulary*, and includes response activities.

TEACHER GUIDE
The accompanying **Teacher Guide** provides teaching strategies and support for using all the Readers, as well as English and Spanish worksheets that focus on vocabulary development. A correlation to the Disciplinary Core Ideas of the Next Generation Science Standards is included.

DIGITAL VERSIONS

All of these Leveled Readers are available online. They are also available in an innovative and engaging format for touchscreen mobile devices. Contact your HMH Sales Representative for more information.

RTI ▶ Response to Intervention

Response to Intervention is a process for identifying and supporting students who are not making expected progress toward essential learning goals.

Component	Location	Strategies and Benefits
The following *ScienceFusion* components have the flexibility to be used to provide Core Classroom Instruction (Tier 1), strategic intervention (Tier 2), and intensive intervention (Tier 3).		
Student Edition, Active Reading prompts, Sum It Up, Brain Check	Active Reading throughout each lesson, Sum It Up and Brain Check at the end of each lesson	Student responses can be used as screening tools to assess whether intervention is needed.
Assessment Guide, Lesson Quizzes	pp. AG 62–AG 66	Student responses can be used as screening tools to assess whether intervention is needed.
Inquiry Flipcharts	Inquiry Flipchart pp. 31, 32, 34	Directed Inquiry for students who learn best through directed or teacher-led hands-on activities.
Teacher Edition, Unit Review Answer Strategies	TE pp. 345–348	Suggestions for intervention, guidance, and remediation for each review question.
Leveled Readers	TE p. 295J	Content support for students not meeting the learning needs during core classroom instruction.
Leveled Readers, Teacher Guides and Vocabulary Worksheets	TE p. 295J	Direct instruction with small groups of students needing additional content at various readability levels.
Extra Support for Vocabulary and Concepts (online worksheets)	Online Resources	Support for individualized instruction with practice in essential content.
Online Student Edition with Audio	Online Resources	Provides learners with multiple-modality access to science concepts and information.
Interactive Digital Lessons and Virtual Labs	Online Resources	Provides individualized learning experiences. Lessons make content accessible through simulations, animations, videos, audio, and integrated assessment.

Differentiated Instruction
English Language Learners

Choose from these instructional strategies to meet the needs of English language learners. Suggestions are provided for adapting the activity for three proficiency levels. Point-of-use strategies also appear within unit lessons.

☑ Unit Vocabulary

Lesson 1	Lesson 2	Lesson 4
rotate	moon phases	solar system
axis		planet
orbit		
constellation		

Vocabulary Cards are provided in Online Resources.

Vocabulary Activity

True or False?

Present statements about the vocabulary words. Students will identify whether the statements are true or false. Statements may be presented in different ways:

- Draw or point to pictures.
- Say statements.
- Write statements.

Beginning	Intermediate	Advanced
Draw or point to pictures in the book as you say statements about the vocabulary words. For example, say *"This is a planet,"* as you point to a planet (or something else). Have students decide whether the statement is true or false. Ask students to correct the false statements by using words or pointing to accurate pictures.	Say statements about the vocabulary words, such as *"Our solar system has two planets,"* or *"The axis is an imaginary line through Earth."* Have students decide whether each statement is true or false. Elicit corrections for the false statements. For example: *Our solar system has eight planets.*	Put students into pairs and have them write statements about the vocabulary words. Students should write both true and false statements. Put pairs into groups of four and have students read their statements aloud and have group members identify whether each statement is true or false. Require students to correct the false statements.

☑ Model Concepts

Our Solar System

Pair students or organize them into small groups. Provide groups with an illustration of the solar system that shows the sun and the eight planets. Alternatively, have students draw a solar system diagram. Students will use the diagrams to identify, describe, and compare the sun and planets in the solar system.

Beginning	Intermediate	Advanced
Have students name the sun and each planet. Assist them in writing labels for each space object. List adjectives on the board, such as *big, small, hot, gas giant, rings,* and *rocky.* Have students discuss the sun and planets, using the adjectives. Provide sentence frames for discussion: *This is _____. It is _____.*	Have students name the sun and each planet. Require them to label each space object. Record as students brainstorm a list of adjectives that describe the sun and planets. Model comparing two or more planets using comparative and superlative adjectives. Then have students use the list of adjectives as they describe where the sun and planets are, what they are like, and how they are the same or different.	Have students name the sun and each planet. Require them to label each space object. Then have students discuss the sun and planets by describing where they are, what they are like, and how they are similar or different. Ask students to write down their descriptions and comparisons as they talk. Then assign each group one solar system object, and have group members collaborate to write a detailed description of that space object and present it to the class.

☑ Model Inquiry Skills

Use Models

Provide students with three balls of different sizes, such as a tennis ball, a beach ball, and a table tennis ball, to represent Earth, the sun, and the moon. Students will use the balls to discuss and model the movements of Earth, the sun, and the moon in space.

Beginning	Intermediate	Advanced
Tell students that the balls represent Earth, the sun, and the moon. Have students match the balls to a picture of the object each represents. Direct students to use the balls to model the rotation and revolution of Earth and the moon. Provide the following sentence frame to describe each movement: *The _____ travels around the _____. _____ rotates, or spins, on its axis.*	Tell students that the balls represent Earth, the sun, and the moon. Have students use words to explain which ball represents each space object. Direct students to describe the sun, Earth, and the moon and model their movements in space. Provide these sentence frames for students to use: *The _____ is/ has _____. The _____ is bigger / smaller / hotter than the _____. The _____ orbits the _____.*	Present students with the three balls. Ask three volunteers to each choose a ball, tell what it represents, and explain why. Then have students use the balls to model the movements of the three objects in space. Direct students to diagram movements of these bodies and write extended captions that describe the movements. Have them display their diagram and explain the movement shown to the class.

Earth and Space

I Wonder Why

Use the images and the question to stimulate interest in the unit topic. Ask students to share what they know about our solar system and space exploration. Students may be familiar with tools scientists use to gather information about space, including different types of telescopes, space probes, space shuttles, and the International Space Station. Tell students that the large image shows a control room at the Johnson Space Center in Houston, Texas. The crewed missions leading up to the moon landings, shown in the inset, were monitored from rooms such as this one.

Here's Why

Have students turn the page and read the response to the question. You may wish to share the following background with students.

More About...

Johnson Space Center

Johnson Space Center (JSC) is the training base for United States astronauts and the site of Mission Control, where crewed space flights are monitored. Operations at JSC include testing of spacecraft systems, development of experiments to be carried out on space flights, scientific engineering and medical research that supports how astronauts function in space, selection and training of astronauts from the United States and space-station partner nations, and operation of human space flights.

UNIT 6

Earth and Space

Big Idea

Objects in space including Earth and its moon move in regular observable patterns.

I Wonder Why

People have studied space for hundreds of years. How has modern space exploration changed our lives? *Turn the page to find out.*

295

Professional Development) **Science Background**

Use the keywords to access

- Professional Development from **The NSTA Learning Center**
- **SciLinks** for additional online content appropriate for students and teachers
- Teacher Science Background in the back of this Teacher Edition and in the Planning Guide

Keywords

exploring space

solar system

SCI LINKS.
THE WORLD'S A CLICK AWAY

Here's Why Space technology has led to many discoveries about our universe. In addition, technology originally invented to explore space has solved many problems here on Earth.

In this unit, you will explore the Big Idea, the Essential Questions, and the Investigations on the Inquiry Flipchart.

Levels of Inquiry Key ■ DIRECTED ■ GUIDED ■ INDEPENDENT

Track Your Progress

Big Idea Objects in space including Earth and its moon move in regular observable patterns.

Essential Questions

Now I Get the Big Idea!

Science Notebook
Before you begin each lesson, be sure to write your thoughts about the Essential Question.

Go Digital

For a complete digital curriculum and resources that provide full coverage of the objectives for this unit, see the Online Resources for this program.

Big Idea and Essential Questions

▶ **Big Idea** Objects in space including Earth and its moon move in regular observable patterns.

Post the Unit Big Idea on the board. Have students read the Essential Questions, which are also the titles of the lessons in this unit.

- Discuss how the Essential Questions can help them focus on the Big Idea.

- Have students read the Big Idea statement. The statement describes the main science concept they will be learning.

- Have students predict other ideas that will be taught in the lessons based on the titles, or have them give examples of pictures they expect to see.

Once they have completed all the lessons, they should have a better understanding of the Big Idea.

▶ **Essential Questions** You may use the following Science Notebook strategy for working with the Essential Questions before students begin the unit or lessons in the unit.

- Strategies for revisiting the Big Idea and Essential Questions are provided in Enduring Understandings on page 345A.

📓 Notebook ▶ Science Notebook

- Have students copy the Essential Questions into their Science Notebooks. Suggest they leave writing lines between questions.

- Ask students to write responses to the Essential Questions. Urge students not to worry about whether their responses are correct. They should expect their ideas to change as they work in the unit. Comment that students will be able to review and revise their answers to the Essential Questions at the end of the unit.

- Tips and strategies for using Science Notebooks are provided throughout this unit, in the Planning Guide, and in Online Resources.

Big Idea and Essential Questions **296**

Options for Inquiry

FLIPCHART P. 31

Students can conduct these optional investigations at any time before, during, or in response to the lesson in the Student Edition.

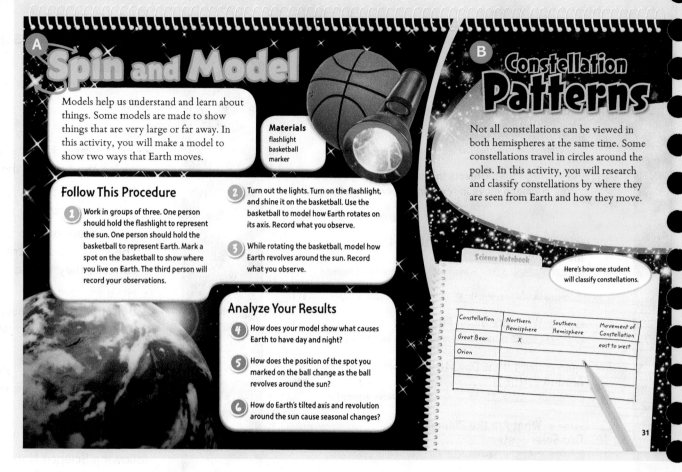

A Spin and Model

Models help us understand and learn about things. Some models are made to show things that are very large or far away. In this activity, you will make a model to show two ways that Earth moves.

Materials
flashlight
basketball
marker

Follow This Procedure

1. Work in groups of three. One person should hold the flashlight to represent the sun. One person should hold the basketball to represent Earth. Mark a spot on the basketball to show where you live on Earth. The third person will record your observations.

2. Turn out the lights. Turn on the flashlight, and shine it on the basketball. Use the basketball to model how Earth rotates on its axis. Record what you observe.

3. While rotating the basketball, model how Earth revolves around the sun. Record what you observe.

Analyze Your Results

4. How does your model show what causes Earth to have day and night?

5. How does the position of the spot you marked on the ball change as the ball revolves around the sun?

6. How do Earth's tilted axis and revolution around the sun cause seasonal changes?

B Constellation Patterns

Not all constellations can be viewed in both hemispheres at the same time. Some constellations travel in circles around the poles. In this activity, you will research and classify constellations by where they are seen from Earth and how they move.

Science Notebook

Here's how one student will classify constellations.

Constellation	Northern Hemisphere	Southern Hemisphere	Movement of Constellation
Great Bear	X		
Orion			east to west

31

Directed Inquiry

A Spin and Model

🕐 15–20 minutes
👥 small groups

Prep and Planning Tips

Before starting, mark a spot on the basketball to represent where you are on Earth. You may also want to mark an axis.

Expected Results

Rotation: Students should find that the side of the basketball facing the flashlight is always illuminated. The side facing away from the flashlight is never illuminated. As Earth spins on its axis, different areas of Earth move into and pass through the sunlit zone. This represents day. As an area passes out of the sunlit zone, it is no longer illuminated, and it is night.

Revolution: Students should note that Earth keeps rotating as it revolves around the sun. If students keep the axis tilted, they should see that the amount of time an area spends in daylight varies as Earth revolves. This variation, which is most evident near the poles, is what causes seasonal changes. Areas at the equator have 12 hours of daylight and 12 hours of darkness year-round.

Independent Inquiry

B Constellation Patterns

🕐 30–40 minutes
👥 small groups

Prep and Planning Tips

See the Planning for Inquiry page for more information. Show students a globe and point out the Northern and Southern Hemispheres, and the North and South Poles. Make sure students understand that people in the different hemispheres see different constellations because of their location on Earth.

Science Notebook

Students can use the Science Notebook page shown on the Flipchart as a model for research. Encourage students to use an online encyclopedia or nonfiction books from the school library to research several constellations. The NASA website is a good source for constellations and their position in the night sky.

Lesson 1

Essential Question

How Do the Sun, Earth, and Moon Interact?

Engage Your Brain!

Find the answer to the following question in this lesson and record it here.

Why is only part of Earth's surface visible?

Only the part of Earth's surface that is facing the sun is visible and has daytime. The part that is not visible is facing away from the sun and has nighttime.

Active Reading

Lesson Vocabulary

List the terms. As you learn about each one, make notes in the Interactive Glossary.

rotate

axis

orbit

constellation

Cause and Effect

Some ideas in this lesson are connected by a cause-and-effect relationship. Why something happens is a cause. What happens as a result of something else is an effect. Active readers look for effects by asking themselves, What happened? They look for causes by asking, Why did it happen?

297

Go Digital

An interactive digital lesson is available in Online Resources. It is suitable for individuals, small groups, or it may be projected or used on an interactive white board.

---

1 Engage/Explore

Objectives

- Describe the motions of Earth, the moon, and the sun in space.
- Explain how the rotation of Earth causes day and night.
- Recognize that the seasons result from the tilt and orbit of Earth around the sun.
- Identify historical contributions to the understanding of the Earth-moon-sun system.

Engage Your Brain!

Have students brainstorm answers to the question, *Why is only part of Earth's surface visible?* Record their responses on the board. Suggest that students think about how the moon appears throughout the month, and compare its changing shape to what they see here.

Remind students to record their final answer to the question when they find it on the first two pages of this lesson.

Active Reading   Annotations

Remind students that active readers "make texts their own" by annotating them with notes and marks that help with comprehension. Encourage students to use pencil, not pen, to make annotations and to feel free to change their annotations as they read. The goal of annotation is to help students remember what they have read.

Vocabulary and Interactive Glossary

Remind students to find and list the yellow highlighted terms from the lesson. As they proceed through the lesson and learn about the terms, they should add notes, drawings, or sentences in the extra spaces provided in the Interactive Glossary.

Lesson 1   **297**

2 Explain

Notebook ▸ Generate Ideas

Read the main heading on this page aloud and then ask: **How do night and day look different?** Prompt students with questions about what the sky looks like during the day as opposed to at night, or what they can see in the daytime sky that they cannot see in the night sky.

Active Reading

Remind students that to find an effect, active readers ask themselves, What happened? To find a cause, active readers ask, Why did it happen?

Develop Science Concepts

Have everyone stand near their seats and face in the same direction. Ask a volunteer to describe what they see. Then have students slowly turn in place to face the opposite direction. Ask several volunteers to describe what they see. **Why did you see different things at different times?** We were facing different directions. Explain that the same principle applies to us on Earth. As Earth rotates, or turns, we face different directions so we see different things in space. When the side of Earth we are on faces the sun, the sky is bright. When the side of Earth we are on faces away from the sun, the sky is dark.

Do the Math!

Use and Represent Numbers

Ask: **Which operation should you use to solve these problems?** subtraction

Remind students that there are 60 minutes in one hour. To subtract minutes, students must first regroup one hour as 60 minutes.

Night and Day

How can it be morning where you live and be nighttime in India at the same time? You cannot feel it, but Earth moves in space.

Active Reading As you read this page, draw one line under a cause of night and day. Draw two lines under an effect of night and day.

People once thought that the sun moved around Earth. After all, the sun seems to rise, to move across the sky, and to set each day. Today we know what makes it seem like the sun moves around Earth. Earth **rotates**, or turns like a top. Earth rotates around an imaginary line, called an **axis**. Earth's axis runs through it from the North Pole to the South Pole. Once every 24 hours, or once a day, Earth rotates about its axis.

Earth's rotation causes day and night. As it rotates, one side of Earth faces the sun. This part of Earth has daytime. The other side of Earth faces away from the sun and has nighttime. As Earth's rotation continues, parts of Earth cycle between day and night.

Each planet rotates at a different rate, so the length of a day is different. For example, Venus rotates so slowly that one day on Venus is equal to 225 days on Earth!

Do the Math!
Use and Represent Numbers

Find the difference between a day on Earth and a day on other planets.
(1 Earth day = 24 hours)

Length of Day:

Mercury: 59 Earth days

58 days
_____

Jupiter: 9 Earth hours, 55 minutes

14 hours, 5 minutes
_____

Neptune: 16 Earth hours, 6 minutes

7 hours, 54 minutes
_____

298

English Language Learners

Multiple-Meaning Word: Face
Students are probably most familiar with *face* used as a noun referring to the front of the head. Explain that *face* is also a verb that means turned in a certain direction. Have one student stand and look toward the board.

Say: [student's name] is facing the board. Have the student turn around. Say: Now [student's name] is facing the class. Have students use the word *facing* in sentences regarding objects in the room that are facing each other, and a side of Earth always facing the sun.

Night

Day

Earth rotates on its axis from west to east. As a result, the sun appears to rise in the east and set in the west.

299

Differentiation — Leveled Questions

Extra Support

China is on the opposite side of Earth from the United States. Suppose during the day you call your friend in China. Will it also be day in China? Why? No, when it is daytime on one side of Earth, it is night on the other side.

Challenge

How would night and day be different if Earth did not rotate? Half of Earth would always face the sun and would always have day, while half of Earth would always face away from the sun and would always have night.

Develop Science Vocabulary

rotates Write these sentences on the board, underlining the words *rotate* and *rotation*: *Today we know that Earth rotates, or turns. This rotation, or turning about its axis, causes day and night.* Point out that *rotates* is a verb; *rotation* is a noun. Spin a world globe to model Earth's rotation. **What other things rotate?** Sample answer: merry-go-rounds, fans, windmills

axis Point to the rod that runs up the center of the globe. Say that Earth's axis is in this position, but emphasize that Earth's axis is imaginary. There isn't really a rod or pole through the center of Earth.

Develop Inquiry Skills

HYPOTHESIZE **What would happen if Earth were to rotate more slowly on its axis?** Days and nights would be longer.

Interpret Visuals

Have students look at the illustration on this page.

Why is one half of Earth lit? It is facing the sun, so the sun is shining on it.

Why is the other half of Earth dark? That half of Earth is facing away from the sun, so there is no light on it.

Where is Earth's axis? through its center

Notebook Summarize Ideas

Tell students to think about what causes day and night. Have them summarize the cause in writing.

2 Explain (continued)

Notebook ▶ Generate Ideas

Have a student read the main head on this page aloud. Then ask: **What is a system?** A system is a group of separate things that work together as a whole. **Challenge students to brainstorm other things that work as a system.** Sample answer: a car engine, the human body **Tell students they will learn how the sun, Earth, and the moon work together as a system.**

Active Reading

Remind students that the main idea may be stated in the first sentence, or it may be stated elsewhere. To find a main idea, active readers ask, What is this paragraph mostly about?

Develop Science Vocabulary

orbit Ask a student to state the definition of *orbit* in his or her own words. Then have two volunteers model an orbit for the rest of the class. Direct one student to stand still while the second walks in a circle around him or her.

Develop Inquiry Skills

USE MODELS Use a tethered ball to describe the force of gravity. Hold the tether as you swing the ball in circles. Tell students you are the sun and the ball is Earth.

What does the string represent? gravity Discuss that the string is the force holding the ball in place and forcing it to move in circles instead of flying off to the edge of the room. Explain that this is like the gravitational force of the sun that keeps Earth circling around it. Earth's gravity also acts on the sun. The sun doesn't move because it is much larger than Earth.

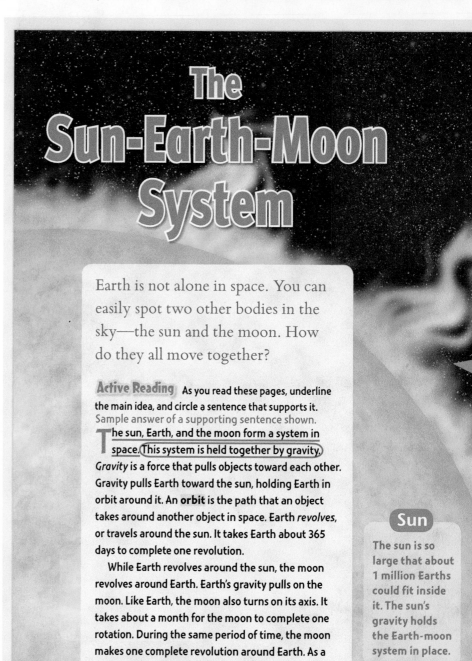

The Sun-Earth-Moon System

Earth is not alone in space. You can easily spot two other bodies in the sky—the sun and the moon. How do they all move together?

Active Reading As you read these pages, underline the main idea, and circle a sentence that supports it. Sample answer of a supporting sentence shown. The sun, Earth, and the moon form a system in space. This system is held together by gravity. *Gravity* is a force that pulls objects toward each other. Gravity pulls Earth toward the sun, holding Earth in orbit around it. An **orbit** is the path that an object takes around another object in space. Earth *revolves*, or travels around the sun. It takes Earth about 365 days to complete one revolution.

While Earth revolves around the sun, the moon revolves around Earth. Earth's gravity pulls on the moon. Like Earth, the moon also turns on its axis. It takes about a month for the moon to complete one rotation. During the same period of time, the moon makes one complete revolution around Earth. As a result, the same side of the moon always faces Earth.

Sun

The sun is so large that about 1 million Earths could fit inside it. The sun's gravity holds the Earth-moon system in place.

300

👥 Differentiation — Leveled Questions

Extra Support

Which force pulls on Earth and holds it in orbit around the sun? the sun's gravity Which force holds the moon in orbit around Earth? Earth's gravity

Challenge

Why does the sun have a much greater force of gravity than Earth? The size (mass) of a body affects the amount of gravitational force it exerts. The sun's gravity is greater because it is a much larger (more massive) body.

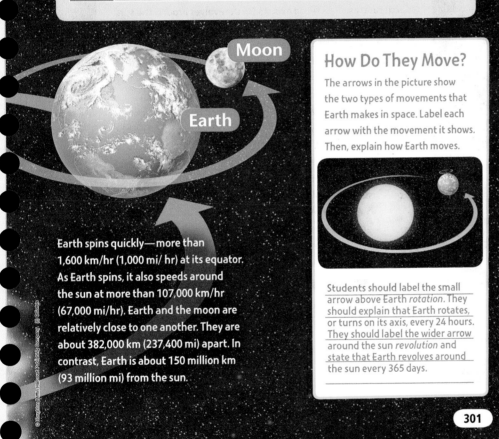

The sun, the moon, and Earth all have distinct characteristics. The sun has the largest diameter of all bodies in the solar system. An object's *diameter* is the distance from one side, through its center, to the other side.

	Makeup	Diameter	Age
Sun	hot, glowing gases; mostly helium and hydrogen	1,391,000 km (864,400 mi)	about 4.6 billion years old
Earth	rocky surface with large oceans; thick atmosphere of nitrogen and oxygen; life forms	12,756 km (7,926 mi)	about 4.5 billion years old
Moon	rocky surface; no atmosphere or water; extreme cold and heat; no known life forms	3,475 km (2,159 mi)	at least 4.5 billion years old

Moon

Earth

Earth spins quickly—more than 1,600 km/hr (1,000 mi/ hr) at its equator. As Earth spins, it also speeds around the sun at more than 107,000 km/hr (67,000 mi/hr). Earth and the moon are relatively close to one another. They are about 382,000 km (237,400 mi) apart. In contrast, Earth is about 150 million km (93 million mi) from the sun.

How Do They Move?

The arrows in the picture show the two types of movements that Earth makes in space. Label each arrow with the movement it shows. Then, explain how Earth moves.

Students should label the small arrow above Earth *rotation*. They should explain that Earth rotates, or turns on its axis, every 24 hours. They should label the wider arrow around the sun *revolution* and state that Earth revolves around the sun every 365 days.

301

Interpret Visuals

Draw students' attention to the table on this page. **How is Earth like the moon?** They both have rocky surfaces. **How is Earth different from the moon?** Earth has oceans and a thick atmosphere. The moon has no known liquid water and no atmosphere.

Based on diameter, what is the order from largest to smallest of the three bodies shown in the table? sun, Earth, moon Remind students that diameter measures the circumference of an object.

Develop Science Concepts

Remind students that both Earth and the moon move in two ways at the same time. **What are the two types of movements of Earth and the moon?** They rotate and they revolve.

What do Earth and the moon revolve around? Earth revolves around the sun. The moon revolves around Earth.

Ask three student volunteers to model the rotation and revolution of Earth and the moon in the sun-Earth-moon system. Then have students complete the Interactivity.

Notebook **Summarize Ideas**

Ask students to write a summary of the main idea in their own words. Students should include that the sun's gravity holds Earth in orbit around it, as Earth's gravity holds the moon in orbit. Earth and the moon travel together as they revolve around the sun.

English Language Learners

Understand Revolve/Revolution
Tell students that the suffix *-tion* changes a verb into a noun. It means the condition of doing the action named by the verb.

Explain that *revolve* is a verb that describes a motion in which one object travels in a path around another, and that *revolution* is the noun that names that motion. Have students pronounce the words. Then have each student write original sentences using the pairs of words.

2 Explain (continued)

Notebook Generate Ideas

Read the main title on the page aloud. Then have students look at the photos on the spread that show the seasons. **What are seasons?** The seasons are distinct times of year often marked by changes in the weather patterns of a place. **How are seasons different from each other?** Sample answer: Some seasons are warm and others are cold. Some might be rainy while others are dry. The trees and other vegetation can change during different seasons.

Active Reading

Remind students that to find an effect, active readers ask themselves, What happened? To find a cause, active readers ask, Why did it happen?

Develop Inquiry Skills

USE MODELS **What causes the seasons?** Earth's tilt on its axis as it revolves around the sun Model sunlight shining on Earth's surface in different seasons with a flashlight and a globe. Have one student point the beam at the globe. Tilt the northern half of the globe toward the beam, and have students observe how the beam strikes the globe's surface. They should notice the light beam being concentrated over a relatively small area. Tell students this represents summer in the Northern Hemisphere. Then point the southern half of the globe toward the beam, and again have students observe how the beam strikes the northern half of the globe's surface. They should notice light being spread over a relatively large area. Tell students this represents winter in the Northern Hemisphere. **Based on your observations, why is winter colder than summer?** Less direct sunlight in winter means temperatures are lower.

Seasons

When it is summer in the United States, it is winter in Chile. How can two places have a different season at the same time of year?

Active Reading As you read this page, underline the cause of the seasons.

Earth rotates on its tilted axis. As Earth revolves around the sun, the direction of its tilted axis doesn't change. The tilt of Earth's axis and its orbit cause the seasons.

Earth is divided into halves called *hemispheres*. The Northern Hemisphere extends from the equator to the North Pole. The Southern Hemisphere extends from the equator to the South Pole. In June, the Northern Hemisphere is tilted toward the sun and gets more direct rays of sunlight. It has more hours of daylight and warmer weather. It is summer there.

In June, in the Southern Hemisphere, the opposite season takes place. Why? The Southern Hemisphere is tilted away from the sun and gets less direct sunlight. It has fewer hours of daylight and cooler weather. It is winter there.

In December, the Northern Hemisphere is tilted away from the sun. As a result, it is winter there. At the same time, the Southern Hemisphere is tilted toward the sun and has summer.

Home Sweet Home

Which season is it where you live? Draw a picture of the sun and Earth in the correct positions to show the season. Include the tilt of Earth's axis in your picture.

Check students' pictures for accuracy.

302

 ### Differentiation — Leveled Questions

Extra Support

Why is it warmer where you live in summer than in winter? In summer the Northern Hemisphere where I live is tilted toward the sun and gets more direct sunlight. In winter, it is tilted away from the sun and gets less direct sunlight.

Challenge

How would seasons be different if Earth's axis were not tilted? There would not be seasons as we know them. Temperatures would generally stay the same in each part of Earth all year.

Seasons in the Northern Hemisphere

When the Northern Hemisphere is tilted away from the sun, that part of Earth has winter. When the Northern Hemisphere is tilted toward the sun, it has summer.

Winter

Fall

Spring

Summer

303

Interpret Visuals

Before students complete the Interactivity on the facing page, have them look carefully at the diagram of the seasons on this page. **In which direction does Earth's Northern Hemisphere point when it is winter there?** away from the sun **In which direction does the Northern Hemisphere point when it is summer there?** toward the sun Continue by having students describe the orientation of Earth when it is either spring or fall in the Northern Hemisphere. The axis is neither pointed toward the sun nor away from it.

After students understand the correlation between Earth's tilt and seasons, have them complete the Interactivity.

⁄⁄ Misconception Alert ⁄⁄

Students often think that Earth's axis changes its orientation as it revolves around the sun. Emphasize that the axis always points in the same direction. It is oriented neither toward nor away from the sun because of Earth's position in its orbit.

Have students refer to the Seasons in the Northern Hemisphere diagram on this page. It might help to use a globe to model the Earth's axis for students.

Develop Inquiry Skills

COMPARE **How are summer and winter different where you live?** Sample answer: Summer is hot and dry. There are lots of flowers and birds. Winter is cold and rainy. Most trees do not have leaves.

Notebook ▸ Summarize Ideas

Students can summarize in writing or orally the effect on Earth when Earth's Northern Hemisphere points toward the sun.

Lesson 1   **303**

2 Explain (continued)

 Generate Ideas

Have a student read the main title aloud for the class. **What do you see when you look up at the night sky?** Sample answer: stars, the moon **Have you ever thought some of the stars form a picture?** It is likely that some students will say they have. Tell students that in ancient times, astronomers saw many patterns in the way stars were arranged in the sky. We still recognize them today.

Active Reading

Remind students that detail sentences give examples, features, characteristics, or facts about a topic. Active readers stay focused on the topic when they ask, What fact or information does this sentence add to the topic?

Develop Science Concepts

Ask students to describe any constellations they have observed in the night sky.

Why do you think you can see some constellations only during certain times of the year? Earth travels in an orbit around the sun, so the positions of the constellations in the night sky, as viewed from Earth, change from season to season.

Why do you think people in the Southern Hemisphere see some different constellations than people in the Northern Hemisphere do? People who live in different hemispheres of Earth see different parts of the sky.

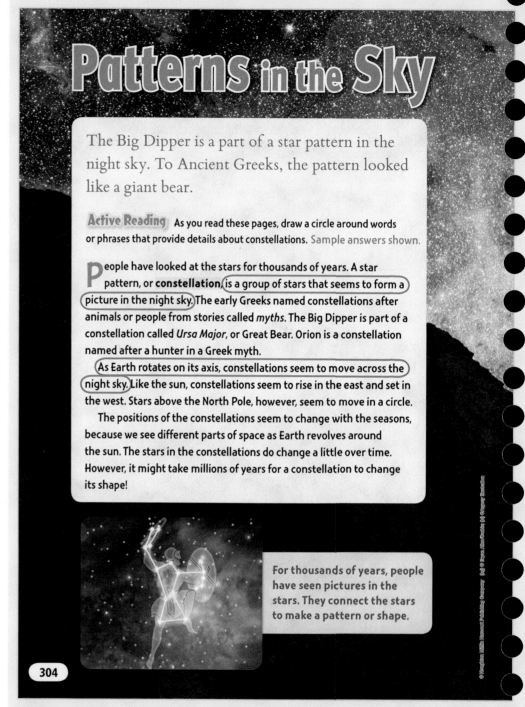

Patterns in the Sky

The Big Dipper is a part of a star pattern in the night sky. To Ancient Greeks, the pattern looked like a giant bear.

Active Reading As you read these pages, draw a circle around words or phrases that provide details about constellations. Sample answers shown.

People have looked at the stars for thousands of years. A star pattern, or **constellation**, (is a group of stars that seems to form a picture in the night sky.) The early Greeks named constellations after animals or people from stories called *myths*. The Big Dipper is part of a constellation called *Ursa Major*, or Great Bear. Orion is a constellation named after a hunter in a Greek myth.

(As Earth rotates on its axis, constellations seem to move across the night sky.) Like the sun, constellations seem to rise in the east and set in the west. Stars above the North Pole, however, seem to move in a circle.

The positions of the constellations seem to change with the seasons, because we see different parts of space as Earth revolves around the sun. The stars in the constellations do change a little over time. However, it might take millions of years for a constellation to change its shape!

For thousands of years, people have seen pictures in the stars. They connect the stars to make a pattern or shape.

 304

Differentiation — Leveled Questions

Extra Support

How did the constellations get their names? Long ago, people looked up at the night sky and saw star patterns that looked like people, animals, or objects. People named these patterns, which became the constellations.

Challenge

Will the constellations we see today always look the same? Explain. No. Over long periods of time, stars in the constellations will move, which will change the shape of the constellations as we know them today.

These pictures show stars seen from the same location during summer (at left) and winter (at right). The constellations seem to change their places in the sky.

Connect the Stars

Connect the stars to draw a constellation. Use all or some of the stars. What is the name of your constellation?

Answers will vary. Encourage students to be creative.

305

Develop Science Vocabulary

constellation Write the term *constellation* on the board and underline the letters *stella*. Tell students this comes from the Latin word that means "star." *Constellation* comes from a Latin word that means "set with stars."

Develop Inquiry Skills

DRAW CONCLUSIONS Tell students that the constellations Canis Major (the Great Dog) and Canis Minor (the Little Dog) seem to follow the constellation Orion (the Hunter) across the sky. Ask: **Which Earth movement would make constellations seem to move across the sky over the course of one night?** Earth's rotation on its axis

Interpret Visuals

Before students complete the Interactivity, allow them to view pictures of constellations that have images of what they are supposed to represent superimposed on top of them. Encourage students to be creative in making their own constellations in the Connect the Stars Interactivity.

Notebook ⮞ **Summarize Ideas**

Ask students to summarize what they have learned by listing three important details about constellations. Students can provide their summaries orally or in writing.

Writing Connections

Names of the Constellations
Ask students to choose a constellation, such as Orion, Ursa Major, Canis Major, or one of the zodiac constellations, such as Taurus the Bull or Aquarius the Water Bearer. Have students research the constellation and write a one-page paper describing the story behind the constellation's name.

2 Explain (continued)

 Generate Ideas

Read the main title, "Our Place in Space," aloud to the class. Have students look at the photos and captions on these two pages. Then ask students to predict what they will read about here.

Develop Science Concepts

Remind students that astronomers once thought that Earth was at the center of the universe. **What evidence did they use to come to this conclusion?** People saw the sun, moon, planets, and stars move from east to west across the sky, so they thought Earth was at the center and these objects moved around it.

How did astronomers determine that this idea was wrong? Sample answer: They found new evidence to prove that Earth and the other planets revolve around the sun.

▨ Misconception Alert ▨

Students often think that early astronomers, such as Copernicus and Galileo, developed an accurate model of the universe because they successfully refuted the Earth-centered model. Note that Copernicus and Galileo were right about the sun standing at the center of the solar system. However, it took many more years of observations and new technology to realize that our solar system is just a tiny part of an even larger system called the Milky Way Galaxy.

Why It Matters

Our Place in Space

At one time, people thought Earth was the center of the universe. How did we learn that this isn't true?

Long ago, astronomers believed Earth was the center of the universe. Daily observations seemed to confirm this belief. When people looked at the sky, they saw the sun, the moon, planets, and stars in motion. Naturally, they concluded that Earth was at the center of the universe. It took hundreds of years, new technology, and new observations for this idea to change.

In the 1500s, a Polish astronomer named Nicolaus Copernicus designed a new *model*, or system, of the universe. Based on new observations about the motion of the planets, he suggested that Earth and the planets revolved around the sun. Then, in the 1600s, scientists gathered more evidence to support this sun-centered model of the solar system.

Using a telescope he made, Galileo Galilei was the first to see moons orbiting Jupiter. His observation showed that all objects in space did not orbit Earth. Around this time, Johannes Kepler correctly described the shape of the planets' orbits around the sun. His calculations showed that the planets revolved around the sun in elliptical [ee•LIP•tih•kuhl] orbits. All these scientists' observations changed our idea about Earth's place in space.

Earth

306

 Differentiation — Leveled Questions

Extra Support

Who was among the first astronomers to design a model in which Earth and the other planets revolved around the sun? Copernicus Which astronomer was the first to make observations with a telescope? Galileo

Challenge

Why did some astronomers challenge the model that had the sun and planets revolving around Earth? They found new evidence that contradicted that model. They used this evidence to make and support a new model.

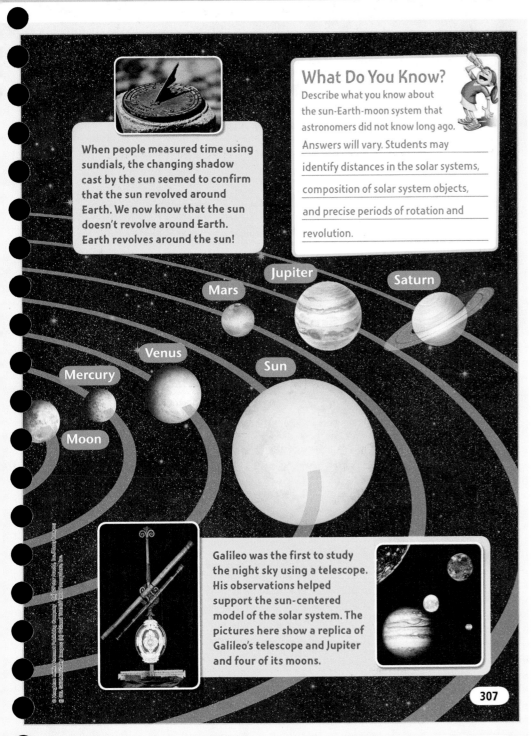

When people measured time using sundials, the changing shadow cast by the sun seemed to confirm that the sun revolved around Earth. We now know that the sun doesn't revolve around Earth. Earth revolves around the sun!

What Do You Know?

Describe what you know about the sun-Earth-moon system that astronomers did not know long ago. Answers will vary. Students may identify distances in the solar systems, composition of solar system objects, and precise periods of rotation and revolution.

Jupiter

Saturn

Mars

Venus

Sun

Mercury

Moon

Galileo was the first to study the night sky using a telescope. His observations helped support the sun-centered model of the solar system. The pictures here show a replica of Galileo's telescope and Jupiter and four of its moons.

307

 Math Connection

Compare Diameters Earth's moon is larger than most moons in the solar system, but where does it fall among the solar system's largest moons? Have students put the Galilean moons and Earth's moon in decreasing size order based on diameter.

Callisto: 4,806 km; Europa: 3,130 km; Ganymede: 5,268 km; Io: 3,600 km; Earth's moon: 3,474 km

Then have students write a statement comparing the size of Earth's moon to the sizes of the Galilean moons.

Develop Science Concepts

Which evidence did astronomers use to support a sun-centered model of the solar system? Copernicus made a model based on his observations of the motion of the planets; Galileo used a telescope and discovered that all objects in space did not orbit Earth; Kepler did calculations that showed the planets revolve around the sun in elliptical orbits.

Interpret Visuals

Reinforce that the large diagram shown on these pages is a representation of the Earth-centered model of the solar system. This diagram shows the order of the planets as astronomers interpreted them from the observations they made. Point out that in our current model, Earth and its moon have traded places with the sun.

Have students use this information as well as the concepts they have learned throughout the lesson to craft their answers to the Interactivity.

Develop Inquiry Skills

DRAW CONCLUSIONS **What is needed before long-held ideas in science can change?** New observations and investigations must present new evidence that supports new ideas.

Notebook **Summarize Ideas**

Have students think about the way the model of the solar system has changed in the past few hundred years. Invite them to summarize the main idea that states this change either orally or in writing.

3 Extend/Evaluate

Sum It Up!

- Before they begin, make sure students understand that they are to correct the blue part of each statement. Suggest that students draw a picture of how Earth moves in space to clarify their understanding of the lesson concepts.

- If students are still having difficulty changing the incorrect part of each statement to make it correct, suggest they circle the key vocabulary terms in each statement and look up the terms in the glossary.

- Have students use the Answer Key to check their answers when they are finished. Tell students to correct any wrong answers so they can use this page to study for tests. Make sure students ask for help with any concepts they still do not understand.

When you're done, use the answer key to check and revise your work.

Read the summary statements below. Each one is incorrect. Change the part of the summary in blue to make the statement correct.

Summarize

1. Day and night are caused by Earth's revolution around the sun.	Day and night are caused by Earth's rotation on its axis.
2. The discovery of moons around Jupiter proved that all objects in space revolve around Jupiter.	The discovery of moons around Jupiter proved that all objects in space do not revolve around Earth.
3. Earth's seasons are caused by Earth's revolution and rotation in space.	Earth's seasons are caused by Earth's revolution and the tilt of its axis.
4. During winter in the Northern Hemisphere, there are more hours of daylight and it is warmer.	During winter in the Northern Hemisphere, there are fewer hours of daylight and it is cooler.
5. When it is spring in the Northern Hemisphere, the season is summer in the Southern Hemisphere.	When it is spring in the Northern Hemisphere, the season is fall in the Southern Hemisphere.
6. Constellations appear to move across the night sky because of Earth's tilt on its axis.	Constellations appear to move across the night sky because of Earth's rotation.

Answer Key: 1. Day and night are caused by Earth's rotation on its axis. **2.** The discovery of moons around Jupiter proved that all objects in space do not revolve around Earth. **3.** Earth's seasons are caused by Earth's revolution and the tilt of its axis. **4.** During winter in the Northern Hemisphere, there are fewer hours of daylight and it is cooler. **5.** When it is spring in the Northern Hemisphere, the season is fall in the Southern Hemisphere. **6.** Constellations appear to move across the night sky because of Earth's rotation.

© Houghton Mifflin Harcourt Publishing Company

308

 **Brain Check**

Name_____

Word Play

1 Unscramble letters to fill in the blanks with the words from the box below. Use the hints to help you unscramble the letters.

1. X A S I   A X I S
   [Hint: an imaginary line through Earth]

2. T E R A O T   R O T A T E
   [Hint: Earth's spinning in space]

3. R I B O T   O R B I T
   [Hint: Earth's path in space]

4. L E O V R E V   R E V O L V E
   [Hint: Earth does this around the sun once a year.]

5. S T E L C O N A L I O N T   C O N S T E L L A T I O N
   [Hint: a pattern of stars in the night sky]

6. H M S I E E P R E H   H E M I S P H E R E
   [Hint: one half of Earth]

7. D O L E M   M O D E L
   [Hint: a representation of the sun-Earth-moon system]

8. N A S S E O   S E A S O N
   [Hint: a time of year with a particular type of weather]

model	revolve	orbit*	hemisphere
axis*	constellation*	rotate*	season

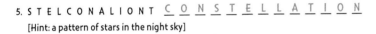

* Key Lesson Vocabulary

© Houghton Mifflin Harcourt Publishing Company

309

Answer Strategies

Word Play

1. If students are having difficulty unscrambling the letters, have them use the word bank and refer to the glossary to look up definitions. As a challenge, have students use each unscrambled word in a sentence that shows its meaning.

Assessment

Suggested Scoring Guide

You may wish to use this suggested guide for the Brain Check.

Item	Points
1	40 (5 points per item)
2	15
3	10
4	10
5	10
6	15
Total	100

Lesson Quiz

See Assessment Guide, p. AG 62.

3 Extend/Evaluate (continued)

Answer Strategies

Apply Concepts

2. Lead a class discussion about the ways Earth moves in space. Ask students to consider which movement Earth makes that causes day and night. Refer students who are having difficulty to the text and image on the second and third pages of this lesson.

3. Refer students to the second and third pages of this lesson, where rotation is defined and described. Ask students to think about why the sun seems to gradually disappear as a place on Earth rotates away from the sun.

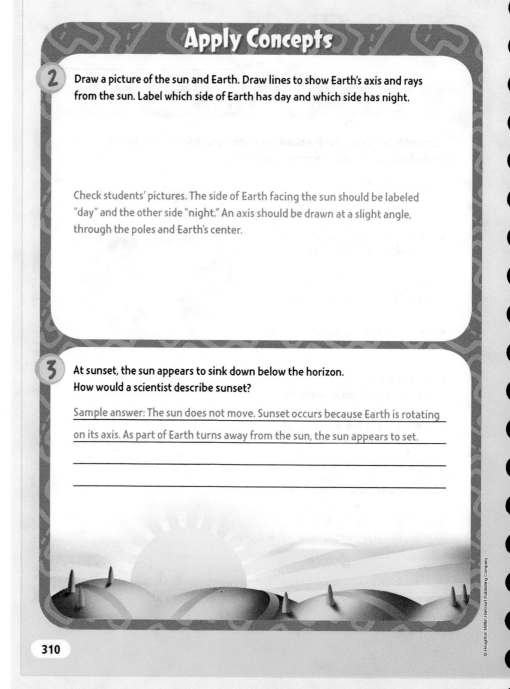

Apply Concepts

2 Draw a picture of the sun and Earth. Draw lines to show Earth's axis and rays from the sun. Label which side of Earth has day and which side has night.

Check students' pictures. The side of Earth facing the sun should be labeled "day" and the other side "night." An axis should be drawn at a slight angle, through the poles and Earth's center.

3 At sunset, the sun appears to sink down below the horizon. How would a scientist describe sunset?

Sample answer: The sun does not move. Sunset occurs because Earth is rotating on its axis. As part of Earth turns away from the sun, the sun appears to set.

310

Name _____

4 The constellation Orion is seen in the night sky during winter in the Northern Hemisphere. During summer, Orion cannot be seen. Why is Orion only seen during part of the year?

Earth revolves around the sun. Many constellations are

seasonal, because we can only see them when Earth is

in the right place in space.

_____

_____

_____

_____

5 Imagine you are going on a ride in a spacecraft next to Earth. Your trip takes one whole year. Describe Earth's tilt in the Northern Hemisphere during your trip. What happens as a result of the tilt?

Sample answer: Earth's Northern Hemisphere is tilted toward the sun for part of

the year. As Earth continues in its orbit around the sun, the Northern Hemisphere

is tilted away from the sun, causing seasonal changes.

_____

_____

311

Answer Strategies

Apply Concepts

4. Have students recall that a constellation is a pattern of stars in the night sky. Remind students that the star patterns seem to change their positions in the sky because of the way Earth moves in space. Ask students to consider what movement Earth makes that would cause star patterns to vary with the seasons. Students who have difficulty can review this concept on the eighth and ninth pages in this lesson.

5. Have students identify the Northern Hemisphere of Earth on the diagram. Then ask students to think about Earth's movements and how the orientation of the Northern Hemisphere changes with the seasons. Remind students that the tilt of Earth itself does not change. It is Earth's rotation around the sun in combination with its tilt that causes different parts of the planet to receive more or less direct sunlight at different times of the year.

3 Extend/Evaluate (continued)

Answer Strategies

Apply Concepts

6. Have students recall the contributions that Galileo made to the development of the sun-centered model of the solar system. If students need a refresher, have them go back and reread Why It Matters: Our Place in Space on the tenth and eleventh pages in this lesson.

Take It Home!

See *ScienceSaurus*® for more information about Earth and its moon. *ScienceSaurus* is a "mini-encyclopedia" students can use to find out more about unit topics. It contains numerous resources including concise content summaries, an almanac, many tables, charts, and graphs, history of science, and a glossary.

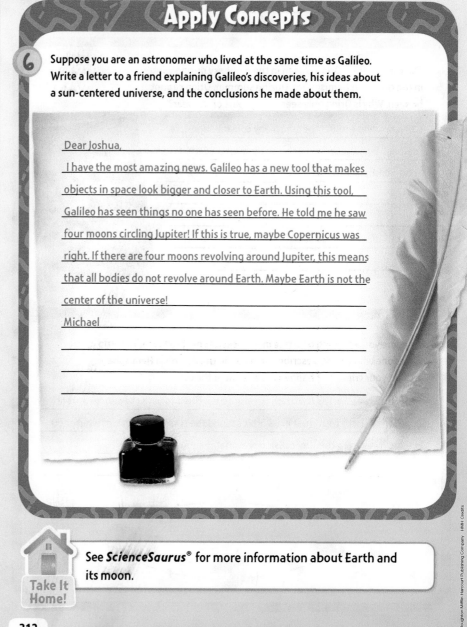

Apply Concepts

6 Suppose you are an astronomer who lived at the same time as Galileo. Write a letter to a friend explaining Galileo's discoveries, his ideas about a sun-centered universe, and the conclusions he made about them.

Dear Joshua,

I have the most amazing news. Galileo has a new tool that makes objects in space look bigger and closer to Earth. Using this tool, Galileo has seen things no one has seen before. He told me he saw four moons circling Jupiter! If this is true, maybe Copernicus was right. If there are four moons revolving around Jupiter, this means that all bodies do not revolve around Earth. Maybe Earth is not the center of the universe!

Michael

Take It Home!

See *ScienceSaurus*® for more information about Earth and its moon.

312

Make Connections

Art Connection

Draw Scenes of the Seasons

In most of North America, there are distinct seasons. Instruct students to divide a large piece of construction paper into four parts, one for each of the four seasons. In each part, students should draw the same object or scene during one of the four seasons. Together, the four parts should show typical seasonal changes and characteristics where you live.

Social Studies Connection

Draw Activities at Different Times of Day

Each day as Earth rotates, day changes to night and back again. Tell students to pinpoint several locations on a world map, labeling each with the time at that location. Then have students draw a small picture of something people are doing at that time of day or night in that part of the world. Encourage students to include at least four different locations in four different time zones on the map.

Math Connection

Make a Time Line

Students learned that astronomers once supported an Earth-centered model of the universe. Over time, new discoveries caused astronomers to change the model to put the sun at the solar system's center. Have students research and make a time line that shows the major scientific events that contributed to acceptance of a sun-centered solar system after centuries of erroneously believing it was Earth-centered. Students can work alone or with a partner.

Writing Connection

Make a Sky Calendar

Constellations can be seen on any clear night, but other objects can also be seen in the sky. Tell students to research what a person can see from your local area with an unaided eye or with a simple telescope at different times of the year. Students can then make a calendar that describes what can be seen, on what date and at what time of day or night, and where in the sky one should look to see the object or event. Students can include events, such as eclipses and meteor showers and objects, such as comets. They can also include any planets that are easy to spot, such as Venus, which is often visible as a bright "morning star" in late fall and winter, and as a shining "evening star" in spring and summer. Students can work in small groups.

People in Science

Objectives

- Describe the roles of scientists.
- Describe that scientists come from all backgrounds.
- Determine the role of technology in the work of scientists.

Notebook ▶ ### Generate Ideas

Ask students why they think climate is an important topic for scientists to study. Have students tell what they know about global climate change, which has become a controversial issue around the world. List students' responses on the board.

Background

- Milutin Milankovitch was an expert in mathematics, astronomy, and physics. He applied knowledge from all three disciplines to develop his ideas about the relationship between Earth's orbit and its climate.

- Milankovitch was a colleague of Alfred Wegener, the scientist who expanded on the theory of continental drift. Milankovitch's work helped Wegener develop his ideas.

- Maureen Raymo is a paleoclimatologist, or a scientist who studies ancient climates. Among her interests are the physical mechanisms that cause ice ages— the same topic that Milankovitch studied.

- Most of Raymo's work is based on data collected from deep-sea sediment.

- The American Geophysical Union is a professional organization of climate scientists. In 2010, the organization announced that 700 of its members would be speaking to the public about the seriousness of global climate change.

People in Science

Meet the Climate Scientists

Milutin Milankovitch

During an ice age, ice sheets cover much of Earth. Why do ice ages happen? Serbian scientist Milutin Milankovitch [mih•LOO•tin mih•LAHNG•koh•vich] spent his career trying to find out. Milankovitch learned that Earth's orbit changes in cycles lasting thousands of years. He determined that these changes affect the amount of sunlight reaching Earth. As a result, during cooler periods, ice ages occur. Today, data from the ocean floor supports Milankovitch's ideas. These climate patterns are called Milankovitch cycles in his honor.

The direction of Earth's axis changes over time as part of a cycle that lasts about 23,000 years. This change affects Earth's temperature.

Dr. Maureen Raymo

Dr. Maureen Raymo is an earth scientist. She studies how Earth's climate has changed over long periods of time. Like Milankovitch, Dr. Raymo studies the relationship between changes in Earth's orbit and climate. During an ice age, much of Earth's water is stored in glaciers. This affects sea level. Dr. Raymo has been able to find evidence of ancient changes in climate by studying rocks and sediment on the ocean floor. Through her research, she has been able to describe the sea level and water flow direction in ancient oceans.

313

Nature of Science

A climate scientist applies a wide range of scientific knowledge. Milankovitch applied principles of astronomy and physics, as well as his skills in mathematics, to develop his theories. In her climate studies, Maureen Raymo uses her knowledge of chemistry to track isotopes of carbon and oxygen in the ocean. Guide students in a discussion about scientific endeavors, such as developing artificial limbs and exploring space, that depend on several branches of knowledge. Record their ideas on the board.

The Road to a New Hypothesis

Use the information below to make a timeline of the events that led Milutin Milankovitch to develop his hypothesis.

1930 Milutin Milankovitch publishes his hypothesis. He bases it on improved methods of calculating differences in Earth's orbit, axis direction, and axis tilt.

1864 James Croll explains ice ages as a result of changes in Earth's axis and the shape of its orbit around the sun.

1960s Continued research shows that Milankovitch's hypothesis explains some climate trends.

1754 Jean le Rond d'Alembert calculates how the direction in which Earth's axis is pointed changes over time.

1824 J. A. Adhemar studies d'Alembert's ideas and suggests that the change in axis direction is responsible for ice ages.

Today Dr. Raymo finds evidence in rocks and sediment on the ocean floor that supports Milankovitch's hypothesis.

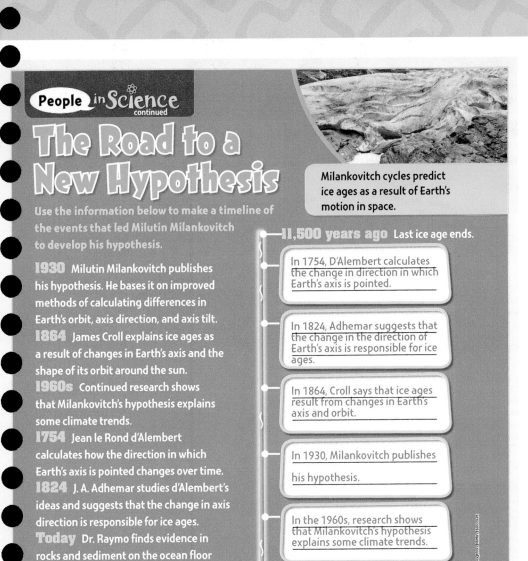

Milankovitch cycles predict ice ages as a result of Earth's motion in space.

11,500 years ago Last ice age ends.

In 1754, D'Alembert calculates the change in direction in which Earth's axis is pointed.

In 1824, Adhemar suggests that the change in the direction of Earth's axis is responsible for ice ages.

In 1864, Croll says that ice ages result from changes in Earth's axis and orbit.

In 1930, Milankovitch publishes his hypothesis.

In the 1960s, research shows that Milankovitch's hypothesis explains some climate trends.

Dr. Raymo finds evidence in rocks and sediment on the ocean floor that supports Milankovitch's hypothesis.

Think About It!

Where should the following event be placed on the timeline?

Scientists find data that conflict with Milankovitch's hypothesis, which falls into disfavor.

between 1930 and the1960s

314

Develop Science Concepts

Discuss the importance of scientists sharing their work with other scientists. For example, Milankovitch developed his theory by researching and applying more than 100 years of discoveries about Earth's movement in space. His work led to new discoveries by other scientists who came after him, including Maureen Raymo. **How do scientists share their work with their colleagues?** Sample answers: They publish their work in scientific journals; they share and discuss their ideas at scientific conferences.

Develop Inquiry Skills

DRAW CONCLUSIONS Point out to students that scientists did not begin to accept Milankovitch's ideas about ice ages until the 1960s. **Why do you think scientists were slow to accept Milankovitch's ideas?** Sample answer: His ideas could not be proven with simple observations. New evidence for his ideas was not discovered until the 1960s.

USE MODELS Discuss the different technologies used in weather and climate science. Ask students to list the technologies used to collect data, such as computers and remote cameras.

Notebook Summarize Ideas

Have students review the biographies of Milankovitch and Raymo and the timeline of important developments in climate science. Then have them summarize the work of climate scientists orally or in writing.

Writing Connection

Write a Report Explain that the study of climate involves large amounts of data that describe air temperature, air pressure, precipitation, and other conditions all over the world. Computers can quickly store, process, and perform calculations based on these data. Cameras aboard satellites also constantly take pictures of Earth's weather. Have students research the use of computers and satellites in weather and climate science. Then have them present their findings in a written report.

Options for Inquiry

FLIPCHART P. 32

Students can conduct these optional investigations at any time before, during, or in response to the lesson in the Student Edition.

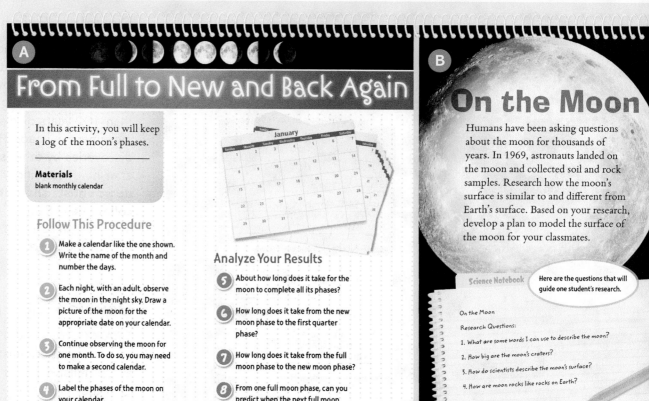

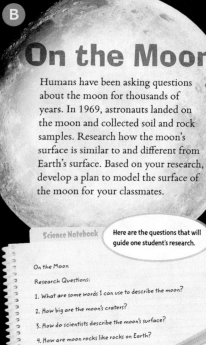

A

From Full to New and Back Again

In this activity, you will keep a log of the moon's phases.

Materials
blank monthly calendar

Follow This Procedure

1. Make a calendar like the one shown. Write the name of the month and number the days.

2. Each night, with an adult, observe the moon in the night sky. Draw a picture of the moon for the appropriate date on your calendar.

3. Continue observing the moon for one month. To do so, you may need to make a second calendar.

4. Label the phases of the moon on your calendar.

Analyze Your Results

5. About how long does it take for the moon to complete all its phases?

6. How long does it take from the new moon phase to the first quarter phase?

7. How long does it take from the full moon phase to the new moon phase?

8. From one full moon phase, can you predict when the next full moon phase will occur? How do you know?

B

On the Moon

Humans have been asking questions about the moon for thousands of years. In 1969, astronauts landed on the moon and collected soil and rock samples. Research how the moon's surface is similar to and different from Earth's surface. Based on your research, develop a plan to model the surface of the moon for your classmates.

Science Notebook   Here are the questions that will guide one student's research.

On the Moon

Research Questions:

1. What are some words I can use to describe the moon?

2. How big are the moon's craters?

3. How do scientists describe the moon's surface?

4. How are moon rocks like rocks on Earth?

32

Directed Inquiry

A From Full to New and Back Again

⏱ 10–15 minutes
👥 individuals

Prep and Planning Tips

Time listed is for initial discussion and distribution of the calendars. Students will carry out the bulk of this activity at home. At the end of the month, set aside time for students to share what they observed.

Prepare a blank calendar grid and distribute a copy to each student. If students are beginning this activity in the middle of a month, they will each need two calendar grids.

Expected Results

Students should find that the moon appears to change shape during its phases, and that it takes approximately 29 days to complete one cycle of phases. Students should observe that there is about 1 week from the new moon phase to the first quarter moon and about 2 weeks between the full moon and new moon phases.

Independent Inquiry

B On the Moon

⏱ 20–25 minutes
👥 pairs

Prep and Planning Tips

See the Planning for Inquiry page for more information. Students will need the initial 20–25 mintues for research. Model design and construction will take additional time. Provide students with a variety of materials to use in their investigations, including clay, newspaper, glue, scissors, and paints.

Science Notebook

Students can use the Science Notebook as a guide for developing their models. Encourage pairs of students to compare their models with those of other groups. How are their models similar? How are they different? Which models are the most effective in showing the concept?

Lesson 2

Essential Question
What Are Moon Phases?

Engage Your Brain!

Find the answer to the following question in this lesson and record it here.

What do you observe about the moon in the night sky?

Sample answer: I observe the moon's phases. The moon's shape appears to change over the course of a month.

Active Reading

Lesson Vocabulary
List the terms. As you learn about each one, make notes in the Interactive Glossary.

moon phases

Sequence
Many ideas in this lesson are connected by a sequence, or order, that describes the steps in a process. Active readers stay focused on sequence when they mark the transition from one step in a process to another.

315

Go Digital

An interactive digital lesson is available in Online Resources. It is suitable for individuals, small groups, or may be projected or used on an interactive white board.

What Are Moon Phases?

Vocabulary
moon phase

The vocabulary word for this lesson is moon phase.
Click the word to learn more about it.

Objectives
- Identify and predict changes in the appearance of the moon.

Engage Your Brain!

Have students brainstorm answers to the question, "What do you observe about the moon in the night sky?" Ask students to think about reasons why the moon appears to change its shape.

Remind students to record their final answer to the question when they find it on the third and fourth pages of this lesson.

Active Reading Annotations

Remind students that active readers "make texts their own" by annotating them with notes and marks that help with comprehension. Encourage students to use pencil, not pen, to make annotations and to feel free to change their annotations as they read. The goal of annotation is to help students remember what they have read.

Vocabulary and Interactive Glossary

Remind students to find and list the yellow highlighted terms from the lesson. As they proceed through the lesson and learn about the terms, they should add notes, drawings, or sentences in the extra spaces provided in the Interactive Glossary.

2 Explain

Notebook **Generate Ideas**

Ask students to preview the visuals and their captions on these two pages, and then read the introductory paragraph. Ask them how they think the moon is different from Earth.

Develop Science Concepts

What does the moon look like from Earth? What do you think the moon is made up of? Students may suggest that the moon is lit up and appears to have dark spots on it. They may suggest that the moon is made up of dust, rocks, craters, mountains, and valleys.

Why does the moon appear to move across the sky? because Earth is rotating on its axis

Why does the moon appear lit at night? because it reflects light from the sun

⚠ Misconception Alert ⚠

Some students may think that the moon makes its own light like the sun does. Point out that the sun is a star, which is a ball of hot, glowing gases. The burning hot gases are the source of light. The moon is made up of rocky substances, similar to Earth, so it does not make its own light.

Our Moon

Neil Armstrong was the first person to walk on Earth's moon. He said of the moon, "The surface is fine and powdery. I can pick it up with my toe."

The moon is Earth's satellite. A satellite is an object that moves around another larger object in space. Earth's moon is the largest and brightest object in the night sky. It looks large because it is close to Earth. But the moon is small compared to Earth. It is only about one-fourth the size of Earth. The moon has no air, wind, or liquid water. We see the moon because light from the sun reflects from it and back to Earth.

The pull of Earth's gravity keeps the moon in its orbit around Earth. We see only one side of the moon from Earth. That is because the moon takes the same amount of time to rotate once as it does to orbit Earth once.

We can see the moon at night (small photo) and sometimes during the day.

316

Differentiation — Leveled Questions

Extra Support

Why can we only see one side of the moon from Earth? because the moon takes the same amount of time to rotate once as it does to orbit Earth once

Challenge

What can scientists learn by studying the features of the moon? Sample answer: They can learn more about what makes up the universe; they can learn about how objects move together in space.

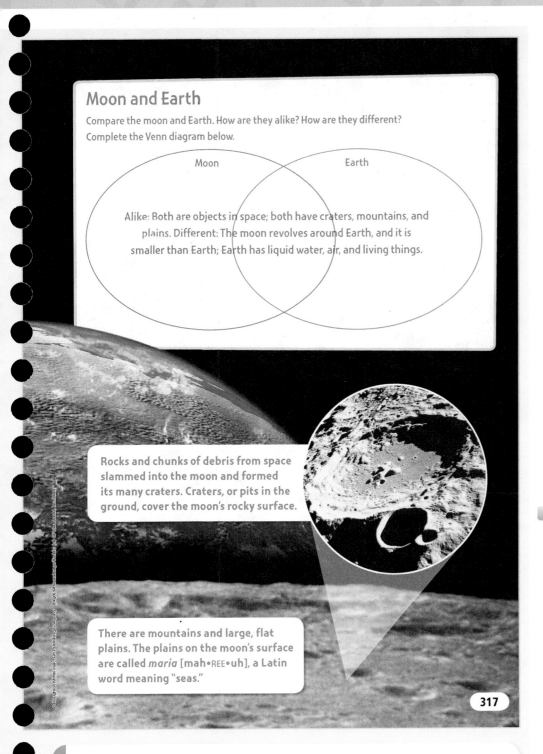

Moon and Earth

Compare the moon and Earth. How are they alike? How are they different? Complete the Venn diagram below.

Moon — **Earth**

Alike: Both are objects in space; both have craters, mountains, and plains. Different: The moon revolves around Earth, and it is smaller than Earth; Earth has liquid water, air, and living things.

Rocks and chunks of debris from space slammed into the moon and formed its many craters. Craters, or pits in the ground, cover the moon's rocky surface.

There are mountains and large, flat plains. The plains on the moon's surface are called *maria* [mah•REE•uh], a Latin word meaning "seas."

317

Interpret Visuals

Call attention to the large visual of the moon. **What are the characteristics of the moon's surface?** The moon is covered in craters, mountains, plains, and chunks of rock and dust.

Have students use the visuals of the moon and Earth, and what they read in the text to complete the Interactivity. Remind students that a Venn diagram compares two things by telling how they are alike and contrasts two things by telling how they are different.

Develop Inquiry Skills

HYPOTHESIZE **Astronauts last walked on the moon in 1972. If astronauts were to visit the moon today, they would still be able to see the footprints of astronauts that walked there long ago. Why do you think this is so?** There is no wind or air on the moon to blow away the dust that makes up the footprints.

Notebook ▸ Summarize Ideas

Have students think about the features of the moon and how the moon is similar to and different from Earth. Ask them to summarize the main idea orally or in writing.

2 Explain (continued)

Notebook ▸ **Generate Ideas**

With students, brainstorm a possible answer to the question in the introductory paragraph. Write their responses on the board. After students read through the lesson, have them make additions or revisions to the list.

Active Reading

Remind students that sequence, or order, is important in text that describes the development of ideas or the steps in a process. Active readers stay focused on sequence when they mark the change from one stage of an idea or step in a process to another.

Develop Science Concepts

What causes the moon's appearance to change in the night sky? As the moon revolves around Earth, different amounts of its lit side can be seen from Earth.

What do you see from Earth when there is a new moon? Explain. During the new moon, you cannot see the moon from Earth because the moon is between Earth and the sun. **What do you see from Earth when there is a full moon?** During the full moon, the moon appears to look like a big, round ball. **What do you think are the positions of the sun, Earth, and the moon during a full moon?** The Earth is between the sun and the moon.

⚡ Misconception Alert ⚡

Some students may think that the phases of the moon are caused by shadows cast on its surface by other objects in the solar system, particularly Earth. Ask students to recall the Flipchart activity in which they modeled the motion of the moon. Reinforce the concept by modeling the moon's phases with a flashlight, a basketball, and a tennis ball.

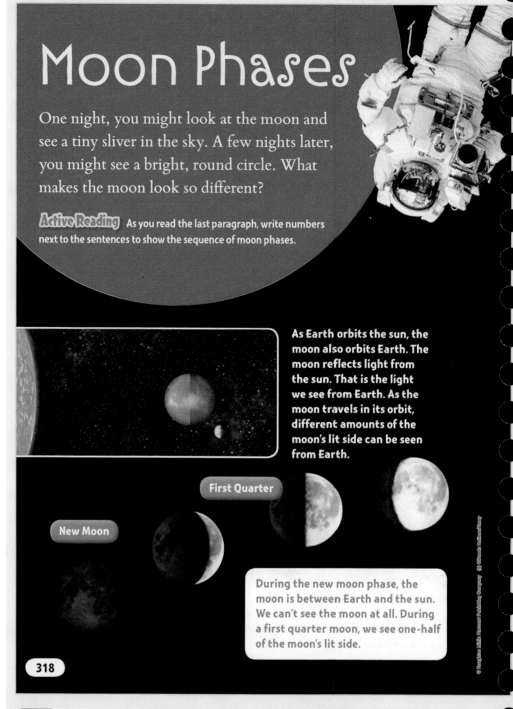

Moon Phases

One night, you might look at the moon and see a tiny sliver in the sky. A few nights later, you might see a bright, round circle. What makes the moon look so different?

Active Reading As you read the last paragraph, write numbers next to the sentences to show the sequence of moon phases.

As Earth orbits the sun, the moon also orbits Earth. The moon reflects light from the sun. That is the light we see from Earth. As the moon travels in its orbit, different amounts of the moon's lit side can be seen from Earth.

First Quarter

New Moon

During the new moon phase, the moon is between Earth and the sun. We can't see the moon at all. During a first quarter moon, we see one-half of the moon's lit side.

318

👥 Differentiation — Leveled Questions

Extra Support

Why are the phases of the moon visible in the night sky? The moon reflects light from the sun.

Challenge

How does the moon's position affect its phases? As the moon orbits around Earth, the portion of the moon's lit surface that we see from Earth changes.

The moon's shape does not change. The changes in the appearance of the moon's shape are known as **moon phases**.

You know that sunlight reflects from the moon to Earth. Yet the sun lights only half of the moon at any time. The motions of Earth and the moon are responsible for the phases you see. As the moon revolves around Earth, the amount of the lit part that we see from Earth changes. These different amounts of the moon's lighted side are the different phases of the moon.

Each phase of the moon has a different shape. It takes about 1 month for the moon to complete all of its phases. Then the cycle repeats.

1 During the new moon phase, we can't see the moon. That is because the lit part of the moon faces away from Earth. As the 2 moon moves in its orbit around Earth, we see more of the moon's lit part. We see a full 3 moon when all of the lit part of the moon faces Earth. Then we see less and less of the lit part again. 4

Do the Math!
Estimate Fractions and Percentages

What fraction and percent of the moon's lit side is seen during each phase? Complete the table.

	Full moon	First quarter	New moon	Third quarter
Fraction	1	$\frac{1}{2}$	0	$\frac{1}{2}$
Percent	100%	50%	0	50%

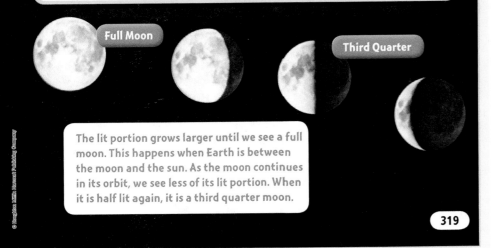

Full Moon

Third Quarter

The lit portion grows larger until we see a full moon. This happens when Earth is between the moon and the sun. As the moon continues in its orbit, we see less of its lit portion. When it is half lit again, it is a third quarter moon.

319

Writing Connection

Write a Poem Find a copy of Vachel Lindsay's poem, *The Moon's the North Wind's Cooky* and read it to the class. Ask the class how the poem describes the moon's phases. Then have students write a creative poem of their own that describes the phases of the moon.

Develop Science Vocabulary

moon phases Tell students that a phase can refer to the stages in a cycle or sequence of events. Point out that the pictures are an illustration of the cycle of the moon's phases.

Interpret Visuals

On the diagram of the moon's revolution, emphasize that the sun is the source of light for the moon. Describe how the phases are caused by the moon's position in relation to Earth.

Develop Inquiry Skills

OBSERVE Have students study the pictures that show the phases of the moon. Ask: **How do a first-quarter moon and a third-quarter moon differ?** The portion of the moon's lit surface that is visible from Earth is reversed from right to left.

Do the Math!
Estimate Fractions and Percentages

Direct students to review the diagram of the moon's phases across the bottom of these pages. Point out that at any given time, one-half of the moon's total surface is lighted. During the first-quarter and third-quarter moons, only one-half of the lit side, or one-fourth of moon's total surface, is visible from Earth.

Notebook ▸ Summarize Ideas

Have students think about what causes the phases of the moon. Ask them to summarize their ideas orally or in writing using a sequence of events to describe the phases.

2 Explain (continued)

Notebook ▸ **Generate Ideas**

Ask students to preview the visuals and their captions on these two pages. Then read the introductory paragraph. Ask them what they already know about how people use calendars and write their responses on the board.

Develop Science Concepts

Ask students to describe the calendar that we use.

What is the difference between a lunar calendar and a solar calendar? A solar calendar is based on Earth's orbit around the sun. The lunar calendar is based on the repeating pattern of the moon's phases.

Which calendar do you use to keep track of the months of the year? Explain. A solar calendar, because it takes 12 months for Earth to revolve around the sun. **How do you use a lunar calendar?** Sample answer: to keep track of the moon's phases

Lunar and Solar Calendars

For thousands of years, people used the phases of the moon to make calendars and track time. These are called lunar calendars. Earth's orbit around the sun also has been used to make calendars and track time. These are called solar calendars.

The Chinese Zodiac Calendar

The Chinese zodiac calendar is based in part on the phases of the moon. Twelve animals stand for cycles of time on the calendar. Some of these animals are the tiger, rabbit, dragon, and snake. Each year is also given an animal name. For example, in 2026, it will be the "Year of the Horse." The year 2027 will be the "Year of the Sheep".

Chinese New Year comes sometime between late January and early February. It is celebrated with fancy dragon costumes.

320

123 Math Connection

Solve Problem Pose this problem: If the phases of the moon take about 29 days, how many days is that for a period of 12 moon cycles? How many days are left over based on the number of days it takes for the sun to revolve around Earth once? 29 x 12 = 348; 365 − 348 = 17 days

The Aztec calendar is based on Earth's orbit around the sun. Each part of the calendar has colorful animals or symbols. These symbols marked important times of the year, such as when to plant crops.

APRIL

| Sunday | Monday | Tuesday | Wednesday | Thursday | Friday | Saturday |

New Year's Day

In the United States, New Year's Day is always January 1. In China, it is on the day of the new moon. Why do you think New Year's Day always falls on a different day each year in China? The new moon comes on different days each month, so the date that the Chinese New Year falls on will be different each year.

Our modern calendar is based on Earth's orbit around the sun. Each month is based roughly on the moon's phases. Once in a while, there are two full moons in one month.

321

Interpret Visuals

Have students study the pictures of the calendars on these two pages. Ask: **How are the Aztec and our modern calendars alike?** Both are based on Earth's orbit around the sun. **How are the Chinese and Aztec calendars alike?** They both use animals to mark cycles of time. **What cycles of time are the Chinese and our modern calendars based on?** Both are divided into 12 cycles representing the phases of the moon.

Develop Inquiry Skills

PREDICT Point out that the Chinese calendar is based on 12-month and 12-year cycles. Ask: **If 2012 is the year of the dragon, when would you expect the next year of the dragon after that? Why do you think so?** It would come in 2024 because each animal of the cycle comes once every 12 years.

Have students use the text and illustration of the Chinese Zodiac calendar to complete the Interactivity.

Notebook ▸ Summarize Ideas

Have students take one more look at the images on these pages. Ask them to think about how their ideas about calendars have changed. Have them summarize the main idea orally or in writing.

English Language Learners

Pronounce and Understand Phase Write this sentence on the board: "The different amounts of the moon's lighted side that we see are the different <u>phases</u>, or forms, of the moon." Review with students the pronunciation of

phase: /FAYZ/. Point out that in English, the letters *ph* often stand for the /f/ sound. Have partners read the sentence aloud and then ask and answer questions about the different phases of the moon.

3 Extend/Evaluate

Sum It Up!

- Point out that the boxes in the center of the diagram represent the main ideas presented in the lesson. The boxes that surround the center boxes represent details.

- Have students use the Answer Key to check their answers when they are finished. Tell students to correct any wrong answers so they can use this page to study for tests. Make sure students ask for help with any concepts that are still unclear.

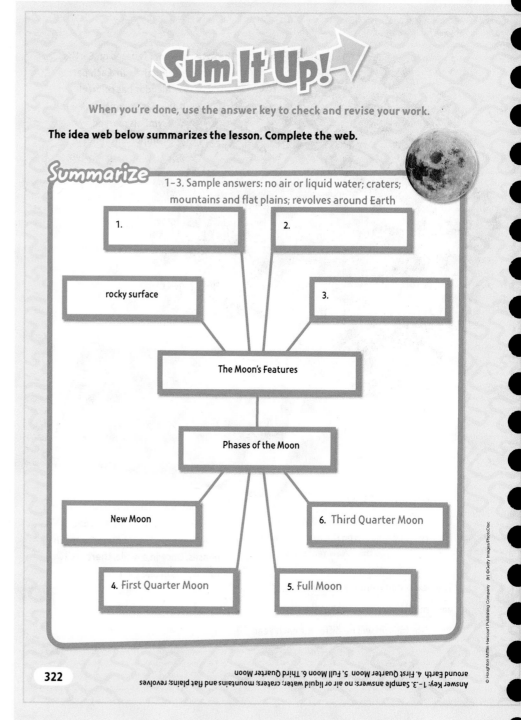

Sum It Up!

When you're done, use the answer key to check and revise your work.

The idea web below summarizes the lesson. Complete the web.

Summarize

1–3. Sample answers: no air or liquid water; craters; mountains and flat plains; revolves around Earth

1.

2.

rocky surface

3.

The Moon's Features

Phases of the Moon

New Moon

6. Third Quarter Moon

4. First Quarter Moon

5. Full Moon

322

Answer Key: 1–3. Sample answers: no air or liquid water; craters; mountains and flat plains; revolves around Earth 4. First Quarter Moon 5. Full Moon 6. Third Quarter Moon

Brain Check

Name_____

Word Play

1 Look at the picture and word clues. Write the answer to each clue on the blanks.

1.

The picture shows a first
q (u) a (r) t e r moon.
   1   2

2.

People use this to track time.
c a (l) e (n) d a r
      3   4

3.

These are pictures of some moon
p _ h _ a _ s _ e(s)_
            5 6

4.

An object that moves around another larger object in space is a
s (a) t e l l i t e .
   7 8

Look at the letters in circles. Match the letter with the number below each space to solve the riddle.

What kind of cartoons does the moon watch?
l u n a r   t u n e s
3 1 4 7 2   8 1 4 5 6

© Houghton Mifflin Harcourt Publishing Company

323

Answer Strategies

Word Play

1. Make sure students can identify each visual image. If students are having trouble filling in the blanks, have them refer back to the student pages and look for vocabulary words and other terms that might answer each question.

   Point out that each blank gets one letter. To solve the riddle, make sure students understand that they must write the letter in each space in the riddle by matching the numbers below the blanks with the numbers of the letters in the picture clues.

3 Extend/Evaluate (continued)

Answer Strategies

Apply Concepts

2. Lead a class discussion in which you describe how Earth and the moon move in space. Ask students to consider the source of the moon's light. Refer students who are having difficulty to the image of Earth, the moon, and the sun on the third page of this lesson.

3. If students are having difficulty, refer them to the pages on which the phases of the moon are illustrated.

4. Again refer students to the pages on which the phases of the moon are shown. Students should realize that as the moon waxes, the amount of its lit side that is visible from Earth increases from right to left. So, for January 10 (one week after a new moon), students should draw a first-quarter moon, during which the right half of the moon's lit surface is visible.

Take It Home!

Encourage students to bring their drawings to class to display on a bulletin board. If binoculars are not available, have students draw what they see with their unaided vision.

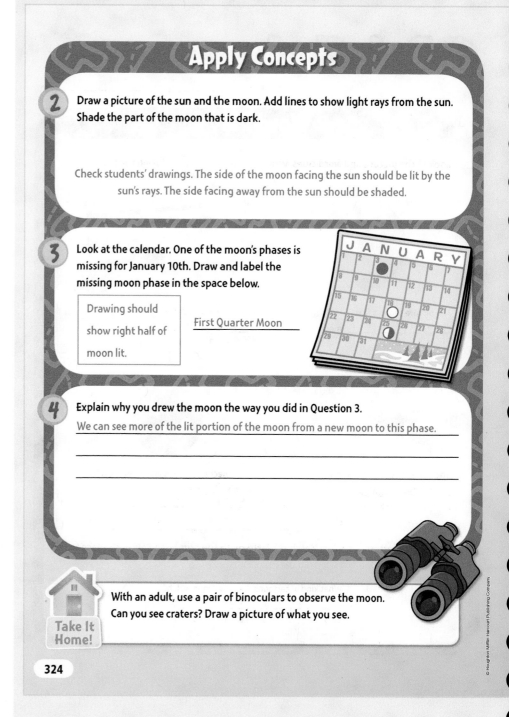

Apply Concepts

2 Draw a picture of the sun and the moon. Add lines to show light rays from the sun. Shade the part of the moon that is dark.

Check students' drawings. The side of the moon facing the sun should be lit by the sun's rays. The side facing away from the sun should be shaded.

3 Look at the calendar. One of the moon's phases is missing for January 10th. Draw and label the missing moon phase in the space below.

Drawing should show right half of moon lit.

First Quarter Moon

4 Explain why you drew the moon the way you did in Question 3.

We can see more of the lit portion of the moon from a new moon to this phase.

Take It Home! With an adult, use a pair of binoculars to observe the moon. Can you see craters? Draw a picture of what you see.

324

Make Connections

Language Arts Connection

Names of the Moon

The Algonquian tribes of New England gave names to the moon representing each month of the year. For example, they called the January moon the Wolf Moon. Ask students to find out the names of the moons for each month as described by the Algonquians. Ask them to tell why the Algonquians named the moons as they did. Have students display their research in an illustrated calendar of the moon months.

Average

Art Connection

A Lunar Calendar

Have students create and illustrate their own lunar calendar. They can choose animals or symbols to represent 12 cycles of the moon's phases. Have them give reasons for their choices. Ask students to compare their calendars to the Chinese Zodiac and Aztec calendars they learned about in this lesson.

Average

Social Studies Connection

Ancient Calendars

Have students use an online encyclopedia or nonfiction books from the school library to research ancient calendars such as the Babylonian, Mayan, and Egyptian calendars. Have them display their research in a poster illustrating the different calendars. Each calendar should include a caption describing whether it is a lunar or a solar calendar.

Challenging

Language Arts Connection

Native American Moon Stories

Many Native American cultures have stories that explain the phases of the moon. Have students use an online encyclopedia or nonfiction books from the school library to research a Native American story. Have students share the stories with the class. Students may want to supplement their stories with illustrations. Encourage students to listen attentively to each speaker and to ask questions as appropriate.

Guided Inquiry

⏱ 30–40 minutes

👥 small groups

Students should follow the directions on the Flipchart. The accompanying Lesson Inquiry pages in the Student Edition provide scaffolding for guided inquiry.

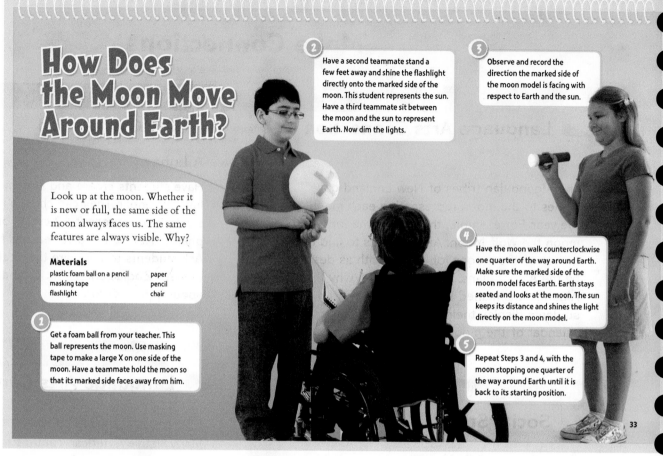

How Does the Moon Move Around Earth?

Look up at the moon. Whether it is new or full, the same side of the moon always faces us. The same features are always visible. Why?

Materials

plastic foam ball on a pencil   paper
masking tape   pencil
flashlight   chair

1 Get a foam ball from your teacher. This ball represents the moon. Use masking tape to make a large X on one side of the moon. Have a teammate hold the moon so that its marked side faces away from him.

2 Have a second teammate stand a few feet away and shine the flashlight directly onto the marked side of the moon. This student represents the sun. Have a third teammate sit between the moon and the sun to represent Earth. Now dim the lights.

3 Observe and record the direction the marked side of the moon model is facing with respect to Earth and the sun.

4 Have the moon walk counterclockwise one quarter of the way around Earth. Make sure the marked side of the moon model faces Earth. Earth stays seated and looks at the moon. The sun keeps its distance and shines the light directly on the moon model.

5 Repeat Steps 3 and 4, with the moon stopping one quarter of the way around Earth until it is back to its starting position.

33

Inquiry Skills Focus Use Models, Observe, Draw Conclusions

Objective

- Observe and sketch apparent changes in the shape of the moon.
- Predict when and how the shape of the moon appears to change.

Prep and Planning Tips

See the Planning for Inquiry page for more information.

- For safety and to save time, prepare the moon ahead of time using plastic foam balls that are about 4 inches in diameter stuck onto the end of a sharpened pencil.
- Students must work in groups of at least three. They can take turns using the equipment. They can take turns playing different roles during the activity.

Expected Results

Students will learn that the same side of the moon always faces Earth, because the period the moon takes to rotate once and the period it takes to revolve once are about the same.

1 Engage/Explore

Attention Grabber

Gather photos of at least three phases of the moon (e.g., full moon, first quarter, waxing gibbous). Printable photos are available on the Internet by searching for the name of a phase plus the word photos. Have students observe the photos one by one. Discuss why the visible surface features of the moon always look the same. If necessary, remind students that the same side of the moon always faces Earth. Tell students that in this investigation, they will model the movements of the moon to find out why the moon always keeps one side facing us—and one side hidden.

Preview Activity

Before beginning the investigation, have students review the directions on the Inquiry Flipchart and the accompanying Student Edition response pages. Then have them complete the response pages as they follow the directions on the Flipchart.

Inquiry Flipchart page 33

Lesson 3

INQUIRY

Name _____

Essential Question

How Does the Moon Move Around Earth?

Set a Purpose
What do you think you will learn from this activity?

I will learn how the moon rotates and

revolves around Earth.

Think About the Procedure
How does the moon have to move for its marked side to always face Earth?

Sample answer: To keep the marked side

of the moon facing Earth, the student

holding the moon must turn slowly as he

or she "revolves" around Earth.

The student holding the flashlight also moves. Why? How is this different from what we know about the sun?

The student with the flashlight moves
to keep the light shining directly on the
moon; however, the sun shines its light on
the moon and Earth without changing
position.

Record Your Data
In the space below, draw the position of the marked side of the moon with respect to Earth and the sun. Show the shaded and lit portions of the moon.

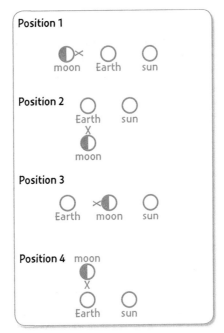

Position 1

moon   Earth   sun

Position 2

Earth   sun
X
moon

Position 3

Earth   moon   sun

Position 4   moon
X
Earth   sun

325

© Houghton Mifflin Harcourt Publishing Company · HMH Credits

Go Digital
A virtual lab experience is available with the Online Resources for this program.

Guide the Investigation

Develop Inquiry Skills

USE MODELS What did you model in this investigation? the movement of the moon in its orbit around Earth **What in the model is the moon? The sun? Earth?** A plastic foam ball on a pencil is the moon; a flashlight is the sun; a person sitting between the sun and moon is Earth.

Students may have found it necessary to have the "sun" move slightly in order to keep the sun's light shining on the moon. Discuss how this is different from what happens in space. You may also wish to discuss that this is an example of the limitations of models—they often cannot exactly reproduce conditions in nature.

OBSERVE The student holding the moon should move in a counterclockwise direction, stopping at three different points before returning to the starting position. Observations are made at all four points in the moon's "orbit." The student representing Earth stays seated throughout the activity, but turns to face the moon and record his or her observations.

Emphasize that the parts of a model must work the same way as the parts of the natural system it models. As a result, the model moon must spin once as it circles Earth. Have students observe that in order to keep the x facing Earth, the person holding the moon must slowly rotate it as she or he revolves around Earth. When the student holding the moon model is in between the Earth and sun, tell him or her to step aside to let light shine on the model, representing a new moon.

GATHER AND RECORD DATA Students should begin by observing the relative positions of the sun, Earth, and the moon at each stop in the moon's orbit. In some cases, they will be in a nearly straight line, while in others they will form a right angle. Students can then indicate the shaded side of the moon and the location of the x.

2 Explain

Develop Inquiry Skills

DRAW CONCLUSIONS Have students recall the model and review their recorded observations as they draw conclusions about the investigation.

ANALYZE AND EXTEND Discuss students' responses to the items.

1. Students can check their recorded observations of this point in the moon's orbit. They should observe the moon's lit side facing away from Earth. The moon is completely in shadow, at new-moon phase.

2. Have students recall that the same side of the moon always faces Earth. As a result, the lit part of the moon seemed to change as different amounts of its lit side faced Earth.

3. Recorded observations should prove this incorrect. For most of its orbit, the moon is next to or in front of Earth with respect to the sun, so Earth's shadow can't be the reason for phases.

4. Remind students that the same side of the moon always faced Earth. Point out the positions of the three bodies at new-moon phase. At this point in the moon's orbit, the side we always see is dark, and the other side is lit. The opposite happens at full moon. Thus, there is not one dark side of the moon.

3 Extend/Evaluate

5. Accept reasonable answers. Students who want to know more about moon phases should carry out the Flipchart investigation "From Full to New and Back Again."

Assessment

Lesson Quiz
See Assessment Guide, p. AG 64.

Draw Conclusions

Where does the moon get its light?
The moon gets its light from the sun.

What happens to the visible part of the moon as it moves through its orbit?
Sample answer: The amount of light on the visible part of the moon changes.

The moon turns as it orbits Earth. When does the moon complete a full rotation?
The moon completes a full rotation at the end of one revolution around Earth.

Analyze and Extend

1. Draw the moon phase that takes place when the moon is between Earth and the sun. Describe how this moon phase would look from Earth.

Students should draw and describe a new moon.

2. **Why does the amount of sunlight on the moon seem to change?**
It seems to change because as the moon revolves around Earth, different amounts of its lighted side are visible from Earth.

3. A friend thinks that Earth's shadow causes moon phases. Use evidence from this investigation to explain why your friend's idea is incorrect.
Students may explain that for most of its orbit, the moon is next to or in front of Earth with respect to the sun. So, Earth's shadow can't be the reason for the moon's phases.

4. The same friend also thinks that the moon has a dark side where the sun never shines. What evidence would you use to explain why your friend's idea is incorrect?
Students may say that in the investigation, half of the moon was always lit by the sun, even when only a portion—or none—of its lit side was visible from Earth.

5. What other questions would you like to ask about moon phases?
Sample answer: How long does each moon phase last? Does the moon ever cast a shadow on Earth?

326

Differentiated Inquiry

Easy

Compare the Moon's Near and Far Sides

- In the investigation students learned that the same side of the moon always faces Earth because its period of rotation and its period of revolution are basically the same.

- Although we can't see it from Earth, lunar probes and observations from crewed missions have given us photographs of the moon's far side. Have students access photos of the moon's near and far sides on the Internet, or you may wish to provide students with these photos.

- Students should compare and contrast the two sides of the moon, with sketches and a brief description. These should present the moon's far side with a rougher and more heavily cratered terrain than the near side.

Average

Make a Sun-Earth-Moon Model

- Students modeled the movements of the moon in the investigation, but the model did not represent Earth's movements.

- Ask students to think about how Earth also rotates and revolves in space and to use that information to modify the investigation. Have them consider whether the sun should move, too.

- Students should put the sun at the center. Earth should walk in a circle around a spinning sun. Earth should also (slowly) rotate as it revolves. At the same time, the moon should walk slowly around Earth and slowly spin to keep the same side facing Earth. Students should correctly represent the movements of the bodies, but need not concern themselves with timing. If you wish, discuss the limitations of this model to accurately represent the speed of the motions.

Average

Investigate a Non-rotating Moon

- Have students repeat the procedure, but have the moon revolve without rotating.

- In this case, the student representing the moon should keep his or her body oriented in the same direction as he or she moves around Earth.

- Ask students to use their observations to determine whether the moon would keep the same face toward Earth if it did not rotate. They will find it would not. Have them also use observations to determine that the moon's phases would still occur if it did not rotate.

Challenging

Investigate Earth's Phases

- Astronauts who landed on the moon were able to observe the phases of Earth.

- Have students redesign the activity to investigate what Earth's phases look like from the moon. Students can use the same materials, but their observations should be taken from the point of view of a person on the moon viewing Earth.

- Challenge students to draw pictures similar to the ones they made in the "How Does the Moon Move Around Earth?" activity. Have students present their drawing to the class.

Options for Inquiry

Students can conduct these optional investigations at any time before, during, or in response to the lesson in the Student Edition.

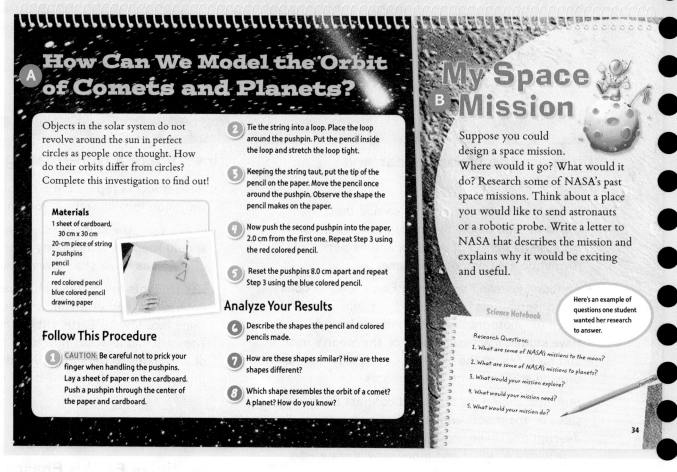

A How Can We Model the Orbit of Comets and Planets?

Objects in the solar system do not revolve around the sun in perfect circles as people once thought. How do their orbits differ from circles? Complete this investigation to find out!

Materials
1 sheet of cardboard, 30 cm x 30 cm
20-cm piece of string
2 pushpins
pencil
ruler
red colored pencil
blue colored pencil
drawing paper

Follow This Procedure

1 CAUTION: Be careful not to prick your finger when handling the pushpins. Lay a sheet of paper on the cardboard. Push a pushpin through the center of the paper and cardboard.

2 Tie the string into a loop. Place the loop around the pushpin. Put the pencil inside the loop and stretch the loop tight.

3 Keeping the string taut, put the tip of the pencil on the paper. Move the pencil once around the pushpin. Observe the shape the pencil makes on the paper.

4 Now push the second pushpin into the paper, 2.0 cm from the first one. Repeat Step 3 using the red colored pencil.

5 Reset the pushpins 8.0 cm apart and repeat Step 3 using the blue colored pencil.

Analyze Your Results

6 Describe the shapes the pencil and colored pencils made.

7 How are these shapes similar? How are these shapes different?

8 Which shape resembles the orbit of a comet? A planet? How do you know?

B My Space Mission

Suppose you could design a space mission. Where would it go? What would it do? Research some of NASA's past space missions. Think about a place you would like to send astronauts or a robotic probe. Write a letter to NASA that describes the mission and explains why it would be exciting and useful.

Here's an example of questions one student wanted her research to answer.

Science Notebook

Research Questions:
1. What are some of NASA's missions to the moon?
2. What are some of NASA's missions to planets?
3. What would your mission explore?
4. What would your mission need?
5. What would your mission do?

34

Directed Inquiry

A How Can We Model the Orbits of Comets and Planets?

 20 minutes   pairs

Prep and Planning Tips

- Cut a piece of corrugated cardboard and tie loops of string for each pair of students. Pencils do not have to be red and blue, as long as they are of two different colors.

- Provide background on ellipses and explain that in the model, the sun is at one of the foci. Describe the extremely elongated shape of the elliptical orbits of most comets. It can be hundreds of years or more between times when they travel through the part of their orbit that brings them closest to the sun.

Expected Results

Students will find that the first setup (pencil) forms a circle, while the second and third (red and blue pencils) form ellipses—the shape of the orbits of planets and comets respectively. Point out that an ellipse looks like a slightly flattened circle. Also, point out that a circle has just one central point, but an ellipse has two—called foci.

Independent Inquiry

B My Space Mission

 20 minutes   pairs

Prep and Planning Tips

- See the Planning for Inquiry page for more information.

- The NASA website has a wealth of information that students can access about past, present, and future space missions to the planets, moons, and other objects in the solar system.

Science Notebook

Students can use the sample Science Notebook page shown on the Flipchart as a model for recording possible research questions. When students are finished with their proposals, encourage volunteers to share what they have written with the rest of the class. The proposals can be used as a springboard to discuss the future of space exploration.

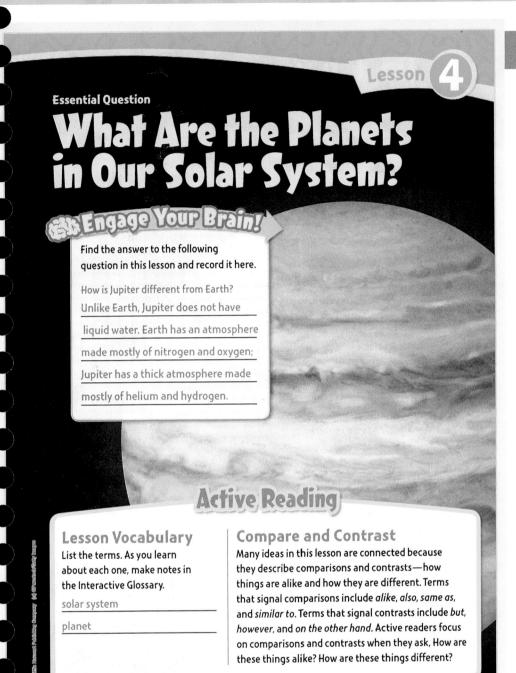

© Houghton Mifflin Harcourt Publishing Company (c) ©ThinkstockGetty Images

Lesson **4**

Essential Question

What Are the Planets in Our Solar System?

Engage Your Brain!

Find the answer to the following question in this lesson and record it here.

How is Jupiter different from Earth?
Unlike Earth, Jupiter does not have
liquid water. Earth has an atmosphere
made mostly of nitrogen and oxygen;
Jupiter has a thick atmosphere made
mostly of helium and hydrogen.

Active Reading

Lesson Vocabulary

List the terms. As you learn about each one, make notes in the Interactive Glossary.

solar system

planet

Compare and Contrast

Many ideas in this lesson are connected because they describe comparisons and contrasts—how things are alike and how they are different. Terms that signal comparisons include *alike, also, same as,* and *similar to.* Terms that signal contrasts include *but, however,* and *on the other hand.* Active readers focus on comparisons and contrasts when they ask, How are these things alike? How are these things different?

327

Go Digital

An interactive digital lesson is available in Online Resources. It is suitable for individuals, small groups, or may be projected or used on an interactive white board.

Objectives

- Identify the major components of the solar system.
- Describe characteristics of planets in the solar system.
- Compare and contrast the inner and outer planets.

Engage Your Brain!

Have students brainstorm possible answers to the question, *How is Jupiter different from Earth?* If possible, show a photo of Earth from space to help students with their comparisons. Remind students to record their final answer to the question when they find it on the second and third pages of the lesson.

Active Reading   Annotations

Remind students that active readers "make texts their own" by annotating them with notes and marks that help with comprehension. Encourage students to use pencil, not pen, to make annotations and to feel free to change their annotations as they read. The goal of annotation is to help students remember what they have read.

Vocabulary and Interactive Glossary

Remind students to find and list the yellow highlighted terms from the lesson. As they proceed through the lesson and learn about the terms, they should add notes, drawings, or sentences in the extra spaces provided in the Interactive Glossary.

2 Explain

 Generate Ideas

Read the main heading on this page aloud and then ask: **What other objects are near Earth in this part of space?** Have students brainstorm a list of the objects as you record their ideas on the board.

Active Reading

Remind students that informational text contains many facts and details. Active readers process informational text with deliberate speed that enables them to focus on and retain the facts presented. Circling details helps active readers focus more readily.

Develop Science Vocabulary

solar system Remind students that Earth is part of our solar system and that the sun is in the center of the solar system.

planet Have a volunteer read the definition aloud. Then discuss the three parts of the definition. Reinforce that *clear orbit* means that the orbit of a planet does not cross the orbit of another body.

⚠ Misconception Alert ⚠

Many students might remember that Pluto was once classified as a planet but is no longer. Explain that astronomers refined the definition of planet to include a clear orbit. Pluto's orbital path crosses that of Neptune, so Pluto no longer fulfills all the requirements to be classified as a planet. It is now classified as a dwarf planet. Other dwarf planets include Eris and Ceres.

Have students use this information as they complete the Interactivity on the facing page.

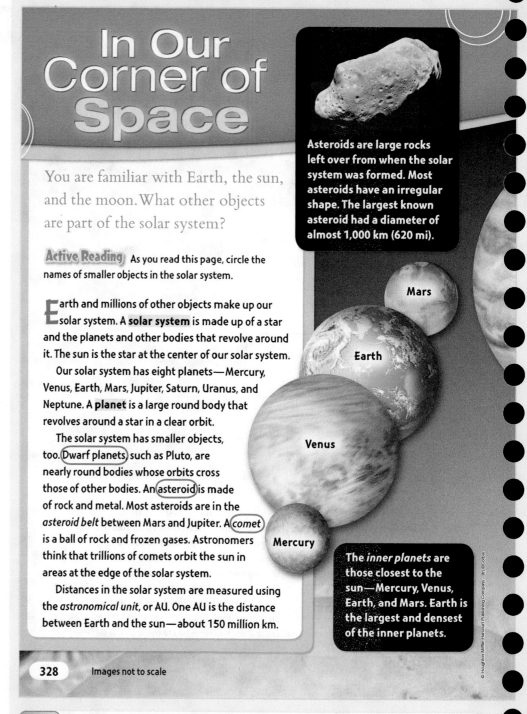

In Our Corner of Space

Asteroids are large rocks left over from when the solar system was formed. Most asteroids have an irregular shape. The largest known asteroid had a diameter of almost 1,000 km (620 mi).

You are familiar with Earth, the sun, and the moon. What other objects are part of the solar system?

Active Reading As you read this page, circle the names of smaller objects in the solar system.

Earth and millions of other objects make up our solar system. A **solar system** is made up of a star and the planets and other bodies that revolve around it. The sun is the star at the center of our solar system.

Our solar system has eight planets—Mercury, Venus, Earth, Mars, Jupiter, Saturn, Uranus, and Neptune. A **planet** is a large round body that revolves around a star in a clear orbit.

The solar system has smaller objects, too. Dwarf planets such as Pluto, are nearly round bodies whose orbits cross those of other bodies. An asteroid is made of rock and metal. Most asteroids are in the *asteroid belt* between Mars and Jupiter. A comet is a ball of rock and frozen gases. Astronomers think that trillions of comets orbit the sun in areas at the edge of the solar system.

Distances in the solar system are measured using the *astronomical unit*, or AU. One AU is the distance between Earth and the sun—about 150 million km.

Mars

Earth

Venus

Mercury

The *inner planets* are those closest to the sun—Mercury, Venus, Earth, and Mars. Earth is the largest and densest of the inner planets.

328 Images not to scale

© Houghton Mifflin Harcourt Publishing Company (tr) ©Corbis

123 Math Connection

Calculate Distance Neptune is the planet farthest from the sun. Have students determine that distance in AUs. Ask them to explain how they would determine how far Neptune is from the sun in kilometers. Provide this information:

Neptune is 30 times as far from the sun as Earth.

Earth is 1 AU from the sun. So Neptune is 30 × 1 AU = 30 AU from the sun. To convert to kilometers, students would multiply the number of kilometers in an AU (150 million) by 30.

The *outer planets* are those farthest from the sun—Jupiter, Saturn, Uranus, and Neptune. These planets are the largest in our solar system. In fact, Jupiter is larger than all of the other planets combined.

As a comet approaches the sun, the sun's heat turns the comet's frozen parts into gas. This gas may look like a fiery tail streaming away from the sun. Comets are less than 10 km (6.2 mi) across but can have tails that are up to 100,000 km (62,137 mi) long.

Compare Planets and Dwarf Planets

In the space below, compare planets and dwarf planets.
Answers will vary. Students might indicate that planets are large solar system bodies. Dwarf planets are smaller than planets and their orbits are not clear of other objects.

329

Develop Science Concepts

Note that the sun and planets are not the only objects in the solar system. Tell students that there are almost 200 moons, several dwarf planets, and millions—perhaps billions—of asteroids and comets.

Which characteristics do astronomers use to classify these different bodies? They use size, shape, composition of the object, its location in the solar system, and the type of orbit it has.

Many characteristics of objects in the solar system differ. For example, a comet is made of rock, and frozen gases; an asteroid is rock and metal. Still, what do all objects in the solar system have in common? They all revolve around the sun.

Interpret Visuals

Draw students' attention to the illustrations on these two pages.

Into what two groups are the planets of the solar system divided? inner and outer planets

In which of these two groups is Earth? inner planets

What is one characteristic of the inner and outer planets that is different? Sample answer: The outer planets are larger than the inner planets.

 Summarize Ideas

Tell students to use the vocabulary terms *solar system* and *planet* in a sentence that summarizes the main idea of these two pages orally or in writing.

Differentiation — Leveled Questions

Extra Support

Which object is at the center of the solar system? the sun What is the sun? a star What are the eight large, round bodies, including Earth, that revolve around the sun? the planets

Challenge

Why are comets sometimes visible with the unaided eye, even though they are smaller than many asteroids? When comets get near the sun, they develop glowing tails that can sometimes be seen from Earth.

2 Explain (continued)

 Generate Ideas

Read the title of this section aloud to the class. **What might this title mean?** Some planets in the solar system are near Earth, and some are far away. Remind students that there are two groups of planets, the outer planets and the inner planets. **Do you recall one way they are different?** The outer planets are larger. **Tell students** they are now going to find out how else the planets are different.

Active Reading

Remind students that authors compare and contrast events, objects, and ideas when they point out ways they are alike and different. Active readers remember similarities and differences because they focus on the events, objects, and ideas being compared.

Develop Science Concepts

What caused the difference in the inner and outer planets? They formed in different parts of the solar system. Inner planets formed in the warmer area nearest the sun, while outer planets formed in a colder area farther away from the sun.

How did this affect the composition of the planets? Rock and metal bits clumped together to form rocky planets in the inner, warmer part of the solar system. In the colder, outer part of the solar system, gases and icy particles clumped together to form the balls of gas and ice that are the outer planets.

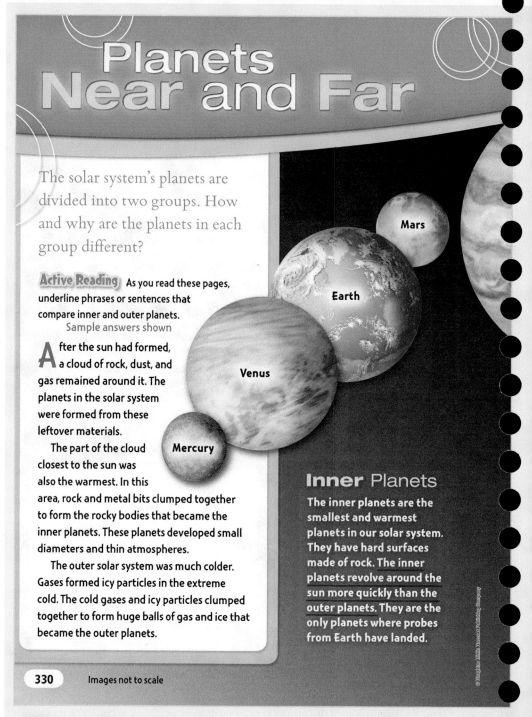

Planets Near and Far

The solar system's planets are divided into two groups. How and why are the planets in each group different?

Active Reading As you read these pages, underline phrases or sentences that compare inner and outer planets.
Sample answers shown

After the sun had formed, a cloud of rock, dust, and gas remained around it. The planets in the solar system were formed from these leftover materials.

The part of the cloud closest to the sun was also the warmest. In this area, rock and metal bits clumped together to form the rocky bodies that became the inner planets. These planets developed small diameters and thin atmospheres.

The outer solar system was much colder. Gases formed icy particles in the extreme cold. The cold gases and icy particles clumped together to form huge balls of gas and ice that became the outer planets.

330   Images not to scale

Inner Planets

The inner planets are the smallest and warmest planets in our solar system. They have hard surfaces made of rock. The inner planets revolve around the sun more quickly than the outer planets. They are the only planets where probes from Earth have landed.

 Differentiation — Leveled Questions

Extra Support

What are the names of the inner planets? Mercury, Venus, Earth, and Mars **What are the names of the outer planets?** Jupiter, Saturn, Uranus, and Neptune

Challenge

The outer planets rotate fast, so they have short days. Do they also have short years? The outer planets are far from the sun, and they travel a longer path as they revolve around the sun. Thus, their years are very long.

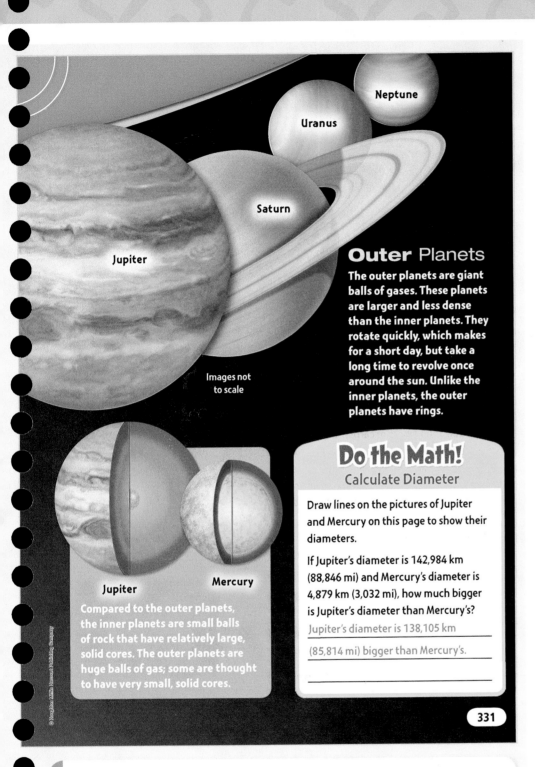

Outer Planets

The outer planets are giant balls of gases. These planets are larger and less dense than the inner planets. They rotate quickly, which makes for a short day, but take a long time to revolve once around the sun. Unlike the inner planets, the outer planets have rings.

Images not to scale

Jupiter

Mercury

Compared to the outer planets, the inner planets are small balls of rock that have relatively large, solid cores. The outer planets are huge balls of gas; some are thought to have very small, solid cores.

Do the Math!
Calculate Diameter

Draw lines on the pictures of Jupiter and Mercury on this page to show their diameters.

If Jupiter's diameter is 142,984 km (88,846 mi) and Mercury's diameter is 4,879 km (3,032 mi), how much bigger is Jupiter's diameter than Mercury's?

Jupiter's diameter is 138,105 km

(85,814 mi) bigger than Mercury's.

331

⫽ Misconception Alert ⫽

Students often think the outer planets have solid surfaces like Earth and the other inner planets. They do not. Remind students that they could never land on the outer planets, which are made of cold gases and liquids. **How would scientists study a planet with no solid surface?** Sample answer: They could send probes to photograph the planet.

Interpret Visuals

Tell students to look carefully at the cross-section diagrams of Mercury and Jupiter. Note that in this diagram, one planet stands as an example of what all the planets in a certain group are like. Given that, ask: **Would a cross-section of Earth look more like that of Jupiter or Mercury?** Like Mercury, Earth would be small with a large, solid core. **Which planet's cross section would one of Saturn resemble?** Like Jupiter, Saturn would be a huge gas ball around a small, solid core.

Do the Math!

Calculate Diameter

Review how the diameter of a circle or sphere is determined. Guide students in drawing lines from one edge to the other through the center of each planet. To determine the differences in size, students should subtract the diameter of Mercury from the diameter of Jupiter.

Notebook ▸ Summarize Ideas

Have students make a two-column chart and compare the characteristics of the inner and outer planets. Have them use their charts to summarize the differences orally or in writing.

2 Explain (continued)

Notebook **Generate Ideas**

Have students read the main title on this page and scan these two pages looking at the photos and main captions. Then ask: **What does _Inside Track_ mean in the title?** The words _inside track_ refer to the part of the solar system made up of the inner planets. Draw an analogy between a running track and the solar system. Point out that people who run on the inside lanes of a track are closer to the center of the track and have a shorter distance to cover to circle the track. This is analogous to the paths followed by the inner planets.

Active Reading

Remind students that active readers annotate, or mark up, text to benefit their own recollection of the information presented. Though students may star different sentences, it is important they are able to offer a reasonable explanation for their annotations.

Develop Science Concepts

How are the inner planets alike? They are small, rocky, and have either no moon or few moons.

How is Earth different from all of the other inner planets? Earth has a lot of liquid water and an atmosphere of nitrogen, oxygen, and carbon dioxide. Earth also has diverse types of life.

Contrast Venus and Mars in terms of temperature. Venus is extremely hot; Mars is freezing cold. **What causes this difference?** Venus is closer to the sun, and it also has a thick atmosphere that holds in the planet's heat. Mars has a very thin atmosphere of carbon dioxide, which does not hold in heat like that on Venus.

The Inside Track

The inner planets are Earth's closest neighbors. Sometimes, these planets look like bright stars in the night sky. How are the inner planets alike and different?

Active Reading As you read these pages, draw a star next to words or phrases that identify characteristics shared by all of the inner planets.

The inner planets are alike in some ways. They are all small and rocky. They have few moons—or none at all. Still, each planet is unique. Mercury has a thin atmosphere of carbon dioxide with a surface like our moon. Venus has a thick carbon dioxide atmosphere, which makes it boiling hot. Drops of acid fall from Venus's clouds. Mars is dry and freezing cold. Huge dust storms blow across Mars's surface. Only Earth has water, soil, and air to support life.

Images taken by the _Venus Express_ probe show one of the more than 1,600 volcanoes on Venus's surface. For a long time, it was hard to study Venus's surface because of the thick clouds hiding it. These same clouds trap heat on Venus, making it the hottest planet.

Venus

Mercury is the smallest planet in our solar system. Images taken by the _Messenger_ space probe show the deep craters on Mercury's surface. Rocky objects slammed into Mercury, leaving deep scars.

Mercury

332   Images not to scale

Differentiation — Leveled Questions

Extra Support

What are the surfaces of the inner planets made of? rock
How do we know what the surfaces of the inner planets look like? Space probes have taken pictures of these planets and sent them back to Earth.

Challenge

What is one advantage that inner planets would have over those that are farther away? Sample answer: The planets closer to the sun would be warmer than those farther away from the sun.

The Mars *Rover Spirit* has sent images of Mars's surface back to Earth. Mars's surface has mountains, wide plains, canyons, and volcanoes. Its surface looks red because of the iron oxide in its soil.

Mars

Satellite images of Earth show large green areas. Earth is the only planet with visible life, a large supply of liquid water, and an atmosphere mostly made of nitrogen, oxygen, and carbon dioxide.

Earth

Survivor—Mars!

Suppose you have the chance to go to Mars. Think about what Mars is like. Make a list of things you would need to survive on Mars, and explain your choices.

Sample answer: I would bring warm clothes

because it's so cold on Mars. I would bring air,

food, and water, because these things are not

found on Mars.

Images not to scale

333

// Misconception Alert //

Students might have thought that the planet closest to the sun, Mercury, is the hottest planet. However, the text states that Venus is the hottest planet. Emphasize that it is Venus's thick atmosphere that allows the temperature to rise so high near its surface. The clouds act like a blanket, holding in the planet's heat. Although Mercury is closer to the sun, its lack of a thick atmosphere means that the planet does not hold in heat.

Develop Inquiry Skills

INFER **Space probes have visited both of Earth's neighbors, Venus and Mars. Why is Mars the planet that astronauts are more likely to visit rather than Venus?** It would probably be easier for people to survive on Mars. Venus is boiling hot with acid raining down on its surface. Mars is cold and has a thin atmosphere, but astronauts could survive on its surface with protective clothing and an air supply.

For the Interactivity, students should first gather information about the conditions on Mars on these pages. Have students then list what they would need to survive such conditions.

Notebook ▸ Summarize Ideas

Have students make a graphic organizer in which they list the unique features of the four inner planets. Common characteristics can be recorded in a center circle along with the title *The Inside Track*. Have students use their graphic organizers to aid them in summarizing the main idea of these pages, either orally or in writing.

English Language Learners

Pair and Share Planet Facts
Pair ELLs and English-proficient students and have them make Planet Cards. The front of the card should contain a planet's name and a drawing of the planet. Students can then hold up a card, with the English-proficient student pronouncing the name and the ELL repeating. After practicing the names, have them work together to write sentences that contain planet names and facts. Have students read their sentences aloud and add the facts to the backs of the cards.

2 Explain (continued)

Notebook ▶ Generate Ideas

Remind students of the running-track analogy. Ask: **If the inside track referred to the inner planets, what do you think the outside track refers to?** the outer planets Ask students to brainstorm what they know about the outer planets, and list their responses on the board. Return to the list after students read these two pages to allow them to review and revise the list.

Active Reading

Remind students that the main idea may be stated in the first sentence, or it may be stated elsewhere. To find a main idea, active readers ask, What is this paragraph mostly about?

Develop Science Concepts

Remind students that the inner planets are rocky, fairly small, and closest to the sun. **What characteristics do the outer planets share?** They are large, made of cold liquids and frozen gases, are surrounded by rings, and have many moons.

Why will astronauts never visit the outer planets? Sample answer: They don't have solid surfaces to land on; they are too far away.

The Outside Track

The outer planets are so far away that even the fastest space probes take many years to reach them.

Active Reading As you read these pages, underline the sentence that contains the main idea.

Astronauts and probes will never land on Jupiter, Saturn, Uranus, or Neptune—the outer planets. The outer planets are very different from the inner planets. These huge planets do not have solid surfaces. They are *gas giants*, made up mostly of gases.

All the outer planets have many moons and are surrounded by rings made of dust, ice, or rock. Jupiter and Saturn are the largest planets in our solar system. Uranus and Neptune are smaller and are the coldest planets.

Jupiter has at least 63 moons. Astronomers think that Europa, one of Jupiter's moons, has an icy surface that covers a cold, slushy ocean. Jupiter's atmosphere is in constant motion. Its Great Red Spot is a swirling storm that has raged for more than 300 years.

Jupiter

Great Red Spot

334

Images not to scale

© Houghton Mifflin Harcourt Publishing Company · (cr) ©Purestock/Getty Images

Differentiation — Leveled Questions

Extra Support

How do the inner and outer planets compare in size? The outer planets are larger. What do all of the outer planets have around them that the inner planets do not have? rings, many moons

Challenge

Based on what you've read about the outer planets, what would conditions be like if you dropped down through the atmosphere of one of them? Sample answer: It would be very cold, with extremely strong winds.

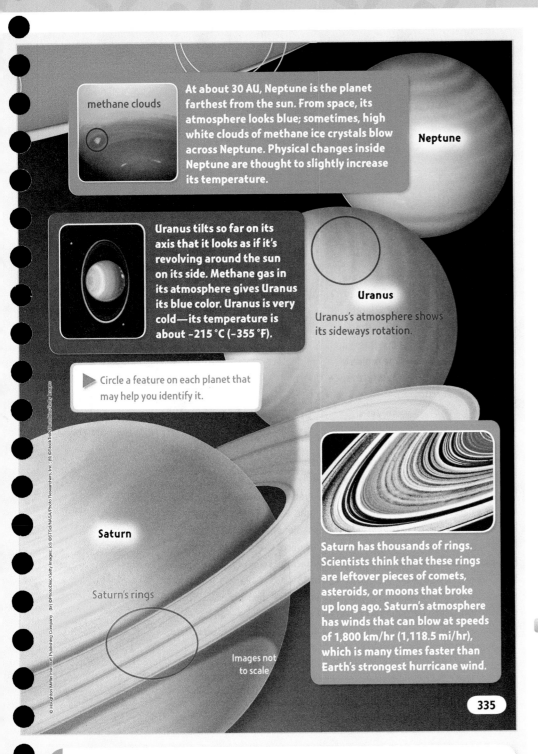

methane clouds

At about 30 AU, Neptune is the planet farthest from the sun. From space, its atmosphere looks blue; sometimes, high white clouds of methane ice crystals blow across Neptune. Physical changes inside Neptune are thought to slightly increase its temperature.

Neptune

Uranus tilts so far on its axis that it looks as if it's revolving around the sun on its side. Methane gas in its atmosphere gives Uranus its blue color. Uranus is very cold—its temperature is about -215 °C (-355 °F).

Uranus

Uranus's atmosphere shows its sideways rotation.

▶ Circle a feature on each planet that may help you identify it.

Saturn

Saturn's rings

Saturn has thousands of rings. Scientists think that these rings are leftover pieces of comets, asteroids, or moons that broke up long ago. Saturn's atmosphere has winds that can blow at speeds of 1,800 km/hr (1,118.5 mi/hr), which is many times faster than Earth's strongest hurricane wind.

Images not to scale

335

Develop Science Concepts

Remind students that all the planets rotate on an imaginary axis as they revolve around the sun. **What is different about the way Uranus revolves around the sun?** Uranus has an extreme tilt, so it looks like it is rolling around on its side as it revolves around the sun. Use a small plastic foam ball stuck onto a sharpened pencil to contrast the slight tilt of Earth with the extreme tilt of Uranus. Then demonstrate the rolling effect of Uranus' rotation/revolution.

Interpret Visuals

Have students look at the individual images of the planets, and read the captions. **How do the appearances of Jupiter and Saturn compare?** They have colorful bands formed by their atmospheres. Unlike Jupiter, Saturn is surrounded by a large and well-developed ring system. Jupiter's rings are not as visible. **How do Uranus and Neptune look alike?** They both appear blue, because of methane in their atmospheres.

Have students locate identifying characteristics of each planet and use them to complete the Interactivity.

Notebook ▸ **Summarize Ideas**

Ask students to elaborate, orally or in writing, on the main idea they underlined on these pages in order to summarize what they have learned about the outer planets.

English Language Learners

Compare Planets Draw a two-column chart, similar to the one shown here, on the board. Work with students to fill in the table. Use simple words and phrases to describe characteristics such as composition, position, size, and number of moons.

Inner Planets	Outer Planets
Smaller	Bigger
Made of rock	Made of gas
Near the sun	Far from the sun
Have few moons	Have many moons

2 Explain (continued)

Notebook > Generate Ideas

Read the title, "The Right Spot," aloud to the class. Have students preview the images and captions on these pages to predict what they will learn.

Develop Science Concepts

What is the solar system's "life zone"? the area where the temperature range allows life to flourish

Where is our solar system's life zone? It extends from outside Venus' orbit to the area just before Mars' orbit.

List objects in the solar system that are within its life zone. Earth, the moon Remind students that the moon is also within the life zone. **Why doesn't the moon have life?** The moon doesn't have the liquid water or the atmosphere needed to support life as we know it.

Emphasize that location within the life zone is necessary for life, but so are other characteristics that only Earth has, such as abundant liquid water on its surface.

▟ Misconception Alert ▟

Students are aware that Earth is the only planet with diverse life as we know it. Make it clear that there still could be life on other planets in the solar system and beyond. Explain that this life, however, might be the type of life that can live only in extreme environments and would likely be microscopic.

Why It Matters

The Right Spot

Living things like those found on Earth do not exist elsewhere in the solar system, which makes Earth a unique place.

Out of the eight planets in our solar system, only Earth has life as we know it. Why? Scientists think it is because Earth is the only planet within the solar system's life zone. The *life zone* is the region of space where the temperature range allows life to thrive.

Our solar system's life zone begins just outside Venus's orbit and ends before the orbit of Mars. If Earth were outside this zone, it would be either too hot or too cold for life to exist on our planet. Earth sits near the center of the life zone.

Our moon is also within the life zone, yet it has no life. Why? The moon doesn't have an atmosphere or liquid water. Earth's atmosphere does many things to support life. It traps solar energy to keep Earth's temperature comfortable. It contains the gases that most living things need. It also protects living things from harmful solar radiation.

Earth's average temperature is about 13 °C (55 °F). Earth's oceans help maintain this temperature. The oceans store and distribute heat from the sun. Ocean currents carry heat away from the equator and toward the poles. Without the oceans to store and distribute heat from the sun, some places on Earth would be extremely cold or extremely hot.

Venus and Earth are sometimes called sister planets, but Earth supports life and Venus does not. It's all because of Earth's position within the solar system's *life zone*.

336

👥 Differentiation — Leveled Questions

Extra Support

Why do we say that Earth is in just the right spot in the solar system? It is in the life zone, the place where the temperature range is just right for Earth's life forms.

Challenge

Why would Earth's position be less useful without its oceans and its atmosphere? The atmosphere protects life from harmful radiation. The atmosphere and the oceans together help maintain temperatures suitable for life.

Life on Venus and Mars?

Explain why life could not thrive on these two planets.

Sample answer: Venus and Mars lay

outside the solar system's life zone.

Their temperatures are too hot or too

cold for life to thrive on them.

The surface of Mars is cold and dry. There is no liquid water on Mars's surface. Much of Mars's water is locked away in the planet's polar icecaps.

The temperature range of Earth is ideal for many living things.

337

Develop Science Concepts

How does Earth's atmosphere help the planet maintain its temperature? It traps heat and prevents heat from escaping into space. **How do Earth's oceans help maintain and regulate its temperature?** They store and distribute heat from the sun, with currents that carry heat away from the equator and release it near the poles.

Develop Inquiry Skills

DRAW CONCLUSIONS **Would Earth have the diverse life it has now if it had its same atmosphere and surface water, but orbited where Mars does?** no Students should conclude that the surface waters would freeze, and the average temperature would be freezing as well, making the diverse life Earth has now impossible.

Interpret Visuals

Have students look at the position of Earth within the life zone. **Is the life zone within the area of the inner planets or the outer planets?** inner planets **How does the position of the sun affect the position of the life zone?** Students should infer that the life zone is close enough to the sun to provide adequate heat, but not so close that the heat is too intense.

In order to complete the Interactivity, have students review the information on Venus and Mars and compare the conditions that exist on those planets with those on Earth.

Notebook ▸ Summarize Ideas

Have students summarize, either orally or in writing, why Earth's position in the solar system makes it just the right spot for life.

Writing Connection

Write a Travel Brochure
Suppose scientists were able to communicate with intelligent beings beyond our solar system. Have students write a brochure that would convince them to visit Earth. Tell students to concentrate on characteristics of Earth that make it comfortable and hospitable for many types of life. Encourage students to use concrete words and sensory details to convey conditions on Earth. Have students then share what they have written with the rest of the class.

3 Extend/Evaluate

Sum It Up!

- Be sure students understand that one set of four clues describes the outer planets and the other set describes the inner planets. Students might find it useful to list the four characteristics for each category side by side, then identify the group each describes.

- If students are still having difficulty deciphering the clues, have them review the characteristics of the inner planets and outer planets discussed throughout this lesson.

- Have students use the Answer Key to check their answers when they are finished. Tell students to correct any wrong answers so they can use this page to study for tests. Make sure students ask for help with any concepts they still do not understand.

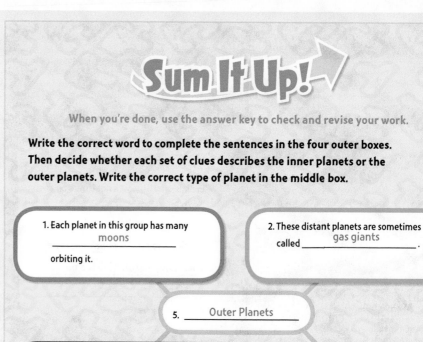

Sum It Up!

When you're done, use the answer key to check and revise your work.

Write the correct word to complete the sentences in the four outer boxes. Then decide whether each set of clues describes the inner planets or the outer planets. Write the correct type of planet in the middle box.

1. Each planet in this group has many __moons__ orbiting it.

2. These distant planets are sometimes called __gas giants__.

5. __Outer Planets__

3. Only the planets in this group have __rings__ around them.

4. Because of their distances from the sun, these planets have lower __temperatures__.

6. Probes have landed on these planets because their surfaces are __hard__.

7. Some planets in this group have one or two __moons__. Others have none.

10. __Inner Planets__

8. None of the planets in this group has __rings__ around it.

9. These planets' __diameters__ are smaller than those of the planets in the other group.

338

Answer Key: 1. moons 2. giants 3. rings 4. temperatures 5. Outer Planets 6. hard 7. moons 8. rings 9. diameters 10. Inner Planets

© Houghton Mifflin Harcourt Publishing Company

338   Unit 6

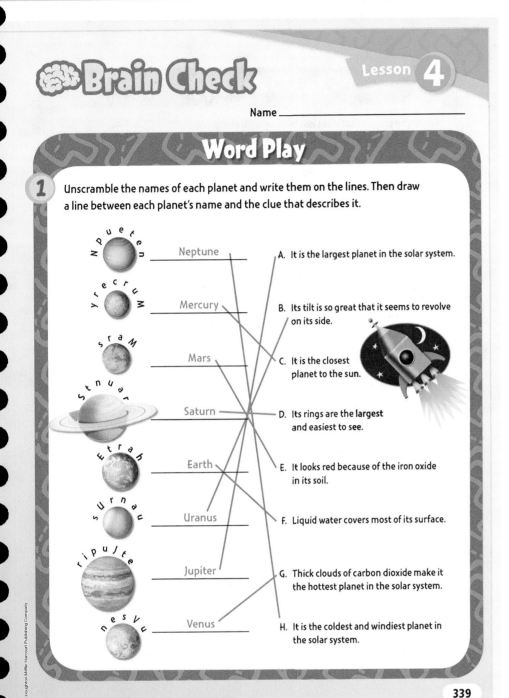

Brain Check

Name _____

Word Play

1 Unscramble the names of each planet and write them on the lines. Then draw a line between each planet's name and the clue that describes it.

N p u e t e n — Neptune

y r e c r u M — Mercury

s r a M — Mars

S t n u a r — Saturn

E t r a h — Earth

s U r n a u — Uranus

r i p u J t e — Jupiter

n e s V u — Venus

A. It is the largest planet in the solar system.

B. Its tilt is so great that it seems to revolve on its side.

C. It is the closest planet to the sun.

D. Its rings are the largest and easiest to see.

E. It looks red because of the iron oxide in its soil.

F. Liquid water covers most of its surface.

G. Thick clouds of carbon dioxide make it the hottest planet in the solar system.

H. It is the coldest and windiest planet in the solar system.

© Houghton Mifflin Harcourt Publishing Company

339

Answer Strategies

Word Play

1. If students are having difficulty unscrambling the letters to identify the planet names, suggest they make a list of the names of the planets as they review the lesson pages. As a challenge, have students make up a crossword puzzle using the planet names for answers and facts about each planet for clues.

Assessment

Suggested Scoring Guide

You may wish to use this suggested guide for the Brain Check.

Item	Points
1	40 (5 points each item)
2	20
3	20
4	20
Total	100

Lesson Quiz

See Assessment Guide, p. AG 65.

3 Extend/Evaluate (continued)

Answer Strategies

Apply Concepts

2. If students are unsure about the appearance of the planets, refer them back to the pages in this lesson where the characteristics of the planets are covered. Have students recall the two distinct groups of planets to which all the planets in the solar system belong.

3. Refer students to the two pages in this lesson where the solar system's life zone is defined and discussed. Have students recall all of the characteristics of Earth itself that play a part in the planet's ability to support diverse life.

4. Suggest that students use drawing paper if they need more space to complete their drawings. If students have difficulty defining the word *planet*, refer them back to the page in this lesson where the term is defined

 Take It Home!

On NASA's website, students and their families can explore the history of space exploration, learn about the objects in the solar system and beyond, and read the latest news on present and future space missions. If families find a mission that is of particular interest, they can search for additional information at other websites.

Apply Concepts

2 Circle the planet that does not belong with the group. Then explain your choice on the lines below.

Venus   Mercury   Mars   Neptune

Sample answer: Neptune does not belong in this group because it is an outer planet. The other planets shown here are all inner planets.

3 Suppose that scientists discover a planet orbiting a star within its life zone. What else might scientists want to know before concluding that this planet could support Earth-like life forms?

Sample answer: Scientists might want to know whether the planet has an atmosphere, similar to Earth's, land, and liquid water like Earth.

4 Draw a picture of a our solar system. Then identify objects found in the solar system. What are planets?

Check students' pictures.

Sample answer: a star, eight planets, some dwarf planets, and many moons, asteroids, comets make up our solar system; Planets are relatively large objects that have clear orbits around the sun.

Take It Home! With a family member, explore NASA's websites to learn more about efforts to detect water on the surface of the moon and Mars. Make a poster or write a report to share your findings with your class.

340

Make Connections

Social Studies Connection

Research Planet Names

Have students look up the names of the eight planets to determine the derivation of each of them. Students can use an encyclopedia, or they can look for the information on the Internet. Each explanation should be one or two sentences long. Students can list the information by planet on a sheet of paper, or organize the information in a table.

Average

Math Connection

Make a Venn Diagram

The inner planets and outer planets share some characteristics and have others that are very different. Instruct students to draw a Venn diagram that compares and contrasts the features of the inner and outer planets. Review the way the diagram should be set up, with one part for listing characteristics of the inner planets, one part for listing characteristics of the outer planets, and a shared section in the middle listing characteristics that both groups of planets have in common.

Average

Writing Connection

Write a Science-Fiction Story

Students have learned about each of the planets in the solar system. Now ask them to write a science-fiction story about the first crewed mission to one of those planets. Students can choose any planet and should write the story in the first person, as if they are writing a journal about their own experiences. Remind students to take into account the planet's distance from Earth, its atmosphere, and conditions on its surface. For planets without surfaces, students should use what they know to describe conditions they would encounter under its upper atmosphere. Encourage students to share their stories.

Challenging

Writing Connection

Report on Extremophiles

Scientists have discovered a surprising number of life forms on Earth living in extreme environments. These extremophiles have given astrobiologists new hope that the extreme environments on other planets might also harbor life. Have students research and write a report on extremophiles and their connection to the expanded possibilities of finding life on other planets.

S.T.E.M.

Engineering and Technology

Objectives

- Identify the benefits and risks of crewed space exploration.
- Identify the benefits and risks of crewless space exploration.
- Compare and contrast the benefits and risks of crewed and crewless space exploration.

Notebook **Generate Ideas**

Ask students to discuss what they know about crewed and crewless space missions, such as the space shuttle missions, the Apollo program, and the more recent crewless missions to Mars. Have students give at least one advantage and one disadvantage of both kinds of missions. Record their responses.

Background

- Astronaut safety has always been a major concern. The first orbiting satellite, *Sputnik 1*, was launched in 1957 by the USSR with no one aboard. Next, animals were launched into space. The first person to go to space was Yuri Gagarin, sent by the USSR in 1961. Since then, only Russia, the United States and China have sent manned vehicles into space.

- More recently, crewless missions have allowed people to research areas of space where human exploration is currently too dangerous or impossible.

Develop Inquiry Skills

DRAW CONCLUSIONS Explain that there is no right answer to the Interactivity. **Why might scientists weigh the benefits and drawbacks of an idea before implementing it?** Sample answer: It is important to consider the costs and materials needed and to determine whether the design is safe for humans and the environment.

S.T.E.M.

Engineering & Technology

Space Exploration

Typically, engineering design problems have many solutions. An engineer often needs to find a balance among many trade-offs to get the best solution. A *trade-off* is the giving up of one design feature to make another design feature better. The charts below show trade-off analyses for spacecraft with and without crew. The benefits and drawbacks of some major design features of each kind of mission are shown. You decide which one should blast off.

Spacecraft with Crew

Design Feature	Benefit	Drawback
living space for crew	people onboard to fix problems and run difficult science experiments	greater cost to build and to fuel; increased weight during liftoff (must store air, food, and water)
heat shield for reentry to Earth's atmosphere	safe return of crew; reusable ship	more fuel needed; less space for everything else

Spacecraft without Crew

Design Feature	Benefit	Drawback
smaller, lighter	less fuel needed; costs less to launch	less room for instruments
no living space for crew	no need to store air, food, water	no one to fix problems or watch experiments
large energy suppy to last many years in space	can learn about faraway objects	spacecraft doesn't return to Earth; it cannot be reused

You Decide

Which type of spacecraft works best for space exploration? Use information from the chart to explain your answer.

Sample answer: Spacecraft without a crew make sense for long-range missions with unsupervised science experiments. They're less expensive with no risk to human health.

341

S.T.E.M.
continued

Analyze Trade-offs

Engineers think about trade-offs before designing a spacecraft. Sometimes, the trade-offs lead them to conclude that a particular solution is not worth trying.

Suppose a crew wants new space suits. Use the features and trade-offs of the old and new space suits to answer the questions below.

Old Space Suit		New Space Suit	
Design Feature	Trade-off	Design Feature	Trade-off
thick space suit protects astronaut against extreme temperatures and debris	hard to move around in	thinner space suit lighter and easier to move around in	may not protect as well as the old suit against extreme temperatures or debris
sturdy material and strong joints	difficult to put on quickly	has newer technologies built in	all technologies may not have been tested in space

What is the most important feature of a space suit?

Sample answer: to protect the astronaut and keep him or her alive

Do you think the benefits of the new space suit outweigh its trade-offs? Why or why not?

Sample answer: The new space suit is not better. While the astronauts may be able

to move around more easily, they may not be able to keep warm or be protected in space.

Build On It!

Rise to the engineering design challenge—complete **Design It: Build a Sundial** on the Inquiry Flipchart.

342

© Houghton Mifflin Harcourt Publishing Company (t) ©NASA; (r) ©NASA

Develop S.T.E.M. Concepts

USING MODELS The Interactivity allows students to analyze trade-offs of a new space suit design that is less bulky.

- Encourage students to refer to the charts to help answer the questions.

- Explain that the design problem involves designing a suit that is less bulky but does not sacrifice other important aspects of the suit, such as safety and function. Explain that the outcome may be that the suit cannot be as lightweight as desired.

- Remind students that some aspects of the suit cannot be compromised, or the suit may malfunction.

Notebook ▸ **Summarize Ideas**

Direct students to briefly summarize how to analyze trade-offs of a technological system. Students can give their summaries orally or in writing.

Build On It!

In **Design It: Build a Sundial**, the design challenge associated with this lesson, students use the steps of the engineering design process to build their own sundial.

See the pages that follow. Other opportunities to apply the design process appear throughout the Inquiry Flipchart.

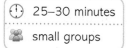

S.T.E.M.
Engineering and Technology

FLIPCHART p. 35

⏱ 25–30 minutes

👥 small groups

S.T.E.M.
Engineering & Technology
Design It: Build a Sundial

What time is it? Most likely, you'll find the answer by looking at a watch or another electronic device. However, thousands of years ago, people used the sun to tell time.

A sundial is a device that uses the position of the sun to tell time. It has an upright rod that casts a shadow onto a number scale that identifies the time of day.

Now that you know about sundials, can you build one, too? Think about how a sundial is used. What materials would work best? A good sundial design should be accurate to within a half hour of the actual time.

Sundial

What to Do

1. Research sundials to learn how they use Earth's motion to tell time.

2. Identify everyday materials you could use to build your sundial.

3. Identify the design criteria your sundial must meet. Then draw a diagram of your design in your Science Notebook.

4. Build and test your design.

5. Use an electronic clock to test the accuracy of your sundial. How can you improve the sundial's performance?

6. If needed, redesign your sundial until it meets your design criteria.

7. Place your sundial outside and use it to tell time.

Keep a record of your work in your Science Notebook.

35

Objectives

- Use the steps of the design process to make a sundial.
- Understand the purpose of sundials in telling time.

Prep and Planning Tips

- Identify resources students can use to learn about sundials.
- Gather materials students may use to build their designs, including sharpened pencils, modeling clay, cardboard or heavy card stock, craft sticks, chalk, game chips, scissors, and tape.
- Review with students the cardinal points.

Expected Results

Students should be able to research, plan, design, and build a sundial. The students' sundial should meet the design criteria. Students should be able to test the sundial for accuracy and improve its design for final use.

1 Engage/Explore

Attention Grabber

Show students pictures of both modern and ancient sundials. Explain the concept of using the sun to tell time. Tell students that the part of a sundial that points straight up forms a shadow that moves throughout the day. The sun's position in the sky is so predictable that we can use it to tell time.

Preview Activity

Before beginning the activity, have students review the directions on the Engineering and Technology Flipchart page. You may wish to have students review the lesson on the engineering design process earlier in this program.

Guide the Activity

Develop Inquiry Skills

OBSERVE Prior to making their sundials, students may need to spend a few days observing the sun's position in the sky throughout the day. Have them pay particular attention to its position in the morning, at midday, and in the early evening, before it sets, as well as how shadows move throughout the day.

INFER Direct students to examine the large photo on the Flipchart page. **Where is the sun in this picture, and how do you know?** The sun is behind and slightly to the right of the people shown in the photo. You can tell from the direction that the shadows point.

Strategies for Success

Review with students the sun's apparent east-west motion across the sky, and have them identify cardinal directions (before noon, facing away from the sun, north is to your right and south is to your left). They can use this as a reference point when placing their sundials.

Remind students that sundials do not work at night, so the scale they put on their sundial needs only to include daylight hours (for example, 7:00 a.m.–7:00 p.m.).

 **Science Notebook**

During the Activity Ask students to describe in their notebooks how a sundial works and how their design will solve the problem of telling time without a watch.

Direct students to record in their notebooks the materials they plan to use to construct their sundial and the steps they will follow during construction. Suggest that students make two designs in case their initial design does not work.

2 Explain

Develop the Engineering Design Process

2. PLAN AND BUILD Suggest to students that if their design includes hash marks to indicate time intervals they should use chalk instead of drawing them on cardboard or card stock. This will make it easier to modify the placement of the hash marks later, if necessary.

3. TEST AND IMPROVE Students should test their designs on a sunny day. It is best to test them from late in the morning through early afternoon.

4. REDESIGN Students may have to test their sundials over several days before they can finalize the design.

3 Extend/Evaluate

Quick Check

Discuss with students what they learned as they went through the design process. Ask:

What part of designing a sundial did you find most challenging? How did you solve this challenge?

Which part or parts of your design required improvement? Why?

What advice would you give to someone who is planning to make a sundial?

 **Science Notebook**

After the Activity Check to see that students have included a detailed drawing of their sundial and an explanation of how it works. Look for evidence of modifications made to initial designs to improve the accuracy of the sundial.

Michael DiSpezio's
Tips & Tricks

In the Beginning To begin, have students explore the movement of shadows by inserting a pencil into a clay base. In sunlight, have students observe and mark the position and length of the shadow over time. Challenge them to incorporate these observations into their design.

Watch the Weather Be aware of the local weather, and if possible, schedule this activity for a day forecast to be clear and sunny. After the device is assembled, have students bring their sundials home and use them as alternate time-keeping devices.

Guided Inquiry

FLIPCHART P. 36

🕐 90 minutes

👥 pairs

Students should follow the directions on the Flipchart. The accompanying Lesson Inquiry pages in the Student Edition provide scaffolding for guided inquiry responses.

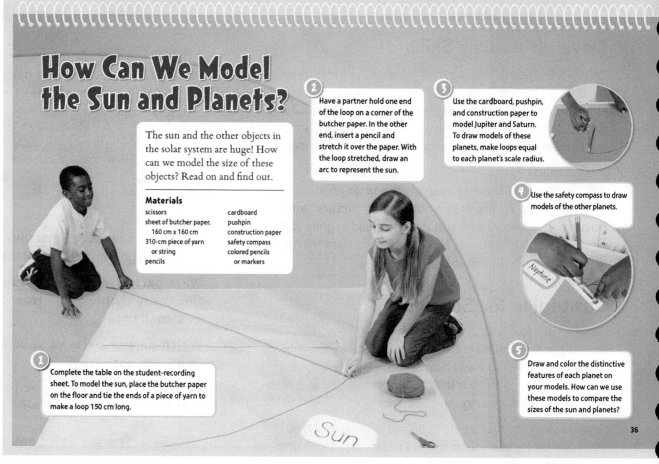

How Can We Model the Sun and Planets?

The sun and the other objects in the solar system are huge! How can we model the size of these objects? Read on and find out.

Materials

scissors	cardboard
sheet of butcher paper, 160 cm x 160 cm	pushpin
	construction paper
310-cm piece of yarn or string	safety compass
	colored pencils or markers
pencils	

1 Complete the table on the student-recording sheet. To model the sun, place the butcher paper on the floor and tie the ends of a piece of yarn to make a loop 150 cm long.

2 Have a partner hold one end of the loop on a corner of the butcher paper. In the other end, insert a pencil and stretch it over the paper. With the loop stretched, draw an arc to represent the sun.

3 Use the cardboard, pushpin, and construction paper to model Jupiter and Saturn. To draw models of these planets, make loops equal to each planet's scale radius.

4 Use the safety compass to draw models of the other planets.

Neptune

5 Draw and color the distinctive features of each planet on your models. How can we use these models to compare the sizes of the sun and planets?

Sun

36

Inquiry Skills Focus Use Models

Objective

- Model the size of the sun and planets in the solar system.
- Compare and contrast the size of the sun and the inner and outer planets.

Prep and Planning Tips

See the Planning for Inquiry page for more information.

- Plan for at least two class periods to complete this activity. It may work best to organize the class into four groups, and assign each group to make one-fourth of the sun and two of the planets. Bring the groups together as a class to assemble the completed model.
- Identify a location that provides the space needed for students to lay out their paper.
- If there is minimal space available in the classroom, groups can work in shifts.

Expected Results

Students will be able to visualize the relative sizes of the sun and planets as the result of completing their scale models.

1 Engage/Explore

Attention Grabber

Display a large map of the 48 contiguous states of the United States. Ask students to identify the largest ones and explain how they made their choices. Students should respond that some states, such as Texas and California, look bigger than the others when seen together. Explain that it is difficult to make this type of visual comparison with the planets because we can't see them side by side. Then tell students there is a way to "see" the planets together and compare their sizes. In this investigation they are going to compare the objects in the solar system by making scale models of them.

Preview Activity

Before beginning the investigation, have students review the directions on the Inquiry Flipchart and the accompanying Student Edition response pages. Then have them complete the response pages as they follow directions on the Flipchart.

Inquiry Flipchart page 36

Lesson 5 INQUIRY

Name _____

Guide the Investigation

Develop Inquiry Skills

Essential Question

How Can We Model the Sun and Planets?

Set a Purpose

What do you think you will learn from this activity?

I will learn how the sizes of the sun, inner

planets, and outer planets compare to

each other.

Think About the Procedure

The word *scale* has several meanings. What does it mean to make a *scale model* of the sun and planets? Answers will vary.

Students might explain that it means using

math to draw models of the sun and planets

that are proportional to the real things.

You know that diameter is any line that passes through the center of a circle and connects two points on its circumference. Based on Step 1 of the activity, how would you define *radius*? Accept any answer that

explains that the radius of a circle is half its

diameter, or is the distance between the center

of a circle and any point on its circumference.

Record Your Data

Complete the chart below. To find the missing values, divide the scale diameter of each object by 2.

Object	Actual Diameter (km)	Scale Diameter (cm)	Scale Radius (cm)
Sun	1,391,900	300.0	150.0
Mercury	4,880	1.0	0.5
Venus	12,104	2.6	1.3
Earth	12,756	2.8	1.4
Mars	6,794	1.5	0.75
Jupiter	142,984	32.0	16.0
Saturn	120,536	25.0	12.5
Uranus	51,118	10.0	5.0
Neptune	49,532	9.8	4.9

343

USE MODELS **What does this investigation model?** It models the sizes of the sun and the planets in our solar system.

MEASURE Emphasize to students that in this investigation, they will be modeling the relative sizes of the planets, not the distances between the planets. Explain that in order to make the model to scale, each body must be the same fraction of its actual size. If this rule is followed, all objects will be proportional to one another.

For example, if I make a model of two cars to scale, and one car is one-tenth its actual size, what fraction of its actual size should the other car be? Students should realize that for both cars to stay the same size relative to each other, both must be one-tenth their actual size.

Emphasize that in this exercise, the sun is an extremely tiny fraction of its actual size, but all the planets are the same extremely tiny fraction of their actual size.

GATHER AND RECORD DATA To fill out the table, students divide the Scale Diameter of each body in half to find the Scale Radius. If necessary, provide students with the scale radius for each object:
Sun: 150.0 cm
Mercury: 0.5 cm
Venus: 1.3 cm
Earth: 1.4 cm
Mars: 0.75 cm
Jupiter: 16.0 cm
Saturn: 12.5 cm
Uranus: 5.0 cm
Neptune: 4.9 cm

Go Digital

A virtual lab experience is available with the Online Resources for this program.

© Houghton Mifflin Harcourt Publishing Company · HMH Credits

2 Explain

Develop Inquiry Skills

DRAW CONCLUSIONS Using the data table, students should note that Mercury has the smallest diameter and Jupiter the largest. If necessary, have them review Lesson 4 to identify the inner planets and the outer planets. Students will find that Earth is the largest inner planet, Neptune is the smallest outer planet, and the sun is much larger than anything else in the solar system.

ANALYZE AND EXTEND Discuss students' responses to the items.

1. Remind students that models often represent things that are too large or too small to study directly. The only way to really see the relative sizes of the sun and the planets is to use a model.

2. Point out that the sun is almost ten times the diameter of the solar system's largest planet. To make the model a reasonable size, the entire sun can't be shown.

3. If the diameter of the circle is 8.6 cm, students should set the compass for the circle's radius, which is half of 8.6 cm, or 4.3 cm.

4. With a diameter of 8.6 cm, the new planet would probably be classified as an outer planet, in terms of its size alone. It would be the smallest outer planet, but it would be more than three times the diameter of the largest inner planet, Earth.

3 Extend/Evaluate

5. Accept all reasonable answers. Students might ask how big a model would have to be to show scale distances within the solar system.

Assessment

Lesson Quiz
See Assessment Guide, p. AG 66.

Draw Conclusions

Which planet has the smallest diameter?

Mercury has the smallest diameter.

Earth is the largest inner planet. What is Earth's diameter? How does it compare to the diameter of the outer planets?

Sample answer: Earth's diameter is 12,756 km. The smallest outer planet is Neptune; however its diameter is almost four times larger than Earth's.

Jupiter is the largest planet in the solar system. How does Jupiter's diameter compare to the sun's diameter?

Sample answer: The sun's diameter is almost 100 times larger than Jupiter's.

Analyze and Extend

1. **Why would a scientist want to model the size of the sun and planets?**

Accept any answer that explains scientists want to present information in different ways. Models help scientists make quick comparisons about properties of objects.

2. **A section of the circumference of a circle is called an *arc*. In this investigation, why did you use an arc to model the sun and not the planets?**

Students should explain that unlike the planets, the sun is so large that it would be difficult to model and display its entire circumference at the specified scale.

344

---

3. **In the space below, use your compass to draw an arc for a circle with a diameter of 8.6 cm.**

> Check students' pictures.

4. **If the circle in item 3 were a model of a new planet in the solar system, based on its size alone, to which group of planets would it belong? Explain.**

Accept any answer that correctly relates the size of the planet in item 3 to its likely position within the outer planets.

5. **Think of other questions you would like to ask about objects in the solar system. Write your questions here.**

Sample answer: How can we model distances in the solar system? How do asteroids, moons, and dwarf planets compare to each other? How can I model the surface of the sun and moon?

Differentiated Inquiry

Easy

Make a Solar System Mobile

- Have students make a solar system mobile. Planets do not have to exhibit relative sizes or distances, but must be hung in the correct order outward from the sun.

- Students first draw and cut out circles of several sizes from cardboard and color them to resemble the planets. Have students punch a small hole in the top of each planet, tie it to a length of string, and hang the string from the bottom of the hanger to make the mobile.

Average

Model Distances in the Solar System

- Have students make a model that represents the distances between the planets to scale.

- Students can choose the scale of the model and use the information in the table below to calculate the distances between bodies. Students will probably have to experiment with several scales to determine the one that is reasonable.

- Students can place markers at the proper scaled distance for each of the solar system's eight planets. These markers can be cardboard planet signs, plastic foam planet models, students holding signs, or another system students propose.

Distance of Planets from the Sun (in Astronomical Units)

Planet	AU	Planet	AU
Mercury	0.4	Jupiter	5.2
Venus	0.7	Saturn	9.5
Earth	1	Uranus	19
Mars	1.5	Neptune	30

Easy

Model One of the Planets

- Have each student choose one planet to model, or allow students to work on the project with a partner. The model should replicate the way the planet's surface or atmosphere looks from space.

- Remind students to look carefully at pictures that show the color of the planet and any distinguishing features such as bands, spots, clouds, or rings. These should be represented in the model, if possible.

- Make a number of materials available that students can use, including construction paper and scissors, modeling clay, plastic foam balls, paint, glue, and glitter.

Challenging

Record a Guided Tour of a Solar System Model

- Have students start with the model made in the "Average" exercise, and make an audio guided tour of the solar system to go with it.

- Students will research the individual planets and make an audiotape viewers can listen to as they walk from the sun to the end of the model. Along the way, the recording will tell viewers something interesting about each planet they pass.

- These tours need to be timed so someone walking slowly through the model will hear about each planet as he or she passes it. Students should work in groups, with different members researching, writing, and recording the script.

Enduring Understandings
Revisit the Big Idea and Essential Questions

Big Idea Objects in space including Earth and its moon move in regular observable patterns.

To explore the Big Idea, post unit vocabulary terms from the unit on the board. Challenge students to find and explain different ways word pairs are connected. Possible responses:

- *Rotate* and *axis* are connected because an object rotates around an imaginary line called the axis.
- *Solar system* and *planet* are connected in that our solar system includes eight planets.
- *Planet* and *orbit* are connected because the planets in our solar system orbit the sun.

Essential Questions

Post the Essential Questions and use the following prompts to guide a discussion.

Lesson/Essential Question	Prompts
L1 How Do the Sun, Earth, and Moon Interact?	• Describe how Earth moves in space. What results from these movements?
L2 What Are Moon Phases?	• Draw a series of pictures that show how the moon's apparent shape changes over a month.
L3 How Does the Moon Move Around Earth?	• Explain why the same side of the moon always faces Earth.
L4 What Are the Planets in Our Solar System?	• Name the eight planets in our solar system, and give three differences between the inner and outer planets.
L5 How Can We Model the Sun and Planets?	• Compare and contrast the sizes of the sun, the inner planets, and the outer planets.

Notebook ▶ **Science Notebook**

You may use the following strategies after students complete the unit or after each lesson.

- Have students review and edit the answers to Essential Questions they drafted at the beginning of the unit. Suggest they cross out sentences or ideas that are unnecessary or inappropriate.

- Challenge students to make a crossword puzzle, using unit concepts and vocabulary terms, to exchange with a classmate. As an added challenge, have them devise riddles for each clue. For example, *I am a planet. If you had a big enough bowl, I would float in water. What am I?* (Answer: Saturn) Have students write their riddles and answers in their Science Notebooks. You may wish to provide grid paper for them to use when constructing their puzzles.

Science Notebook

Essential Questions	Answers
How Do the Sun, Earth, and Moon Interact?	
What Are Moon Phases?	
How Does the Moon Move Around Earth?	
What Are the Planets in Our Solar System?	
How Can We Model the Sun and Planets?	

Unit 6 Review

Name _____

Vocabulary Review

Use the terms in the box to complete the sentences.

axis
constellation
moon phase
orbit
planet
rotate
solar system

1. A change in the appearance of the moon's shape is known

   as a(n) ____moon phase____.

2. When things turn like a top, they ____rotate____.

3. Earth turns around an imaginary line called

   a(n) ____axis____.

4. The path that one object takes around another object in space

   is its ____orbit____.

5. A star and the planets and other objects that revolve around it

   make up a(n) ____solar system____.

6. A large round body that revolves around a star in a clear orbit

   is a(n) ____planet____.

7. A group of stars that seems to form a pattern in the night sky

   is a(n) ____constellation____.

©Houghton Mifflin Harcourt Publishing Company (border) ©NGDak/Age Fotostock

Unit 6   345

Item Analysis

Items	Depth of Knowledge	Cognitive Complexity
1–7	1	Low

Unit Review

Answer Key

Vocabulary Review (3 points each)

1. **moon phase**

   Direct students to Lesson 2 in this unit, which covers the phases of the moon.

2. **rotate**

   Model the difference between rotation and revolution. Refer students to diagrams that show each type of movement in the section titled "The Sun-Earth-Moon System" in Lesson 1.

3. **axis**

   Spin a world globe for students, demonstrating the way it rotates around a central axis. Emphasize that Earth's axis is imaginary, unlike the axis on the globe.

4. **orbit**

   Note that planets follow an orbit when they revolve around the sun. On the board, draw the sun, Earth, and Earth's orbit represented by an arrow around the sun.

5. **solar system**

   Direct students to review Lesson 4. Then have students list the objects that are part of the solar system as you write them on the board. Emphasize that the sun, a star, is at the center of our solar system.

6. **planet**

   Have students review the first two pages of Lesson 4 to identify the eight planets of the solar system. As an exercise, ask students to write the names of all the planets.

7. **constellation**

   Refer students to the section titled "Patterns in the Sky" in Lesson 1 to see examples of constellations. Discuss with students patterns they might have seen in the night sky.

Assessment

Unit 6 Test and Performance Assessment

See Assessment Guide, pp. AG 67–AG 73, for Unit Test and Performance Task with Long Option rubric.

Unit Review *continued*

Answer Key

Science Concepts (5 points each)

8. A

Students should recognize that the illustration shows Earth's rotation. It takes Earth one day to rotate once.

9. A

Students should recall that as Earth rotates, one side of the planet has day while the other has night.

10. D

Students should recall that when the Northern Hemisphere tilts toward the sun, as it does in August, temperatures are warmer and the season is summer. In January, the Northern Hemisphere is tilted away from the sun and it is winter.

11. D

Have students reread the section titled "Planets Near and Far" in Lesson 4 and look for the art and caption where the sizes of the cores of inner and outer planets are compared.

12. B

Refer students to the order of the moon's phases in Lesson 2, and the sketches of moon phases they made in Lesson 3.

13. D

Reinforce that we see the stars differently at various points as we orbit the sun.

14. A

Use greater-than/less-than statements to help students analyze the data. For example, *Earth's rotation takes less time than that of Mercury.* After students analyze the data, have them reexamine the answer choices for the one that matches their analysis.

Science Concepts

Fill in the letter of the choice that best answers the question.

8. The picture below is a two-dimensional model of how Earth moves in space.

How long does it take for Earth to complete one full movement?

- (A) 1 day
- (B) 1 week
- (C) 1 month
- (D) 1 year

9. A fourth grader in the United States does an experiment in her science class. At the same time, a fourth grader in China is asleep. Why is it daytime in the United States while it is nighttime in China?

- (A) Earth's rotation
- (B) Earth's revolution
- (C) the moon's revolution
- (D) Earth's path as it orbits the sun

10. In the United States, an August day is usually hotter than a January day. Why is this true?

- (A) The sun gives off more heat in the summer.
- (B) Earth is closer to the sun in summer and farther away in winter.
- (C) Earth's rotation slows down in the summer and speeds up in winter.
- (D) Earth's North Pole tilts toward the sun in summer and away from it in winter.

11. Which characteristic do all the inner planets in our solar system have?

- (A) rings
- (B) many moons
- (C) lower densities
- (D) relatively large cores

12. Ashley notices changes in the moon over the course of a month. Which of the following sequences could Ashley have seen?

(A)
Full moon · New moon · Third quarter moon · First quarter moon

(B)
New moon · First quarter moon · Full moon · Third quarter moon

(C)
New moon · First quarter moon · New moon · Third quarter moon

(D)
Full moon · New moon · First quarter moon · Third quarter moon

13. Some constellations are visible from different places on Earth only during part of the year. Why are these constellations not visible from every location on Earth year-round?

- (A) because of the sun's rotation
- (B) because of the moon's revolution
- (C) because of Earth's rotation
- (D) because of Earth's revolution

Item Analysis *(continued)*

Items	Depth of Knowledge	Cognitive Complexity
8	3	High
9–12	2	Moderate
13	3	High
14	2	Moderate

14. The table below contains data showing how long it takes each planet to make one complete rotation and revolution. The numbers are in Earth days.

Planet	Time needed to make one complete rotation (Earth days)	Time needed to make one complete revolution (Earth days)
Mercury	58.6	87.96
Venus	243.0	224.7
Earth	1.0	365.26
Mars	1.02	687.0

According to the data table, which one of these statements is correct?

(A) Earth takes less time to orbit the sun than does Mars.

(B) Venus takes more time to orbit the sun than does Mars.

(C) Venus takes less time to orbit the sun than does Mercury.

(D) Mercury takes more time to orbit the sun than does Earth.

15. Each planet in the solar system has its own characteristics. Which set of characteristics describes Mars?

(A) boiling hot; thick clouds

(B) iron oxide in soil; fourth planet from the sun

(C) made of frozen gases; stormy atmosphere

(D) similar size to Earth; atmosphere rich in carbon dioxide

16. The same side of the moon always faces Earth. Why is this?

(A) Half the moon faces the sun.

(B) The moon does not rotate like Earth does.

(C) The moon's revolution and rotation are about the same length.

(D) Earth blocks part of the sunlight that shines on the moon's surface.

17. Pluto was once classified as a planet. Now it is classified as a dwarf planet. What is one reason for this change?

(A) Pluto is too big to be a planet.

(B) Pluto has a core that is too small.

(C) Pluto's orbit crosses the orbit of another body.

(D) Pluto is too far from the sun to be in the solar system.

18. Which of the following correctly lists the planets of the solar system in order of distance from the sun?

(A) Jupiter, Saturn, Uranus, Neptune, Mercury, Venus, Earth, Mars

(B) Mercury, Venus, Earth, Mars, Jupiter, Saturn, Uranus, Neptune

(C) Mars, Venus, Earth, Mercury, Jupiter, Saturn, Uranus, Neptune

(D) Venus, Mercury, Earth, Saturn, Jupiter, Neptune, Mars, Uranus

Item Analysis (continued)

Items	Depth of Knowledge	Cognitive Complexity
15	3	High
16–18	2	Moderate

Unit Review continued

Answer Key

Science Concepts (5 points each)

15. B

After students review the characteristics of the planets in Lesson 4, challenge them to identify the descriptions of the other planets.

16. C

Have students recall modeling the moon's periods of revolution and rotation in Lesson 3.

17. C

Have students return to the first section of Lesson 4 to review the definition of a dwarf planet. Only choice C fits the definition.

18. B

An overview of the order of the planets outward from the sun is provided on the first pages of Lesson 4.

Short Option Performance Assessment

Task

Construct Space Objects

Ask students to use art supplies to make representations of objects in outer space. Tell students to make, label, and describe these objects: sun, Earth, four moon phases, star, and constellation.

Rubric

Preparation Provide several colors of construction paper (including black to use as a background), glue, scissors, and markers.

Scoring Rubric—Performance Indicators

___ Accurately represents objects in space.

___ Accurately labels all objects.

___ Accurately portrays relationships among objects.

Observations and Rubric Scores

3   2   1   0

Unit Review *continued*

Answer Key

Apply Inquiry and Review the Big Idea

(8 points each)

19. See student page for sample answer.
   Have students refer to Lesson 2 for information on how the moon reflects light from the sun.

20. See student page for sample answer.
   Refer students to the comparative descriptions of the inner and outer planets presented in Lesson 4.

21. See student page for sample answer.
   Draw students' attention to the section titled "Our Place in Space" in Lesson 1, which discusses early Earth-centered theories about the structure of the solar system, and new discoveries that supported a sun-centered model.

Apply Inquiry and Review the Big Idea

Write the answers to these questions.

19. The diagram below shows Earth, the moon, and the sun. This diagram is not drawn to scale.

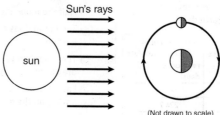

Sun's rays

sun

(Not drawn to scale)

Use the diagram to explain why you can see the moon from Earth.

Sample answer: The moon does not make its own light. We can see the moon because sunlight is reflected from its surface.

20. Scientists classify the planets in our solar system into two groups—inner planets and outer planets. The planets in each group share several characteristics. List four ways in which the inner planets are similar. Then list four ways that the outer planets are similar.

Inner Planets: Students may list four of the following: relatively small and rocky; few or no moons; no rings; short periods of revolution; slow rotation/long days; large solid cores

Outer Planets: Students may list four of the following: giant balls of frozen or liquid gases; fast rotation/short days; long period of revolution; ring; many moons; small solid cores

21. Astronomers before Copernicus and Galileo knew about Earth's moon. They also knew about the planets Mars, Jupiter, and Saturn. Do you think they knew about the moons of Mars, Jupiter, and Saturn? Explain your answer.

Sample answer: No. Most astronomers before Copernicus and Galileo thought Earth was the center of the universe and that all bodies revolved around Earth. Knowledge of moons orbiting other planets would have contradicted this Earth-centered model.

348   Unit 6

Item Analysis *(continued)*

Items	Depth of Knowledge	Cognitive Complexity
19	3	High
20	2	Moderate
21	4	High

Planning Guide Resources

Professional Development

References and Resources

Teacher Notes

Enduring Understandings

Big Ideas, Essential Questions

by Marjorie Frank

It goes without saying that a primary goal for your students is to develop understandings of science concepts that endure well past the next test. The question is, what is the best way to achieve that goal?

Research and learning experts suggest that students learn most effectively through a constructivist approach in which the learner is aware of an end result and is encouraged to figure out how to reach that result. Within constructivism, the teacher's guidance, called scaffolding, is essential to students' success. A key tenet of constructivism is drawn from schema theory—that knowledge is arranged into units called schemas, that information is stored in these units, and that they are interconnected with one another. As teachers, we are uniquely positioned to guide learners to create new schemas, to broaden and deepen existing schemas, and to connect them to others. Informed by these understandings, we set about organizing *ScienceFusion,* beginning with the Big Ideas of science.

Big Ideas are generalizations—broad, powerful concepts that connect facts and events that may otherwise seem unrelated. Big Ideas are implicit understandings that help the world make sense. Big Ideas define the units of *ScienceFusion.* Each is a statement that articulates the overarching teaching and learning goals of a unit.

Essential Questions define the information in a unit. Each Essential Question identifies the conceptual focus of a lesson that contributes to your students' growing understanding of the associated Big Idea. As such, Essential Questions give your students a sense of direction and purpose.

With *ScienceFusion,* our goal is to provide you with a tool that helps you help your students develop Enduring Understandings in science. Our strategy for achieving that goal has been to provide lesson plans with 5E-based learning experiences organized in a framework informed by constructivism and schema theory.

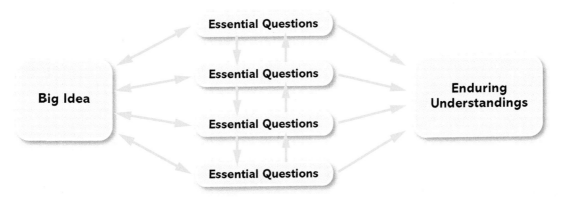

21st Century Skills/STEM

Skills Redefined

Our world has changed. Globalization and the digital revolution have redefined the skill set that is essential for student success in the classroom and beyond. Known collectively as 21st Century Skills, these areas of competence and aptitude go beyond the three Rs of reading, writing, and arithmetic. 21st Century Skills incorporate a battery of high-level thinking skills and technological capabilities.

by
Michael A. DiSpezio

21st Century SKILLS — A Sample List

Learning and Innovation Skills

- Creativity and Innovation
- Critical Thinking and Problem Solving
- Communication and Collaboration

Information, Media, and Technology Skills

- Information Literacy
- Media Literacy
- ICT (Information, Communications, and Technology) Literacy

Life and Career Skills

- Flexibility and Adaptability
- Initiative and Self-Direction
- Productivity and Accountability
- Leadership and Responsibility

S.T.E.M.

Curriculum that integrates Science, Technology, Engineering, and Mathematics

21st Century Skills are best taught in the context of the core subject areas. Science makes an ideal subject for integrating these important skills because it involves many skills, including inquiry, collaboration, and problem solving. An even deeper level of incorporating these skills can be found with Science, Technology, Engineering, and Mathematics (STEM) lessons and activities. Hands-on STEM lessons that provide students with engineering design challenges are ideal for developing Learning and Innovation Skills. Students develop creativity and innovation as they engineer novel solutions to posed problems. They communicate and collaborate as they engage higher-level thinking skills to help shape their inquiry experience. Students assume ownership of the learning. From this emerges increased self-motivation and personal accountability.

As profiled in the Next Generation Science Standards, the application of content to real-world scenarios, as well as elevating engineering to the same level as scientific inquiry, offers the ideal landscape on which to nurture this skill set. With STEM lessons and activities, related disciplines are seamlessly integrated into a succinct *problem–based* scenario and further extended into a *project–based* learning experience that becomes far more than the sum of its parts. Learners emerge with an operational understanding of 21st Century Skills constructed through their usage and application across STEM examples.

ScienceFusion provides deep science content and STEM lessons, activities, and Video-Based Projects that incorporate and develop 21st Century Skills. This provides an effective learning landscape that will prepare students for success in the workplace—and in life.

Professional Development

Differentiated Instruction

Skills Redefined

Your students learn in different ways, at different speeds, and through different means. Channeling the energy and richness of that diversity is part of the art of teaching. A classroom atmosphere that encourages academic risk-taking encourages learning. This is especially true in science, where learning involves making predictions (which could turn out to be inaccurate), offering explanations (which could turn out to be incomplete), and doing things (which could result in observable mistakes).

by Marjorie Frank

Like most people, students are more likely to take risks in a low-stress environment where they feel accepted and respected. Science, with its emphasis on exploring through hands-on activities and interactive reading, provides a natural vehicle for low-stress learning. Low stress, however, may mean different things to different people. For students with learning challenges, low stress may mean being encouraged to respond at the level they are able. For a classroom of diverse learners, it may mean instructional tools that are flexible, inviting, and interactive. *ScienceFusion* addresses the needs of diverse students at every step in the instructional process.

As You Plan

Select from these resources to meet individual needs.

- The planning pages at the beginning of each unit in the Teacher Editions identify resources and strategies geared to diverse learners.

- Online Resource: Digital lessons and virtual labs appeal to all students, especially struggling readers and visual learners. Extra Support for Vocabulary and Concepts are reproducible pages for use with struggling readers and students who need additional reinforcement.

- Student Edition with Audio for use with students who have vision impairments or learning difficulties.

- Leveled Readers reinforce, enrich, and extend concepts. A Teacher Guide for each Reader provides instructional strategies and includes reproducible vocabulary worksheets.

As You Teach

Take advantage of these point-of-use features.

- A mix of Directed Inquiries and Independent Inquiries suitable for different kinds of learners

- Interactive digital lessons

- Leveled questions for Extra Support, Enrichment, and English Language Learners

- Make Connections: Easy, Average, and Challenging follow-up activities.

 **As You Reach Out to Families**

Look for these school-home connections.

- Take It Home! at the end of every lesson in the Student Edition and Teacher's Edition

- Customizable School-Home Connection Letters for every lesson, available online.

The 5E Model and Levels of Inquiry

How do students best learn science? Extensive research and data show that the most effective learning emerges from situations in which one builds understanding based upon personal experiences. Learning is not transmitted from instructor to passive receiver; instead, understanding is constructed through the experience.

by
Michael A. DiSpezio

The 5E Model for Effective Science Lessons

In the 1960s, Robert Karplus and his colleagues developed a three-step instructional model that became known as the Learning Cycle. This model was expanded into what is today referred to as the 5E Model. To emulate the elements of how an actual scientist works, this model is broken down into five components for an effective lesson: Engage, Explore, Explain, Extend (or Elaborate), and Evaluate.

Engage—The engagement sets the scene for learning. It is a warm-up during which students are introduced to the learning experience. Prior knowledge is assessed and its analysis used to develop an effective plan to meet stated objectives. Typically, an essential question is then posed; the question leads the now motivated and engaged students into the exploration.

Explore—This is the stage where the students become actively involved in hands-on process. They communicate and collaborate to develop a strategy that addresses the posed problem. Emphasis is placed on inquiry and hands-on investigation. The hands-on experience may be highly prescribed or open-ended in nature.

Explain—Students answer the initial question by using their findings and information they may be reading about, discussing with classmates, or experiencing through digital media. Their experience and understanding of concepts, processes, and hands-on skills is strengthened at this point. New vocabulary may be introduced.

Extend (or Elaborate)—The explanation is now extended to other situations, questions, or problems. During this stage the learner more closely examines findings in terms of context and transferable application. In short, extension reveals the application and implication of the internalized explanation. Extension may involve connections to other curriculum areas.

Evaluate—Although evaluation is an ongoing process, this is the stage in which a final assessment is most often performed. The instructor evaluates lesson effectiveness by using a variety of formal and informal assessment tools to measure student performance.

The 5E lesson format is used in all the *ScienceFusion* Teacher Edition lessons.

Directed, Guided, and Independent Inquiry

Today, most instructional strategies integrate an inquiry-based approach to learning science. Under the conceptual umbrella of the Next Generation Science Standards' term "science practices," this methodology is founded in higher-level thinking and facilitates the students' construction of understanding from experience. When offered opportunities to ask questions, design investigations, collect and analyze data, and communicate their findings, each student assumes the role of an active participant in shaping his or her own learning process.

The degree to which any activity engages the inquiry process is variable, from highly prescribed steps to a completely learner-generated design. Researchers have established three distinct levels of inquiry: directed (or structured) inquiry, guided inquiry, and independent (or open) inquiry. These levels are distinguished by the amount of guidance offered by the instructor.

Directed Inquiry In this level of inquiry, the instructor poses a question or suggests an investigation, and students follow a prescribed set of instructions. The outcome may be unknown to the students, but it is known to the instructor. Students follow the structured outline to uncover an outcome that supports the construction of lesson concepts.

Guided Inquiry As in Directed Inquiry, the instructor poses to the students a question to investigate. While students are conducting the investigation, the instruction focuses on developing one or more inquiry skills. Focus may also be provided for students to learn to use methods or tools of science. In *ScienceFusion*, the Teacher Edition provides scaffolding for developing inquiry skills, science methods, or tools. Student pages accompany these lessons and provide prompts for writing hypotheses, recording data, and drawing conclusions.

Independent Inquiry This is the most complex level of inquiry experience. A prompt is provided, but students must design their own investigation in response to the prompt. In some cases, students will write their own questions and then plan and perform scientific investigations that will answer those questions. This level of inquiry is often used for science fair projects. Independent Inquiry does not necessarily mean individual inquiry. Investigations can be conducted by individual students or by pairs or teams of students.

Response to Intervention

In a traditional model, assessments mark the end of an instructional cycle. Students work through a unit, take a test, get a grade, and move on. The test functions as an assessment of student achievement. It is summative. Current research supports the use of formative assessments; that is, assessments embedded within the learning cycle and used to inform teaching and learning activities going forward. Within this model, assessments are used to identify students who may need intervention.

by Marjorie Frank

Formal Assessments

Every student interaction has the potential to be a formative assessment. Whether its potential is realized depends on you, the teacher/listener.

- Suppose you ask a question. You can judge the answer as correct or incorrect. Or, you can use it as "data." Does it indicate comprehension? Does it reveal a misconception, a misunderstanding, a mistake? If so, intervention may be needed.

- Suppose students offer explanations of a phenomenon, such as a volcanic eruption. You can judge the explanations as correct or incorrect. Or, you can listen and assess the knowledge underlying them. Is it consistent with scientific understanding? If not, intervention may be needed.

- Suppose students draw a diagram, such as a depiction of an atom. The diagram itself may reveal the source of a misunderstanding and the need for intervention.

As the examples indicate, assessing students' understandings can—and should—be an integral part of the instructional cycle and be used to make decisions about the next steps of instruction. For students making good progress, the next steps might be exploring a related concept, a new lesson, or an additional challenge. For students who are not making adequate progress, intervention may be needed.

Assessment and intervention are tightly linked. Assessment leads to intervention—fresh approaches, different groupings, new materials—which, in turn, leads to assessment. Response to Intervention (RTI) gives shape and substance to this linkage.

RTI Response to Intervention

Response to Intervention is a process for identifying and supporting students who are not making expected progress toward essential learning goals.

RTI is a three-tiered approach based on an ongoing cycle of superior instruction, frequent monitoring of students' learning (formative assessments), and appropriate interventions. Students who are found not to be making expected progress in one Tier move to the next higher Tier, where they receive more intense instruction.

- **Tier I:** Students receive whole-class, core instruction.

- **Tier II:** Students work in small groups that supplement and reinforce core instruction.

- **Tier III:** Students receive individualized instruction.

How RTI and *ScienceFusion* Work

ScienceFusion provides many opportunities to assess students' understanding and many components appropriate for students in all Tiers.

TIER III Intensive Intervention
Individualized instruction, with options for auditory, visual, and second language learners. Special education is a possibility.

Online Student Edition

ScienceFusion Components

Online Student Edition lessons with audio recordings

Appropriate for:
- Auditory learners

Online Extra Support for Vocabulary and Concepts

Appropriate for:
- Struggling readers
- Second-language learners

Extra Support

Students achieving at a lower level than their peers in Tier II

TIER II Strategic Intervention
Small Group Instruction in addition to core instruction

ScienceFusion Components

Extra Support Leveled Readers

Leveled Reader Teacher Guide

Vocabulary Worksheets

Appropriate for:
- Struggling readers
- Visual learners
- Second-language learners
- Screening tools to assess students' responses to Tier II instruction

Students achieving at a lower level than their peers in Tier I

TIER I Core Classroom Instruction
With the help of extensive point-of-use strategies that support superior teaching, students receive whole-class instruction and engage productively in small-group work as appropriate.

Teacher Edition

Student Edition

Assessment Guide

ScienceFusion Components

Student Edition
Teacher Edition
Assessment Guide
Online Digital Curriculum

Appropriate for:
- Screening tools to access students' responses to Tier I instruction
- Tier I intervention for students unable to complete the activity independently

Digital Curriculum

Science Notebooks

The What, Why, Who, When, Where and How!

Science Notebooks are powerful tools, and they play an important role in every teacher's inbox. They lead your students deep into the learning process, and they provide you with a window into that process as well as a means to communicate about it.

by Marjorie Frank

Notebook ▸ What Are Science Notebooks?

A notebook contains the writer's ideas, observations, and perceptions of events and endeavors. A Science Notebook contains ideas about and observations of scientific processes, data, conclusions, conjectures, and generalizations.

A Science Notebook can be in many formats—spiral bound, tablet, loose pages in a binder, or digital. Like an ordinary notebook, it functions much like a storehouse, a place where things are collected and held. The "things" in a Science Notebook can be just about anything related to what students are doing and learning in science:

- observations and data
- drawings and diagrams of structures and processes
- graphs
- charts
- summaries of new concepts or a textbook lesson
- vocabulary words with definitions and drawings
- graphic organizers showing how ideas are connected
- responses to lessons or a specific learning experience
- reflections about their work and the meaning they derived from science experiences
- responses to questions
- new questions
- predictions and plans for an investigation
- observations and conclusions
- drawings or sketches from field trips
- original stories and poems about science topics
- science applications in daily life

A Science Notebook is especially important when students do inquiry-based or project-based learning. It offers students a single place to record their observations, consider possibilities, and organize their thoughts. As such, it is a learner's version of the logs professional scientists keep.

Notebook ▸ **Why** Bother with Science Notebooks?

No doubt, it takes time and effort to help students set up and maintain Science Notebooks, not to mention the time it takes you to review them and provide meaningful feedback. The payoff better be worth it, you're probably saying to yourself. And it is. Here's why.

Keeping a Science Notebook:

- leads each learner to engage with ideas (not just those who raise their hands in class)
- engages students in writing—an active, thinking, analytical process
- causes students to organize their thinking
- helps students develop 21st Century organizational skills
- enables students to express themselves creatively
- provides students with multiple opportunities and modes to process new information
- makes learning experiences more personal
- provides students with a record of their own progress and accomplishments
- doubles as a study guide for formal assessments
- creates a vehicle for students to improve their reading and writing skills

Notebook ▸ **Who** Should Keep a Science Notebook?

Every single student, regardless of age, aptitude, or language background.

Science Notebooks are well suited for differentiating instruction. By allowing students to draw about their investigations and use the glossary to label their drawings, you can include all students in the process. Students can also work in pairs to do shared writing.

Kindergarten and first grade learners may dictate brief captions to pictures that tell their science story. Or, they may benefit from working as a class to construct a science "big book."

Notebook ▸ **When** Should Students Work in Their Science Notebooks?

During every single science class.

On some days, students may only write a summary of a lesson, or write a response to an experience. On other days, they may attach a data sheet they completed during an investigation, or write a longer entry that includes diagrams, data, conclusions, and reflections.

Notebook ▸ **Where** Should Science Notebooks Be Stored?

In school. The Notebooks can be stored in a basket, in a bin, or behind a colored tab in a file cabinet. If students are working in groups or teams, each team may have its own basket or bin. Use color-coding for easy identification. Store the Notebooks near the science materials if there's space.

Notebook ▸ **How** Can I Get Started with Science Notebooks in My Class?

You'll want to have students set up their Science Notebooks as soon as possible after school begins. You might want to follow these steps or modify them to suit your needs.

1. After deciding on a Notebook format—spiral, pad, loose leaf in a binder, or digital—invite students to make a cover with their name, your name, the class period, and a decoration.

2. Use the first three or four pages to create a Table of Contents. Remind students to write "Table of Contents" at the top of each page.

3. Set up three columns on each Contents page and label the columns *Page, Activity,* and *Dates.*

4. Number the pages. While this may seem like a tedious task, it will pay off many times over during the year.

5. Although *ScienceFusion* has an interactive glossary at the back of the Student Edition, you may want students to use the last ten or twelve pages of their Science Notebooks for a glossary.

Now your students are all set!

For each activity or concept, students should start a new page. Many teachers have students use the pages as pairs, with the right page for input (e.g., information they receive from reading, viewing videos, and listening) and the left page for output (e.g., student-made diagrams, concept maps, drawings, observations, and questions related to the input). After students complete their work, they should return to the Table of Contents and fill in the information.

 TIP **Keeping Place in the Notebooks**

Students can lose valuable time trying to find their place in their Notebook. Here are some ways to get around the problem:

- Have students use a binder clip to hold all the unused pages. During each lesson, they can remove newly used pages from the clip.

- Suggest that students tape a string to the spiral or spine of a binder and place the string between the used and unused pages.

- Encourage students to use a sticky-note to mark the last used page or first unused page.

How Can I Give My Students Feedback on Their Notebooks?

Giving feedback is one of the most important strategies you can use to support students' learning. You'll want to review your students' Notebooks as often as possible. This is a case where *more* really is better. Students need to know their Notebooks are important. Regular feedback sends that message.

Many teachers provide critical feedback to coincide with points in the curriculum where mastery is key to moving on—for example, in the middle and at the end of a unit.

- Be sure you have a clear understanding of the lesson objective. This will help you decide how to comment on whether a student has met the objective. In *ScienceFusion*, a full answer to an Essential Question articulates the content of lesson objectives.
- Provide positive feedback directly in a Student's Notebook.
- Make suggestions for additional thought or work on sticky-notes, which can be removed when the work is completed.
- When possible, couch your suggestions as guiding questions such as, What conclusions can you draw from the evidence? Which of the variables will you need to control?

You may wish to have students conduct a self-evaluation of their Science Notebook. This page is available in the *ScienceFusion* Assessment Guide.

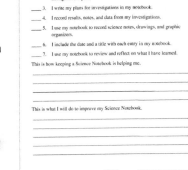

Science Notebooks and *ScienceFusion*

Notebook ▸ *ScienceFusion* Teacher Editions and the Inquiry Flipcharts include point-of-use suggestions and strategies for Science Notebook entries. Look for the Science Notebook features.

⊙ Strategies for using Science Notebooks with all the *ScienceFusion* Inquiry activities are provided in Online Inquiry Support in Online Resources.

Notebook ▸ The Teacher Editions also include suggestions for summarizing ideas after each two-page spread. The Science Notebook is an ideal place for students to write their summaries.

As you and your students embrace Notebooking, you will surely find it to be an engaging, enriching, and very valuable endeavor.

Active Reading

Reading is a complex process in which readers use their knowledge and experience to make meaning from text. Though rarely accompanied by obvious large-muscle movement, reading is very much an active endeavor.

by Marjorie Frank

Think back to your days as a college student when you pored over your textbooks to prepare for class or for an exam—or, more recently, concentrated on an article or book with information you wanted to remember.

▶ You probably paid close attention to the text.

▶ Perhaps you paused to ask yourself questions.

▶ You might have broken off temporarily to look up an important, but unfamiliar, word.

▶ You may have stopped to reread a challenging passage or to "catch up" if your mind wandered for a moment.

If you owned the reading material, you also may have used a pencil or marker to interact with the text right there on the page (or in a digital file).

In short, you were having a conversation with yourself about the text. You were engaged. You were thinking critically.

These are the characteristics of active readers. This is precisely the kind of reader you want your students to be, because research suggests that active reading enables readers to understand and remember more information.

Active Reading involves interacting with text cognitively, metacognitively, and quite literally. You can actually see active readers at work. They are not sitting quietly as they read; they're underlining, marking, boxing, bracketing, drawing arrows, numbering, and writing comments. Here is what they may be noting:

▶ key terms and main ideas

▶ questions they have, opinions, agreements, and disagreements

▶ important facts and details

▶ sequences of events

▶ words, such as *because, before,* and *but,* that signal connections between ideas

▶ problems/solutions

▶ definitions and examples

The very process of interacting actively with text helps keep readers focused, thinking, comprehending, and remembering. But interacting in this way means readers are marking up the text. This is exactly why *ScienceFusion* Student Editions are consumable. They are meant to be marked up.

Active Reading and *ScienceFusion*

ScienceFusion includes Active Reading prompts and strategies on most pages of the Student Editions. The prompts appear at the beginning of each lesson and on most two-page spreads.

The first page of each lesson includes an Active Reading prompt. Beginning in Grade 3, these prompts give readers a heads-up about the text structure of the lesson—the way the ideas are organized. Reading experts suggest that knowledge of text structure improves comprehension since readers approach the text ready to think about ideas in the same way the writer has organized them. Cause and effect, sequence, compare/contrast, problem/solution, and main idea and details are ways to organize text.

Cause and Effect

Some ideas in this lesson are connected by a cause-and-effect relationship. Why something happens as a result of something else is an effect. Active readers look for effects by asking themselves, What happened? They look for causes by asking, Why did it happen?

Each prompt also includes a specific idea for readers to keep in mind, engaging self-monitoring or metacognitive strategies. For example, a prompt may give readers specific questions to ask themselves so they remain focused on causes and effects, comparisons, events in sequence, or other relationships. Other prompts urge readers to look for specific words that signal a text structure or to preview the text, turning headings into questions the text will answer.

Examples of **Active Reading** Prompts

- Draw a star next to the names of animals that hatch from eggs and a check mark next to the names of animals that are born live.

- As you read these two pages, circle lesson vocabulary each time it is used.

- Find and underline four clues that a chemical change has occured.

- Put a *P* next to the sentences that describe a problem. Put an *S* next to the sentences that describe a solution.

Students' Responses to Active Reading Prompts

Active Reading has benefits for you as well as for your students. You can use students' responses to Active Reading prompts and the other interactive prompts in *ScienceFusion* as ongoing assessments. A quick review of students' responses provides a great deal of information.

▶ Are students comprehending the text?

▶ How deeply do they understand the concepts developed?

▶ Did they get the main idea? the cause? the order in which things happen?

Answers to these questions are available in students' responses to Active Learning prompts throughout a lesson—long before you might see poor results on a test. These frequent and regular assessments are integral parts of an effective Response to Intervention program.

The Active Reading prompts in *ScienceFusion* help make everyone a winner.

Project-Based Learning

For a list of the *ScienceFusion* Video-Based Projects, see page T21.

**by
Michael R. Heithaus**

When asked why I decided to become a biologist, the answer is pretty simple. I was inspired by spending almost every day outdoors, exploring under every rock, getting muddy in creeks and streams, and fishing in farm ponds, rivers, and—when I was really lucky—the oceans. Combine that with the spectacular stories of amazing animals and adventures that I saw on TV and I was hooked. As I've progressed in my career as a biologist, that same excitement and curiosity that I had as a ten-year-old looking for a salamander is still driving me.

But today's kids live in a very different world. Cable and satellite TV, Twitter, MP3 players, cell phones, and video games all compete with the outdoors for kids' time and attention. Education budget cuts, legal issues, and the pressures of standardized testing have also limited the opportunities for students to explore outdoors with their teachers.

How do we overcome these challenges so as to inspire kids' curiosity, help them connect with the natural world, and get them to engage in science and math? This is a critical issue. Not only do we need to ensure our national competitiveness and the conservation of our natural resources by training the next generation of scientists, we also need to ensure that every kid grows up to appreciate the environment that supports us and to understand how scientists work and why their work is important.

How do we do this? First, we must grab students' attention and get them to actively engage in the learning process. Research shows that students who are active and engaged participants in their learning have greater gains in concept and skills development than students who are passive in the classroom.

Project-based learning is one way to engage students. And when the stimulus for the project is exciting video content, engaged and active learning is almost guaranteed. Nothing captures a student's attention faster than an exciting video. I have noticed that when my university students have video to accompany a lesson, they learn and retain the material better. It's no different for younger students! Videos need to do more than just "talk at" students to have a real impact. Videos need to engage students and require participation.

Teachers and students who use *ScienceFusion* video-based projects have noticed the following:

- The videos use captivating imagery, dynamic scientists, and cool stories to inspire kids to be curious about the world around them.
- Students connect to the projects by having the videos present interesting problems for them to solve.
- The videos engage students with projects woven into the story of the video so students are doing the work of real scientists!
- When used *before* a unit is presented, students are able to grasp and apply the information more quickly and retain it more effectively.
- Students are excited to learn and apply math and graphing skills to answer the questions *they* developed during the project.

The start-to-finish nature of the video projects, where students do background research and develop their own hypotheses, should lead to students' personal investment in solving the challenges that are presented. By seeing real scientists who are excellent role models gather data that they have to graph and interpret, students will not only learn the science standards being addressed, but they will also see that they can apply the scientific method to their lives. One day, they too could be a scientist!

Based on my experiences teaching in the university classroom, leading field trips for middle school students, and taking the first project-based videos into the classroom, project-based learning has considerable benefits. The video-based projects generate enthusiasm and curiosity. They also help students develop a deeper understanding of science content as well as how to go about a scientific investigation. If we inspire students to ask questions and seek answers for themselves, we will go a long way toward closing achievement gaps in science and math and facilitate the development of the next generation of scientists and scientifically literate citizens.

(c) ©Adam Rosenblatt; (b) ©David Ponton/Design Pics/Corbis

Developing Visual Literacy

Science teachers can build the bridges between students' general literacy and their scientific literacy by focusing attention on the particular kinds of reading strategies students need to be successful. One such strategy is that of knowing how to read and interpret the various visual displays used in science.

by
Donna M. Ogle

Many young readers receive little instruction in reading charts, tables, diagrams, photographs, or illustrations in their language arts/reading classes. Science is where these skills can and must be developed. Science provides a meaningful context where students can learn to read visually presented forms of information and to create their own visual representations. Research studies have shown that students take longer to read science materials containing combinations of visual displays and narrative texts than they do to read narrative text alone. The process of reading the combination materials is slower and more difficult because the reader must relate the visual displays to the narrative text and build a meaning that is based on information from both.

We also know that students benefit when teachers take time to explain how each visual form is constructed and to guide students in the thinking needed to make sense of these forms. Even the seemingly simple act of interpreting a photograph needs to be taught to most students. Here are some ways to help students develop the ability to think more critically about what they view:

▶ Model for students how to look carefully at a photograph and list what they notice.
▶ Divide the photograph into quadrants and have students think more deeply about what the photographer has used as the focus of the image and what context is provided.
▶ Have students use language such as *zoom, close-up, foreground, background,* or *panorama views* to describe photographs.

The ability to interpret a photograph is clearly a part of the scientific skill of engaging in careful observation. This skill helps students when they are using print materials, observing nature, and making their own photographs of aspects of their experiments.

Attention to the other forms of visual displays frequently used in science is also important to students' learning of scientific concepts and processes. For example, students in grades 4 through 8 need to learn to interpret and then construct each of the types of graphs, from circle graphs and bar graphs to more complex line graphs.

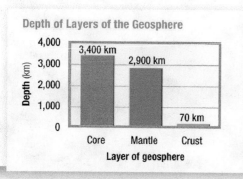

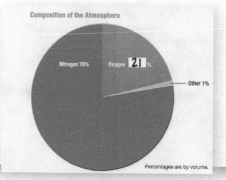

Students also need to be able to read diagrams and flow charts. Yet, in a recent study asking students to think aloud and point to how they visually scan tables and diagrams, we learned how inadequate many students were as readers of these visual forms. Because so much of the scientific information students will encounter is summarized in these visual formats, it is essential that students learn to interpret and construct visual displays.

A second aspect of interpreting visual displays is connecting the information in the visual formats with the narrative text information.
Some students misinterpret what they see in visuals when even a few words differ between the text and the illustration. For example, in this page from a Middle School Student Edition, the text says, "the arm of a human, the front leg of a cat, and the wing of a bat do not look alike . . . but they are similar in structure."

The diagram labels (lower right) showing the bat wing and the cat's leg use *front limb*, not *wing* or *leg*. For students who struggle with English, the differing terms may cause confusion unless teachers show students how to use clues from later in the paragraph, where limb and wing/arm are connected, and how to connect this information to the two drawings. In some cases teachers have students draw lines showing where visual displays connect with the more extensive narrative text content. Developing students' awareness of how visual and narrative information support each other and yet provide different forms in which information can be shared is an important step in building scientific literacy.

Reading science requires students to use specific reading strategies. The more carefully science teachers across grade levels assess what students already know about reading scientific materials, the more easily they can focus instruction to build the scaffolds students need to gain independence and confidence in their reading and learning of science. Time spent explaining, modeling, and guiding students will yield the rewards of heightened student enjoyment, confidence, and engagement in the exciting world of scientific inquiry.

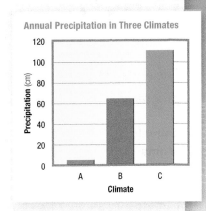

Annual Precipitation in Three Climates

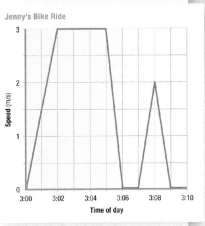

Jenny's Bike Ride

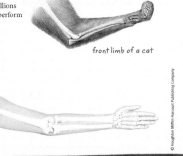

Common Structures

Scientists have found that related organisms share structural traits. Structures reduced in size or function may have been complete and functional in the organism's ancestor. For example, snakes have traces of leglike structures that are not used for movement. These unused structures are evidence that snakes share a common ancestor with animals like lizards and dogs.

Scientists also consider similar structures with different functions. The arm of a human, the front leg of a cat, and the wing of a bat do not look alike and are not used in the same way. But as you can see, they are similar in structure. The bones of a human arm are similar in structure to the bones in the front limbs of a cat and a bat. These similarities suggest that cats, bats, and humans had a common ancestor. Over millions of years, changes occurred. Now, these bones perform different functions in each type of animal.

front limb of a bat

front limb of a cat

 Visualize It!

10 Relate Do you see any similarities between the bones of the bat and cat limbs and the bones of the human arm? If so, use the colors of the bat and cat bones to color similar bones in the human arm. If you don't have colored pencils, label the bones with the correct color names.

Teacher Science Background

These pages provide concise science background for the major topics and concepts in this program. The information is organized according to the following key words:

animals	engineering and	landforms	properties of matter
atoms	technology	light	rocks
cells	engineering design	magnetism	scientific methods
changes in matter	process	measuring matter	scientific tools
climate	exploring space	meteorology	simple machines
earthquakes	food chains and food	minerals	solar system
Earth's changing	webs	motion	sound
surface	forces	natural resources	states of matter
ecosystems	fossils	oceans	volcanoes
electricity	heredity	planetary cycles	water
energy	human body	plants	water cycle
	inquiry skills	plate tectonics	

Additional background information is provided in ⊘ Online Resources. The online content, appropriate for teachers and students, provides the following benefits:

• Free up-to-date web content to extend and expand student understanding

• Lessons, assessments, and deeper exploration of content for teachers

• Content that is constantly reviewed and vetted by experienced NSTA educators (National Science Teachers Association)

• Activities to bring science alive in the classroom

Animals

Adaptation

An adaptation is a characteristic of a plant or an animal that allows the organism to survive in a particular environment. Some adaptations have developed over many generations. Some, however, occur within a single generation. The key to adaptation is variation, or difference, within a species. In order for a species to survive, it must be able to adapt, or change, to better fit new circumstances that arise within an environment. Adaptations can take the form of changes both in an organism's body (physical adaptation) and in its behavior (behavioral adaptation). An example of the former is the long, pointed beak of the hummingbird, which is designed to fit inside tubular flowers. An example of the latter is the nest-building and courting-dance activity of the male bower bird that helps him attract a mate. These adaptations do not happen during one animal's lifetime, but over many generations. The shape of a bird's beak, the placement of a fish's eyes, and the shape of a mammal's teeth are just a few adaptations that help animals survive.

How Animals Are Born and Grow

All animals produce offspring in one of two ways. Some animals hatch from eggs, while others develop inside the mother before she gives birth. Some animals look like their parents when they are born and others do not. Some need a lot of parental care; others need little. All need food, water, air, and shelter to survive. Either the parent helps the young meet these needs, or the young are equipped to meet them. In species where there is little or no parenting, the adults produce many offspring to compensate for those lost to predators. An animal's body covering also changes as the animal grows. Young animals that have to fend for themselves tend to develop mature body coverings faster than animals that receive parental care.

Protective Body Coverings

An animal's body covering protects an animal from the harmful elements of its environment. The hard outer shell of an insect and the sharp quills of a porcupine act as shields around these organisms. Body coverings also protect animals from extreme temperatures. Thick hair traps an animal's body heat to insulate it in a cold environment. Thin porous skin enables an animal to release body heat and keep cool in a warm environment.

Animal Classification

Living things can be grouped into domains and kingdoms. Two of the kingdoms are the plant kingdom and the animal kingdom. To organize the thousands of different species in the animal kingdom, zoologists group animals into categories according to their genetic makeup and their physical similarities and differences. Zoologists divide the animal kingdom into smaller and smaller groups called *subkingdoms*, *phyla*, and *subphyla*. This classification system is called a *taxonomy*. Animals can further be divided into smaller groups. The science of animal classification has been developing for more than 300 years. Because contemporary scientists can study the genetic makeup of animals, scientists can now group them in more ways. They have even found some new groups. Some animals may seem to belong to one group but actually belong to another. For example, a whale lives in water like a fish, but it is a mammal. It feeds milk to its young, and it has lungs instead of gills.

Vertebrates and Invertebrates

The terms *vertebrate* and *invertebrate* are used by scientists as a matter of convenience. The terms do not indicate a natural division in the animal kingdom because the divisions do not indicate the real relationships among the animals in the groups. Some invertebrates are more closely related to the vertebrates than they are to other invertebrates. For example, echinoderms (the group that includes sand dollars, sea stars, and sea urchins) belong to a group of animals called *deuterostomes*. The term describes the animals' embryonic development. All vertebrates are deuterostomes. Most other groups of invertebrates, however, belong to a group called *protostomes*. Thus, echinoderms are inferred to be more closely related to vertebrates than to other invertebrate groups.

Atoms

Models of the Atom

The model of the atom has gone through several changes.

- In 1911, Ernest Rutherford proposed his nuclear theory of the atom, suggesting that an atom contains electrons and protons. At the time, no one understood how their opposite charges could exist together.

- In 1915, Niels Bohr proposed that electrons orbit the nucleus in the same way that planets orbit the sun. His model gained acceptance for a while, but it didn't explain some properties of some elements.

- In the 1920s, Erwin Schrödinger developed the current electron "cloud" model, which models the probability of finding an electron in a region outside the nucleus.

Cells

Cells into Tissues

Most multicellular organisms are made up of many different kinds of cells, each kind specialized to do a certain job. Cell specialization occurs during the development of a new organism. After fertilization, the genetic material contained in the zygote's nucleus directs each new cell produced by mitosis to enter one of several different pathways for development. In flowering plants, for example, a fertilized egg gives rise to at least 15 different kinds of specialized cells. In vertebrates, the egg gives rise to more than 100 specialized cell types. In both plants and animals, similar specialized cells that work together to carry out a specific task for the organism are known as a tissue.

Stages of Cell Division

Mitosis occurs in a predictable series of phases.

- **Interphase:** The cell prepares for cell division. The chromosomes copy themselves, and the cytoplasm of the cell increases in volume.

- **Prophase:** The chromosomes become thicker and visible with a microscope. The membrane surrounding the nucleus disappears.

- **Metaphase:** The chromosomes line up across the center of the cell.

- **Anaphase:** The chromosomes divide and move to opposite poles of the cell.

- **Telophase:** The end of mitosis. New nuclear membranes form around the chromosomes at each end of the cell. In animal cells, the cell membrane pinches in, dividing the cell into two identical daughter cells.

Changes in Matter

Changes in Matter

Cutting, bending, and wetting things with water are ways to cause physical changes in matter. When a physical change takes place, the substance itself does not change. Paper remains paper, no matter how it is changed physically. Matter can also be changed chemically, but chemical changes affect the basic nature of a substance. Chemical changes can occur when a substance burns, oxidizes, or is dissolved in an acid. When a chemical change takes place, a new substance is formed, and the change is permanent.

Gases

Like solids and liquids, gases are a form of matter with properties that can be observed and described. Gases spread out to fill whatever empty space they occupy, from balloons and bubbles to rooms, or Earth's atmosphere. Water vapor, oxygen, and carbon dioxide are some gases that students are familiar with. They can see carbon dioxide bubbles in soda water and oxygen bubbles on the *elodea* plant in fish tanks. They can observe water evaporate and become invisible as water vapor. Many gases are odorless and colorless, but others can smell like rotten eggs or swampy muck.

Students can experience how gases act when they squeeze an inflated balloon, open a bottle of soda water, or stand in front of a fan.

Climate

Climate

Recording and charting daily weather helps people understand the climate of an area. People make generalizations about climate based on recorded average weather conditions of an area over a long period of time. There are different kinds of climates, the three main types being polar, temperate, and tropical. In general, the greater a region's distance from the equator, the cooler the climate will be.

Earthquakes

Moment Magnitude Scale

The moment magnitude scale measures earthquake magnitude more precisely than the Richter Scale. The moment magnitude scale measures the total energy that an earthquake releases. This is measured by multiplying the distance the ground moves along the fault by the area of the fault's rupture surface. This scale is particularly accurate for measuring large earthquakes.

Seismology

The study of earthquake waves, known as *seismology*, dates back almost 2,000 years to the Chinese. Today's seismographs work by suspending a weight from a support that is attached to bedrock.

- When waves from an earthquake reach the seismograph, the inertia of the weight keeps it stationary while Earth and the support vibrate.

- The vibrations used to be recorded on a rotating drum; now all seismographs are recorded digitally.

- The resulting record, called a seismogram, reveals two main types of waves: surface waves, which travel along Earth's surface, and the body waves, which travel through Earth's interior.

Earthquake Waves

An earthquake produces primary waves (P waves), secondary waves (S waves), and surface waves.

- P waves and S waves both travel through Earth's interior.

- P waves are "push-pull," or compression waves. They push (compress) and pull (expand) rocks in the same direction that the wave is moving. P waves can travel through solids, liquids, and gases.

- S waves, on the other hand, vibrate the particles at right angles to the waves' direction of travel. The vibrations can travel only through solids, so gases and liquids do not transmit S waves.

- Surface waves travel along Earth's outer layer, moving up and down and side to side. It is the side-to-side motion that is particularly damaging.

Earth's Changing Surface

Creep

Creep is a slow type of ground movement. During creep, soil gradually shifts downhill because of gravity. Unlike other types of ground movements such as landslides, creep is so slow that changes in landforms are hard to observe directly. The land may move only a few centimeters each year. But while creep cannot be seen occurring, over time it can move fences, utility poles, roads, and railroad tracks.

Types of Glaciers

There are two main kinds of glaciers. Valley glaciers are found in high mountain valleys. They flow slowly down mountainsides, eroding the mountain under them and forming U-shaped valleys. Only a few valley glaciers remain in North America, and even those are melting rapidly. Continental glaciers are ice sheets that cover large areas of Earth. They cover almost all of Greenland and Antarctica today. Thousands of years ago, when the global climate was colder, continental glaciers covered Europe, Canada, and the northern United States. The Great Lakes formed as retreating continental glaciers melted.

Erosion

Gravity is a force that pulls objects toward each other. It causes objects to fall toward Earth's surface and to roll down hills. Gravity can help erode mountains and hills by causing loose debris such as boulders and rocks to tumble down the slopes. Other agents, such as water, ice, wind, plants, and animals, also weather and erode rock, sand, and soil. In turn, rock, sand, and soil can further erode other rock. For example, a rolling boulder can cause erosion by breaking up rocks, causing material to fall, and destroying plants. Of all of the agents of erosion, water is the most powerful. A large drop of water can splash sand grains 30 cm (1 ft) or more into the air.

How Animals Help Plants

Animals help plants in two basic ways. First, they help plants grow better. Animals enrich the soil by leaving behind their wastes. They also enrich it by mixing humus, or dead organic matter, into the soil. This helps recycle nutrients plants need to grow. Small animals, such as earthworms and moles, also aerate the soil when they dig tunnels. Plant roots get air and water more easily in loose, aerated soil. Animals also help plants make new plants. Some plants need animals to scatter plant seeds and pollen, which is necessary for reproduction. Many plants cannot make seeds unless they receive pollen from another plant, and they depend on animals such as insects, birds, and even some mammals to bring them the pollen they need. They produce sweet nectar to attract the animals to the part of the flower where the pollen is located.

Ecosystems

Scientists define an ecosystem as any group of organisms interacting with each other and with their physical environment. Thus, an ecosystem can be as small as a drop of pond water or as large as the entire Earth. The Earth ecosystem is called the biosphere. Organisms within an ecosystem compete with each other for food, energy, and space. They also interact with the nonliving components of the ecosystem, for example, by taking minerals from the soil, consuming water and oxygen, and anchoring topsoil against erosion.

Limiting Factors

In an ecosystem, all populations tend to increase until they reach the carrying capacity of the ecosystem. The carrying capacity is the number of organisms that the environment can support. Factors that limit this growth include the amounts of available food, water, oxygen, and space. Other factors include the number of predators, competition within a population, and parasitism. For plants, limiting factors also include the amount of sunlight, the richness of the soil, the temperature range, the strength of the winds, and so on. A factor that limits one population, such as scarce water limiting the growth of grass, can be an indirect limiting factor for the population that eats the grass—and for the population that eats the grass-eaters.

Primary Succession

Volcanoes that erupt periodically, such as those on the Hawaiian Islands, offer scientists a chance to study the stages of succession in an ecosystem. After a new lava flow, organisms immediately begin to arrive from nearby ecosystems. In Hawai'i, the first ones are likely to be wolf spiders. They eat other insects that wander onto the cooled lava. Soon the wind and rains bring seeds and spores that slip into cracks and pockets in the lava. The pockets catch rainwater, allowing ferns and shrubs to sprout. In time, these plants form a layer of vegetation, catching bits of leaves, bark, and roots from other plants. Decomposers help turn this dead matter into nutrients for more plants. In Hawai'i, a forest can develop on a lava flow in only 150 years.

Electricity

Electric Components

Most circuits use a few basic electric parts, also called components. Here are a few:

- Resistors are components that limit the amount of electric current that can flow. Limiting electrical currents in a circuit with a resistor is like using a smaller garden hose to limit the amount of water running through a hose.

- Capacitors are components that collect static charge on a plate so the static charge can be used at a later time to make an electric current.

- Transformers are like small electromagnets. They use electric current to make a magnetic field and then use the magnetic field to make an electric current in another wire.

- Transistors use an electric current through one wire to control the electric current going through another wire.

Uses of Static Electricity

If you have ever unloaded clothing from a dryer, you have probably seen and felt the effects of static electricity. Static electricity might seem like a nuisance, but it does have some practical uses. African American inventor Granville T. Woods invented a telegraph system in 1887 that used static electricity. In this system, messages were sent through static electricity created by a train to telegraph wires running beside the track. The messages then traveled along the wires to other trains and depots. The ability to send messages this way helped improve train safety. Today, one use of static electricity is in photocopy machines. Static electricity charges are applied to the ink so the ink sticks to the paper.

Conductors, Insulators, and Resistance

Some materials, called conductors, allow electric charges to move through them easily. Most metals are good conductors of electricity. That's why wires and the working parts of electrical outlets are made of metal. Other materials, called insulators, do not easily permit the flow of electricity. Rubber, plastic, and glass are insulators. Wires and electric plugs are covered in insulators for safety. Resistance is the degree to which any material resists the flow of electricity. Resistance (abbreviated R), is measured in ohms (Ω). A wire's thickness and length affect its resistance. Comparing the resistance of various wires requires that they be the same thickness and length.

Conductors and Insulators

Whether a material is a good electrical insulator or conductor depends on how easily negative charges move through the material. Metals are good conductors because their outer electrons are loosely bound and move freely through the material. The outer electrons in nonmetals, such as glass, rubber, wood, and plastic, are tightly bound. The repulsion of electrons added to the materials is not enough to push the outer electrons through the material. A stream of water is attracted or repelled by a charged object because its molecules have a positive and negative end. However, pure water is an insulator. When salts dissolve in water, they form ions—charged particles that can move freely through the water. The ions will then conduct electricity.

Electromagnetism

Until the 1800s, electricity and magnetism were thought to be separate forces. Experimental evidence then began to accumulate, suggesting that electricity and magnetism are actually two aspects of the same phenomenon. In 1905, Einstein's theory of relativity confirmed the dual nature of a single electromagnetic force. We encounter this dual nature in visible light, ultraviolet radiation, microwaves, and radio waves. We use it in practical applications in which magnetic fields generate current electricity (generators) and current electricity produces magnetic fields (electromagnets).

Energy

Energy

The scientific definition of *energy* is "the ability to cause changes in matter." Without energy, matter does not change. Energy can be divided into two broad categories: kinetic energy and potential energy. Kinetic energy is the energy of motion. Anything that is moving has kinetic energy. Potential energy is stored energy. An object that has potential energy has the potential to move or change. A book on a shelf has potential energy—it could fall to the floor. A child on the raised end of a seesaw has potential energy—she could drop back to the ground. In these cases, the object gained potential energy as it was raised into its position. The higher an object is raised, the more potential energy it acquires.

Energy Resources

Energy resources are crucial factors in our economic and political systems as well as in our daily lives. For 150 years, most of humanity's energy has come from fossil fuels—oil, coal, and natural gas. Because these fuels take so long to form, supplies are finite. Remedies such as finding new reserves and reducing demand will work for a while, but they only delay the inevitable. At some point, people will have to switch to renewable energy resources such as wind power and solar power. Before this can happen, technological advances are required to make these renewable sources as powerful and efficient as current sources.

Forms of Energy

There are ways to categorize different forms of energy other than as potential and kinetic energy. Energy that comes from the sun is called solar energy. Solar energy itself consists of many different kinds of electromagnetic energy—infrared, light, ultraviolet, radio waves, gamma rays, and X rays. (All of these are electromagnetic waves; each has a different wavelength.) Other forms of energy include chemical energy, mechanical energy, electrical energy, and sound energy. In both technology and everyday life, energy is constantly changing from one form to another.

Heat Transfer

All matter in the universe is made of atoms and molecules. These particles have kinetic energy; they are always moving. The particles of a solid stay in a fixed place and vibrate. The particles of a liquid slide easily past each other. The particles of a gas fly all over the place. This form of random, kinetic energy is called thermal energy. The average amount of thermal energy in all the particles of a substance is the substance's temperature. The higher the temperature, the more thermal energy there is and the more movement there is. Natural movement of thermal energy is called heat, and it can occur in one of three ways—by conduction, convection, or radiation. If two substances contact each other, thermal energy will move from the warmer substance to the cooler one; this is conduction.

Mechanical Energy

The term *mechanical energy* is sometimes used to describe kinetic energy, or energy of motion. For example, falling water has mechanical energy. This mechanical energy can move a turbine. The turbine changes the mechanical energy to electric energy. Or, perhaps a person turns a crank on a generator. The mechanical energy of the turning crank is changed into electric energy. The mechanical energy of two sticks rubbing together is turned into heat energy by friction. The mechanical energy of a spring uncoiling makes a wind-up toy move. Although not technically correct, this meaning often appears in textbooks. You may need to explain this to students who are confused by the conflicting definitions.

Engineering

Engineering is the use of science knowledge to design products that solve problems and meet people's needs and wants. The products of engineering are *technology*. Technology can be as simple as a pencil or as complex as a car or computer. We're used to thinking of technology as only high-tech electronics. Actually, nearly everything that we see on a daily basis came from a factory that was designed by engineers—paper, aluminum cans, plastic cups, mirrors, roads, cars, fabric, ink pens, and on and on. Processes are also technology, for example, the steps for making steel, a cookie recipe, or a trouble-shooting script for computer hardware.

Engineering Design Process

The Engineering Design Process

Engineers often follow an iterative design process to develop a solution to a problem. The steps of the process vary and the divisions between steps are somewhat arbitrary. *ScienceFusion* uses a simplified five-step engineering design process:

1. **Find a Problem** Identify a problem; describe an unmet need or want and who will use the solution.

2. **Plan and Build** Decide the criteria the solution must meet to succeed; brainstorm designs; consider constraints, or limitations, such as budget, size, weight, and available materials; choose materials; draw detailed plans; and finally, construct a prototype.

3. **Test and Improve** Test the prototype against the design criteria. If it is successful, make improvements to enhance its performance.

4. **Redesign** Often, the first attempt at a solution fails to meet the design criteria. Engineers take what they learned from testing and start over with a new design.

5. **Communicate** Document work throughout the process and communicate with team members. At the end of the process, engineers share the final design, explain the test results, and often write directions for how to use the product.

Exploring Space

Mars

People dream about space travel to other planets. Many scientists are now considering the possibility of humans traveling to Mars.

- The distance from Earth to Mars is approximately 80,000,000 km (49,700,000 mi). The trip would take a spacecraft many months to complete.

- Two rovers, *Spirit* and *Opportunity,* arrived on Mars in January 2004. Each rover carries a sophisticated set of instruments that allows it to search for evidence that liquid water may have been present on Mars in the past.

- Mars has an atmosphere that would not support life as we know it. NASA hopes to change that with ambitious plans to thicken the atmosphere of Mars and even melt its polar ice caps.

Trip to the Moon

- The *Saturn V* rocket had three stages. Each stage was mounted on top of the previous stage. The first stage produced more than 33 million N of thrust at liftoff.

- A command and service module (CSM) at the top of the *Saturn V* carried three astronauts into space and toward the moon. The CSM traveled the 384,000 km (about 239,000 mi) from Earth to the moon in four days.

- For comparison, it takes about four days to drive a car across the continental United States, a distance of about 5,000 kilometers (about 3,100 miles).

Food Chains and Food Webs

Food Chains and Food Webs

Organisms get the energy they need from food. A food chain traces the path of energy as it moves from one organism to the next in an ecosystem. In most ecosystems, energy begins with the sun, so producers (organisms that use the sun's energy to make food) always form the base, or starting point, of a food chain. Arrows are typically used to show the direction of energy movement in a food chain.

A food chain only shows one energy path in an ecosystem. But most organisms are part of more than one food chain. Scientists often use a food web to show a more complete picture of the flow of energy in an ecosystem. A food web is a system of several overlapping food chains.

In most ecosystems, the energy starts with the sun. This energy is taken in by producers (plants) and converted to food energy. The energy in food moves through different levels of consumers. The first to feed on plants is a primary consumer. The secondary consumers feed on primary consumers. A third feeder is the tertiary consumer. The final link is filled by bacteria and fungi that act as decomposers. These organisms feed on and break down the remains of consumers when they die.

Forces

Force

Force is what makes all objects move. Force can be either a push or a pull. Force can start or stop motion, speed up or slow down motion, or change the direction of motion. When a child slides down a slide, gravity pulls him toward Earth. When a child pushes a toy truck, her muscles contract and pull her bones to make her arm move and push. When a flag is blowing and waving, the wind is pushing it back and forth.

Units of Force

Standardized units of measurement, such as centimeters for length, have been developed to make measurements consistent everywhere. There are two common systems—the customary (English) system, and the SI (metric) system. Scientists generally use the SI, or metric, system. SI units of mass are grams and kilograms. Because weight is a measure of force between objects, units of weight are also units of force. In the English system, the unit of force is pounds. In the SI system, it is newtons, abbreviated N and named for Isaac Newton. A newton is defined as the force needed to accelerate a 1-kg mass 1 m/s^2.

Fossils

Fossil Formation

Fossils rarely form. Whether plant or animal remains become fossils depends on what the organism is, where it lived, and whether the remains were protected from exposure. Organisms that are buried quickly and remain protected from air, water, bacteria, and scavengers are more likely to become fossils, because the remains will not be eaten and they will not decay too quickly. Hard materials such as bones, teeth, wood, and shells are more likely to become fossils than soft tissues. Marine organisms are more likely to become fossils than land-dwelling organisms. In a few cases, organisms such as woolly mammoths (prehistoric elephant-like animals) were preserved intact when they froze in the Arctic tundra.

Dinosaur Trace Fossils

When most people think of dinosaur fossils, they think of bones and large skeletons. Such "body fossils" are not the only types of fossil evidence, however. A trace fossil is indirect evidence of ancient life. It is not a body part but evidence of an organism's behavior. Examples of trace fossils left by dinosaurs include tracks, tooth marks, eggs, nests, gastroliths, and coprolites. A coprolite is fossilized animal droppings. Dinosaur coprolites reveal what dinosaurs consumed. Coprolites can contain either body fossils of plant material (indicating a herbivorous diet) or bones (indicating a carnivorous diet). Gastroliths, or "gizzard stones," can be difficult to distinguish from polished stones. Those most easily identified are found in the rib cages of dinosaur skeletons, which is where the dinosaur's stomach was.

Paleontology

Paleontology is the study of ancient life through analysis of plant and animal fossils.

- Paleontologists focus on the biology of ancient life. Their work involves investigating ancient life, trying to discover its connection to current life forms on Earth, and developing an understanding of the ancient forms' interrelationship with their environment.

- Paleontologists are also concerned with geology and have a major influence in determining the facts about the layers of rock that make up Earth. Using index fossils and other information about the rocks in which fossils occur, paleontologists aid petroleum geologists in their search for oil and gas.

Heredity

Nature Versus Nurture

- Behavior is the response of an organism to its surroundings.

- Behavior may be inherited—passed from parent to offspring—or learned.

- Instincts are behaviors that are inherited responses to stimuli and do not require learning. In newborn humans, instincts include crying.

- Some instinctive behaviors are influenced by learning. For example, a tiger is born with the instinct to hunt, but it must learn skills to hunt effectively.

- Learned behaviors are acquired completely as a result of experience. In humans, reading is a learned behavior.

Human Body

Parts of the Skeleton

The human skeleton is divided into two parts: the axial skeleton and the appendicular skeleton. The axial skeleton contains the bones that make up the face, skull, rib cage, and vertebral column. The main function of the axial skeleton is to protect vital organs of the body, such as the brain, heart, and spinal cord. The remaining bones of the skeleton make up the appendicular skeleton.

Bones

About 206 bones together form the human skeleton. The head bones make up the skull, which sits on top of the spine. At the top of the spine sit the shoulder bones, which are linked to the arm bones. Twelve pairs of rib bones curve around the spine and connect at the front of the chest. At the bottom of the spine, pelvic bones connect to the leg bones. At birth, a human baby has as many as 350 bones in its body, yet an adult has only 206 bones. The difference is due to the fusing of certain bones that occurs as humans mature. The places where bones meet are called **joints**. Knuckle and knee joints act like hinges and can bend naturally in only one way. Ball-and-socket joints in the shoulders and hips allow bones to move in a complete circle. There are more than 600 **muscles** in the human body. Some of these work under voluntary control, such as arm and thigh muscles. Others, such as those in the stomach, are involuntary.

How Bodies Grow

The human body grows, changing in both shape and size, from infancy to about the age of 20. Growth is rapid during the first year of life. Weight will triple and height will increase by one half before a child turns one. When a baby is born, its head is 25% of its total body height. As the baby grows, the body's proportions will change. Arms, legs and torso grow so that the head becomes 12.5% of the body's size in an adult. During childhood, the growth rate is steady. It speeds up again between the ages of 10 and 16 when the child's body matures and becomes adult. This stage is called puberty. The adult body does not change much but may experience weight gain, shrinking, skin wrinkles, and loss of hair and muscle.

The Five Senses

The five senses are sight, hearing, smell, touch, and taste. Receptors for each sense are found on our faces in our eyes, ears, noses, mouths, and skin. Receptors for the sense of touch are also found in the skin on all parts of our bodies. Our senses send signals about their environment to the brain through the nervous system. The brain then processes the information from the senses. This enables us to learn about the world and to make decisions. The senses are survival tools because they send signals to the brain that help us detect danger and pain.

Human Organ Systems

In addition to its solo function, each organ in the human body is also a part of an **organ system**. The human body has 11 organ systems; each carries out specific tasks for the body. The function of six systems is as follows: the circulatory system carries oxygen and nutrients to cells of the body; the respiratory system exchanges carbon dioxide for oxygen; the skeletal system provides support, protects internal organs, and produces blood cells; the muscular system allows the body to move and produces heat to keep it warm; the nervous system directs activities of all systems and responds to stimuli; the excretory system eliminates wastes from the body.

Inquiry Skills

Inferring and Concluding

The word *infer* is often defined as "concluding by reason." Students may have difficulty distinguishing between inferring and concluding.

- In scientific inquiry, drawing a conclusion is deciding whether an experiment supports the hypothesis being tested.

- *Inferring* is used in a much less specific way to describe reasoning from specific evidence to a general conclusion. For example, if one observes a bus arrive at the same corner at almost the same time each morning, one can infer that the bus is on a regular route and is following a schedule. No experiment is necessary, unless one wishes to convert the inference to a hypothesis and test it.

The Null Hypothesis

It may not occur to students that a hypothesis does not have to imply a difference. A null hypothesis can be used.

- A hypothesis might state that a round parachute, rather than parachutes of other shapes, will be better at keeping an egg from breaking. A null hypothesis might be that the shape of the parachute will make no difference.

- Often, scientists will state a null hypothesis because it helps prevent them from looking for a certain outcome. For example, they might test round parachutes and square ones, without stating that either type will be better.

What Is a Model?

Students may think that a model is always a small version of something larger. Point out that a model does not have to be a real object that they build.

- A model can be an idea that they get from nature, such as the way a leaf falls. When people first tried to fly, they thought of birds as models. They tried to make airplanes look and behave like birds.

- Sometimes people get ideas for models from things that are very different from the problem they're trying to solve. The man who invented Velcro got his idea from burrs that stuck to his clothes when he walked through some weeds!

Landforms

What Are Landforms?

Landforms are natural features that make up Earth's surface. There are many kinds of landforms, including mountains, hills, valleys, plains, plateaus, beaches, and dunes. Some landforms, such as mountains and plateaus, form as a result of upward movement of rock. Mountains can be found both on the ocean floor and on land. Other landforms are caused by erosion and by deposition of earth materials. Canyons are narrow, deep gorges that are cut into Earth by the action of running water, while valleys can be the result of erosion by streams and rivers and by glacial action. Landforms can also be caused by the movement of Earth's crust and by volcanic activity.

Light

Properties of Light

When light strikes a surface, the light may be reflected, refracted, or absorbed. What happens to light depends on the surface it hits. When light hits a smooth, shiny surface, it is reflected, or thrown back. Reflected light enables you to see yourself in a mirror. When light passes from one substance into another, it is refracted, or bent. That is why an object partially immersed in water appears to bend at the water line. Many surfaces absorb light. Some surfaces are opaque. They don't let light pass through, and you can't see through them. Surfaces that let some light through, such as wax paper, are translucent. Surfaces that let most light through are transparent. You can see through them.

Lasers

Laser light is very different from regular light.

- Laser light is **monochromatic**. It contains one specific wavelength of light. The color depends on the type of material used to make the laser.

- Laser light released is **coherent**—the light waves move as one, similar to the feet of marching soldiers, rather than moving off randomly.

- The light is **directional**. A laser has a very narrow beam that is bright and tight. Light from a flashlight, by contrast, spreads out.

Although laser light spreads out a little as it travels from the source, it has been used to measure the distance to the moon. Astronauts left a mirror on the moon. Scientists aim a laser at the reflector to measure how long the light takes to reach the moon and return.

Visible Light

Visible light is the small range of electromagnetic waves to which the human eye is sensitive. Visible light ranges from red, with a wavelength of about 7×10^{-5} cm, to violet, with a wavelength of about 4×10^{-5} cm. When all the wavelengths are present, the effect is white light.

- All electromagnetic waves, including visible light, travel at about 300 million meters per second through a vacuum.

- When electrons are energized, they move to higher energy levels farther from the nucleus. As they return to lower energy levels, they emit energy of various wavelengths, some of which can be visible light. In the visible light spectrum, red has the longest wavelength and lowest frequency. Violet has the shortest wavelength and highest frequency.

Waves

Waves are part of our daily experience, although we cannot always see them. The sounds we hear and the light we see are waves. Waves are regular, repeating disturbances or deformations. For example, we hear sounds because of pressure deformations of the air, water, or other medium. The waves "propagate" through the medium. Electromagnetic waves such as visible light and radio waves can travel through space. There are several different types of waves. Longitudinal waves vibrate in the same direction as they are traveling. Sound waves are an example of longitudinal waves. Electromagnetic waves are transverse. They vibrate at right angles to the direction of travel. We can also classify waves as traveling or standing. Traveling waves move, while standing waves oscillate in place and do not travel.

Magnetism

Magnets

A magnet is a solid, such as a piece of metal or a stone, that attracts objects that are made of iron or of steel, which contains iron. Natural magnets, called *magnetite* or *lodestone*, are formed inside Earth. Centuries ago, sailors navigated by suspending a lodestone from a string to detect North. Today, magnets are found in computers and many appliances. They activate speakers in televisions, radios, stereos, and telephones. They are used as door latches and to separate items in recycling centers. To avoid damage, do not place magnets near computers or software. Do not drop, strike, or heat magnets, as demagnetization can result. Magnets attract only iron and a few other metals, such as nickel and cobalt.

Magnetic Force

Magnets can be used to make some things move, even without touching them, because magnetic force reaches beyond the magnet. This area where the force extends is called the magnetic field. How far the force reaches, or the size of the magnetic field, depends on a magnet's strength. Most magnets used by students have small fields extending an inch or less. Earth has a magnetic field that extends more than 37,000 miles into space. Magnetic force happens in an iron object when groups of atoms, called domains, align. The domains cause an electromagnetic force that reaches beyond the object. The force is strongest within the magnet, and decreases as distance from the magnet increases. Scientists hypothesize that Earth's magnetic force comes from its core of hot iron surrounded by a fluid outer core.

Magnetic Poles

The poles of a magnet are named for the direction in which they point. Thus, a bar magnet suspended from a string tied around its center will swing until its north-seeking pole points north and the south-seeking pole points south. If a bar magnet is broken into two pieces, each piece will have its own north- and south-seeking poles. The poles of disk and circular magnets are not as easy to identify. For example, ring magnets can be magnetized so the inner edge is one pole, and the outer edge, the other pole; the two surfaces of a disk magnet may be the poles, and so on.

Measuring Matter

Mass and Weight

The mass and weight of an object are not the same; they are different properties. Mass is the amount of matter an object has. Weight is the amount of pull that gravity has on an object. The mass of an object stays the same regardless of where it is. Its weight can change depending on the strength of the gravitational force that is pulling on it. An object would weigh more on Earth than on the moon because Earth has more gravity than the moon. Mass is measured with a balance. Weight is measured with a scale.

Meteorology

Anemometers and Hygrometers

An anemometer is a tool that measures wind speed. One kind of anemometer has four cups connected at right angles to an upright shaft. The wind pushes the cups, which causes the shaft to turn. A system of gears converts the number of turns per minute into wind speed. Another kind of anemometer has an L-shaped tube, with one end open to the flow of air and the other end connected to a device that measures the pressure of the air blowing into it. Hygrometers measure humidity. A hair hygrometer, for example, measures the changes in length of a human hair that occur due to the absorption of water. The hair gets longer in humid air and shorter in dry air.

Clouds and Rain

Liquid water is constantly evaporating from Earth's surface. When water evaporates, it changes to a gas called *water vapor*. Water vapor condenses back to a liquid in the form of tiny droplets after 9 or 10 days. These tiny droplets make up clouds, or fog, or the dew we see on grass in the morning. If the tiny droplets form a cloud, and conditions allow, then the droplets grow until they are heavy enough to fall back to Earth as precipitation. Depending on the temperature conditions, precipitation can fall as either rain, snow, or ice, which might be either sleet or hail. About three-fourths of all Earth's precipitation falls over the ocean. The rest soaks into the ground or runs off into streams and rivers that flow into the ocean. Before long, the sun's heat causes the water to evaporate again, and the water cycle repeats.

Wind

Moving air is called wind. The whole body of air surrounding Earth is constantly moving, in part because of Earth's spin, and because of an uneven distribution of heat in Earth's land and water. Since air is a gas, it expands and contracts according to its temperature and the temperature of whatever it moves across. Air over warm regions that has been heated by strong sunshine is less dense than air over cooler regions. The greater the difference in density between the two air masses, the faster the wind will move. This movement, plus the more complicated movements caused by Earth's spin, produces wind conditions that affect our weather. Wind can be both harmful and helpful. Strong unpredictable winds such as those found in hurricanes or tornadoes can be life threatening, if people do not take shelter. But predictable, steady winds can be helpful when people use them to power wind turbines that generate electricity.

Fronts

Cold fronts and warm fronts are only two types of fronts. Sometimes the cold and warm air masses remain in the same position, or are stationary, for a time. The boundary dividing these air masses is a *stationary front*. Locations along a stationary front may have the same weather for days. Differences in air temperature occur in locations on either side of the front. Sometimes a warm air mass is trapped between two cold air masses to form an *occluded front*. This occurs because cold fronts travel about twice as fast as warm fronts travel.

Earth's Magnetosphere

Earth is surrounded by a large magnetic field that protects it from harmful, charged-particle radiation from the sun. It is a magnetosphere.

- The magnetic north and south poles of Earth's magnetosphere are close to—not directly over—the North Pole and the South Pole of Earth.

- When charged particles from the sun run into the magnetosphere, the magnetic field catches the particles, causing them to be funneled toward the magnetic north and south poles.

- The southern lights—*aurora australis*—form around Earth's South Pole. They are seen less frequently than the northern lights because fewer people live at the magnetic south pole.

Minerals

Minerals

There are more than 2,000 known minerals on Earth. For a material to be classified as a mineral, it must meet certain requirements. The material must be a solid, naturally occurring substance that has a definite chemical composition and internal arrangement of atoms, which is reflected in the mineral's outward appearance when the mineral has enough space to grow. The chemical makeup is responsible for the mineral's color, crystal shape, hardness, luster, streak, and other properties. People often think of minerals as gems, but not all minerals are gems. Many minerals are metal ores and salts. Likewise, not all gems are minerals. For example, pearls and amber are both produced through biological processes.

Motion

Action-Reaction Forces

Students may wonder how forces produce acceleration if there is always an equal but opposite reaction force. Point out the following facts:

- Forces are balanced only if they act on the *same* object.

- Action-reaction forces act on *different* objects.

If you push a box across the floor, the box pushes back on you with an equal but opposite force. However, your mass is greater than that of the box, so there is a net force on the box that makes it move.

Laws of Motion

Sir Isaac Newton was an English physicist and mathematician who lived from 1643 to 1727. He formulated three fundamental laws of motion. These laws state that (1) an object at rest will remain at rest, and an object in motion will continue to move at the same speed and direction unless acted upon by an external force; (2) an external force acting on an object causes acceleration, and the amount of acceleration depends on the strength of the force and the mass of the object; and (3) for every force there is an equal and opposite force. In the twentieth century, quantum physics and Albert Einstein's theory of relativity suggested that Newton's laws of motion do not apply to atomic and subatomic particles or to objects moving close to the speed of light.

Relative Motion

Everything in the universe, from atoms to galaxies, is moving. Even objects on the surface of Earth that appear to be standing still, such as buildings, are moving from west to east at about 1600 km/hr (1000 mi/hr) as Earth rotates. Therefore, the motion of an object must be measured relative to other objects. For example:

- A passenger seated in a bus may not be moving with respect to the bus but moving with respect to the road on which the bus is traveling. The person is moving at yet another speed with respect to Earth.

- People riding in trains going in opposite directions find it difficult to judge whether their train, the other train, or both are moving, because they have no stationary frame of reference.

Natural Resources

Energy Resources

Natural resources that provide people with energy are called *energy resources*. Sunlight is an energy resource that provides light and heat. The energy of sunlight can also be changed into electricity. Other energy resources include wind (moving air), tidal or current (moving water), and fuels such as wood, coal, gasoline, and oil.

Material Resources

Minerals, water, plants, animals, rocks, and soil are all *material resources*. Some of these things can be used to make different products. For example, sand is used to make glass, and wheat kernels are ground up to make flour. Renewable resources are those that are regularly replaced or replenished by nature. Plants, animals, and water are **renewable resources**. Plants and animals reproduce to make more of their own kind. Thus when some plants are harvested, new plants can be grown to take their place. Water is replaced through the water cycle. Some natural resources are forever lost when used. Others take many years to be replaced by natural processes. **Nonrenewable resources** are those that can be used only once, or those that are not replaced by nature nearly as quickly as they are used. Oil, coal, and natural gas are considered nonrenewable resources because it takes millions of years for them to form. Minerals, including metals, are also considered nonrenewable resources. All natural resources must be used with care. Nonrenewable resources can be used up, making them unavailable to people in the future. Even renewable resources can be polluted or destroyed if not treated carefully.

Oceans

Ocean Plants and Animals

Algae are plantlike organisms that live in the oceans. They are not considered to be true plants because they have no transport system to carry water and nutrients. Algae include seaweeds and kelp. Some, such as kelp, can grow up to 30.5 m (100 ft) long. Others are single cells and can be seen only with a microscope. Ocean animals live where they can meet their needs. Most ocean plants and animals live in or near shallow water or near the surface of the open ocean.

Oceans and Sea Water

One large body of water covers almost three-fourths of Earth's surface. This body of water is separated into five regions—the Pacific, Atlantic, Indian, Southern, and Arctic Oceans. The largest ocean is the Pacific Ocean. It covers a third of Earth's surface and extends from the Arctic Ocean to Antarctica's Ross Sea. It contains about half of all the water on Earth. Oceans border all of Earth's large landmasses.

Salinity

The Arctic and Southern Oceans are less salty than other saltwater seas and oceans for several reasons, including freshwater precipitation, low evaporation, and melting of the ice. By checking the salinity of the water and the expected temperatures, scientists can predict when ice will form around ships and in harbors. Ocean water contains, in some amount, all the elements found on Earth. The seven most abundant elements in seawater are chlorine, sodium, magnesium, sulfur, calcium, potassium, and bromine. They make up 99 percent of ocean salinity, with the other elements present in trace amounts. Scientists estimate that these trace amounts include about 9 million tons of gold!

Planetary Cycles

Rotation and Revolution

Earth has two primary motions within the solar system. It rotates, or spins, on its axis once every 23 hours, 56 minutes, 4.1 seconds. A point at the equator spins at about 1,600 km per hour (about 1,000 mph); a point at 45° North rotates more slowly at approximately 1,073 km per hour (about 667 mph). In addition to its spinning motion, Earth is also revolving around the sun in an elliptical orbit. Traveling through space at about 106,000 km per hour (66,000 mph), it takes approximately 365 days for Earth to make one complete revolution around the sun, the length of one year. Every four years, the calendar includes an extra day to accommodate the additional time.

Plants

Flowers

The blossoms of flowers are often arranged in groups. They appear in tightly packed clusters, broad clusters, or along a single stalk, such as the puya. The *puya* is an ancient treelike angiosperm that grows in the Andes Mountains of South America. Its flowers form spikes of up to 8000 bright-green blossoms. This plant, classified as a bromeliad, forms flowerstalks that can be nearly 5.4 m (18 ft) tall.

Roots

The two basic root systems found in plants are a taproot system and a fibrous root system. In a taproot system, such as in a carrot, a large root grows down into the soil, producing smaller lateral roots. A fibrous root system, such as in grasses, begins with a primary root that is shortly replaced by many roots that form from the stem. Both root systems have adaptations to perform certain functions. For example, taproots of beets and carrots are modified to store food. In mangrove trees, large, woody prop roots develop from adventitious roots on horizontal branches.

Tropism

The response of a plant to stimuli in its environment is called *tropism*. This response is triggered by plant hormones called *auxins*. A plant that grows toward a stimulus is said to display a positive tropism, while one that grows away from a stimulus displays a negative tropism. Most plants show tropisms to light, or phototropism, and gravity, or gravitropism. The root displays a positive gravitropism and a negative phototropism. As the stem grows upward, it shows a negative gravitropism and a positive phototropism.

Unusual Pollinators

The tiny Australian honey possum feeds on pollen and nectar from desert flowers such as the *Banksia* and, in the process, pollinates the plants. The South American creeper is a plant that gives off a bad odor that attracts flies. When a fly enters the flower, it becomes trapped overnight. During its "incarceration," the fly pollinates the plant. The flower fades by morning and the fly escapes.

Photosynthesis

Photosynthesis is a series of chemical reactions that plants and some protists and bacteria use to convert solar energy into chemical energy. The basic photosynthetic reaction converts six molecules of water and six molecules of carbon dioxide into one molecule of glucose (sugar) and six molecules of oxygen. Chlorophyll and other pigments enable the chemical reaction by absorbing energy from different wavelengths of sunlight. Additional chemical reactions convert and store the glucose as complex sugars and starches.

Plant Adaptation

An adaptation is a characteristic of a plant or an animal that allows the organism to survive in a particular environment. Some adaptations have developed over many generations. Some, however, occur within a single generation. The key to adaptation is variation, or difference, within a species. In order for a species to survive, it must be able to adapt, or change, to better fit new circumstances that arise within an environment.

Types of Plants

Plants can be divided into two groups—flowering plants and nonflowering plants. Flowering plants have special parts that make seeds. Seeds are the first stage of growth for many plants. Roses and lilies are kinds of plants that have flowers. A conifer is one type of nonflowering plant. Conifers are plants that have cones instead of flowers. The seeds are made inside of cones which hold and protect the seeds. After some time, the seeds will be ready to grow into new plants. When this happens, the cone will open and the seeds will fall out. Most conifers have needle-shaped leaves that stay green all year. Many conifers do not shed their leaves like other plants. Pines, spruce, firs, cypress, and yews are kinds of conifers.

What Plants Need

Plants need light, water, and air to produce food through a process called *photosynthesis*. This process takes place in a plant's leaves and green stems. These parts contain chlorophyll, which enables the plant to use water, carbon dioxide from the air, and light energy from the sun to make sugars. Plants then use the sugar to grow and to form flowers, seeds, and fruit, which enables them to reproduce. Soil supplies nutrients, which are certain chemical elements that plants need to live. Plants grown hydroponically, or in a growing solution, get these nutrients from the solution. Plants that grow aeroponically, or in air, get the nutrients and moisture they need from air.

Plant Nutrients

All plants need certain chemical elements to live. Elements they need in large amounts, called macronutrients, include carbon, hydrogen, oxygen, sulfur, phosphorus, nitrogen, potassium, calcium, and magnesium. Nutrients needed in smaller amounts, called micronutrients, include copper, zinc, iron, nickel, and other minerals. Plants get oxygen and carbon through their leaves and absorb other elements through their roots. Most root absorption takes place from the soil; however, plants grown hydroponically, or in water, obtain the minerals they need from a mineral-rich growing solution. Plants grown aeroponically, or in air, have their roots sprayed with a mineral-rich solution.

Plant Parts

Plants have parts that are adapted to get what the plant needs. Most roots grow underground and absorb water and nutrients. Roots also anchor the plant. Some roots, called taproots, are thick. Other roots, called fibrous roots, are thin and spread out. Stems support a plant's leaves and flowers and improve the plant's ability to absorb water and nutrients. Some stems, such as tree trunks and limbs, are woody. Leaves make most of the food that the plant needs in a process called photosynthesis. The leaves contain chlorophyll, which enables them to use light energy to combine water and carbon dioxide to make the plant's food. Some plants reproduce from seeds. Seed plants are divided into two main groups. In flowering plants, the fruit protects the seeds. In conifers, such as pines and firs, seeds are made in cones.

Seeds

Seeds contain the food they need to start the growing process, but they have three other requirements for continued growth—warmth, oxygen, and water. The roots are necessary for further plant development. Seeds use their stored food to initiate sprouting. They absorb water through their covers from the soil. They get oxygen from air, which is trapped between soil particles. Warmth is usually provided by the sun.

Parts of a Seed

Seeds come in many different sizes, shapes, and colors. The outside of a seed is the seed coat. This covering protects the seed. Some seeds, such as those of the coconut palm, have additional protection in the form of shells or husks. The fleshy part of the seed, called the cotyledon, is food for the embryo, which is the beginning of a new plant. The radicle is the first part of the plant to grow from the seed. It is the root of the plant embryo. The radicle holds the seedling in the soil and absorbs water that the seedling needs for growth. The shoot, which consists of both stems and leaves, emerges after the root.

Fruit

Most fruits contain seeds. Through fruits, plants are able to disperse their seeds with the help of various animals. Oranges, cherries, and tomatoes are all considered a type of berry. Blackberries and strawberries are a different type of berry. Both types ripen into a sweet, moist fruit, which is attractive to the animals that eat them. Then the seeds pass, unharmed, through the animal's digestive tract and are deposited on the soil in a new location. Fruits are an important part of the human diet because they provide the body with vitamins, such as vitamin C, and dietary fiber. Humans eat fruit in the forms of fresh fruit, jams, jellies, and pickles. Fruits can be packed in cans or jars or frozen to preserve them or transport them.

Plate Tectonics

Plate Tectonics

According to the theory of plate tectonics, Earth's outer shell consists of about 20 rigid plates (seven of these are major plates). The plates are moving continuously, although very slowly, at a rate of only a few centimeters a year. Most of the large plates include both continental and oceanic crust. In general, continental crust is thick and oceanic crust is thin. Each plate moves as a distinct unit, so interactions between plates occur along plate boundaries. There are divergent boundaries, convergent boundaries, and transform fault boundaries. A plate is often bounded by a combination of these zones.

Plate Boundaries

At the spreading center of a divergent boundary, plates are moving apart. New crust is constantly being produced by magma pushing up from the mantle. However, because the total surface area of Earth remains constant, crust must also be reabsorbed into the mantle. This can happen where two plates collide along a convergent boundary, or the edges of the plates can fold and bend forming mountain ranges. One plate is subducted, that is, it sinks below the other. At a transform fault boundary, plates grind past one another without producing or subducting crust. Movement along these faults often causes earthquakes. The San Andreas fault zone in California is an example.

Properties of Matter

Chemical Properties and Changes

The chemical properties of a substance include what it is composed of and what chemical changes it can undergo.

- A chemical change is independent of physical properties. For example, hydrogen and helium are both colorless gases at room temperature. However, hydrogen reacts with many other elements and compounds.

- In a chemical change, one or more substances are converted into one or more new substances. When pennies tarnish, some of the copper and zinc atoms in them combine with oxygen, forming metal oxides. The compounds are chemically different from either of the elements that formed them and also have different properties.

Density

The density of a material is a measure of how close together its matter is packed. An object with a low density, such as a block of balsa wood, floats because its material is less dense than water. The opposite is true of a high density object, such as a golf ball. A golf ball sinks because it is denser than water. A large ship can float because its mass is spread out and a large part of its volume is air, so its average density is lower than that of water.

Matter

Matter refers to everything in the universe that occupies space and has mass. Matter is made up of microscopic particles called atoms. Matter generally exists in three states: solid, liquid, and gas. Although there is a fourth state called plasma, it is not common in our everyday world. Each kind of matter can be identified by its specific properties, or special qualities, such as smell, taste, size, shape, color, mass, and solubility. All matter shares two properties: taking up space and having mass. However, two objects cannot occupy the same place at the same time. All substances are made from more than 110 different elements, which, when combined differently, produce millions of materials with different properties.

Rocks

Rocks and How They Are Used

Rocks are naturally occurring solid objects made of one or more minerals. Rocks are found all over the surface of Earth, from the tops of mountains to the ocean floor. They vary in color, depending on the kinds of minerals in them, or in texture, depending on the size of the mineral grains. Earth's crust is made up of three different groups of rocks. Igneous rocks form when molten rock such as magma or lava cools. Granite and basalt are types of igneous rocks. Sedimentary rocks form when sediments are cemented together or when chemicals precipitate from ocean water. Sandstone, limestone, and shale are types of sedimentary rock. Metamorphic rocks form when any type of rock is subjected to enough heat and pressure to change it without melting. Slate and marble are types of metamorphic rock. Most kinds of rocks can easily be found in one region of the world or another. People use rocks for building roads and structures, as well as for jewelry and other products, including materials such as chalk.

Rocks and the Rock Cycle

Igneous rocks are formed when molten rock cools and solidifies beneath the surface. On Earth's surface, any type of rock can weather and the sediment be deposited in layers, often in the ocean. Over a long time, the sediment fuses and becomes sedimentary rock. If pulled deep inside Earth, any type of rock can be converted to metamorphic rock through great heat and pressure (but not great enough to melt rock).

Weathering

Weathering is the process that changes the surface of rocks. There are two types of weathering, physical and chemical. During physical weathering, rocks are broken down into smaller rocks by force. One example of physical weathering is when water seeps into the cracks of large rocks. When this water freezes, it expands and breaks the rock into smaller pieces. Plant roots can also grow in the cracks of rocks and cause weathering. Physical weathering can also be caused by thermal expansion, which is the constant heating and cooling of rocks. Chemical weathering is when the makeup of a rock changes into a new substance when reacting to a chemical. Oxidation, hydrolysis, and acid rain are examples of chemical weathering.

Scientific Methods

How Science Works

Scientists make certain assumptions about nature that lead them to use the scientific method.

- The world can be understood through study and experimentation.

- The basic rules by which the universe works are the same everywhere.

- Scientific ideas can change. No matter how well one theory explains a set of observations, it is possible that another theory may fit just as well or better as our knowledge grows.

- Scientific knowledge is long-lasting. For example, calculations used to send people to the moon were based on Newton's laws, developed in the 1600s.

- There are many matters that cannot be examined in a scientific way, such as people's beliefs or issues of morality or religion. A hypothesis in these areas is not valid because it cannot be disproved.

Scientific Methods

Scientific methods are based on evidence instead of belief. They permit the acquisition of new scientific knowledge that is based on physical evidence. The essential elements of the scientific methods can be summarized in four steps—characterization of the subject of the investigation, which is accomplished by observation; the formulation of a hypothesis, which provides a casual explanation of the subject; the statement of a prediction that can be experimentally assessed; and the design of an experiment to test the hypothesis. The scientific process is iterative, which means that at any stage, scientists may repeat a part of the process. The results must also be verifiable, which means the results must be replicable by others.

Scientific Tools

Units of Measurement

It is important for students to understand that units of measurement, such as inches or meters, do not exist in nature. They are simply amounts that people have agreed to use as a standard so that they can communicate measurements and have someone else reproduce them.

- The earliest units of measurement were based on body parts. A cubit was the length of a person's forearm, from elbow to fingertip. A foot was the length of a man's foot. One problem was that men's arms and feet can vary in length by several inches!

- The Babylonians were the first to use a standard set of stones to measure weight. Other early cultures used wheat seeds and other grains as standards of weight and length.

- Roman soldiers kept track of the distance they traveled by counting paces.

Temperature and Temperature Scales

Temperature is a measure of how hot or cold something is. It should not be confused with heat, a form of energy that flows. Temperature can be measured on three scales: Fahrenheit, Celsius, and Kelvin. On the Fahrenheit scale, the temperature of boiling water is 212°F and of melting ice is 32°F. There are 180°F between them. On the Celsius scale, the temperature of boiling water is 100°C and of melting ice is 0°C. Each degree is one-hundredth of the difference between the two points on the scale. The Kelvin scale begins at the lowest theoretically possible temperature, which is called absolute zero, zero K, or zero Kelvins. This is the same as -273°C.

History of the Microscope

Magnifiers are mentioned in writings dating from the first century A.D. The earliest simple microscope, called a flea glass, was a tube with a plate for the object at one end and a lens at the other. Late in the sixteenth century, two Dutch spectacle makers developed the forerunner of the compound microscope and telescope. In 1609, Galileo made an instrument with a focusing device. The father of microscopy, Anton van Leeuwenhoek, of Holland, taught himself to grind and polish tiny lenses with great curvature that yielded magnifications. This led to his building microscopes and his famous biological discoveries. He was the first to see and describe bacteria, yeast cells, and to observe that a single drop of pond water is teeming with life.

Science Tools

Scales and balances are scientific tools used in homes as well as in scientific laboratories. A balance measures the mass of an object. The most basic tool for measuring mass is the pan balance. A pan balance uses a bar with a pan hanging from each end. At the center of the bar is a support, called a fulcrum, on which the bar can balance. The Egyptians used a balance of this type as early as 2500 B.C. Scales measure weight and other forces.

Simple Machines

Simple Machines

A simple machine is a device that makes work easier. There are six types of simple machines: the inclined plane, the wedge, the screw, the lever, the wheel-and-axle, and the pulley. All simple machines transfer force. Some change the direction of force, while others change the magnitude, or strength, of force. Still others change both the direction and the magnitude of force.

Most simple machines make work easier by allowing you to move things farther and/or faster. In these machines, a larger force is required, but over a shorter distance.

An inclined plane is really just a ramp, a flat surface that slopes. This type of simple machine is the only one that doesn't move. Instead, objects are moved over it in order to raise them. It takes less force to move an object up an inclined plane than it does to lift the object straight up. The trade-off is that the object must be moved a greater distance—the entire length of the inclined plane—to achieve the same height.

A wedge is an inclined plane that moves. Wedges are used to split or lift objects. Force is applied to the wide end of the wedge and gets transferred to the sides. In the process, the object either splits apart or gets lifted. It takes less force to drive a wedge into or under an object than it does to separate the object yourself. Cutting tools such as axes, scissor blades, saw blades, nail points, and plows are all examples of wedges.

A screw is an inclined plane wrapped around a cylinder. The spiral ridges around the shaft of the screw are called threads. As the screw is turned, the threads pull the object up the shaft. It takes less force to turn a screw than to pound a nail the same size. However, a screw must be turned many times, while a nail can be driven in just a few blows of a hammer.

A lever is a long rigid bar that rests on and pivots around a support called a fulcrum. Applying a force called the effort to one part of the lever causes the load at another place on the lever to move.

A wheel-and-axle is a simple machine that consists of a shaft, called the axle, inserted through the middle of a wheel. Any force that gets applied to the wheel gets transferred to the axle, and vice versa. A pulley is a wheel with a rope or chain wrapped around it. The wheel rotates around a fixed axle. The rope rides in a groove in the wheel. When the rope is pulled, the wheel turns.

Solar System

The Moon

Although students may think the moon and sun are the same size, the sun is really about 400 times the size of the moon. What we call moonlight is actually sunlight reflecting off the moon's surface. The moon itself has no light. We see half of the illuminated side of the moon when looking at a first-quarter or third-quarter moon. The first-quarter phase of the moon is labeled as such because it is one-quarter of the way through the lunar cycle. The third-quarter moon is three-quarters of the way through the cycle.

Satellites

An artificial, or human-made, satellite is any object placed into orbit around Earth and used for scientific and technological purposes. Most satellites are used for communication, military purposes, or scientific research. Scientific research satellites are used to explore Earth's atmosphere and space near Earth, to make images of Earth's surface or ocean floor, to track weather patterns, and to image astronomical objects without the interference of Earth's atmosphere. *Sputnik 1*, launched by the Soviet Union on October 4, 1957, was the world's first artificial satellite. *Sputnik 1* was about the size of a basketball. Then on November 3, the Soviets launched a second satellite. It contained a small dog, named Laika. Three months later, the United States launched its first satellite, *Explorer 1*. Today, many satellites orbit Earth. A balance between gravity and inertia makes this happen.

- The International Space Station, a satellite of Earth, is about 360 km (224 mi) above Earth's surface. It orbits Earth 16 times per day.

- The moon is a natural satellite of Earth; it is about 384,000 km (about 239,000 mi) from Earth and orbits Earth once every 27.3 days.

Sound

Loudness

The loudness of a sound refers to how strong the sound seems to people when they hear it. The intensity of a sound is determined by the amount of energy in the sound waves. Sound wave energy is less concentrated as it spreads outward in all directions from a source. As a result, the loudness of a sound decreases as the distance increases between the listener and the source of the sound. The word *volume* is also used to refer to the loudness of a sound.

Making Sound

All sounds—whether they are high or low, loud or soft—are made by a vibration. When an object vibrates, it causes the air around it to vibrate. The vibrations travel away from their point of origin in all directions. The vibrations can travel through gases, liquids, and solids. Humans produce sound in a section of the throat called the larynx. Two folds of tissue, called the vocal cords, cross the larynx. Between the vocal cords is an opening, or slit. When the vocal cords are relaxed, air rushes through the slit causing little or no vibration. When the vocal cords are tight, such as during speech, the rushing air causes the vocal cords to vibrate, which, in turn, causes sound. The tighter the vocal cords are, the faster the vibration and the higher pitched the sound is.

Sound Quality

Students may wonder why different musical instruments playing the same pitch sound different.

- The basic properties of sound are pitch, loudness, and quality. Sound "quality" is what allows the ear to distinguish between sounds.

- When an instrument plays a certain pitch, called the *fundamental*, some parts of it also vibrate, producing different pitches called *overtones*.

- The sound wave produced by the instrument is a complex combination of the fundamental tone and the overtones.

- When a sound wave reaches the ear, it creates an equally complex vibration of the eardrum. The person learns to associate the complex vibration with a particular instrument.

States of Matter

Physical Properties of Water

Water is the only common substance that exists in all three physical states under normal atmospheric conditions on Earth. However, its properties are not the same everywhere on Earth.

- At sea level, atmospheric pressure is 1 atmosphere (atm), and water boils at 100°C.

- At higher altitudes, atmospheric pressure is less than 1 atm, and liquid water boils at lower temperatures. For example, Twin Sisters Peak in Colorado's Rocky Mountain National Park is nearly 3,500 meters (11,450 feet) above sea level. Atmospheric pressure is about 0.65 atm, and water boils at 87°C. It takes almost twice as long to boil an egg at this elevation as at sea level.

Solubility of Gases

Solutions of gases in liquids are fairly common. All natural water contains dissolved oxygen (O_2) and nitrogen (N_2) along with other gases found in air. Carbonated beverages are solutions of carbon dioxide (CO_2) in water, along with sugar and flavoring. The solubility of a gas depends on its temperature and pressure.

- The gases dissolved in water become less soluble as the temperature increases. For example, at 30°C, the amount of dissolved O_2 in water is only about half of that found at 0°C. Fish depend on dissolved oxygen in water, and many of them cannot survive in warm water.

- The solubility of gases in water increases as the pressure increases. Carbonated beverages are bottled under pressure. When the cap is removed, the pressure drops and the solubility decreases, which accounts for the formation of bubbles.

Volcanoes

How Quickly Can a Mountain Form?

The natural processes to build a mountain are usually very slow. It takes hundreds of thousands of years for mountains ranges such as the Alps and the Rockies to form. Volcanic mountains can form very quickly, however. In early February 1943, the location where Paricutín Mountain (in Mexico) is now located was a flat cornfield. By the end of the month, a fissure had opened, and ash was accumulating. Within a year, that pile of ash was 335 m (1,100 ft) high. Within two years, the volcano had almost completely buried the village of Paricutín. Nine years later, when the volcanic eruption ended, Paricutín Mountain was about 425 m (1,400 ft) high and covered about 25 km^2 (10 mi^2).

Layers of Earth

The deepest hole ever drilled into Earth's crust was only 12 km (7 mi) deep. To learn about deeper layers of Earth, scientists study lava from volcanoes as well as seismic waves produced by earthquakes. Waves travel at different speeds through different types of materials. These waves reveal that oceanic crust is on average about 6 km (3 mi) thick and continental crust is on average about 30 km (18 mi) thick. The crust and a small part of the mantle (collectively called the lithosphere) float on a soft, pliable portion of the mantle known as the asthenosphere. Magma is less dense than some material in the asthenosphere and in the crust, so it rises up through these layers and erupts on Earth's surface.

Predicting Volcanic Eruptions

Although it is not currently possible to predict exactly when a volcano will erupt, there are warning signs that sometimes indicate that an eruption may be imminent. As the magma in a volcano rises to the surface, there may be a series of small earthquakes. The rising magma may also cause the volcano to bulge, crack, or become distorted. The ground and any springs in the area may increase in temperature. These clues, unfortunately, can be unpredictable or misleading. Some or all of these events might continue to occur for days, weeks, months, or even years before the volcano actually erupts. Also, the pre-eruption events may occur and yet not be followed by an eruption.

Water

Point Pollution and Nonpoint Pollution

Point pollution and nonpoint pollution are the two ways that land and water are polluted.

- Point sources of pollution include discharge from oil spills, factory pipes, and sewage that flows directly from the source. These are more easily monitored than other kinds of pollution, because the source of the problem is often a pipe or another easily identifiable source.

- Nonpoint pollution is more dispersed. It's often more difficult to find the source and treat it. One example of nonpoint pollution is the runoff from farms that may include animal waste and pesticides sprayed onto field. Urban storm drains that collect water from rainstorms are another source of nonpoint pollution.

Water Cycle

The Water Cycle

Facts about the water cycle:

- People are part of the water cycle. A large percent of the human body is water. In fact, 75% of the brain is water!

- Earth contains the same amount of water today as it did when it first formed. Because water cycles continuously, the water you used to brush your teeth this morning could include water once used by dinosaurs.

- Water is one of the few substances that expands instead of shrinks when it freezes. Frozen water is less dense. This is why ice floats on liquid water.

- Only about 3% of Earth's water is fresh water (mostly ice); the rest is salt water.

Teacher Notes

Science Trade Books

Bibliography

Grade 4

Actual Size by Steve Jenkins (Houghton Mifflin, 2004) invites readers to see how they measure up against a variety of different animals. Provides fun facts and physical dimensions of these critters. CHILDREN'S CHOICE; BOOKLIST EDITORS' CHOICE

Almost Invisible Irene by Daphne Skinner (Kane, 2003) tells the story of a shy girl who, after learning about animal camouflage, tries to avoid attracting attention to herself by blending in with her surroundings.

Animals by Miranda Smith (Kingfisher, 2009) provides vivid, three-dimensional illustrations that show a variety of animals in their natural habitats. Students will discover how animals hunt, build their homes, and adapt to their surroundings.

Arctic Lights, Arctic Nights by Debbie S. Miller (Walker, 2007) portrays arctic animals and weather; each two-page spread features a different time of year, complete with the total number of sunlight hours and average daily temperatures. NSTA TRADE BOOK; OUTSTANDING SCIENCE TRADE BOOK

Brilliant Bees by Linda Glaser (Millbrook, 2003) describes the pollination process, hive structure and social order, methods of communication, and life cycle of the honeybee. NSTA TRADE BOOK; OUTSTANDING SCIENCE TRADE BOOK

Cell Division and Genetics by Robert Snedden (Heinemann, 2002) provides detailed information on the structure and function of cells. AWARD-WINNING AUTHOR

Claws, Coats and Camouflage: The Ways Animals Fit into Their World by Susan E. Goodman (Millbrook, 2001) poses questions that promote careful observations, critical analysis, and more inquiry into how well different animals, from insects to humans, are adapted for surviving in their environments. NSTA TRADE BOOK; OUTSTANDING SCIENCE TRADE BOOK

Dandelions: Stars in the Grass by Mia Posada (Carolrhoda, 2000) presents rhyming text with information about the dandelion, not as a weed, but as a flower of great beauty. Includes fun science activities to further engage young minds. NSTA TRADE BOOK; OUTSTANDING SCIENCE TRADE BOOK

Day Light, Night Light by Franklyn M. Branley (HarperCollins, 1975) discusses the properties of light, particularly its source in heat. AWARD-WINNING AUTHOR

Disgusting Plants by Connie Colwell Miller (Capstone, 2007) describes ten unusual plants and the characteristics that make them gross and disgusting.

Down Comes the Rain by Franklyn M. Branley (HarperCollins, 1997) explains the stages of the water cycle. AWARD-WINNING AUTHOR

Drip! Drop!: How Water Gets to Your Tap by Barbara Seuling (Holiday House, 2000) introduces students to JoJo and her dog Willy, who explain the water cycle and introduce fun experiments about filtration, evaporation, and condensation. AWARD-WINNING AUTHOR

Electrical Circuits: Harnessing Electricity by David Dreier (Compass Point, 2008) provides information about currents, how electricity works, and how circuits allow currents to flow in a continuous loop.

Energy by Christine Webster (Capstone, 2005) introduces the concept of energy and provides instructions for an activity to demonstrate some of its characteristics.

Energy by Don Herweck (Compass Point, 2009) describes the different forms of energy and how we use it in our everyday lives.

Find the Constellations by H.A. Rey (Houghton Mifflin, 2008) teaches readers how to recognize various constellations. Helpful charts and tables are provided in the back of the book. AWARD-WINNING AUTHOR AND ILLUSTRATOR

Flick a Switch: How Electricity Gets to Your Home by Barbara Seuling (Holiday House, 2003) describes how electricity was discovered, how early devices were invented to make use of it, and how it is generated in power plants and then distributed for many different uses. AWARD-WINNING AUTHOR

Flicker Flash by Joan Bransfield Graham (Houghton Mifflin, 1999) is a collection of poems celebrating light in its various forms, from candles and lamps to lightning and fireflies. NSTA TRADE BOOK; OUTSTANDING SCIENCE TRADE BOOK; SLJ BEST BOOK; NOTABLE CHILDREN'S BOOK IN THE LANGUAGE ARTS

Force and Motion: Laws of Movement by Don Nardo (Compass Point, 2008) focuses on English scientist Isaac Newton as well as his three laws of motion and how they govern the way we live. AWARD-WINNING AUTHOR

Forces and Motion: From Push to Shove by Christopher Cooper (Heinemann, 2003) discusses what happens when you push or pull an object and how forces can change the shape of an object. AWARD-WINNING AUTHOR

Forces: Science All Around Me by Karen Bryant-Mole (Heinemann, 2002) explains the basic principles of forces and movement through direct observation and through looking at everyday experiences.

From Seed to Daisy: Following the Life Cycle by Laura Purdie Salas (Picture Window, 2008) offers information about the Shasta daisy's life cycle from tiny seed to beautiful bloom.

Fully Charged: Electricity by Steve Parker (Heinemann, 2005) describes how electricity is generated, harnessed, and used, and explains the difference between electricity, including static electricity, and electrons. AWARD-WINNING AUTHOR

Girls Think of Everything: Stories of Ingenious Inventions by Women by Catherine Thimmesh (Houghton Mifflin, 2000) tells the story of how women throughout the ages have responded to situations confronting them in daily life by inventing various useful products. NSTA TRADE BOOK; OUTSTANDING SCIENCE TRADE BOOK; TEACHERS' CHOICE; SMITHSONIAN NOTABLE BOOK; IRA CHILDREN'S BOOK AWARD

Green Plants: From Roots to Leaves by Louise and Richard Spilsbury (Heinemann, 2004) provides information about the various parts of a plant via informational text and fun experiments and demonstrations.

Gulls . . . Gulls . . . Gulls by Gail Gibbons (Holiday House, 2001) uses detailed text and clear illustrations to describe nearly every aspect of gulls, from their appearance to migration and more. NSTA TRADE BOOK; OUTSTANDING SCIENCE TRADE BOOK

A History of Super Science: Atoms and Elements by Andrew Solway (Raintree, 2006) offers a basic introduction to atoms, elements, and various other components of chemistry, including the Periodic Table and famous alchemists.

Hot and Cold by Karen Bryant-Mole (Heinemann, 2002) introduces the scientific properties of heat and cold, examining such topics as temperature, thermometers, freezing, and melting.

If You Find a Rock by Peggy Christian (Harcourt, 2000) celebrates the variety of rocks, including skipping rocks, chalk rocks, and splashing rocks. NOTABLE CHILDREN'S BOOK IN THE LANGUAGE ARTS

Inventions by Glenn Murphy (Simon & Schuster, 2009) brings inventions to life with state-of-the-art, three-dimensional illustrations and informational text about inventions through the years—from prehistoric times up until today.

Jane Goodall: Legendary Primatologist by Brenda Haugen (Compass Point, 2006) tells the story of Jane Goodall, her research on chimpanzee behavior, and how she went on to found a conservation organization to improve the environment for all living things.

Life Processes: From Reproduction to Respiration by Louise and Richard Spilsbury (Heinemann, 2004) describes the processes by which living things abide in order to thrive and survive.

Light and Sound by Dr. Mike Goldsmith (Kingfisher, 2007) takes students on a journey of discovery as they learn how light is made, how light makes electricity, and how sound travels.

Light: From Sun to Bulbs by Christopher Cooper (Heinemann, 2003) invites students to investigate the dazzling world of physical science and light through fun experiments. AWARD-WINNING AUTHOR

Light: Look Out! by Wendy Sadler (Raintree, 2006) enlightens readers about the way light is present in their everyday lives. Offers information about color, reflection, and electricity.

Lightning by Seymour Simon (Collins, 2006) uses spectacular photos to introduce readers to the forms of lightning, to streamers called stepped leaders, and to the main lightning bolt itself. NSTA TRADE BOOK; OUTSTANDING SCIENCE TRADE BOOK; CHILDREN'S CHOICE

A Log's Life by Wendy Pfeffer (Aladdin, 2007) introduces readers to the life cycle of a tree and explains how animals depend on the tree for food and shelter, as well as how animals assist in the decay process. NSTA TRADE BOOK; OUTSTANDING SCIENCE TRADE BOOK

Matter by Jane Weir (Compass Point, 2009) explores the different states of matter, the elements of the Periodic Table, and atoms—the smallest particles that make up elements.

Matter by Mir Tamim Ansary (Heinemann, 2002) looks at the physical world and the properties and behavior of different kinds of matter.

A Matter of Survival: Properties of Matter by Ann Weil (Raintree, 2006) provides information about the states of matter as well as mass, density, volume, buoyancy, and the physical and chemical changes of matter. AWARD-WINNING AUTHOR

The Moon by Seymour Simon (Simon & Schuster, 2003) tells about the work of early scientists and takes the reader through the moon explorations of the Apollo astronauts. NSTA TRADE BOOK; OUTSTANDING SCIENCE TRADE BOOK; ALA NOTABLE BOOK

Muscles: Our Muscular System by Seymour Simon (HarperCollins, 2000) takes the reader on a tour through the human muscular systems, explaining the different types of muscles and their functions and purposes, and the effects that exercise has on muscles. NSTA TRADE BOOK; OUTSTANDING SCIENCE TRADE BOOK

My Light by Molly Bang (Blue Sky, 2004) is told from the sun's point of view and describes how various forms of energy are derived from the heat and light of the sun. ALA NOTABLE BOOK

Neo Leo: The Ageless Ideas of Leonardo da Vinci by Gene Barretta (Henry Holt, 2009) tells the story of artist, inventor, engineer, and scientist Leonardo da Vinci, accompanied by brightly colored illustrations. AWARD-WINNING AUTHOR

Next Stop Neptune: Experiencing the Solar System by Alvin Jenkins (Houghton Mifflin, 2004) takes readers on a virtual tour of our solar system, providing fun facts about planets, moons, and asteroids.

Night Wonders by Jane Ann Peddicord (Charlesbridge, 2005) takes readers on a journey through space, providing information about stars, the sun and moon, planets, nebulae, and galaxies. IRA CHILDREN'S BOOK AWARD

Oak Tree by Gordon Morrison (Houghton Mifflin, 2000) describes the impact of the changing seasons on an old oak tree and the life that surrounds it. AWARD-WINNING AUTHOR

One Giant Leap: The Story of Neil Armstrong by Don Brown (Houghton Mifflin, 1998) discusses the life and accomplishments of astronaut Neil Armstrong, from his childhood in Ohio to his famous moon landing. PARENTS' CHOICE

One Tiny Turtle by Nicola Davies (Walker, 2008) describes the life cycle of the loggerhead sea turtle. TEACHERS' CHOICE

Physics: Why Matter Matters! by Dan Green (Kingfisher, 2008) combines science and art to bring the world of physics to life with fun and wacky characters to explain the building blocks of our universe.

Postcards from Pluto: A Tour of the Solar System by Loreen Leedy (Holiday House, 2006) offers readers a virtual tour of the solar system, describing each planet. BOOKLIST EDITORS' CHOICE

Pumpkin Circle: The Story of a Garden by George Levenson (Tricycle, 2004) captures each phase of the pumpkin's life cycle with time-lapse photography: seeds sprouting, flowers blooming, bees buzzing, pumpkins growing, and finally, a pumpkin returning to the earth. NSTA TRADE BOOK; OUTSTANDING SCIENCE TRADE BOOK

Rachel: The Story of Rachel Carson by Amy Ehrlich (Silver Whistle, 2003) describes the life and work of pioneer nature writer and activist Rachel Carson, who was a leader in the environmental movement. NSTA TRADE BOOK; OUTSTANDING SCIENCE TRADE BOOK; NOTABLE SOCIAL STUDIES TRADE BOOK

Raptors, Fossils, Fins, and Fangs by Brad Matsen and Ray Troll (Tricycle, 2004) introduces lesser-known prehistoric creatures, including the giant sea scorpion called eurypterid, the Helicoprion shark, and the carnivorous land dinosaur Deinonychus.

Saving Birds: Heroes Around the World by Pete Salmansohn and Stephen W. Kress (Tilbury House, 2005) features fascinating stories of six bird species that were saved from extinction with the help of naturalists, residents, and community leaders. NSTA TRADE BOOK; OUTSTANDING SCIENCE TRADE BOOK

Sea Clocks: The Story of Longitude by Louise Borden (Margaret K. McElderry, 2004) tells the story of Englishman John Harrison who, with no scientific training, worked tirelessly for more than forty years to create an accurate clock. AWARD-WINNING AUTHOR

Seeing by Mary Mackill (Heinemann, 2006) provides information on the sense of sight, the parts of the eye, how we see, and tools that can help us see.

Slugs by Anthony D. Fredericks (Lerner, 2000) describes the physical characteristics, habitat, and behavior of these slimy creatures that spend their lives crawling on their stomachs. NSTA TRADE BOOK; OUTSTANDING SCIENCE TRADE BOOK

Snowflake Bentley by Jacqueline Briggs Martin (Houghton Mifflin, 1998) is the story of Wilson "Snowflake" Bentley, a self-taught scientist and photographer, who developed a technique to photograph snowflakes. NSTA TRADE BOOK; OUTSTANDING SCIENCE TRADE BOOK; ALA NOTABLE BOOK; BOOKLIST EDITORS' CHOICE

Solar Power by Josepha Sherman (Capstone, 2004) introduces the history, uses, production, advantages and disadvantages, and future of solar energy as a power resource.

The Stars by Patricia Whitehouse (Heinemann, 2004) provides information about stars, including star nurseries, star energy, star color and temperature, and twinkling. Combines information text with stunning photographs.

States of Matter: A Question and Answer Book by Fiona Bayrock (Capstone, 2006) explores the composition of matter, its changing states, and the effects of changing between states.

Summer Ice: Life Along the Antarctic Peninsula by Bruce McMillan (Houghton Mifflin, 1995) informs readers about the coldest continent and how, despite its frigid temperatures, various plants and animals can survive there. NSTA TRADE BOOK; OUTSTANDING SCIENCE TRADE BOOK

Sun by Steve Tomecek (National Geographic Society, 2006) describes the physics and characteristics of the sun. AWARD-WINNING AUTHOR

Temperature by Rebecca Olien (Capstone, 2005) introduces the concept of temperature and provides instructions for an activity to demonstrate some of its characteristics.

The Top of the World: Climbing Mount Everest by Steve Jenkins (Houghton Mifflin, 1999) describes the conditions and terrain of Mount Everest, attempts that have been made to scale this peak, and information about the equipment and techniques of mountain climbing. ALA NOTABLE BOOK; SLJ BEST BOOK; BOSTON GLOBE - HORN BOOK AWARD; ORBIS PICTUS HONOR

Tornadoes by Seymour Simon (HarperCollins, 2001) explains where and how tornadoes develop, how they are tracked, and the dangers associated with them. NSTA TRADE BOOK; OUTSTANDING SCIENCE TRADE BOOK

Under Pressure: Forces by Ann Fullick (Heinemann, 2005) provides an overview of what forces are and how they affect the way we live, describing such forces as gravity, pressure, balanced and unbalanced forces, and motion on a curve.

Water Dance by Thomas Locker (Voyager/ Harcourt, 2002) involves readers in a question-and-answer format, observing the natural movement of water. NSTA TRADE BOOK; OUTSTANDING SCIENCE TRADE BOOK; TEACHERS' CHOICE; NOTABLE CHILDREN'S BOOK IN THE LANGUAGE ARTS

Weather Patterns by Monica Hughes (Heinemann, 2004) describes different types of climate in various places and the weather that occurs during the seasons. AWARD-WINNING AUTHOR

What Do You Do When Something Wants to Eat You? by Steve Jenkins (Houghton Mifflin, 1997) introduces young readers to the specialized adaptations animals use to avoid the constant threat of becoming another animal's meal. NSTA TRADE BOOK; OUTSTANDING SCIENCE TRADE BOOK; BOOKLIST EDITORS' CHOICE

What's the Matter in Mr. Whiskers' Room? by Michael Elsohn Ross (Candlewick, 2007) tells the story of a teacher who encourages his students to be scientists as they explore matter through an array of hands-on exploration experiments. AWARD-WINNING AUTHOR

Your Bones by Terri DeGezelle (Bridgestone, 2002) introduces bones, their makeup and function, and bone diseases, and ways to keep bones healthy.

COMMON CORE

Correlation

Correlations to the Common Core State Standards for English Language Arts are provided on these pages.

Grade 4 Standard Code	Descriptor	Teacher Edition Page Citations
Range of Reading and Level of Text Complexity		
RL.4.10	By the end of the year, read and comprehend literature, including stories, dramas, and poetry, in the grades 4–5 text complexity band proficiently, with scaffolding as needed at the high end of the range.	See the Science Trade Books Bibliography on pp. TR44–TR47 for some suggested titles.
Reading Standards for Informational Text		
Key Ideas and Details		
RI.4.1	Refer to details and examples in a text when explaining what the text says explicitly and when drawing inferences from the text.	5, 7, 9, 11, 13, 19, 21, 23, 29, 31, 33, 35, 37, 47, 49, 51, 65, 67, 69, 71, 81, 83, 85, 87, 89, 105, 107, 109, 111, 119, 121, 123, 125, 127, 137, 139, 141, 143, 145, 175, 177, 179, 181, 183, 191, 193, 195, 197, 199, 209, 211, 213, 215, 217, 223, 225, 227, 229, 247, 249, 251, 253, 261, 263, 265, 267, 269, 275, 277, 279, 281, 289, 299, 301, 303, 305, 307, 317, 319, 321, 329, 331, 333, 335, 337, 351, 353, 354, 355, 357, 359, 361, 375, 377, 379, 393, 395, 397, 399, 407, 409, 411, 413, 431, 433, 435, 437, 439, 449, 451, 453, 465, 467, 469, 485, 487, 489, 491, 503, 505, 507, 509, 519, 521, 523, 525, 539, 541, 543, 545, 547

Grade 4 Standard Code	Descriptor	Teacher Edition Page Citations
RI.4.2	Determine the main idea of a text and explain how it is supported by key details; summarize the text.	Use the Summarize Ideas sections to provide opportunities for students to summarize concepts. For example, see pages 5, 7, 9, 11, 13, 19, 21, 23, 29, 31, 33, 35, 37, 47, 49, 51, 65, 67, 69, 71, 81, 83, 85, 86, 87, 89, 105, 107, 109, 111, 119, 121, 123, 125, 127, 137, 139, 141, 143, 145, 175, 177, 179, 181, 183, 191, 193, 195, 197, 199, 209, 211, 213, 215, 217, 223, 225, 227, 229, 247, 249, 251, 253, 260, 261, 263, 265, 267, 269, 270, 275, 277, 278–279, 282, 289, 299, 301, 303, 305, 307, 317, 319, 321, 329, 331, 333, 335, 337, 353, 355, 357, 358, 359, 361, 375, 377, 379, 431, 433, 435, 437, 439, 449, 451, 453, 465, 467, 469, 539, 541, 543, 545, 547
RI.4.3	Explain events, procedures, ideas, or concepts in a historical, scientific, or technical text, including what happened and why, based on specific information in the text.	5, 7, 9, 11, 13, 19, 21, 23, 29, 31, 33, 35, 37, 47, 49, 51, 65, 67, 69, 71, 81, 83, 85, 86, 87, 89, 105, 107, 109, 111, 119, 121, 123, 125, 127, 137, 139, 141, 143, 145, 175, 177, 179, 181, 183, 191, 193, 195, 197, 199, 209, 211, 213, 215, 217, 223, 225, 227, 229, 247, 249, 251, 253, 260, 261, 263, 265, 267, 269, 270, 275, 277, 278–279, 282, 289, 299, 301, 303, 305, 307, 317, 319, 321, 329, 331, 333, 335, 337, 353, 355, 357, 358, 359, 361, 375, 377, 379, 431, 433, 435, 437, 439, 449, 451, 453, 465, 467, 469, 539, 541, 543, 545, 547

Grade 4 Standard Code	Descriptor	Teacher Edition Page Citations
Craft and Structure		
RI.4.4	Determine the meaning of general academic and domain-specific words or phrases in a text relevant to a grade 4 topic or subject area.	Use the strategies in the Develop Science Vocabulary entries in the side margins of the Teacher Edition. Use the Interactive Glossary with every lesson.
RI.4.5	Describe the overall structure (e.g., chronology, comparison, cause/effect, problem/solution) of events, ideas, concepts, or information in a text or part of a text.	4, 6, 8, 10, 12, 18, 20, 22, 28, 30, 32, 34, 36, 46, 48, 50, 70, 80–81, 82, 84, 86, 88, 104, 106, 108, 110, 118, 120, 122, 124, 126, 136, 138, 140, 142, 144, 167A, 174, 176, 178, 180, 182, 190, 191, 192, 194, 196, 198, 208, 210, 212, 214, 216, 222, 224, 226, 228, 246, 248, 250, 252, 260, 262–263, 264, 266, 268, 274, 276, 278, 280, 298, 300, 302, 304, 306, 316, 318, 320, 328, 330, 332, 334, 336, 352, 354, 356, 358, 360, 374, 376, 378, 392, 394, 396, 398, 406, 408, 410, 412, 430, 432, 434, 436, 438, 448, 450, 452, 464, 466, 468, 484, 486, 488, 490, 502, 504, 506, 508, 518, 520, 522, 524, 538, 540, 542, 544, 546
Integration of Knowledge and Ideas		
RI.4.7	Interpret information presented visually, orally, or quantitatively (e.g., in charts, graphs, diagrams, time lines, animations, or interactive elements on Web pages) and explain how the information contributes to an understanding of the text in which it appears.	Use the strategies in the Interpret Visuals entries in the side margins of the Teacher Edition.
RI.4.9	Integrate information from two texts on the same topic in order to write or speak about the subject knowledgeably.	Texts with topics related to the Student Edition can be found in the Leveled Readers.

Grade 4 Standard Code	Descriptor	Teacher Edition Page Citations
Range of Reading and Level of Text Complexity		
RI.4.10	By the end of year, read and comprehend informational texts, including history/social studies, science, and technical texts, in the grades 4–5 text complexity band proficiently, with scaffolding as needed at the high end of the range.	See the Science Trade Books Bibliography on pp. TR44–TR47 for some suggested titles.
Reading Standards: Foundational Skills		
Phonics and Word Recognition		
RF.4.3	Know and apply grade-level phonics and word analysis skills in decoding words.	
RF.4.3.a	Use combined knowledge of all letter-sound correspondences, syllabication patterns, and morphology (e.g., roots and affixes) to read accurately unfamiliar multisyllabic words in context and out of context.	87, 109, 110, 154, 181, 190, 209, 321, 374, 466, 508, 520
Fluency		
RF.4.4	Read with sufficient accuracy and fluency to support comprehension.	
RF.4.4.a	Read on-level text with purpose and understanding.	Reproducible student worksheets addressing oral reading fluency are provided with each Leveled Reader Teacher Guide.
RF.4.4.b	Read on-level prose and poetry orally with accuracy, appropriate rate, and expression on successive readings.	135
Writing Standards		
Text Types and Purposes		
W.4.1	Write opinion pieces on topics or texts, supporting a point of view with reasons and information.	
W.4.1.a	Introduce a topic or text clearly, state an opinion, and create an organizational structure in which related ideas are grouped to support the writer's purpose.	51, 227, 229, 234A, 366A, 397, 410, 467, 507
W.4.1.b	Provide reasons that are supported by facts and details.	51, 227, 229, 366A, 397, 410, 467, 507
W.4.1.d	Provide a concluding statement or section related to the opinion presented.	51, 227, 229, 234A, 366A, 397, 410, 467, 507
W.4.2	Write informative/explanatory texts to examine a topic and convey ideas and information clearly.	

Grade 4 Standard Code	Descriptor	Teacher Edition Page Citations
W.4.2.a	Introduce a topic clearly and group related information in paragraphs and sections; include formatting (e.g., headings), illustrations, and multimedia when useful to aiding comprehension.	7, 20, 26A, 29, 40A, 71, 76A, 92A, 111, 120, 134A, 136, 150, 177, 188A, 213, 215, 235, 284A, 305, 312A, 337, 340A, 366A, 375, 402A, 407, 412, 416A, 421, 436, 458A, 529
W.4.2.b	Develop the topic with facts, definitions, concrete details, quotations, or other information and examples related to the topic.	7, 20, 26A, 54A, 71, 76A, 92A, 111, 120, 134A, 136, 150, 152, 177, 188A, 204A, 213, 215, 232A, 235, 284A, 305, 337, 340A, 366A, 375, 402A, 416A, 421, 436, 529
W.4.2.c	Link ideas within categories of information using words and phrases (e.g., another, for example, also, because).	71, 76A, 92A, 136, 150, 177, 188A, 215, 220A, 235, 305, 421, 529
W.4.2.d	Use precise language and domain-specific vocabulary to inform about or explain the topic.	7, 20, 26A, 71, 76A, 92A, 106, 107, 111, 120, 132A, 136, 150, 152, 177, 188A, 204A, 213, 215, 220A, 232A, 235, 284A, 305, 337, 340A, 366A, 375, 402A, 407, 412, 416A, 421, 436, 458A, 514A, 529
W.4.2.e	Provide a concluding statement or section related to the information or explanation presented.	7, 20, 71, 76A, 92A, 120, 134A, 136, 150, 188A, 215, 232A, 235, 284A, 305, 337, 366A, 375, 402A, 416A, 421, 436, 514A, 529
W.4.3	Write narratives to develop real or imagined experiences or events using effective technique, descriptive details, and clear event sequences.	
W.4.3.a	Orient the reader by establishing a situation and introducing a narrator and/or characters; organize an event sequence that unfolds naturally.	82, 86, 114A, 124, 132A, 159, 164A, 177, 195, 220A, 265, 272A, 281, 340A, 355, 382A, 412, 449, 523, 528A, 545
W.4.3.b	Use dialogue and description to develop experiences and events or show the responses of characters to situations.	82, 107, 114A, 124, 132A, 159, 161, 164A, 177, 195, 265, 272A, 281, 340A, 382A, 412, 449, 523, 528A, 545
W.4.3.c	Use a variety of transitional words and phrases to manage the sequence of events.	82, 124, 132A, 177, 195, 272A, 281, 523, 528A
W.4.3.d	Use concrete words and phrases and sensory details to convey experiences and events precisely.	82, 86, 107, 114A, 124, 132A, 159, 164A, 177, 195, 220A, 248, 265, 272A, 281, 319, 340A, 355, 382A, 397, 412, 449, 523, 528A, 545

Grade 4 Standard Code	Descriptor	Teacher Edition Page Citations
W.4.3.e	Provide a conclusion that follows from the narrated experiences or events.	82, 86, 114A, 124, 159, 177, 195, 265, 272A, 281, 340A, 382A, 412, 523, 528A, 545

Production and Distribution of Writing

W.4.4	Produce clear and coherent writing in which the development and organization are appropriate to task, purpose, and audience. (Grade-specific expectations for writing types are defined in standards 1–3 above.)	7, 20, 26A, 40A, 51, 54A, 71, 76A, 82, 86, 92A, 107, 110, 114A, 120, 124, 132A, 136, 150, 177, 188A, 195, 204A, 213, 215, 220A, 227, 229, 232A, 234A, 235, 248, 265, 272A, 281, 284A, 305, 312A, 319, 337, 340A, 355, 366A, 375, 382A, 402A, 407, 412, 416A, 421, 436, 449, 458A, 507, 514A, 523, 528A, 529, 545
W.4.6	With some guidance and support from adults, use technology, including the Internet, to produce and publish writing as well as to interact and collaborate with others; demonstrate sufficient command of keyboarding skills to type a minimum of one page in a single sitting.	The Go Digital Path allows students to use digital tools to present a topic.

Research to Build and Present Knowledge

W.4.7	Conduct short research projects that build knowledge through investigation of different aspects of a topic.	76A, 92A, 114A, 132A, 136, 150, 161, 164A, 188A, 204A, 213, 215, 227, 232A, 234A, 272A, 305, 312A, 340A, 402A
W.4.8	Recall relevant information from experiences or gather relevant information from print and digital sources; take notes and categorize information, and provide a list of sources.	76A, 82, 114, 120, 132A, 136, 150, 161, 188A, 204A, 213, 258A, 312A, 324A, 340A, 444A, 458A, 472A, 528A
W.4.9	Draw evidence from literary or informational texts to support analysis, reflection, and research.	
W.4.9.b	Apply grade 4 Reading standards to informational texts (e.g., "Explain how an author uses reasons and evidence to support particular points in a text").	235

Range of Writing

W.4.10	Write routinely over extended time frames (time for research, reflection, and revision) and shorter time frames (a single sitting or a day or two) for a range of discipline-specific tasks, purposes, and audiences.	528A

Grade 4 Standard Code	Descriptor	Teacher Edition Page Citations
Speaking and Listening Standards		
Comprehension and Collaboration		
SL.4.1	Engage effectively in a range of collaborative discussions (one-on-one, in groups, and teacher-led) with diverse partners on grade 4 topics and texts, building on others' ideas and expressing their own clearly.	
SL.4.1.a	Come to discussions prepared, having read or studied required material; explicitly draw on that preparation and other information known about the topic to explore ideas under discussion.	Use the Generate Ideas sections to access prior knowledge and to provide opportunities for students to discuss their own ideas about a topic. For example, see pages 4, 6, 8, 10, 12, 18, 20, 22, 28, 30, 32, 34, 36, 46, 48, 50, 64, 66, 68, 70, 80, 82, 84, 86, 104, 106, 108, 110, 118, 120, 122, 124, 126, 136, 138, 140, 142, 144, 174, 176, 178, 180, 182, 190, 192, 194, 196, 198, 208, 210, 212, 214, 216, 222, 224, 226, 228, 246, 248, 250, 252, 260, 262, 264, 266, 268, 274, 276, 278, 280, 298, 300, 302, 304, 306, 316, 318, 320, 328, 330, 332, 334, 336, 352, 354, 356, 358, 360, 374, 376, 378, 392, 394, 396, 398, 406, 408, 410, 412, 430, 432, 434, 436, 438, 448, 450, 452, 464, 466, 468, 484, 486, 488, 490, 502, 504, 506, 508, 518, 520, 522, 524, 538, 540, 542, 544, 546
SL.4.1.b	Follow agreed-upon rules for discussions and carry out assigned roles.	104, 106, 108, 109, 110, 164A, 333, 324A, 430

Grade 4 Standard Code	Descriptor	Teacher Edition Page Citations
SL.4.1.c	Pose and respond to specific questions to clarify or follow up on information, and make comments that contribute to the discussion and link to the remarks of others.	4, 6, 8, 10, 12, 18, 20, 22, 28, 30, 32, 34, 36, 46, 48, 50, 64, 66, 68, 70, 80, 82, 84, 86, 104, 106, 108, 110, 118, 120, 122, 124, 126, 136, 138, 140, 142, 144, 174, 176, 178, 180, 182, 190, 192, 194, 196, 198, 208, 210, 212, 214, 216, 222, 224, 226, 228, 246, 248, 250, 252, 260, 262, 264, 266, 268, 274, 276, 278, 280, 298, 300, 302, 304, 306, 316, 318, 320, 324A 328, 330, 332, 334, 336, 352, 354, 356, 358, 360, 374, 376, 378, 392, 394, 396, 398, 406, 408, 410, 412, 430, 432, 434, 436, 438, 448, 450, 452, 464, 466, 468, 538, 540, 542, 544, 546
SL.4.1.d	Review the key ideas expressed and explain their own ideas and understanding in light of the discussion.	5, 7, 9, 11, 13, 19, 21, 23, 29, 31, 33, 35, 37, 47, 49, 51, 65, 67, 69, 71, 81, 83, 85, 86, 87, 89, 105, 107, 109, 111, 119, 121, 123, 125, 127, 137, 139, 141, 143, 145, 175, 177, 179, 181, 183, 191, 193, 195, 197, 199, 209, 211, 213, 215, 217, 223, 225, 227, 229, 247, 249, 251, 253, 260, 261, 263, 265, 267, 269, 270, 275, 277, 278–279, 282, 289, 299, 301, 303, 305, 307, 317, 319, 321, 329, 331, 333, 335, 337, 353, 355, 357, 358, 359, 361, 375, 377, 379, 431, 433, 435, 437, 439, 449, 451, 453, 465, 467, 469, 539, 541, 543, 545, 547
Presentation of Knowledge and Ideas		
SL.4.4	Report on a topic or text, tell a story, or recount an experience in an organized manner, using appropriate facts and relevant, descriptive details to support main ideas or themes; speak clearly at an understandable pace.	76A, 178, 215, 324A, 402A, 436

Grade 4 Standard Code	Descriptor	Teacher Edition Page Citations
Language Standards		
Conventions of Standard English		
L.4.1	Demonstrate command of the conventions of standard English grammar and usage when writing or speaking.	
L.4.1.f	Produce complete sentences, recognizing and correcting inappropriate fragments and run-ons.	407
L.4.1.g	Correctly use frequently confused words (e.g., to, too, two; there, their).	158
L.4.2	Demonstrate command of the conventions of standard English capitalization, punctuation, and spelling when writing.	
L.4.2.d	Spell grade-appropriate words correctly, consulting references as needed.	194, 381, 455, 471
Knowledge of Language		
L.4.3	Use knowledge of language and its conventions when writing, speaking, reading, or listening.	
L.4.3.a	Choose words and phrases to convey ideas precisely.	123, 174, 178, 398, 406, 409, 447, 520, 522, 523, 528A
L.4.3.b	Choose punctuation for effect.	125
Vocabulary Acquisition and Use		
L.4.4	Determine or clarify the meaning of unknown and multiple-meaning words and phrases based on grade 4 reading and content, choosing flexibly from an array of strategies.	
L.4.4.a	Use context (e.g., definitions, examples, or restatements in text) as a clue to the meaning of a word or phrase.	34, 66, 84, 174, 193, 194, 209, 210, 218, 246, 251, 298, 317, 331, 352, 374, 392, 395, 406, 409, 430, 454, 504, 505
L.4.4.b	Use common, grade-appropriate Greek and Latin affixes and roots as clues to the meaning of a word (e.g., telegraph, photograph, autograph).	67, 110, 502, 514A, 520, 522, 524
L.4.4.c	Consult reference materials (e.g., dictionaries, glossaries, thesauruses), both print and digital, to find the pronunciation and determine or clarify the precise meaning of key words and phrases.	The Vocabulary and Interactive Glossary feature allows students to use digital glossaries to add notes, illustrations, and sentences to vocabulary words.
L.4.5	Demonstrate understanding of figurative language, word relationships, and nuances in word meanings.	
L.4.5.b	Recognize and explain the meaning of common idioms, adages, and proverbs.	378, 451, 540

Grade 4 Standard Code	Descriptor	Teacher Edition Page Citations
L.4.5.c	Demonstrate understanding of words by relating them to their opposites (antonyms) and to words with similar but not identical meanings (synonyms).	4, 8, 174, 210, 224, 226, 398, 520
L.4.6	Acquire and use accurately grade-appropriate general academic and domain-specific words and phrases, including those that signal precise actions, emotions, or states of being (e.g., quizzed, whined, stammered) and that are basic to a particular topic (e.g., wildlife, conservation, and endangered when discussing animal preservation).	1L–1M, 5, 7, 9, 19, 31, 33, 35, 47, 49, 61J–61K, 65, 67, 81, 101L–101M, 107, 108, 110, 118, 120, 122, 126, 142, 143, 146, 147, 152, 154, 159, 171L–171M, 175, 176, 179, 181, 190, 191, 193, 197, 200, 201, 209, 210, 219, 227, 228, 243J–243K, 247, 249, 251, 261, 269, 274, 276, 279, 295L–295M, 299, 300, 305, 319, 328, 349J–349K, 353, 356, 359, 374, 375, 378, 389J–389K, 393, 397, 407, 409, 411, 427J–427K, 431, 433, 437, 449, 451, 453, 455, 464, 465, 467, 470, 471, 481J–481K, 487, 490, 502, 504, 507, 519, 520, 522, 523, 524, 525, 528A, 535H–535I, 539, 542, 544

Correlations to the Common Core State Standards for Mathematics are provided on these pages.

Grade 4 Standard Code	Descriptor	Teacher Edition Page Citations
Mathematical Practices		
4.MP.1	Make sense of problems and persevere in solving them.	23, 119, 139, 307, 320, 325, 434, 469, 509, 514A, 528A
4.MP.2	Reason abstractly and quantitatively.	199
4.MP.4	Model with mathematics.	11, 16A, 23, 123, 132A, 164A, 176, 198, 199, 204A, 217, 232A, 312A, 320, 340A, 357, 394, 397, 408
4.MP.5	Use appropriate tools strategically.	35, 49, 357, 394, 449
4.MP.6	Attend to precision.	23, 137, 211, 357, 397, 449, 509, 514A
4.MP.7	Look for and make use of structure.	176
4.MP.8	Look for and express regularity in repeated reasoning.	319, 509, 514A
Operations and Algebraic Thinking		
Use the four operations with whole numbers to solve problems.		
4.OA.2	Multiply or divide to solve word problems involving multiplicative comparison, e.g., by using drawings and equations with a symbol for the unknown number to represent the problem, distinguishing multiplicative comparison from additive comparison.	249, 528A
4.OA.3	Solve multistep word problems posed with whole numbers and having whole-number answers using the four operations, including problems in which remainders must be interpreted. Represent these problems using equations with a letter standing for the unknown quantity. Assess the reasonableness of answers using mental computation and estimation strategies including rounding.	182, 188A, 214, 223, 227, 328, 528A
Gain familiarity with factors and multiples.		
4.OA.4	Find all factor pairs for a whole number in the range 1–100. Recognize that a whole number is a multiple of each of its factors. Determine whether a given whole number in the range 1–100 is a multiple of a given one-digit number. Determine whether a given whole number in the range 1–100 is prime or composite.	253

Grade 4 Standard Code	Descriptor	Teacher Edition Page Citations
Generate and analyze patterns.		
4.OA.5	Generate a number or shape pattern that follows a given rule. Identify apparent features of the pattern that were not explicit in the rule itself. *For example, given the rule "Add 3" and the starting number 1, generate terms in the resulting sequence and observe that the terms appear to alternate between odd and even numbers. Explain informally why the numbers will continue to alternate in this way.*	153, 514A
Number and Operations in Base Ten		
Generalize place value understanding for multi-digit whole numbers.		
4.NBT.1	Recognize that in a multi-digit whole number, a digit in one place represents ten times what it represents in the place to its right. *For example, recognize that 700 ÷ 70 = 10 by applying concepts of place value and division.*	253
Use place value understanding and properties of operations to perform multi-digit arithmetic.		
4.NBT.4	Fluently add and subtract multi-digit whole numbers using the standard algorithm.	26A, 33, 36, 87, 127, 263, 281, 284, 298, 328
4.NBT.5	Multiply a whole number of up to four digits by a one-digit whole number, and multiply two two-digit numbers, using strategies based on place value and the properties of operations. Illustrate and explain the calculation by using equations, rectangular arrays, and/or area models.	83, 87, 127, 227, 253, 258A, 458A, 472A, 542
4.NBT.6	Find whole-number quotients and remainders with up to four-digit dividends and one-digit divisors, using strategies based on place value, the properties of operations, and/or the relationship between multiplication and division. Illustrate and explain the calculation by using equations, rectangular arrays, and/or area models.	48, 214, 249, 284, 320, 458A, 543
Number and Operations—Fractions		
Extend understanding of fraction equivalence and ordering.		
4.NF.1	Explain why a fraction a/b is equivalent to a fraction $(n \times a)/(n \times b)$ by using visual fraction models, with attention to how the number and size of the parts differ even though the two fractions themselves are the same size. Use this principle to recognize and generate equivalent fractions.	49, 68, 123, 413
4.NF.2	Compare two fractions with different numerators and different denominators, e.g., by creating common denominators or numerators, or by comparing to a benchmark fraction such as 1/2. Recognize that comparisons are valid only when the two fractions refer to the same whole. Record the results of comparisons with symbols >, =, or <, and justify the conclusions, e.g., by using a visual fraction model.	413

Grade 4 Standard Code	Descriptor	Teacher Edition Page Citations
Build fractions from unit fractions by applying and extending previous understandings of operations on whole numbers.		
4.NF.3	3. Understand a fraction a/b with $a > 1$ as a sum of fractions $1/b$. a. Understand addition and subtraction of fractions as joining and separating parts referring to the same whole. b. Decompose a fraction into a sum of fractions with the same denominator in more than one way, recording each decomposition by an equation. Justify decompositions, e.g., by using a visual fraction model. *Examples: 3/8 = 1/8 + 1/8 + 1/8 ; 3/8 = 1/8 + 2/8; 2 1/8 = 1 + 1 + 1/8 = 8/8 + 8/8 + 1/8.* c. Add and subtract mixed numbers with like denominators, e.g., by replacing each mixed number with an equivalent fraction, and/or by using properties of operations and the relationship between addition and subtraction. d. Solve word problems involving addition and subtraction of fractions referring to the same whole and having like denominators, e.g., by using visual fraction models and equations to represent the problem.	11, 105, 108, 123, 153, 155, 413, 525
4.NF.4	Apply and extend previous understandings of multiplication to multiply a fraction by a whole number. a. Understand a fraction a/b as a multiple of $1/b$. *For example, use a visual fraction model to represent 5/4 as the product 5 × (1/4), recording the conclusion by the equation 5/4 = 5 × (1/4).* b. Understand a multiple of a/b as a multiple of $1/b$, and use this understanding to multiply a fraction by a whole number. *For example, use a visual fraction model to express 3 × (2/5) as 6 × (1/5), recognizing this product as 6/5. (In general, n × (a/b) = (n × a)/b.)* c. Solve word problems involving multiplication of a fraction by a whole number, e.g., by using visual fraction models and equations to represent the problem. *For example, if each person at a party will eat 3/8 of a pound of roast beef, and there will be 5 people at the party, how many pounds of roast beef will be needed? Between what two whole numbers does your answer lie?*	108, 119, 188A, 528A
Understand decimal notation for fractions, and compare decimal fractions.		
4.NF.6	Use decimal notation for fractions with denominators 10 or 100. *For example, rewrite 0.62 as 62/100; describe a length as 0.62 meters; locate 0.62 on a number line diagram.*	11, 123, 153
4.NF.7	Compare two decimals to hundredths by reasoning about their size. Recognize that comparisons are valid only when the two decimals refer to the same whole. Record the results of comparisons with the symbols >, =, or <, and justify the conclusions, e.g., by using a visual model.	464

Grade 4 Standard Code	Descriptor	Teacher Edition Page Citations
Measurement and Data		
Solve problems involving measurement and conversion of measurements from a larger unit to a smaller unit.		
4.MD.1	Know relative sizes of measurement units within one system of units including km, m, cm; kg, g; lb, oz.; l, ml; hr, min, sec. Within a single system of measurement, express measurements in a larger unit in terms of a smaller unit. Record measurement equivalents in a two-column table. *For example, know that 1 ft is 12 times as long as 1 in. Express the length of a 4 ft snake as 48 in. Generate a conversion table for feet and inches listing the number pairs (1, 12), (2, 24), (3, 36), ...*	33, 76A, 83, 132A, 160, 162, 199, 249, 259A, 281, 287A, 288, 284A, 298, 307, 542
4.MD.2	Use the four operations to solve word problems involving distances, intervals of time, liquid volumes, masses of objects, and money, including problems involving simple fractions or decimals, and problems that require expressing measurements given in a larger unit in terms of a smaller unit. Represent measurement quantities using diagrams such as number line diagrams that feature a measurement scale.	87, 164A, 227, 357
4.MD.3	Apply the area and perimeter formulas for rectangles in real world and mathematical problems. *For example, find the width of a rectangular room given the area of the flooring and the length, by viewing the area formula as a multiplication equation with an unknown factor.*	40A
Represent and interpret data.		
4.MD.4	Make a line plot to display a data set of measurements in fractions of a unit (1/2, 1/4, 1/8). Solve problems involving addition and subtraction of fractions by using information presented in line plots. *For example, from a line plot find and interpret the difference in length between the longest and shortest specimens in an insect collection.*	132A, 288A, 394

Correlation to
ScienceSaurus

ScienceSaurus, **A Student Handbook,** is a "mini-encyclopedia" students can use to find out more about unit topics. It contains numerous resources including concise content summaries, an almanac, many tables, charts, and graphs, history of science, and a glossary. **ScienceSaurus** is available from Houghton Mifflin Harcourt.

ScienceFusion Grade 4	*ScienceSaurus* Topics	*ScienceSaurus* Pages
Unit 1 Studying Science		
Lesson 1 What Do Scientists Do?	Doing Science, Scientific Investigation Doing Science, Working Safely	pp. 2–27 pp. 28–37
Lesson 2 What Skills Do Scientists Use?	Doing Science, Scientific Investigation Doing Science, Using Science Tools and Equipment Doing Science, Using Tables and Graphs Almanac, Numbers in Science Almanac, Solving Math Problems in Science	pp. 2–27 pp. 38–59 pp. 60–73 pp. 371–379 pp. 380–385
Lesson 3 How Do Scientists Collect and Use Data?	Doing Science, Scientific Investigation Doing Science, Using Science Tools and Equipment Doing Science, Using Tables and Graphs Almanac, Maps	pp. 2–27 pp. 38–59 pp. 60–73 pp. 403–407
Lesson 4 Why Do Scientists Compare Results?	Doing Science, Scientific Investigation Doing Science, Using Science Tools and Equipment Doing Science, Using Tables and Graphs Almanac, Numbers in Science	pp. 2–27 pp. 38–59 pp. 60–73 pp. 371–379
People in Science—John Diebold/ Martin Culpepper	Science, Technology, and Society, Science and Society Yellow Pages, History of Science Yellow Pages, Science Time Line Yellow Pages, Famous Scientists and Inventors	pp. 364–369 p. 412 pp. 413–423 pp. 424–435
Lesson 5 What Kinds of Models Do Scientists Use?	Doing Science, Scientific Investigation Earth Science, Weather and Climate	pp. 2–27 pp. 198–217
Lesson 6 How Can You Model a School?	Doing Science, Scientific Investigation	pp. 2–27

ScienceFusion Grade 4	*ScienceSaurus* Topics	*ScienceSaurus* Pages
Unit 2 The Engineering Process		
Lesson 1 What Is an Engineering Design Process?	Science, Technology, and Society, Science and Technology	pp. 356–363
Lesson 2 How Can You Design a Solution to a Problem?	Science, Technology, and Society, Science and Technology	pp. 356–363
Lesson 3 What Is Technology?	Science, Technology, and Society, Science and Technology	pp. 356–363
	Science, Technology, and Society, Science and Society	pp. 364–369
Lesson 4 How Do We Use Technology?	Science, Technology, and Society, Science and Technology	pp. 356–363
	Science, Technology, and Society, Science and Society	pp. 364–369
People in Science—Ayanna Howard	Science, Technology, and Society, Science and Technology	pp. 356–363
	Science, Technology, and Society, Science and Society	pp. 364–369
	Yellow Pages, History of Science	p. 412
	Yellow Pages, Science Time Line	pp. 413–423
	Yellow Pages, Famous Scientists and Inventors	pp. 424–435

ScienceFusion Grade 4	*ScienceSaurus* Topics	*ScienceSaurus* Pages
Unit 3 Plants and Animals		
Lesson 1 What Are Some Plant Structures?	Life Science, Characteristics of Living Things Life Science, Cells, Tissues, Organs, and Systems	pp. 76–91 pp. 98–109
S.T.E.M. Engineering and Technology—Water Irrigation System	Science, Technology, and Society, Science and Technology Science, Technology, and Society, Science and Society	pp. 356–363 pp. 364–369
Lesson 2 How Do Plants Reproduce?	Life Science, Characteristics of Living Things	pp. 76–91
Lesson 3 How Can We Observe a Plant's Life Cycle?	Life Science, Characteristics of Living Things	pp. 76–91
Lesson 4 How Do Animals Reproduce?	Life Science, Characteristics of Living Things	pp. 76–91
Careers in Science—Animal Behaviorist	Life Science, Animal and Plant Behavior Science, Technology, and Society, Science and Technology Science, Technology, and Society, Science and Society	pp. 92–97 pp. 356–363 pp. 364–369
Lesson 5 How Are Living Things Adapted to Their Environment?	Life Science, Characteristics of Living Things Life Science, Animal and Plant Behavior Life Science, Ecology Life Science, Classifying Organisms	pp. 76–91 pp. 92–97 pp. 126–138 pp. 139–155
Lesson 6 Why Do Bird Beaks Differ?	Life Science, Characteristics of Living Things Life Science, Animal and Plant Behavior Life Science, Ecology Life Science, Classifying Organisms	pp. 76–91 pp. 92–97 pp. 126–138 pp. 139–155

ScienceFusion Grade 4	*ScienceSaurus* Topics	*ScienceSaurus* Pages
Unit 4 Energy and Ecosystems		
Lesson 1 What Are Populations, Habitats, and Niches?	Life Science, Ecology Natural Resources and the Environment, Conserving Resources	pp. 126–138 pp. 344–353
Lesson 2 What Are Food Chains?	Life Science, Ecology Natural Resources and the Environment, Conserving Resources	pp. 126–138 pp. 344–353
Lesson 3 How Can We Model a Food Web?	Life Science, Ecology Natural Resources and the Environment, Conserving Resources	pp. 126–138 pp. 344–353
Lesson 4 What Are Natural Resources?	Earth Science, Earth's Structure Natural Resources and the Environment, Natural Resources	pp. 158–169 pp. 320–333
Lesson 5 How Do People Impact Ecosystems?	Life Science, Ecology Natural Resources and the Environment, Pollution Natural Resources and the Environment, Conserving Resources	pp. 126–138 pp. 334–343 pp. 344–353
Lesson 6 How Do People Affect Their Environment?	Life Science, Ecology Natural Resources and the Environment, Pollution Natural Resources and the Environment, Protecting Resources	pp. 126–138 pp. 334–343 pp. 344–353
People in Science— Wangari Maathai/Willie Smits	Science, Technology, and Society, Science and Society Yellow Pages, History of Science Yellow Pages, Science Time Line Yellow Pages, Famous Scientists and Inventors	pp. 364–369 p. 412 pp. 413–423 pp. 424–435
S.T.E.M. Engineering and Technology—Underwater Exploration	Life Science, Ecology Science, Technology, and Society, Science and Technology Science, Technology, and Society, Science and Society	pp. 126–138 pp. 356–363 pp. 364–369

ScienceFusion Grade 4	ScienceSaurus Topics	ScienceSaurus Pages
Unit 5 Weather		
Lesson 1 What Is the Water Cycle?	Earth Science, Earth's Structure Earth Science, Water on Earth	pp. 158–170 pp. 187–197
Lesson 2 What Are Types of Weather?	Earth Science, Weather and Climate	pp. 198–217
Lesson 3 How Is Weather Predicted?	Earth Science, Weather and Climate	pp. 198–217
S.T.E.M. Engineering and Technology—Beaufort Wind Scale	Earth Science, Weather and Climate Science, Technology, and Society, Science and Technology Science, Technology, and Society, Science and Society	pp. 198–217 pp. 356–363 pp. 364–369
Lesson 4 How Can We Observe Weather Patterns?	Earth Science, Weather and Climate	pp. 198–217
People in Science—N. Christina Hsu	Science, Technology, and Society, Science and Society Yellow Pages, History of Science Yellow Pages, Science Time Line Yellow Pages, Famous Scientists and Inventors	pp. 364–369 p. 412 pp. 413–423 pp. 424–435
Unit 6 Earth and Space		
Lesson 1 How Do the Sun, Earth, and Moon Interact?	Earth Science, Earth and Its Moon Earth Science, The Solar System and Beyond	pp. 218–225 pp. 226–239
People in Science— Milutin Milankovitch/Maureen Raymo	Science, Technology, and Society, Science and Society Yellow Pages, History of Science Yellow Pages, Science Time Line Yellow Pages, Famous Scientists and Inventors	pp. 364–369 p. 412 pp. 413–423 pp. 424–435
Lesson 2 What Are Moon Phases?	Earth Science, Earth and Its Moon	pp. 218–225
Lesson 3 How Does the Moon Move Around Earth?	Earth Science, Earth and Its Moon	pp. 218–225
Lesson 4 What Are the Planets in Our Solar System?	Earth Science, The Solar System and Beyond	pp. 226–239
S.T.E.M. Engineering and Technology—Space Exploration	Science, Technology, and Society, Science and Technology Science, Technology, and Society, Science and Society	pp. 356–363 pp. 364–369
Lesson 5 How Can We Model the Sun and Planets?	Earth Science, The Solar System and Beyond	pp. 226–239

ScienceFusion Grade 4	*ScienceSaurus* Topics	*ScienceSaurus* Pages
Unit 7 Properties of Matter		
Lesson 1 What Are Physical Properties of Matter?	Physical Science, Matter	pp. 242–259
Lesson 2 How Are Physical Properties Observed?	Physical Science, Matter	pp. 242–259
Careers in Science—Materials Scientists	Science, Technology, and Society, Science and Technology	pp. 356–363
	Science, Technology, and Society, Science and Society	pp. 364–369
Lesson 3 What Is Conservation of Mass?	Physical Science, Matter Physical Science, Changes in Matter	pp. 242–259 pp. 260–267
Lesson 4 What Are the States of Water?	Physical Science, Changes in Matter	pp. 260–267
S.T.E.M. Engineering and Technology—Refrigeration	Science, Technology, and Society, Science and Technology	pp. 356–363
	Science, Technology, and Society, Science and Society	pp. 364–369
Unit 8 Changes in Matter		
Lesson 1 What Are Some Physical Changes?	Physical Science, Changes in Matter	pp. 260–267
Lesson 2 How Can We Make a Solution?	Physical Science, Matter Physical Science, Changes in Matter	pp. 242–259 pp. 260–267
Lesson 3 What Are Some Chemical Changes?	Physical Science, Changes in Matter	pp. 260–267
S.T.E.M. Engineering and Technology—Body Armor	Science, Technology, and Society, Science and Technology	pp. 356–363
	Science, Technology, and Society, Science and Society	pp. 364–369
Lesson 4 How Can You Tell When a New Substance Forms?	Physical Science, Changes in Matter	pp. 260–267
People in Science—Ruth Rogan Benerito/Hèctor Abruña	Science, Technology, and Society, Science and Society	pp. 364–369
	Yellow Pages, History of Science	p. 412
	Yellow Pages, Science Time Line	pp. 413–423
	Yellow Pages, Famous Scientists and Inventors	pp. 424–435

ScienceFusion Grade 4	ScienceSaurus Topics	ScienceSaurus Pages
Unit 9 Energy		
Lesson 1 What Are Some Forms of Energy?	Physical Science, Energy Physical Science, Heat Physical Science Electricity and Magnetism Physical Science, Light and Sound	pp. 284–287 pp. 288–294 pp. 295–307 pp. 308–317
Lesson 2 Where Does Energy Come From?	Physical Science, Energy	pp. 284–287
Lesson 3 What Is Heat?	Physical Science, Heat	pp. 288–294
Lesson 4 How Is Heat Produced?	Physical Science, Heat	pp. 288–294
Careers in Science— Geothermal Technician	Physical Science, Heat Science, Technology, and Society, Science and Technology Science, Technology, and Society, Science and Society	pp. 288–294 pp. 356–363 pp. 364–369
Lesson 5 What Are Conductors and Insulators?	Physical Science, Heat	pp. 288–294
Lesson 6 Which Materials Are Conductors?	Physical Science, Heat	pp. 288–294
S.T.E.M. Engineering and Technology—Piezoelectricity	Science, Technology, and Society, Science and Technology Science, Technology, and Society, Science and Society	pp. 356–363 pp. 364–369
Unit 10 Electricity		
Lesson 1 What Is Electricity?	Physical Science, Electricity and Magnetism	pp. 295–307
Lesson 2 How Do Electric Charges Interact?	Physical Science, Electricity and Magnetism	pp. 295–307
Lesson 3 What Is an Electric Circuit?	Physical Science, Electricity and Magnetism	pp. 295–307
Lesson 4 What Are Electric Circuits, Conductors, and Insulators?	Physical Science, Electricity and Magnetism	pp. 295–307
Careers in Science—Electrician	Physical Science, Electricity and Magnetism Science, Technology, and Society, Science and Technology Science, Technology, and Society, Science and Society	pp. 295–307 pp. 356–363 pp. 364–369
Lesson 5 How Do We Use Electricity?	Physical Science, Electricity and Magnetism	pp. 295–307

ScienceFusion Grade 4	*ScienceSaurus* Topics	*ScienceSaurus* Pages
Unit 10 Electricity (continued)		
S.T.E.M. Engineering and Technology—The Electric Grid	Science, Technology, and Society, Science and Technology	pp. 356–363
	Science, Technology, and Society, Science and Society	pp. 364–369
Unit 11 Motion		
Lesson 1 What Is Motion?	Physical Science, Forces and Motion	pp. 268–283
Lesson 2 What Is Speed?	Physical Science, Forces and Motion	pp. 268–283
Careers in Science—Air Traffic Controller	Science, Technology, and Society, Science and Technology	pp. 356–363
	Science, Technology, and Society, Science and Society	pp. 364–369
S.T.E.M. Engineering and Technology—Gyroscopes	Science, Technology, and Society, Science and Technology	pp. 356–363
	Science, Technology, and Society, Science and Society	pp. 364–369
All Units		
These topics may be used with all units and lessons.	Almanac, Numbers in Science	pp. 371–379
	Almanac, Solving Math Problems in Science	pp. 380–385
	Almanac, Study Skills	pp. 386–393
	Almanac, Test-Taking Skills	pp. 394–402
	Almanac, Maps	pp. 403–407
	Almanac, Measurement Tables	pp. 408–410
	Yellow Pages, Science Word Parts	pp. 436–437
	Yellow Pages, Glossary of Science Terms	pp. 438–493
These topics may be used with all investigations.	Doing Science, Scientific Investigation	pp. 2–27
	Doing Science, Working Safely	pp. 28–37
	Doing Science, Using Science Tools and Equipment	pp. 38–59
	Doing Science, Using Tables and Graphs	pp. 60–73
These topics may be used with all S.T.E.M. features and S.T.E.M. investigations.	Science, Technology, and Society, Science and Technology	pp. 356–363
	Science, Technology, and Society, Science and Society	pp. 364–369
These topics are covered at another grade.	Human Body Systems	pp. 110–125
	Earth Science, Earth's Changing Surface	pp. 170–186

Grade-Level Materials Lists

Quantities are indicated for one group of students.

▶ Guided Inquiry and S.T.E.M. Lessons

The following list provides materials needed for all the Guided Inquiry
and STEM Lessons—the core activities—in this grade level.

Nonconsumable Materials

Material	Quantity per Group	Teacher Edition Page
apron, lab	varies	403A
balance	1	41A, 367A, 371A
ball, foam	1	325A, 445A
ball, tennis	1	367A
battery holder	1	499A
beaker, 250 mL	1	403A
bin, plastic, large	1	233A
books	varies	93A, 367A
bowl, plastic, small	varies	165A
chair	1	325A
classroom objects	varies	41A, 367A, 371A
comb, plastic	1	476A
compass	1	342A
compass, drawing	1	343A
computer	1	55A
container, plastic, clear 16 oz	1	558A
dowel, wooden	1	459A
dropper	1	165A, 418A
flashlight	1	325A
forceps	1	133A, 165A, 419A
graduated cylinder, 100 mL	1	165A
hand lens	1	419A
jar, plastic, clear, 16 oz	1	476A
key	1	367A

Nonconsumable Materials (continued)

Material	Quantity per Group	Teacher Edition Page
knife, metal, butter	1	473A
lid, metal	1	93A
light bulb holder	1	459A
light socket, mini	varies	499A
light socket, porcelain	varies	459A
marble	varies	93A, 558A
media resources	varies	116A, 238A, 286A, 342A, 384A, 418A, 476A, 530A, 558A
nails, finishing	varies	530A
needle	1	459A
petri dish	1	419A
pictures, bird	varies	165A
pushpin	varies	343A
safety goggles	varies	403A, 418A, 419A, 459A
scissors	1	205A, 342A, 343A, 459A
spoon, slotted	1	165A
spring scale, 5 kg/50 N	1	41A, 93A, 384A
stopwatch	1	473A, 553A
switch with clips	1	499A, 530A
tape measure	1	41A, 55A, 553A
thermometer	1	476A
tubing	varies	558A
weather check tool	1	287A
weather station	1	287A

Nonconsumable Materials (continued)

Material	Quantity per Group	Teacher Edition Page
wire cutter, stripper	1	165A
wood, blocks	varies	93A

Consumable Materials

Material	Quantity per Group	Teacher Edition Page
alcohol	1	403A
apple core	1	233A
bag, freezer, 1 gal	1	77A
baking soda	varies	418A
banana peel	1	233A
battery, size D	varies	325A, 499A, 530A
box, cardboard	1	55A, 77A
butter	varies	473A
can, soda	1	233A
cardboard	varies	558A
classroom art supplies	varies	286A
clay, modeling	varies	205A, 342A, 384A
cotton balls	varies	77A
cup, clear plastic, 16 oz	1	233A, 403A, 473A
cup, plastic, 9 oz	1	133A
egg	1	77A
fabric	varies	77A
fiber fill	varies	77A
foil, aluminum	varies	476A
gloves, disposable	1	233A, 403A
glue stick	1	205A
grapes	varies	165A
graphite, pencil lead	varies	499A
gummy worms	varies	165A

Consumable Materials (continued)

Material	Quantity per Group	Teacher Edition Page
index cards	varies	205A, 384A
juice	1	165A
knife, plastic	1	473A
lettuce	1	165A
light bulb, miniature	1	499A
magazines	varies	205A
markers	1	133A, 205A, 342A, 343A, 384A, 473A
newspaper	varies	233A
paint, black	varies	476A
paper	varies	116A, 238A, 286A, 325A, 342A, 384A, 459A
paper, butcher block	varies	343A
paper, construction	varies	205A, 343A
paper, drawing	varies	55A
paper, graph	varies	55A
paper, towel	varies	133A, 403A
paper clips	varies	367A, 384A, 499A, 530A
peanuts, foam	varies	77A
pencil	1	116A, 238A, 286A, 325A, 342A, 343A, 367A, 384A, 459A
plastic wrap	varies	133A, 476A
plate, plastic	varies	418A
rice	varies	165A
rubber band	1	384A

Consumable Materials (continued)

Material	Quantity per Group	Teacher Edition Page
sand, fine	varies	165A
seeds, lima bean	1	133A
seeds, pumpkin	1	133A
seeds, sunflower	varies	133A, 165A
shoebox	1	205A, 476A
soil, potting	varies	233A
spoon, plastic	1	233A, 403A, 418A
steel wool	varies	419A
sticks, craft	varies	499A
straw, plastic, drinking	varies	165A
string, cotton	varies	93A, 205A, 343A
sugar	varies	403A
tape, masking	varies	133A, 325A, 384A, 553A, 558A
thread	varies	459A
toothpicks	varies	205A
vinegar	1	418A
wire, insulated	varies	499A, 530A
yarn	varies	77A

▶ Directed and Independent Activities

The following list provides materials needed for the optional Directed and Independent activities in this grade level. The * indicates materials that also appear on the Guided Inquiry materials list.

Nonconsumable Materials

Material	Quantity per Group	Teacher Edition Page
apron, lab *	varies	391A, 403A, 447A
balance *	1	41A, 351A, 367A, 371A
ball, foam *	1	325A, 445A
ball, tennis *	1	367A, 553A
basketball	1	297A
battery holder *	1	499A, 501A
beaker, 250 mL *	1	221A, 245A, 351A, 373A, 403A
bin, plastic, large *	1	233A
blender	1	207A
board, flat	1	207A
books *	varies	93A, 367A
bottle, spray trigger	1	173A
bowl, plastic, large	1	151A
bowl, plastic, small	varies	165A
box, plastic	1	259A
bulb, compact *	varies	459A
chair *	1	325A
classroom objects *	varies	41A, 63A, 351A, 367A, 371A
cloth, silk	1	497A
cloth, wool	1	483A, 497A
clothespin *	varies	165A
comb, plastic *	1	476A, 483A
compass *	1	342A, 517A
compass, drawing *	1	343A

Nonconsumable Materials (continued)

Material	Quantity per Group	Teacher Edition Page
computer *	1	55A
container, plastic, clear 16 oz *	1	27A, 558A
dominoes	varies	79A
dowel, wooden *	1	445A, 459A
dropper *	1	165A, 391A, 418A
fan	1	245A
flashlight	1	297A, 325A
forceps *	1	133A, 165A, 419A
fur, fake	1	151A, 483A
graduated cylinder, 100 mL *	1	165A, 351A
hand lens *	1	117A, 135A, 419A
jar, plastic, clear, 16 oz *	1	135A, 447A, 476A, 483A
key	1	367A
knife, metal, butter	1	473A
lid, metal *	1	93A, 135A
light bulb holder *	1	459A
hook	varies	79A
hot plate	1	373A
lamp	1	135A, 447A, 517A
light socket, mini	varies	499A, 501A
light socket, porcelain *	varies	459A
marble *	varies	79A, 93A, 558A
media resources *	varies	27A, 63A, 116A, 117A, 151A, 173A, 189A, 238A, 273A, 286A, 297A, 315A, 327A, 342A, 384A, 418A, 429A, 463A, 476A, 530A, 558A
mesh screen	1	207A

Nonconsumable Materials (continued)

Material	Quantity per Group	Teacher Edition Page
mitts, oven	1	373A
nails, finishing *	varies	517A, 530A
needle *	1	459A
pan, aluminum, 13" x 9" x 2"	1	245A, 259A
pennies	varies	45A
petri dish *	1	419A
pictures, bird *	varies	165A
pitcher	1	273A
pushpin *	varies	327A, 343A
refrigerator	1	135A
ruler	1	17A, 27A, 45A, 463A
safety goggles *	varies	3A, 173A, 373A, 391A, 403A, 405A, 418A, 419A, 445A, 447A, 459A
scissors *	1	3A, 17A, 45A, 189A, 205A, 342A, 343A, 459A, 463A
spoon, measuring 4-in-1	1	221A
spoon, slotted *	1	165A
spring	1	445A
spring scale, 5 kg/50 N *	1	41A, 93A, 384A
stopwatch *	1	17A, 151A, 273A, 473A, 537A, 553A

Nonconsumable Materials (continued)

Material	Quantity per Group	Teacher Edition Page
switch with clips *	1	499A, 501A, 530A
table	2	45A
tape measure *	1	3A, 17A, 27A, 41A, 45A, 55A, 79A, 103A, 221A, 327A, 445A, 537A, 553A
thermometer *	1	151A, 259A, 447A, 463A, 476A
tubing *	varies	558A
washer, metal, 1 ½"	varies	17A
washer, metal, ¾"	varies	17A
weather check tool *	1	287A
weather station *	1	287A
wire cutter, stripper *	1	165A
wood, blocks *	varies	93A

Consumable Materials

Material	Quantity per Group	Teacher Edition Page
alcohol *	1	351A, 391A, 403A
antacid tablets	varies	405A
apple core *	1	233A
bag, freezer, 1 gal *	1	77A, 151A
baking powder	varies	17A
baking soda	varies	17A, 405A, 418A
ball, foam	1	445A
balloon, round	1	497A
banana peel *	1	233A
battery, size D *	varies	297A, 325A, 499A, 501A, 517A, 530A
bottle, clear, plastic, 16 oz	1	447A
bottle, clear, plastic, 2 L	2	173A
box, cardboard *	1	55A, 77A
brine shrimp	1	135A
butter *	varies	473A
calendar, blank	1	315A
candy	1	79A
can, soda *	1	233A
cardboard *	varies	327A, 558A
cardboard, strip	varies	79A
celery, leafy	1	103A
cereal, puffed rice	1	483A
classroom art supplies *	varies	207A, 221A, 286A, 429A
clay, modeling *	varies	27A, 205A, 342A, 384A, 447A

Consumable Materials (continued)

Material	Quantity per Group	Teacher Edition Page
corn syrup	1	391A
cotton balls *	varies	77A
cup, clear plastic, 16 oz *	1	103A, 233A, 259A, 273A, 403A, 473A
cup, paper, 12 oz	1	45A
cup, plastic, 9 oz *	1	133A, 405A
detergent	1	391A
dryer sheet	1	483A
egg *	1	77A
eggshells	varies	405A
fabric *	varies	77A
fiber fill *	varies	77A
flower	1	117A
foil, aluminum	varies	463A, 476A
food coloring	1	103A, 447A
gloves, disposable *	1	151A, 173A, 233A, 403A
glue	1	189A, 463A
glue stick *	1	205A
glycerin	1	391A
grapes *	varies	165A
graphite, pencil lead *	varies	499A
gummy worms *	varies	165A
ice cubes	varies	151A, 245A, 273A, 373A
index cards *	varies	3A, 205A, 245A, 259A, 384A, 537A
index cards, blue	varies	429A

▶ Directed and Independent Activities (continued)

Consumable Materials (continued)

Material	Quantity per Group	Teacher Edition Page
index cards, yellow	varies	429A
juice *	1	165A
knife, plastic	1	473A
lettuce *	1	165A
light bulb, incandescent	1	459A
light bulb, fluorescent	1	459A
light bulb, miniature *	1	499A, 501A
magazines *	varies	189A, 205A
markers *	set	27A, 63A, 133A, 189A, 205A, 207A, 221A, 245A, 297A, 342A, 343A, 384A, 473A
molasses	1	351A
newspaper *	varies	207A, 233A
oil, vegetable	1	351A, 391A
paint, black *	varies	476A
paper *	varies	3A, 17A, 27A, 45A, 63A, 79A, 103A, 116A, 117A, 173A, 189A, 238A, 245A, 286A, 297A, 325A, 327A, 342A, 351A, 384A, 391A, 429A, 459A, 463A, 483A
paper, butcher block	varies	343A
paper, construction *	varies	189A, 205A, 343A, 447A
paper, drawing *	varies	55A
paper, graph *	varies	55A

Consumable Materials (continued)

Material	Quantity per Group	Teacher Edition Page
paper, towel *	varies	103A, 133A, 403A
paper clips *	varies	3A, 45A, 367A, 384A, 499A, 517A, 530A
peanuts, foam *	varies	77A
pebbles	varies	173A
pencil *	1	3A, 17A, 27A, 45A, 63A, 79A, 103A, 116A, 117A, 173A, 189A, 238A, 245A, 259A, 286A, 297A, 325A, 327A, 342A, 343A, 351A, 367A, 384A, 391A, 429A, 459A, 463A, 483A
pencil, colored	varies	117A, 173A, 327A
pen	1	429A
plants	2	103A, 173A, 221A
plastic wrap *	varies	133A, 173A, 476A, 483A
plate, plastic *	varies	391A, 418A, 483A
poster board	1	463A
rice *	varies	165A
rubber band *	1	173A, 384A
salt	varies	373A
sand, coarse	varies	173A
sand, fine *	varies	165A, 259A
seeds, lima bean *	1	133A
seeds, pumpkin *	1	133A
seeds, sunflower *	varies	133A, 165A
shoebox *	1	79A, 205A, 476A

Consumable Materials (continued)

Material	Quantity per Group	Teacher Edition Page
shoebox lid	1	463A
shortening	1	151A
soil, potting *	varies	173A, 233A
spoon, plastic *	1	173A, 233A, 403A, 405A, 418A
steel wool	varies	419A
straw, plastic, drinking *	varies	45A, 165A, 447A
sticks, craft *	varies	499A
string, cotton *	varies	17A, 79A, 93A, 189A, 205A, 327A, 343A, 463A, 497A
sugar *	varies	17A, 403A
tape, masking *	varies	45A, 79A, 133A, 325A, 384A, 445A, 447A, 497A, 537A, 553A, 558A
tape, transparent	varies	517A
thread *	varies	459A
toothpicks *	varies	205A, 373A
vinegar *	1	17A, 221A, 405A, 418A
wax worm	varies	135A
wax worm, food	varies	135A
wire, insulated *	varies	517A, 499A, 501A, 530A
yarn *	varies	77A

For more information about Materials Kits, contact your Houghton Mifflin Harcourt sales representative.

Interactive Glossary

Interactive Glossary

As you learn about each term, add notes, drawings, or sentences in the extra space. This will help you remember what the terms mean. Here are some examples.

Fungi [FUHN•jeye] A kingdom of organisms that have a nucleus and get nutrients by decomposing other organisms

A mushroom is from the kingdom Fungi.

physical change [FIZ•ih•kuhl CHAYNJ] Change in the size, shape, or state of matter with no new substance being formed

When I cut paper, the paper has a physical change.

Glossary Pronunciation Key

With every glossary term, there is also a phonetic respelling. A phonetic respelling writes the word the way it sounds, which can help you pronounce new or unfamiliar words. Use this key to help you understand the respellings.

Sound	As in	Phonetic Respelling	Sound	As in	Phonetic Respelling
a	bat	(BAT)	oh	over	(OH•ver)
ah	lock	(LAHK)	oo	pool	(POOL)
air	rare	(RAIR)	ow	out	(OWT)
ar	argue	(AR•gyoo)	oy	foil	(FOYL)
aw	law	(LAW)	s	cell	(SEL)
ay	face	(FAYS)		sit	(SIT)
ch	chapel	(CHAP•uhl)	sh	sheep	(SHEEP)
e	test	(TEST)	th	that	(THAT)
	metric	(MEH•trik)		thin	(THIN)
ee	eat	(EET)	u	pull	(PUL)
	feet	(FEET)	uh	medal	(MED•uhl)
	ski	(SKEE)		talent	(TAL•uhnt)
er	paper	(PAY•per)		pencil	(PEN•suhl)
	fern	(FERN)		onion	(UHN•yuhn)
eye	idea	(eye•DEE•uh)		playful	(PLAY•fuhl)
i	bit	(BIT)		dull	(DUHL)
ing	going	(GOH•ing)	y	yes	(YES)
k	card	(KARD)		ripe	(RYP)
	kite	(KYT)	z	bags	(BAGZ)
ngk	bank	(BANGK)	zh	treasure	(TREZH•er)

R1

Interactive Glossary

A

acceleration [ak•sel•er•AY•shuhn] Any change in the speed or direction of an object's motion (p. 544)

adaptation [ad•uhp•TAY•shuhn] A trait or characteristic that helps an organism survive (p. 154)

air mass [AIR MAS] A large body of air that has the same temperature and humidity throughout (p. 276)

air pressure [AIR PRESH•er] The weight of the atmosphere pressing down on Earth (p. 261)

atmosphere [AT•muhs•feer] The mixture of gases that surround Earth (p. 247)

axis [AK•sis] The imaginary line around which Earth rotates (p. 298)

B

behavioral adaptation [bih•HAYV•yu•ruhl ad•uhp•TAY•shuhn] Something an animal does that helps it survive (p. 159)

C

carnivore [KAHR•nuh•vawr] An animal that eats only other animals (p. 192)

change of state [CHAYNJ uhv STAYT] A physical change that occurs when matter changes from one state to another, such as from a liquid to a gas (p. 378)

chemical change [KEM•ih•kuhl CHAYNJ] A change in one or more substances, caused by a reaction, that forms new and different substances (p. 408)

chemical energy [KEM•ih•kuhl EN•er•jee] Energy that can be released by a chemical reaction (p. 437)

chemical property [KEM•ih•kuhl PRAHP•er•tee] A property that involves how a substance interacts with other substances (p. 406)

chemical reaction [KEM•ih•kuhl ree•AK•shuhn] A chemical change (p. 411)

chlorophyll [KLAWR•uh•fihl] A green pigment in plants that allows plant cells to make food using sunlight (p. 110)

circuit [SER•kuht] A path along which electric charges can flow (p. 504)

R2

R3

Interactive Glossary

community [kuh•MYOO•nih•tee] All of the organisms that live in the same place (p. 176)

complete metamorphosis [kuhm•PLEET met•uh•MAWR•fuh•sis] A complex change that most insects undergo that includes larva and pupa stages (p. 141)

computer model [kuhm•PYOO•ter MOD•l] A computer program that models an event or object (p. 49)

condensation [kahn•duhn•SAY•shuhn] The process by which a gas changes into a liquid (pp. 248, 379)

conduction [kuhn•DUK•shuhn] The movement of heat between two materials that are touching (p. 450)

conductor [kuhn•DUK•ter] A material that lets heat or electricity travel through it easily (pp. 464, 502)

conservation [kahn•ser•VAY•shuhn] The use of less of something to make its supply last longer (p. 228)

constellation [kahn•stuh•LAY•shuhn] A pattern of stars that form an imaginary picture or design in the sky (p. 304)

consumer [kuhn•SOOM•er] Animals that eat plants or other animals to get energy (p. 181)

convection [kuhn•VEK•shuhn] The transfer of heat within a liquid or a gas (p. 451)

D

data [DEY•tuh] Individual facts, statistics, and items of information (p. 35)

decomposer [dee•kuhm•POHZ•er] A living thing that gets energy by breaking down wastes and the remains of plants and animals (p. 181)

density [DEN•suh•tee] The amount of matter present in a certain volume of a substance (p. 358)

design [dih•ZYN] To conceive something and to prepare the plans and drawings for it to be built (p. 66)

E

ecosystem [EE•koh•sis•tuhm] A community of organisms and the physical environment in which they live (p. 174)

electric current [ee•LEK•trik KER•uhnt] The flow of electric charges along a path (p. 490)

R4

R5

electric motor [ee•LEK•trik MOHT•er] A device that changes electrical energy into mechanical energy (p. 519)

electrical energy [ee•LEK•trih•kuhl EN•er•jee] Energy that comes from electric current (p. 437)

electromagnet [ee•lek•troh•MAG•nit] A temporary magnet caused by an electric current (p. 523)

endangered species [en•DAYN•jerd SPEE•sheez] Organisms whose whole population is at risk of dying out (p. 228)

energy [EN•er•jee] The ability to cause changes in matter (p. 431)

engineering [en•juh•NIR•ing] The use of scientific and mathematical principles to develop something practical (p. 65)

environment [en•v•ruhn•muhnt] All the living and nonliving things that surround and affect an organism (p. 152)

evaporation [ee•vap•uh•RAY•shuhn] The process by which a liquid changes into a gas (pp. 247, 379)

F

fertilization [fur•tl•i•ZAY•shuhn] The joining together of a sperm and an egg cell (p. 120)

food chain [FOOD CHAYN] The transfer of food energy in a sequence of living things (p. 190)

food web [FOOD WEB] A diagram that shows the relationships among different food chains in an ecosystem (p. 196)

force [FAWRS] A push or a pull (p. 544)

front [FRUHNT] The boundary between two air masses (p. 276)

G

gas [GAS] The state of matter that does not have a definite shape or volume (p. 374)

generator [JEN•er•ayt•er] A device that makes an electric current by converting mechanical energy to electrical energy (p. 525)

germination [jer•muh•NAY•shuhn] The sprouting of a seed (p. 116)

groundwater [GROWND•waw•ter] Water located within the gaps and pores in rocks below Earth's surface (p. 250)

H

habitat [HAB•ih•tat] The part of an ecosystem that meets the needs of an organism (p. 179)

heat [HEET] The energy that moves between objects of different temperatures (p. 448)

herbivore [HER•buh•vawr] An animal that eats only plants or other producers (p. 192)

humidity [hyoo•MID•uh•tee] The amount of water vapor in the air (p. 261)

hypothesis [hy•PAHTH•uh•sis] A possible explanation or answer to a question; a testable statement (p. 9)

I

incomplete metamorphosis [in•kuhm•PLEET met•uh•MAWR•fuh•sis] Developmental change in some insects in which a nymph hatches from an egg and gradually develops into an adult (p. 143)

inference [IN•fer•uhns] An untested conclusion based on observations (p. 19)

instinct [IN•stinkt] A behavior an animal knows how to do without having to learn it (p. 159)

insulator [IN•suh•layt•er] A material that does not let heat or electricity move through it easily (pp. 466, 502)

investigation [in•ves•tuh•GAY•shuhn] A procedure carried out to gather data about an object or an event (p. 7)

K

kinetic energy [kih•NET•ik EN•er•jee] The energy of motion (p. 432)

L

law of conservation of mass [LAW UHV kahn•ser•VAY•shuhn UHV MAS] The idea that you cannot make or destroy matter (p. 370)

leaf [LEEF] The part of a plant that makes food, using air, light, and water (p. 108)

liquid [LIK•wid] The state of matter that has a definite volume but no definite shape (p. 374)

Interactive Glossary

M

magnet [MAG•nit] An object that attracts iron and a few other—but not all—metals (p. 520)

mass [MAS] The amount of matter in an object (p. 352)

matter [MAT•er] Anything that has mass and takes up space (p. 352)

maturity [muh•TYOOR•ih•tee] The stage at which organisms can reproduce (p. 118)

mechanical energy [muh•KAN•ih•kuhl EN•er•jee] The total potential and kinetic energy of an object (p. 432)

microscope [MY•kruh•skohp] A tool that makes an object look several times bigger than it is (p. 31)

mixture [MIKS•cher] A combination of two or more different substances that retain their identities (p. 396)

model [MOD•l] A representation of something real that is too big, too small, or has too many parts to investigate directly (p. 47)

moon phase [MOON FAYZ] A change in the appearance of the moon's shape as it orbits Earth (p. 319)

motion [MOH•shuhn] A change of position of an object (p. 539)

N

natural resource [NACH•er•uhl REE•sawrs] Materials found in nature that people and other living things use (p. 208)

niche [NIHCH] The role a plant or an animal plays in its habitat (p. 179)

nonrenewable resource [nahn•rih•NOO•uh•buhl REE•sawrs] A natural resource that cannot be replaced in a reasonable amount of time (p. 210)

nymph [NIMF] An immature form of an insect that undergoes incomplete metamorphosis (p. 143)

O

observation [ahb•zuhr•VAY•shuhn] Information collected by using the five senses (p. 7)

omnivore [AHM•nih•vawr] An animal that eats both plants and other animals (p. 192)

R10

R11

Interactive Glossary

orbit [AWR•bit] The path of one object in space around another object (p. 300)

P

pan balance [PAN BAL•uhns] A tool that measures mass (p. 32)

parallel circuit [PAIR•uh•lel SER•kit] An electric circuit that has more than one path for the electric charges to follow (p. 507)

photosynthesis [foht•oh•SIHN•thuh•sis] The process in which plants use energy from the sun to change carbon dioxide and water into sugar and oxygen (p. 110)

physical adaptation [FIZ•ih•kuhl ad•uhp•TAY•shuhn] An adaptation to a body part. (p. 155)

physical change [FIZ•ih•kuhl CHAYNJ] A change in which a new substance is not formed (p. 393)

physical property [FIZ•ih•kuhl PRAHP•er•tee] A characteristic of matter that you can observe or measure directly (p. 352)

planet [PLAN•it] A large, round body that revolves around a star in a clear orbit (p. 328)

pollination [pol•uh•NEY•shuhn] The transfer of pollen from the male parts to the female parts of seed plants (p. 122)

pollution [puh•LOO•shuhn] Harmful substances mixed with water, air, or soil (p. 226)

population [pahp•yuh•LAY•shuhn] A group made up of the same type of individuals in an ecosystem (p. 177)

position [puh•ZISH•uhn] The location of an object in relation to a nearby object or place (p. 539)

potential energy [poh•TEN•shuhl EN•er•jee] Energy that an object has because of its position or its condition (p. 432)

precipitation [pree•sip•uh•TAY•shuhn] Water that falls from clouds to Earth's surface (p. 249)

producer [pruh•DOOS•er] A living thing, such as a plant, that can make its own food (p. 181)

prototype [PROH•tuh•typ] The original or model on which something is based (p. 67)

R12

R13

R

radiation [ray•dee•AY•shuhn] The movement of heat without matter to carry it (p. 453)

renewable resource [rih•NOO•uh•buhl REE•sawrs] A natural resource that can be replaced within a reasonable amount of time (p. 209)

root [ROOT] A plant part that is usually underground and absorbs water and minerals from the soil (p. 106)

rotate [ROH•tayt] To turn about an axis (p. 298)

runoff [RUN•awf] Water that does not soak into the ground and instead flows across Earth's surface (p. 251)

S

science [SY•uhns] The study of the natural world (p. 5)

scientist [SY•uhn•tist] A person who asks questions about the natural world (p. 5)

series circuit [SIR•eez SER•kit] An electric circuit in which the electrical charges have only one path to follow (p. 507)

solar system [SOH•ler SIS•tuhm] A star and all the planets and other objects that revolve around it (p. 328)

solid [SAHL•id] The state of matter that has a definite shape and a definite volume (p. 374)

solution [suh•LOO•shuhn] A mixture that has the same composition throughout because all the parts are mixed evenly (p. 397)

speed [SPEED] The measure of an object's change in position during a certain amount of time (p. 542)

spore [SPAWR] A reproductive structure of some plants, such as mosses and ferns, that can form a new plant (p. 126)

spring scale [SPRING SKAYL] A tool that measures forces, such as weight (p. 32)

states of matter [STAYTS uhv MAT•er] The physical forms (such as solid, liquid, and gas) that matter can exist in (p. 374)

static electricity [STAT•ik ee•lek•TRIS•uh•tee] The buildup of electric charges on an object (p. 487)

stem [STEM] The part of a plant that holds it up and has tubes that carry water, minerals, and nutrients through the plant (p. 107)

T

technology [tek•NOL•uh•jee] Any designed system, product, or process used to solve problems (p. 81)

three-dimensional model [THREE-di•MEN•shuh•nuhl MOD•l] A model that has the dimension of height as well as width and length (p. 49)

tool [TOOL] Anything used to help people shape, build, or produce things to meet their needs (p. 80)

two-dimensional model [TOO-di•MEN•shuh•nuhl MOD•l] A model that has the dimensions of length and width only (p. 47)

V

velocity [vuh•LAHS•uh•tee] The speed of an object in a particular direction (p. 542)

volume [VAHL•yoom] The amount of space an object takes up (p. 356)

W

water cycle [WAWT•er SY•kuhl] The process in which water continuously moves from Earth's surface into the atmosphere and back again (p. 247)

weather [WETH•er] What is happening in the atmosphere at a certain place and time (p. 260)

Index